WORLD JEWRY TODAY

WORLD
JEWRY TODAY

Edited by

S. FEDERBUSH

New York • THOMAS YOSELOFF • London

TABLE OF CONTENTS

TABLE OF CONTENTS

Preface

THE NEED for a comprehensive reference book comprising all Jewish communities and their institutions the world over has long been felt. Complying with the request voiced by many communities and organizations, this publication sponsored by the World Jewish Congress attempts, for the first time, to meet this requirement.

The growing dispersion of the Jewish people makes intercourse among the various communities increasingly difficult. Never before has our dispersion been so widespread. The Jewish settlements are now scattered over one hundred and three countries. At the same time, the preservation of common spiritual values uniting the Jews of all countries renders even more urgent the maintenance of permanent links between the distant communities. This applies especially to the small, remote, and isolated Jewish settlements, which, menaced by rapid assimilation, are looking to the larger Jewish communities for the inspiration and guidance necessary for their survival. This directory therefore seeks to facilitate mutual communication between distant segments of world Jewry and thus promote the sense of unity of our people.

The State of Israel is accorded a prominent place, as it occupies a central position in Jewish life, and the bonds between it and the Diaspora constitute a significant factor in the Jewry of today. The President of Israel, in his letter published below, also expresses the hope that the Directory including as it does both Israel and the Diaspora, the two main aspects of present Jewish existence, may strengthen the spiritual ties between them.

The statistics of the Jewish population in the various countries are based in the main on direct reports from the communities. The figures, although carefully checked, are at times necessarily approximate due to the lack of a governmental census of the Jewish population in the various countries with the exception of Israel.

This is the first attempt to give a concise history and an account of the present spiritual, economic and political situation, the various institutions, press and communal leaders of all Jewries in the world, including inaccessible communities never before dealt with in any publication.

I shall be grateful for any comments and observations, which will be taken into consideration in the preparation of succeeding editions of this directory.

I hope that the years of effort invested in this work, as well as its general reviews and surveys by the most outstanding Jewish personalities of our time, will find its reward by proving useful to the communities and contributing to the enhancement of Jewish consciousness.

DR. SIMON FEDERBUSH
Editor

Introduction

by the President of Israel, Izhak Ben-Zvi

נשיא מדינת ישראל

ירושלים, ז׳ בשבט תשי״ד ; 11.1.54

ד״ר פדרבוש נכבד,

הנני לברך את הקונגרס היהודי העולמי על משימתו החשובה לפרסם מדריך,
שמטרתו לקשר את קבוצי ישראל הנדחים בכל ירכתי תבל עם הישובים הגדולים
במרכזיהם השונים.

מובטחני שהספר יהיה שוה וראוי לשמו וישמש גורם נוסף לחזק קשר של קיימא
בין עדות ישראל ויסייע ביתר שאת שאיש את אחיו להכיר.

תבורך יזמת הקונגרס היהודי העולמי לחזק את הקשר הזה בין בני עמנו עם
ארץ־ישראל ומדינת ישראל.

יצחק בן־צבי

(TRANSLATION)

Dear Dr. Federbush:

*I hereby congratulate the World Jewish Congress on its important
project of publishing a World Jewish Directory, aimed at strengthening the ties between the remote Jewish communities the world over
and the large Jewish centers.*

*I am confident that the publication will be worthy of its name, that
it will serve as an additional factor to enhance the existing relations
between the Jewish communities, and that it will promote their
mutual acquaintance.*

*May the initiative of the World Jewish Congress succeed in fortifying
the ties between our people and the State of Israel.*

IZHAK BEN-ZVI

The Position of World Jewry

by Dr. Nahum Goldmann

ONE OF the major problems we face today is the illusion we share that we have mastered our problems and that we face a bright future. There are a number of factors which contribute to this sense of well being. In the first place, more than one half of our people live in the United States where the innate optimism of the Jew is wedded to the infinite capacity of the American for wishful thinking. Moreover, in the United States the Jews live in the presence of a magnificent facade, consisting of an ever-increasing array of new synagogues and new centers, supported by large budgets and administered by large professional staffs and lay leaders. It would be difficult to resist the conclusion that Jewish life in the United States is dynamic and vibrant.

If the foregoing were not sufficient to induce widespread euphoria, the very period in which we are living would help in developing this frame of mind. It must be noted that we are a generation of Jews that has gone through a period of history, for which there are few, if any, parallels in terms of drama and tragedy. We have witnessed two World Wars, world-shaking revolutions, the ghastly bloodletting of the Hitler tyranny which, before it had spent itself, had annihilated six million of our people, and, finally, the realization of a two thousand year old dream in the re-establishment of the Jewish State.

Is it any wonder that the Jew should, after a succession of these experiences, want to enjoy peace and quiet? After all, there is a limitation to what human beings can absorb. The Jew is not unique in this respect. History demonstrates that after a people has gone through a period of great tension, accompanying war or revolution, they yield, often prematurely, to the natural impulse to return to an emotional and mental normal life. To use a popular American phrase—on which the orthodox lexicographers frown—they want to return to "normalcy." And there was sufficient cause for the Jew, viewing his post-war world superficially, to believe that he was entitled to the relaxation for which he yearned. To him, the ingredients of the post-war world had special significance: the democracies had achieved a smashing victory over the Nazis, the Jews had won an unprecedented political victory at the United Nations which resolved that a Jewish State should be re-established, and Israel had successfully defended this decision on the field of battle against the combination of the entire Arab world.

As a result of this confluence of events, what visions did the Jew conjure up before his eyes? The Hitler defeat gave him a sense of physical security, and the heroic and victorious fight for the State of Israel gave him a sense of added dignity in his own eyes and, he felt, in the eyes of the world. He fancied that he had no worries. He would have to help Israel and make it more secure and more beautiful. But such problems as remained were incomparably small as compared with the major problems of the previous two or three generations which had been satisfactorily resolved.

I am convinced that if the illusion of well-being under which we live is not abandoned, and if we do not re-dedicate ourselves to the task of insuring Jewish survival, including the survival of the State of Israel, we will be defaulting upon a responsibility which will have tragic consequences for the Jewish people. A people's fate is determined not by its armies or by its economy, but by its "internal front"—its capacity and its readiness to make sacrifices for its survival. This front cannot be maintained and made secure unless the people have a realistic view of their own position.

The Jew does not live in a state of isolation. He lives in a world which is in a state of ferment and in a period which is characterized by the cold war. All we can presently hope for is that the cold war should not be converted into a real war, with all that it implies for the future of civilization. This cold war is not the making of a few "wicked people in the Kremlin" nor, according to the men in the Kremlin, the by-product of the "conspiracy of the warmongers in Washington."

Great historical developments have their roots in objective causes and not in the caprices of a few men. What the cold war indicates is a tension in the world for which there is no parallel in the history of mankind.

The cold war is unique inasmuch as it embraces the entire world. Any past crisis of which we have any record was invariably defined to a limited area. For example, what did the Europeans one hundred years ago care about what happened in China? And what did China fifty years care about what happened in the United States? By way of contrast, we live today in a period where a bomb dropped in Formosa would instantaneously place the city of New York in peril. The struggle today not only involves all of humanity, but in its intensity is without precedent. The struggle is both social and political. We live in a period in which hundreds of millions of people have awakened and are demanding their share of the world's wealth. Today it is five hundred million Chinese and three hundred million Indians who are pressing these claims. Tomorrow—it may take two to ten years—and the entire African continent will put forward its demands, and this will inevitably spread to the other parts of the world.

Decades may pass before these conflicts will be resolved. Experience fortifies the belief that people do not readily surrender what they have acquired. If our generation or the next succeeds in solving these problems peaceably, it will be one of the miraculous achievements of creative statesmanship of all times.

In the circumstances in which we are

living, no people in the world, not even the strongest, can feel safe. This is clearly the motivation behind the American policy which is designed to cultivate friends and acquire allies. When powerful nations tremble for their future, certainly no small people in the world can feel secure.

If this is true of small people generally, it has greater relevance for the Jews, the classic minority of the world. Jewish history abounds with examples that only in a period of general stability is the Jew physically secure. Perhaps the most glorious period of Jewish history in the Diaspora was the 19th Century—the century of emancipation. It was a century marked by stability, in which the world was very neatly distributed among Great Britain, France, and, toward the end, Germany. Buttressed by colonies and vast empires, these nations could afford to be liberal, generous, and tolerant and care little whether the Jew or any other minority got some of the world's assets. What mattered is that they were the uncontested rulers of the world. But this picture has in recent years taken an entirely different complexion. Today, these countries are no longer the *balebatim*. Those who cling to the residue of their colonies know that they are rapidly losing their grasp and that inevitably they will have to be content to retire to their own national boundaries.

It is manifest that the distinction between the century in which we are living and the 19th century is not the difference between bad people and the great liberals of the halcyon days of Gladstone. The difference is much more profound. It is a difference in the world situation itself. The simple fact is that we are living in a brutal period which will remain brutal, with its disregard for minorities, tolerance, and decency, until the world is reorganized and again becomes stabilized. So far as the Jew is concerned, it is true that today there is little anti-Semitism of the blatant variety. People may still feel sufficiently ashamed of the horrible manifestations of anti-Semitism during the Hitler era to succumb to those who would spread the venom of Jew-hatred today only twelve years after the defeat of the Nazis. But this does not mean that our people, the vast majority of whom are dispersed all over the world, are by any means safe and secure.

Let us consider the position of the Jewish communities in the major areas where they live.

There are about three million Jews behind the iron curtain. At least, for the time being, these people are no less secure physically than their fellow citizens. But from the standpoint of Jewish survival, much is to be desired with respect to this segment of Jewry. Should a crisis of either an internal or external character develop in that part of the world, there is no question that the Jew will be selected as the natural scapegoat, and be, as he has traditionally been, the first victim. While today anti-Semitism in these countries is suppressed, it nevertheless exists in a latent form under the surface, waiting for the moment when it can freely burst forth in violent form—precisely because it is suppressed. In brief, from the long range point of view, it is an illusion to think of these three million Jews as being safe.

There are 500,000 Jews in North Africa.

These Jews, in effect, live on a volcano. To put it mildly, the French position in North Africa is unsafe, and in the eyes of the Arabs the Jew is identified with the French who are, in fact, responsible for the only rights and measure of security which the Jews have enjoyed in that part of the world. In general, this area is in a state of ferment, and no one can say with any assurance that the morrow of the Jews there holds out any promise of physical security.

Over 600,000 Jews live on the South American continent. Their economic position is relatively good. However, the countries are beset with unsolved social tensions and conflicts. This explains the existence of dictatorships in some parts of the South American continent. While tensions are held in check, the Jew is safe, but once social conflicts manifest themselves in attempts to solve the problems giving rise to the tensions, the Jew will be in a most vulnerable position.

Consequently, out of the 12 million Jews which survived the Hitler holocaust, at least 4 million Jews live in the shadow of physical insecurity.

Our internal position, as distinguished from our external one, is no more comforting. In the course of our history, we experienced great tragedies and periods of annihilation. There were periods in our history when our numbers had shrunk to two or three million. Yet we managed to survive. Our survival was the result of our determination to maintain our internal front, which, from the standpoint of the future of the Jew, is far more important than the external front.

Even assuming that the State of Israel will flourish and make its contributions to world Jewry, an inescapable fact bearing on the internal position of our generation and of generations ahead is the annihilation of the 6 million European Jews. None of us even began to appreciate what the disappearance of these people has meant in terms of the inner strength of our people. To speak of the numerical loss of one-third of our people, which in itself is staggering, is only one side of the coin. What is equally tragic is that we lost the Jewish communities which were the main repositories of the Jewish heritage, of what thousands of years of Jewish civilization had created. These Polish, Galician, Hungarian, German, Latvian, Lithuanian, and Russian Jews embodied the whole complex of Jewish values which generations of Jews had brought into being. It can hardly be disputed that the rest of Jewry lives morally and spiritually on the values preserved and generated by these centres of Jewish life.

In addition to the six million whom we have lost both physically and spiritually, we are in grave danger of losing another three-million—the Jews of the Soviet orbit. We shall lose them not as a result of physical extermination but as a consequence of spiritual suffocation. What is the likelihood of a young Jewish boy in Prague, in Moscow, in Odessa, or in Jassy remaining a Jew when in his lifetime he has not made the acquaintance of the Bible, when he has not learned a word of Hebrew, when he is a stranger to Jewish history, and when he has never heard the name of King David or Rabbi Akiva?

The process of erosion has cut so deep into the fabric of the Jewish soul that it is by no means sure that even if freedom of religion were restored in this part of the world, there would be any interest in the revival of Jewish life there.

The composite picture in Western Europe is also a disheartening one. Every visit to the Jewish communities on the European continent, once centers teeming with Jewish life, is today a heartrending experience. Some of these communities, for all practical purposes decimated by the Hitler tyranny, are making heroic efforts to maintain a semblance of Jewish life. No part of the Jewish people deserves as much credit and admiration as do the small Jewish communities of Florence, Turin, Antwerp, Strassbourg, Metz, etc. for their attempts to rise from their ashes and live again. But there is a limit to what may be expected concretely to result from these feats of heroism. There are times in life when a quantitative factor becomes qualitative as well. What a community of a hundred thousand can accomplish cannot conceivably be achieved by a community of a thousand. These small isolated communities are fighting a heroic rearguard fight to establish and maintain a school for their children, to rebuild a synagogue, or to reorganize a Zionist group. But their struggle, heroic as it is, is a struggle against almost impossible odds. Let us not be mistaken: this applies as well to the Jewish communities in the democratic West where Jews enjoy the full freedom to live their own lives. What about American Jewry? In my opinion, there never was a period in Jewish history when the danger of assimilation was as great as it is today—and in the very United States, a country rich in a Jewish population with vast material resources. The form of assimilation which threatens the Jewish people everywhere, including the United States, is different from the assimilation we once knew in Europe. There, in the days of Herman Cohen and others, it represented a way of life and thinking of a small group of people. It was dynamic and something tangible which one could oppose. But today Jewish assimilation is anonymous—it is a form of indifference, of aloofness, of an absence of interest in the Jewish tradition. This form of assimilation is elusive and difficult, if not impossible, to fight.

Toynbee, a great historian despite his biased chapter on Zionism, has a theory of history which he calls the theory of "challenge and counterchallenge." There is much substance to this interpretation of the historical development of peoples, of their rise and decline. When Jews were persecuted and oppressed, they were heroic. When their position improved, they relaxed and often became demoralized. It takes a people a long period of development to learn how to remain strong in times free of conflict. Apparently we have not had the time to learn this lesson.

Today we seem to live in a period when the Jew is not challenged. Nazism—without intending to do so—helped us in reclaiming millions of our people who were in the process of moving away from us. American Jewry responded as no other community with new institutions and unprecedented philanthropy when confronted with the challenge of Hitler's determination to destroy the Jewish people. Today, thank God, this challenge no longer exists. Here and there anti-Semitism crops up; again we count ourselves fortunate that it is not of a spectacular variety. Although the problems of Israel are many and complex, the challenge of Israel is no longer the same challenge as it was in the days of illegal immigration and the fight for a Jewish State. Because, basically, there seems to be no challenge to consolidate the Jewish people and inspire them to creative effort, assimilation is rampant everywhere.

I would regard the Jewish position today as virtually hopeless were it not for the existence of the State of Israel. But the mere existence of Israel does not insure the survival of the Jewish Diaspora. For the Jewish people to derive lasting benefits from the creation of that State there must be a spiritual merger with Israel. Diaspora Jewry has given striking evidence of its partnership with Israel— in the form of financial and political support. But if Israel is to become the source of new Jewish creativeness, the interdependence between Israel and the Diaspora will have to be felt much more deeply both by the individual Jew and by the Jewish communities throughout the world

than it is today. I am confident that once the day-to-day problems of Israel are solved and Israel will be able to devote itself to the role for which it was created, to serve as the center of Jewish spiritual life and Jewish values, it will play its proper role in insuring the survival of our people.

Diaspora Jewry, on the other hand, will have to be prepared to participate as partners in the culture which will be nourished in Israel, just as Jewish communities were conditioned to be partners in what was created in Vilna and Lublin. The problem involved in developing this receptiveness is a complex one. The technical aspect of the problem alone—the learning of Hebrew as a common language—is in itself a problem which will not be easy to solve. If our generation lives up to its obligations, it will have to make titanic efforts to promote the Hebrew education of our youth and thus give them the technical facility to receive and appreciate what will emanate from Israel. Once we recognize the important role which Israel must play in Jewish survival, we will find the way to make the Jewish people the true beneficiaries of Israel's cultural achievements. This is the challenge which our generation will have to meet.

Rebirth of Israel

by David Ben-Gurion

ISRAEL is the outcome of the timeless vision of redemption of the Jewish people. It is not the only State to achieve freedom and realize a national dream come true after the struggle of a popular movement. In the nineteenth and twentieth centuries, many countries were restored to independence in Europe and Asia by the momentum of revivalist ecstasy which remade and emancipated subject peoples. But the State of Israel was uniquely reborn. For, behind the veil of dreams elsewhere was the solid fact of a people living in its own land, even if under alien rule. By that, the national movement was sustained, and to accomplish its aim had only to break the foreign yoke. That done, its aspiration to nationhood was achieved in full. Not so with Israel. With us the vision lived only within and on itself, out of the people's soul; and all the hard facts were arrayed against it. The people was strewn and scattered far and wide; the land was ruled by strangers. And not only that. It was occupied by strangers, and ravaged and made desolate. Other than spiritual strength, nothing could have kept the vision alive.

Nor does the State mean its fulfilment. For, by far the greater part of the people is still divided among the nations, and so the State is not yet the consummation but only the instrument of redemption and its principal means. But by its establishment, the State gave the vision body and a basis in reality, and surpassing all else, became a force to weld together and unify the Diaspora.

Theodor Herzl, creator of the Zionist Organization, found the perfect definition of Zionism, as he understood it, though it has been forgotten and forsaken by most of the workers of the Movement. He said: "Zionism is the Jewish nation on the way," and he meant the Jewish people on its way back to its Land. This profound truth was soon garbled and turned into the meaningless dictum that the Zionist Organization was a State on the way.

There is no such thing as a State on the way. A State either is or it is not. When Napoleon said of his army that it was France on the march, that meant something, for everywhere the army went, there France was. But the Jewish State could not come from within "the Jewish nation on the way." It could not be created out of zero. Its embryo and its evolution over the years came not out of the Zionist Organization but out of the flowering of the Yishuv, its growth, and its fruition. It was built by the immigrants of all the generations of Aliyah and it will continue being rebuilt and made strong and firm by immigrant hands. Only Aliyah, "the Jewish nation on the way," as Herzl described it, is the constructive and corporeal essence of the Zionist dream. This is the truth and the whole truth of Zionism, that without Aliyah the Yishuv would not have been, without it the State would not have been, and without it the State will not endure.

Israel has become an inseparable part of the being and experience of the Diaspora. It has enriched the life of the nation and of every Jew as such. A Diaspora without the State, and moreover a State that has sloughed typical poverty and contentiousness, is conceivable no longer.

Equally, we cannot conceive of the growth or missionary fulfillment of the State without the whole of Israel's people in partnership. Between the two there is an interaction, obligatory, organic, historical and vital that is without like or precedent in the relations between nations and States. For, the two differ only in essence.

The Jewish people is not an abstract notion or just a collective name for myriads of isolated and scattered individuals in various countries. It is a conglomerate whose actuality, will, and common destiny are not open to question. But in the nature of things it has no fixed or rigid framework of uniform, planned effect; the conditions differ and conflict at each point of dispersion. The territorial groups are not fitted into a single pattern, for, every Jew, like every non-Jew, is subject to the laws and policy of his country, although his ties with his brethren depend upon the exercise of his free-will and personal inclinations. It was this difficulty that Herzl had to overcome in wishing to marshal the Jewish people and gather it together anew, independent in its own Homeland. That is why he brought the Zionist Organization into being, founding it upon voluntary association and voluntary effort, with no hint of coercion or obligatory duty. It voices the combined historic will of the Jewish people in its longing to be redeemed. For fifty years, it led the people back home and bore, at times alone, the main responsibility for establishing the State.

A universal attachment to social and international justice is engraved deep upon the nation's soul. Our Prophets inveighed passionately against violence, usurpation, oppression, and lawlessness in human and international affairs. The Prophet Isaiah was among the first to foretell the social revolution: 'For he bringeth down them that dwell on high; the lofty city, he layeth it low; he layeth it low, even to the ground; he bringeth it even to the dust. The foot shall tread it down, even the feet of the poor, and the steps of the needy ... for when thy judgments are in the earth, the inhabitants of the world will learn righteousness.' And the minstrel of Israel sings praises of the hero and his qualities: 'Gird thy sword upon thy thigh, O most mighty ... ride prosperously because of truth and meekness and righteousness ... Thou lovest righteousness and hatest wickedness: therefore God ... hath anointed thee ...'

The State will not be true to its prophetic heritage or to the vision of salvation in the "End of Days" unless in a spirit of gratitude and respect for the truth it

supports every venture fostering just relations between men and peoples based on
compassion and endeavors to build human
society on foundations of equality and
mutual help and not upon rivalry and exploitation. And who like the Jewish people
has endured the sins of the wicked and
the presumption of tyrants?

Our long acquaintance with history has
taught us that not in wrongdoing can
righteousness abide, that the salvation of
peoples will not be brought about by alien
compulsion but from within. Israel does
not believe that any powerful State has
the right to impose its will on a weaker
one even under the cloak of reforms. The
crying need of mankind is peace among
the nations, and peace will not come unless powerful States cease to meddle in
the domestic affairs of the small and weak
ones. The sincerity of those pretending to
strive for peace will be judged only in-
sofar as they establish truly peaceful relations even with countries whose regime
differs from their own which they regard
as attractive.

Therefore the Government of Israel
considers it a duty to promote relations of
friendship and reciprocity with every
peace-loving country without prying into
its internal constitution and to support
every step which makes for peace, guarantees the rights of man and the equality of
people, and enhances the authority and
effectiveness of the United Nations.

* * *

The huge undertaking of Israel's cultural development, no less than the Ingathering of Exiles and the reconstruction—again and again I must say it—
cannot be carried out solely with the internal resources of this young and troubled
State. Just as in the case of the absorption of immigration and the expansion of
agriculture, industry, and communications,
so the cultivation of the new wisdom of
Israel, in its general as in its limited meaning, is impossible without the devoted and
constant cooperation of the whole Jewish
people. Again I say, the State was made
not for its citizenry but for all the people
of Israel, for those, too, who do not purpose to dwell in it. The free State of Israel
has enhanced the prestige of Jews in those
lands as well where there exists neither
the will nor the inclination to Aliyah in
large numbers. Our army's victories and
our achievements in agriculture, industry,
and development projects redound to the
credit of every Jew in the world and the
aura of statehood emanating from Israel
bathes in its glow every Jewish soul
wherever it may be.

In scientific research, physics, biology,
sociology, politics, and history, in all
branches of art, literature, religion, and
ethics, we must develop a reliable partnership between the scholars and creative
forces in Israel and corresponding Jewish
elements in the Diaspora. Only by this
common effort can we fulfil the mission
of culture and education which history
has entrusted to us.

We cannot, we may not, do without
the cooperation of any Jewish group
whatsoever, in the Old World or the New.
And if that be the case in the material
and political spheres, how much more so
in the spiritual! Strength and greatness
of spirit are not conditioned by numbers,

and Moses our leader "was worth six hundred thousand ordinary men." But sometimes quantity at a certain point changes into quality. Outside Israel, there is not at this moment a single Jewish community to equal the Jewry of America in material, political, and financial strength, in cultural and spiritual power. The whole future of the Jewish people, the destiny of this State, rests on close and faithful collaboration between Israel in its Land and Jewry in America. But the interdependence will not last if it represents only a partnership between money and politics. There must also be a partnership of the pioneering spirit and intellect, a partnership of body and soul, embracing the elite of American Jewish youth and scholarship to build, together with us, the State and the civilization of Israel.

Pioneers coming to Israel from abroad will make its deserts verdant shoulder to shoulder with the country's native sons. Among them, the place of young American Jews will not be wanting. Above all, we shall need the scholars and intellectuals so as to expand the new 'wisdom of Israel' on which all our economic, military, and educational undertakings will be founded.

'Is a land born in one day? Is a nation brought forth at once?' asked the Prophet Isaiah. Not many asked themselves the question on the 14th day of May, 1948.

Since that day, in these brief years, the young State has performed breathtaking feats and launched incomparable ventures at a speed and in proportions to which our history offers no parallel. But— let no one delude himself! There is still work here for the State to do for its own people and for Jews throughout the world; and the work is still in its very beginnings. The difficulties and the exertions, the trials and the danger are not behind us, but ahead of us. Ahead of us, too, are the campaigns and the achievements, the splendors and the portents still to come. Long and hard is the way—'and it shall be called the way of holiness.'

Tercentenary of American Jewry

by Dr. Israel Goldstein

IN AMERICAN Jewry, the year 1954-55 was a year of stocktaking because it was a historic milestone marking the 300th anniversary of the settlement of Jews in the United States. American Jewry has become the largest Jewish community in the world and the greatest source of moral and financial help to the Jewish people in general and Israel in particular.

The twenty-three Jews who sailed into the harbor of New Amsterdam in September, 1654, little dreamed that they were opening up a path which would become a highway to millions of Jews in years and generations to come. They were refugees from parts of the new continent where already Jewish communities had flourished, so that in Brazil they spoke of a "new Jerusalem" with scholars and rabbis and Jewish congregations. They fled from Brazil when that land changed hands and religious freedom was abrogated and religious persecution, substituted. They fled to New Amsterdam where religious freedom, though not altogether complete, was at least tolerable. After them there came streams and streams of other refugees across the generations and centuries, escaping religious, racial, and political persecution, down to the recent chapter of our own time.

It is to the credit of the early pioneers that they held fast to their faith, established synagogues, and maintained footholds of Jewish community life upon which subsequent generations of Jews enlarged. It is to the credit of America that it became more and more a bulwark of religious freedom in the world.

Volumes have been written on the influence of our Bible, the Old Testament, upon the foundations of American democracy, the molding of the climate of American democracy from its beginnings in colonial times, the place of Hebrew in the culture of important leaders in colonial days, and the ideal of *Shivat Zion*, which found deep lodgement not only in the hearts of Jews such as Mordecai Noah with his project of Ararat but also in the hearts of non-Jews such as the second president of the United States, John Adams. He declared himself a friend of the cause of restoration of the Jewish people to its ancient homeland. He set a precedent for the presidents of our time who endorsed the Balfour Declaration and supported Medinat Israel.

It is important to bear in mind, however, in connection with this retrospect of three hundred years that it had three periods: one, the period of sporadic immigration; second, the period of mass immigration; and third, the period in which we are now living, of restricted immigration, during which all the elements which have gone into the building of American Jewry are being consolidated and integrated more than ever before.

I believe that it is fair to say that the most significant period of American Jewish history has been one which brought the mass immigration from the lands of Eastern Europe. They built upon the foundations of Jewish life which had been laid before them by the Spanish and Portuguese Jews from Central European countries. They brought with them a deeper Jewish culture and a more intensive Jewish will to live, great contributions to the labor movement in America, and the great infusing of Zionist idealism among American Jewry. For all these things, we shall remember this latter period as the decisive one in the life of American Jewry.

American Jewry at this milestone recalls its 300 years not with any feeling of smug complacency or self-satisfaction but with a feeling of humility and gratitude. It is not unaware of its shortcomings and it is not unaware of its achievements. It has contributed worthily to the making of America. Particularly in this last half century, Jews have been in the forefront of industrial and commercial enterprise. They have played a significant part in the development of a strong and responsible labor movement. In culture, the arts and professions, religious life, civic and political thought and action, and in philanthropy Jews have participated prominently. Thus the American Jewish community has added substance and character to American achievement.

During the latest period of restricted immigration, Jewish groups have assimilated with one another regardless of their countries of origin. The *landsmanschaften,* which had served a useful purpose in sending aid to their townsfolk back home and in helping new immigrants in their adjustment to the new environment, were gradually losing their *raison d'etre.* Jewish cultural values, too, became weaker without new supplementation. Yet, there are tenacious zealots of Hebrew culture, and Yiddish is struggling desperately to hold its place. In the meantime, however, the New World has begun to generate its own Jewish values. Rabbinical schools and teachers' seminaries are turning out American-born and bred rabbis and teachers. The Synagogue has become a central institution in the life of Americanized Jewish communities. More attention is being paid to standards of Jewish pedagogy although the content of Jewish education is meager and the majority of Jewish children are still outside its orbit.

There is much to criticize in the New World values of American Jewish life. The chief activity centers about philanthropy and defense programs against anti-Semitism. The whole community is overorganized; and yet, despite the plethora of organizations, many of them duplicating and overlapping, there is not sufficient organization. Too many organizations and not enough organization. New York Jewry, the leading Jewish community in America and in the world has failed in its attempt to organize a Kehilla. Because there exists no overall framework of democratic unity in American Jewish life, emergency after emergency demands ad hoc committees for action. Only in the field of philanthropy, both on local and national levels, has a modicum of unity been achieved.

The American Jewish community has recognized its responsibility to its brothers and sisters overseas and has been a stay and a staff to millions. The height of its career, however, was reached when it responded to the call of the Yishuv in Palestine for help in its material and political struggles, and above all, when it won the support of the American people and government for the Jewish National Home and then for the Jewish State. Barriers between Zionists and Non-Zionists were broken down or thinned. American Jewry rallied to Medinat Israel through many channels of activity. This latest chapter has in turn brought strength to American Jewry itself, has broadened its Jewish outlook, and deepened its Jewish feeling.

American Jewry has received blessings from America but it has given in the same measure as it has received. It has made significant contributions to America's culture and spirit, as well as to its commerce, industry, and science in times of peace, and to its defense in times of war. The Jewish labor movement in America is one of its great democratic forces.

American Jewry counted it a solemn duty and privilege to come to the aid of distressed Jewish communities in Europe in the period spanned by the two world wars and their aftermaths. And it continues to extend the hand of fellowship. It considers its greatest privilege to have been its help in laying the economic and then the political foundations for the establishment of Medinat Israel. But it feels it has received from Israel more than it has given—new dimensions of pride, dignity, and inspiration.

Israel has taken over what used to be America's unique role as the haven for the oppressed. It is worth recalling the words from the pen of a great American Jewish poetess of that day, Emma Lazarus, which have been inscribed at the foot of the Statute of Liberty. America's restrictionist immigration policy renders these words no longer applicable to America. They would well apply to Israel which, in proportion to the size of its population, has admitted more immigrants than any nation in the world:

Mother of exiles, from her beacon hand
Glows world-wide welcome . . .
Give me your tired, your poor,
Your huddled masses yearning to be
*   free*
The wretched refuse of your teeming
*   shore,*
Send these, the homeless, tempest-tost
*   to me,*
I lift my lamp beside the golden door.

American Jewry will continue to give moral and material support to Israel so that it may be able to fulfill the high purpose for which it was established.

It may be safely predicted that American Jewry will never stand apart from the needs and problems of Jews in other parts of the world, be those problems economic, political, or spiritual in character. The date 1840 is an important date in American Jewish history because, for the first time, the Jews of the United States united with Jewish communities in other parts of the world for a protest action and for securing the intercession of governments on behalf of a Jewish community abroad threatened with a ritual murder libel. It was the Damascus Affair of 1840 Since then, American Jewry has engaged in many joint actions with Jewish communities all over the world in defense of the rights and the life of the Jewish people.

Sometimes the united voice of the Jewish people is heard, as it was heard in the Damascus Affair of 1840, or in the United Nations in 1947. Sometimes it is ignored.

But always the voice of our people must be raised in defence of justice and humanity.

American Jewry's future will depend upon the future of the world, whether it shall be *chayim* (life) or *mavet* (death) at this time when the line between the two is so narrow. American Jewry's future will depend upon the direction of American democracy. American Jewry's future will depend upon the future of Israel. American Jewry's future will depend also upon its own capacity to dig deep into the religious and cultural traditions of our past, of our Torah.

World Jewish Population

TABLE 1

Distribution of Jewish Population, by Continents

Continent	Number
Europe (incl. Asiatic USSR and Turkey	3,757,977
America (North and South) . . .	6,207,434
Asia	1,990,730
Africa	686,746
Australia and New Zealand . . .	60,500
TOTAL	12,603,387

TABLE 2

Estimated Jewish Population in Europe, by Countries

Country	Number
Albania	200
Austria	12,000
Belgium	35,000
Bulgaria	6,000
Cyprus	160
Czechoslovakia	23,000
Denmark	6,500
England	450,000
Finland	1,800
France	250,000
Germany	27,280
Gibraltar	650
Greece	6,000
Hungary	100,000
Irish Republic	5,400
Italy	33,000
Lichtenstein	30
Luxembourg	1,200
Malta	42
Netherlands	25,000

Country	Number
Northern Ireland.	1,800
Norway	1,000
Poland	35,000
Portugal	2,000
Rumania	190,000
Saar	415
Soviet Union	2,500,000
Spain	3,500
Sweden	13,000
Switzerland	20,000
Trieste	1,500
Yugoslavia	6,500
TOTAL	3,757,977

TABLE 3

Estimated Jewish Population in North and South America, by Countries

Country	Number
Alaska	120
Canada	241,000
Hawaii	1,000
United States	5,300,000
TOTAL NORTH AMERICA .	5,542,020
Argentina	400,000
Aruba	130
Barbados	104
Bolivia	4,200
Brazil	120,000
British Guiana	30
Chile	36,000
Colombia	9,000
Costa Rica	1,200
Cuba	10,000
Curaçao	700

Country	Number
Dominican Republic . . .	600
Surinam, Dutch Guiana . .	410
Ecuador	3,000
El Salvador	275
Guatemala	1,000
Haiti	200
Honduras	150
Jamaica	1,500
Mexico	25,000
Nicaragua	200
Panama	2,000
Paraguay	1,100
Peru	4,000
Puerto Rico	250
Trinidad	180
Uruguay	40,000
Venezuela	5,900
Virgin Islands	85
TOTAL SOUTH AMERICA .	665,314

TABLE 4
Estimated Jewish Population in Asia, by Countries

Country	Number
Aden	800
Afghanistan	4,000
Bahrein	400
Burma	210
China	400
Fiji	70
Hadhramaut.	500
Hong Kong	230
Indonesia	450
Iran	75,000
Iraq	6,000
Israel	1,800,000
Japan	900

Country	Number
Lebanon	10,000
Pakistan	600
Philippines	300
Singapore	650
India	25,000
Syria	4,500
Thailand	120
Turkey	60,000
Yemen	600
TOTAL	1,990,730

TABLE 5
Estimated Jewish Population in Africa, by Countries

Country	Number
Algeria	130,000
Belgian Congo	2,500
Egypt	25,000
Ethiopia	25,300
Kenya	1,000
Libya	3,000
Morocco (incl. Tangier) .	246,300
Northern Rhodesia	
Southern Rhodesia . .	7,200
Tunisia	75,000
Union of South Africa . .	110,000
TOTAL	686,746

TABLE 6
Estimated Jewish Population in Australia and New Zealand

Country	Number
Australia	56,000
New Zealand	4,500
TOTAL	60,500

Jewish Press of the World

by Joseph Fraenkel

LINGUISTIC DISTRIBUTION

Languages	Dailies	Weeklies	Fort-nightlies	Monthlies	Other Papers	Total	Per-centage
Diaspora and Israel: 1,036 Papers							
English	1	82	17	115	138	253	34.07
French	1	3	5	26	22	57	5.50
German	2	8	7	18	2	37	3.57
Hebrew	14	33	10	99	138	294	28.38
Spanish-Portuguese		8	6	28	13	55	5.31
Yiddish	13	39	15	43	51	161	15.54
Other Languages	3	39	6	24	7	79	7.63
TOTAL	34	212	66	353	371	1036	100.00%
Diaspora: 620 Papers (59.85%)							
English	—	78	16	95	99	288	46.45
French	—	2	4	29	10	45	7.26
German	—	6	6	14	2	28	4.52
Hebrew	—	1	2	10	14	27	4.35
Spanish-Portuguese	—	8	6	28	13	55	8.87
Yiddish	12	36	12	40	46	146	23.55
Other Languages	—	9	3	16	3	31	5.00
TOTAL	12	140	49	226	193	620	100.00%
Israel: 416 Papers (40.15%)							
English	1	4	1	20	39	65	15.63
French	1	1	1	3	6	12	2.88
German	2	2	1	4	—	9	2.16
Hebrew	14	32	8	89	124	267	64.18
Yiddish	1	3	3	3	5	15	3.61
Other Languages	3	30	3	8	4	48	11.54
TOTAL	22	72	17	127	178	416	100.00%

GEOGRAPHIC DISTRIBUTION

	Number of Papers	Percentage
Europe	158	15.25
Africa	45	4.34
Asia	422	40.73
Australia and New Zealand	16	1.55
Canada	18	1.74
United St.tes	254	24.52
Central and South America	123	11.87
Total	1036	100.00%

I. EUROPE

AUSTRIA

Monthlies

Die Stimme, Universitaetsstrasse 4, Vienna, IX.

Juedisches Echo, Seitenstettengasse 2, Vienna, I.

Neue Welt, Hutweidengasse 34, Vienna, XIX.

Renaissance, Seitenstettengasse 2, Vienna, I.

Tribuene, Judenplatz 8, Vienna, I.

BELGIUM

Fortnightly

Tribune Sioniste, 6, rue de Crayer, Bruxelles.

Monthly

Kehilatenou, 2, rue Joseph Dupont, Bruxelles.

Lebn un Sholem (Yiddish), 375, rue Haute, Bruxelles.

Menorah, 11 rue de la Concorde, Bruxelles.

Quarterly

La Centrale (Flemish-Yiddish), Lange Leemstraat 155, Antwerpen

BULGARIA

Monthly

Yevreysky Vesti, Exarch Josif No. 61, Sofia.

CZECHOSLOVAKIA

Monthly

Vestnik, Maislova 18, Prague.

DENMARK

Monthlies

Israel, Ny Kongensgade 6, Copenhagen.

Jodisk Samfund, Olgasvej 42, Vedbaek.

EIRE

Annual

Irish Jewish Year Book, Zion School, Bloomfield Avenue, Dublin.

FRANCE

News Agencies

Informations de l'Agence de Presse Juive, 27, rue du Mont-Thabor, Paris, 1e.

Nouvelles Juives Mondiales, 27, rue de Berri, Paris, 8e.

Yiddish Dailies

Naje Presse, 127, Fg. Poisonnière, Paris 9e.

Unzer Stimme, 20 rue Ferdinand Duval, Paris 4e.

Unzer Wort, 45, rue de Chabrol, Paris, 10e.

Weeklies

Sionistiche Schtime (Yiddish), 2, square Trudaine, Paris, 9e.

La Tribune Sioniste, 135, Avenue de Wagram, Paris, 17e.

Unzer Weg (Yiddish), 4, rue Martel, Paris, 10e.

Fortnightlies

Arbeter Wort (Yiddish), 15, rue Béranger, Paris, 3e.

Bulletin de nos Communautés, 18, rue de l'Observatoire, Strasbourg.

Journal de la Communautés, 17, rue St. Georges, Paris, 9e.

Terre Retrouvée, 12, rue de la Victoire, Paris, 9e.

Monthlies

A Jovö (Hungarian), 56 rue St., Georges, Paris 9e.

Al Hamischmar, 17, rue de la Victoire, Paris, 9e.

Ami, 14, rue Georges Berger, Paris, 8e.

Amif-Association des Médicins Israélites de France, 7, rue de Bucarest, Paris, 8e.

Amitiés: France-Israel, 135 Avenue de Wagram, Paris, 17e.

Bulletin d'Information de l'Association Culturel Israélite de Grenoble, 20 rue de Paris, Grenoble.

Bulletin Mensuel de la Circonscription Consistonale Israélite de Lyon, 13, quai de Tilsitt, Lyon.

Cale Bianca, 44 rue Blanche, Paris, 9e.

Conversation avec les Jeunes, 80, rue St. Antoine, Paris, 4e.

Droit et Liberté, 10, rue de Châteaudun, Paris, 9e.

Evidences, 30, rue de Boëtie, Paris, 8e.

Far Ounzere Kinder (Yiddish), 36 Rue Amelot, Paris 11e.

Freie Horizonten (Yiddish), 306, rue des Pyrénées, Paris, 20e.

La Femme-Pionniere (French-Yiddish), 106, rue Vieille du Temple, Paris, 4e.

La Revue Juive de Lorraine, 16, rue du Grand Rabbin Haguenauer, Nancy.

La Voix Sioniste, 2, square Trudaine, Paris, 9e.

Le Rayon, 24 rue Copernic, Paris, 16e.

Les Cahiers de l'Alliance Israélite Universelle, 45, rue La Bruyère, Paris, 9e.

Notre Drapeau, 13, rue de Lancry, Paris, 10e.

Notre Volonté (French-Yiddish), 18, rue des Messageries, Paris, 10e.

Renaissance, 117, rue de Breteuil, Marseilles.

Revue de la WIZO, 24, rue du Mont-Thabor, Paris, 1e.

Theater Spigel (Yiddish), 25, rue de Lancry, Paris, 11e.

Trait d'Union, 31, rue de Montevideo, Paris, 16e.

Quarterly

Fonds Social Juif Unifié, 19 rue de Teheran, Paris, 9e.

Frailand (Yiddish), 6, rue Quatrefages, Paris, 6e.

Les Lettres Juives Francaises, 17, rue St. Georges, Paris 9e.

Le Monde Juif, 27, rue Guénégaud, Paris, 6e.

Periodicals

Agir, 46, rue St. Didier, Paris, 16e.

Far Ounzere Kinder (Yiddish), 36, rue Amelot, Paris, 11e.

Freie Horizonten (Yiddish), 306, rue des Pyrénées, Paris, 20e.

Images de la Vie, 232, rue de Charenton, Paris, 12e.

Kadimah, 6, rue Lalande, Paris, 14e.

La Revue d'Histoire de Médecine Hébraïque (French-Hebrew), 55 rue de Clichy, Paris, 9e.

La Revue Juive de Champagne, 16 rue Charbonnet, Troyes.

La Vie Juive, 78, Avenue des Champs-Elysées, Paris, 8e.

Les Cahiers Séfardis, 18, Boulevard Bineau, Neuilly-sur-Seine.

Notre Communauté, 6, rue de l'As de Carreau, Belfort.

Targoum, 89 rue de Seine, Paris, 6e.

Volksguezunt (Yiddish), 2 bis, Avenue de Villars, Paris, 7e.

Irregular

La Semaine Juive, 23 bis, rue Dufrénoy, Paris, 16e.

Les Eclaireurs Israélites, 27 avenue de Ségur, Paris, 7e.

GERMANY

Weeklies

Allgemeine Wochenzeitung der Juden in Deutschland, Hildener Strasse 35a, Duesseldorf-Benrath.

Neue Juedische Zeitung (Yiddish), Heberl Strasse 7, Munich.

Three times per month

Muenchener Juedische Nachrichten, Liebher Strasse 19,, Munich.

Monthlies

Frankfurter Juedisches Gemeindeblatt, Hebel Strasse 17, Frankfurt a. main.

Juedische Illustrierte, Hildener Strasse 35a, Duesseldorf-Benrath.

Juedische Sozialarbeit, Hebel Strasse 17, Frankfurt a. Main.

Mitteilungsblatt der Israeliten Badens, Kriegsstrasse 154, Karlsruhe.

Quarterlies

Baderech, Joachimstaler Strasse 13, Berlin, W. 15.

GREAT BRITAIN

News Agencies

Jewish Chronicle Feature and News Service, 37, Furnival Street, London, E.C.4. Tel.: HOLborn 9252.

The Jewish Telegraphic Agency, 58, Fleet Street, London, E.C.4. Tel.: CENtral 3821.

Jewish World News Agency, Yiddish, 66, Woodlands, London, N.W.11. Tel.: SPEedwell 7935.

Weekly News Digest, 77, Great Russell Street, London, W.C.1. Tel.: MUSeum 3817.

World Jewish Affairs, News and Feature Service, 55, New Cavendish Street, London, W.1. Tel.: WELbeck 0335.

Weeklies

Jewish Chronicle, 32, Furnival Street, London, E.C.4. Tel.: HOLborn 9252.

Jewish Echo, 252, Crown Street, Glasgow, C.5. Tel.: SOUth 2466.

Jewish Gazette, 151, Cheetham Hill Road, Manchester, 8.

Jewish Observer and Middle East Review, 129, Salisbury Square House, London, E.C.4.; Tel.: CENtral 3879

Jewish Telegraph, Levi House, Bury Old Road, Manchester, 8.

Jewish Voice (Yiddish), 11-13, New Road, London, E.1.; Tel.: BIShopsgate 9804.

Fortnightlies

Jewish Post (English-Yiddish), 257, Seven Sisters Road, London, N.4.; Tel.: ARChway 4200.

Jewish Review, 345, Grays Inn Road, London, W.C.1.; Tel.: TERminus 9594.

Jewish Vanguard, 2, Bloomsbury Place, London, W.C.1.; Tel. MUSeum 4702.

Monthlies

A.J.R. Information, 8, Fairfax Mansions, Finchley Road, London, N.W.3.; Tel.: MAIda Vale 9096.

Ex-Servicemen, 3, Circus Road, London, N.W.8.; Tel.: PRImrose 6020.

Iton Bnei Akivah, 345 Gray's Inn Road, London, W.C.1. Tel.: TERminus 0417.

Jewish Gazette, 3 Centreville Road, Liverpool, 18.

Jewish Recorder, 51 Westfield Road, Birmingham, 16.

Labour Israel, 37, Broadhurst Gardens, London, N.W.6.; Tel.: MAIda Vale 1993.

Liberal Jewish Monthly, 28, St. John's Wood Road, London, N.W.6.; Tel.: CUNningham 5181.

Loshen un Lebn (Yiddish). 129-131, Cavell Street, London, E.1.; Tel.: BIShopsgate 0268.

Maccabi Times, 73, Compayne Gardens, London, N.W.6.; Tel.: MAIda Vale 3755.

Synagogue Review, 33, Seymour Place, London, W.1.; Tel.: PADdington 4404.

Young Zionist, 77 Great Russell St., London, W.C.1. Tel.: MUSeum 3815.

Bi-Monthlies

Boneh, 36, Wellington Street, London, W.C.2.; Tel.: TEMple Bar 7646

Jewish Woman's Review, 107, Gloucester Place, London, W.1.; Tel.: WELbeck 0506.

Pioneer Women News, 57, Eton Avenue, London, N.W.3.; Tel.: PRImrose 9632.

Tarbuth (Hebrew), 77, Great Russell Street, London, W.C.1.; Tel.: MUSeum 3817.

Wiener Library Bulletin, 19, Manchester Square, London, W.1.; Tel.: WELbeck 4991.

Quarterlies

A.J.A. Quarterly, Woburn House, Upper Woburn Place, London, W.C.1. Tel.: EUSton 5937.

Cajex, 71 Canada Road, Heath, Cardiff.

Gates of Zion, (Hebrew-English), 77, Great Russell Street, London, W.C.1.; Tel.: MUSeum 3817.

Habimah, Savile Mount, Leeds 7.

Hamoreh, 28, East Bank, London, N. 16. Tel.: STAmford Hill 1436.

Illustrated Technion News, 83 Wimpole St., London, W.1. Tel.: HUNter 0356.

Iton Habonim, 36, Wellington Street, London, W.C.2.; Tel.: TEMple Bar 7646.

Jewish Quarterly, 68 Worcester Crescent, London, N.W.7; Tel.: MILl Hill 2268.

Jewish Youth, 33, Berner St., London, E.1.

Journal of Jewish Studies, Stenecourt, Singleton Road, Salford 7.

Le Judaisme Sephardi (English-French), 67/68 Hatton Garden, London, E.C.1, Tel.: CHAncery 4556.

Menorah, Woburn House, Upper Woburn Place, London, W.C.1.; Tel.: EUSton 3825.

Sheffield Jewish Journal, 23, Bowling Green St., Sheffield, 3.

Youth Aliyah Review, 233, Baker Street, London, N.W.1.; Tel. WELbeck 3855.

Periodicals

Bulletin of the Technion, 83, Wimpole Street, London, W.1.; Tel.: HUNter 0356.

Chayenu, 345, Gray's Inn Road, London, W.C.1. Tel.: TERminus 0417.

Jewish Academy, 1, Endsleigh St., London, W.C.1. Tel.: EUSton 8843.

Jewish Clarion, 27 Bedford St., London, W.C.2.

Sifrut, 77, Great Russell St., London, W.1. Tel.: MUSeum 3815.

Yidische Shriften (Yiddish), 31, Balfour Road, London, N.5.

Annuals

Jewish Annual, Clifton House, Worship St., London E.C.2.

Hashanah, 6, Dixon St., Glasgow.

Jewish Year Book, 37, Furnival Street, London, E.C.4.; Tel.: HOLborn 9252.

Joint Palestine Appeal Year Book, 75, Great Russell Street, London, W.C.1.; Tel.: MUSeum 3815.

Moledet, 65, Southampton Row, London, W.C.1.; Tel.: MUSeum 6111.

Shalom, Zion House, 8, Princes Road, Liverpool, 8.

Zionist Year Book, 77, Great Russell Street, London, W.C.1.; Tel.: MUSeum 3817.

GREECE

Fortnightly

Evraiki Estia, 24, Alikarnassou Street, Athens, 2.

HOLLAND

Weekly

Nieuw Israelietisch Weekblad, Utrechtsestraat 44, Amsterdam-C.

Fortnightly

De Joodse Wachter, Johannes Vermeerstraat 22, Amsterdam-Z

Monthly

Niw Hanoar, Utrechtsestraat 44, Amsterdam-C.

HUNGARY

Monthly

Uj Elet, Sip-utca 12, Budapest, VII.

ITALY

Weeklies

Israel, Corso Vittorio Emanuele 173, Roma.

Monthlies

Voce della Comunita di Roma, Lungotevere Cenci (Tempio), Roma.

Bollettino della Comunità Israelitica, Via Guastella, 19, Milano.

He-Chaluz, Tel Broshim, S. Marco, Cevoli (Pisa).

Rassegna Mensile di Israel, Lungotevere Sanzio, 9, Roma.

NORWAY

Monthly

SJUF Bladet (Norwegian-Swedish), Hovedledelsen, P.O.B. 740, Oslo.

POLAND

Four times a week

Folks-Sztyme (Yiddish), Nowogrodzka 5, Warsaw.

Monthly

Idisze Szriftn (Yiddish), Nowogrodzka 5, Warsaw.

Quarterlies

Bleter far Geszichte (Yiddish), Gen. Swierczewskiego 79, Warsaw.

Biuletyn Zydowskiego Instytutu Historycznego, ul. Gen. Swierczewskiego 79, Warsaw.

RUMANIA

Weekly

Viata Noua, str. Matei Basarab 2a Bucarest.

RUSSIA

Three times weekly

Birobidzhaner Shtern (Yiddish), Birobidzhan.

SWEDEN

Fortnightly

Judisk Krönika, Valhallavägen 106, Stockholm.

Monthlies

Judisk Tidsskrift, Rättviksvägen 30, Bromma.

Judisk Hem, Mössebergsvägen 114, Bromma.

Quarterly

Församlingsbladet, Wahrendorffsgatan 3, Stockholm, 7.

SWITZERLAND

Weeklies

Israelitisches Wochenblatt, Uraniastrasse 9, Zurich.

Juedische Rundschau Maccabi, Postfach 14, Basel, 12.

Monthly

Das Neue Israel, Bederstrasse 78, Zurich.

TURKEY

Weeklies

La Vera Luz (Ladino-Turkish), Tahtakale, Djaddesi Prevuayans Han 12, Istanbul.

La Luz de Türkiya (Ladino-Turkish), Mumhane Caddesi No. 102 (P.O.B.) Posta kutusu 1812, Galata, Istanbul.

L'étoile du Levant (French), Beyoglu Galipdede Cad 59, Istanbul.

Salom (Ladino-Turkish), Sair Ziya Pasa Caddesi, Bereket Han 24/5, Galata.

YUGOSLAVIA

Monthly

Bilten Saveza Jevrejskih Opstina Jugoslavije, Sedmoga Jula ul. 71, Beograd.

Annual

Jevrejski Almanah, Sedmoga Jula ul. 71, Beograd.

II. AFRICA

ALGIERS

Monthly

Information Juive, 21, Boulevard Bugeaud, Alger.

Annual

Annuaire du Judaisme Nord-Africain, 21, Boulevard Bugeaud, Alger.

KENYA
Monthly

East African Jewish Review. P.O. Box 5211, Nairobi.

MOROCCO (French)
Monthly

La Voix des Communautés, 12, rue Delcasse, Rabat.

Bulletin des Jeunes,
12 rue Prom, Casablanca.

SOUTH AFRICA
Agency

Jewish Telegraphic Agency, P.O. Box 7594, Johannesburg.

Weeklies

African Jewish Newspaper (Yiddish), 45, Old Arcade, 100, Market Street, Johannesburg.

Jewish Herald,, 19/24, Stability Building, 106, Fox Street, Johannesburg.

South African Jewish Chronicle, P.O. Box 2000, Cape Town.

South African Jewish Times, Eagle House, 19, Rockey Street Doornfontein, Johannesburg.

Zionist Record, P.O. Box 150, Johannesburg.

Fortnightlies

Jewish Family Magazine (German-English), 202, Enfield Court, Kapteijn St., Hillbrow, Johannesburg.

South African Jewish Frontier, 45, Shakespeare House, Commissioner Street, Johannesburg.

Monthlies

Barkai (Hebrew), 60, Shakespeare House, Commissioner Street, Johannesburg.

Eetar, Amsterdam House, Quartz House, Johannesburg.

Dapim (Hebrew), P.O. Box 5486, Johannesburg.

Dorem Afrike (Yiddish), 62, Security Building, 95, Commissioner Street, Johannesburg

Federation Chronicle, 24, Raleigh Street, Yeoville, Johannesburg.

Habinyan, Vanguard House, Cor. Troye & Market Sts., Johannesburg.

Hamadrich, Vanguard House, Cor. Troye & Market Sts., Johannesburg.

Hamatmid, P.O.Box 18, Johannesburg.

Hasholom, P.O. Box 2198, Durban.

Jewish Affairs, P.O. Box 1180, Johannesburg.

Jewish Guild Newsletter, P.O. Box 2934, Johannesburg.

Lanoar, P.O.B. 1588, Capetown.

Looking Ahead, 10, Unity House, 100, Fox Street, Johannesburg.

News and Views, P.O. Box 18, Johannesburg.

Pretoria Jewish Review, 36 Tudor Chambers, Church St., Pretoria.

Shtilim Post, Cor. Troye & Market Streets, Johannesburg.

South African Jewish Observer (Yiddish-English), 8, Store Bros. Building, Eloff Street, Johannesburg.

Temple David Review, P.O.B. 1874, Durban.

World Ose News, 10, Unity House, 100, Fox St., Johannesburg.

Zionist Mirror, 201, Commissioner House, 50 Commissioner St., Johannesburg.

Quarterlies

Ha-Yam, P.O.Box 4023, Cape Town.

Judean, P.O. Box 3995, Johannesburg.

Progressive Jew, P.O. Box 8133, Johannesburg.

Irregulars

Hakinor, University of Capetown.

H.O.D. Journal, 138, Marshall Street, Johannesburg.

Oif Afrike's Erd (Yiddish),
P.O.Box 4241, Johannesburg.

S. A. Maccabi News,
P.O.Box 18, Johannesburg.

Timorim, P.O. Box 9165, Johannesburg.

Annuals

Jewish Guild Annual, P.O.Box 2934, Johannesburg.

South African Jewish Year Book, Fieldhill Publishing House, 19, Rockey Street, Johannesburg.

South African Rosh-Hashanah Year Book, P.O. Box 4263, Johannesburg.

Union of Jewish Women Review, 408, Automutua'l House, 57, De Villiers, Johannesburg.

SOUTHERN RHODESIA

Monthlies

Rhodesian Jewish Times, P. O. Box 1844, Salisbury.

III. ASIA

INDIA

Fortnightly

News from Israel. 50, Pedder Road, Cumballa Hill, Bombay.

Monthlies

Maccabi, Plot No. 50, Ai Mai Merwanji Road, Parel, Bombay 12.

Shema, Morton Bldgs., 1/2, Old Court House Corner, Calcutta.

IRAN

Weekly

Alame Yahoud, 35 Churchill Street, Teheran.

ISRAEL

Dailies

Al Hamishmar, Hamasger Street, Tel Aviv.

Bamahaneh La'Oleh, Israel Defence Forces.

Davar, 45, Sheinkin Street, Tel Aviv.

Echo d'Israel (French), 113 Givat Herzl St., Tel Aviv.

El-Yom (Arabic), Street 10, No. 6, Jaffa.

Ha'aretz, 56, Maze Street, Tel Aviv.

Haboker, 32, Harakevet Street, Tel Aviv.

Hakol, P.O. Box 700, Jerusalem.

Hamodia, 1, Yehudit Street, Jerusalem.

Hatzofeh, 16, Herzl St., Tel Aviv.

Herut, 38, King George Street, Tel Aviv.

Israelski Far (Bulgarian), 11 Sharon Street, Tel Aviv.

Jerusalem Post (English), P.O. Box 81, Jerusalem.

Kol Ha'am, Eilat Street, Tel Aviv.

Lamerhav, 9 Rothschild Blvd., Tel Aviv.

Letzte Neies (Yiddish), 52 Levinsky St., Tel Aviv.

Omer, 45, Sheinkin Street, Tel Aviv.

She'arim, 34, Ahad Ha'am Street, Tel Aviv.

Uj Kelet (Hungarian), 11 Hanegev Street, Tel Aviv.

Yedioth Chadashoth (German), 66, Harakevet Street, Tel Aviv.

Yedioth Hayom (German), 11, Bialik Street, Tel Aviv.

Evening Papers

Ma'ariv, 20 Bnei Brak Street, Tel Aviv.

Yediot Aharonot, P.O.Box 109, Tel Aviv.

Bi and Tri-Weeklies

Al-Ittihad (Arabic), P.O. Box 104, Haifa.

Express Israelski (Polish), 6, Lilienblum St., Tel Aviv.

Kurier Israelski (Polish), 6, Lilienblum St., Tel Aviv.

Lumea Noastra (Rumanian) 52, Harakevet St., Tel Aviv.

Nowiny Poranne (Polish), 85, Allenby Rd., Tel Aviv.

Ora (Rumanian), P.O.B. 736, Tel Aviv.

Viata Noastra (Rumanian), 52, Harakevet Street, Tel Aviv.

Vointa (Rumanian), 12, Erlanger Street, Tel Aviv.

Zerile (Rumanian), II, Hanegev St., Tel Aviv

Weeklies

Adverul (Rumanian), 18, Tarshish St., Jaffa.

Al Hurriya (Arabic), 38, King George St., Tel Aviv.

Al Mirsad (Arabic), 20, Rothschild Blvd., Tel Aviv.

Bakibbutz, 21, Rothschild Blvd., Tel Aviv.

Bamahaneh, Israel Defence Forces.

Davar Liladim, 45, Sheinkin Street, Tel Aviv.

Devar Hashavua, 45, Sheinkin Street, Tel Aviv.

Dimineata (Rumanian), 33, Hahashmal St., Tel Aviv.

Echo, 19, Gruzenberg Street, Tel Aviv.

Ehad Efes, Shikun Havatikim, Ramat Gan.

El Tiempo (Ladino), 99, Ben Yehuda St., Tel Aviv.

Frei Yisroel (Yiddish), 6 Hamagid Street, Tel Aviv.

Glasul Populurui (Rumanian), P.O.B. 2675, Tel Aviv.

Ha'aretz Shelanu, 56, Maze Street, Tel Aviv.

Haifa Haovedet, P.O.B. 4931, Haifa.

Ha'iton Hademocrati, 5, Yavne St., Tel Aviv.

Hakidmah (German), 15, Rambam Street, Tel Aviv.

Hakikat al Amr (Arabic), 2, Mikveh Israel, Tel Aviv.

Hakulmos, P.O.Box 666, Tel Aviv.

Hamodia Hatzair, 1, Yehudit Street, Jerusalem.

Ha'olam Hazeh, 8, Glickson Street, Tel Aviv.

Hapoel Hatzair, P.O. Box 36, Tel Aviv.

Hashavua—A Hét (Hungarian) P. O. Box 1442, Tel Aviv.

Hashavua Bakibbutz Ha'Artzi, Merhavya.

Hasifrut Hazionit, P.O.B. 92, Jerusalem.

Hatzofeh Liladim, 16, Herzl Street, Tel Aviv.

Haye Sha'a, P.O.Box 2670, Tel Aviv.

Hed Hahinnuch, Executive Committee Bldg., 93, Arlosoroff Street, Tel Aviv.

Herut Lanoar, P.O.B. 1878, Tel Aviv.

Herut Lanoar, 38, King George St., Tel Aviv.

Iggeret Lahaverim, 123, Hayarkon Street, Tel Aviv.

Iggeret Lashlihim, P.O.B. 92, Jerusalem.

Isgrev (Bulgarian), 38, Zevulun Street, Tel Aviv.

Israeli Kepeslap (Hungarian), 11, Hanegev Street, Tel Aviv.

Jewish Agency's Digest of Press & Events (English), P.O.B. 92, Jerusalem.

Kolnoa, 28, Kalisher Street, Tel Aviv.

Koresh (Persian), Shekhunat Makkabi Hahadasha, Tel Aviv.

Labour in Israel (English), Histadrut Bldg., Arlosoroff St., Tel Aviv.

La'isha, 7, Pin Street, Tel Aviv.

Lamerhav (Arabic), 9, Rotschild Blvd., Tel Aviv.

Lamerhav (Bulgarian), 9, Rothschild Blvd., Tel Aviv.

La Semaine d'Israel (French), P.O.B.1607, Tel Aviv.

La Verdad (Ladino), 40, Petah Tikva St., Tel Aviv.

Mahanayim, Z.H.L.

Massa, 60, Rothschild Boulevard, Tel Aviv.

Mishmar Liladim, Hamasger Street, Tel Aviv.

Mishmeret, P.O.Box 5069, Jerusalem.

Mitteilungsblatt (German), 15, Rambam Street, Tel Aviv.

Narodno Dielo (Bulgarian), 110, Hayarkon Street, Tel Aviv.

Narodne Glas (Bulgarian), P.O. Box 2675, Tel Aviv.

Neiwelt (Yiddish), P.O.Box 2719, Tel Aviv.

Oif der Wach (Yiddish), P.O.Box 806, Tel Aviv.

Olam Hakolnoa, 2, Pinsker Street, Tel Aviv.

Piskei Din Shel Beit Hamishpat Ha'elyon Le-Israel, Ministry of Justice.

Podem (Bulgarian), 101, Jerusalem Blvd., Jaffa.

Przeglad (Polish), 10, Karl Netter Street, Tel Aviv.

Realitatea Ilustrata (Rumanian), 22, Lilienblum Street, Tel Aviv.

Reshumot (Hebrew-Arabic), Government Printer.

She'arim Lanoar, 34, Ahad Haam Street, Tel Aviv.

Svoboda Rasvet (Bulgarian), 4, Ben Shemen St., Haifa.

Sport La'am, P.O. Box 714, Tel Aviv.

Yalkut Agaf Hamechez Vehablo, Haifa.

Fortnightlies

Al Rabita (Arabic) P.O.Box 279, Haifa.

Bama'aleh, 2, Mikve Israel Street, Tel Aviv.

Bemahane Gadna, Israel Defence Forces.

Cronicas (Spanish), P.O.B. 92, Jerusalem.

Dos Yiddishe Licht (Yiddish), P.O.Box 5071, Jerusalem.

Folk un Zion (Yiddish), P.O.B. 92, Jerusalem.

Hameshek Hashitufi, P.O.B. 130, Tel Aviv.

Harefuah, 9, Yavneh Street, Tel Aviv.

Israel Tourist (English), 35, Nahmani Street, Tel Aviv.

Kalkalan, P.O.B. 7052, Jerusalem.

Michtav Lehaver, Mesillat Yesharim Street, Jerusalem.

Modiin, P.O.B. 588, Jerusalem.

Revue de la Presse et des Evènéments (French), P.O.B. 92, Jerusalem.

Sada al Tarbieh (Arabic), 2, Mikve Israel Street, Tel Aviv.

Tatzpit, 33, Yehuda Halevy St., Tel Aviv.

Unser Ziel (German), P.O.Box 900, Tel Aviv.

Zammlung (Yiddish), Ministry of Defence.

Monthlies

Al Akhbar al Kanassiyah (Arabic), P.O.Box 1796, Haifa.

Al Hamishmar (Bulgarian), P.O.Box 806, Tel Aviv.

Al Jadid (Arabic), P.O.Box 104, Haifa.

Al Mujtama (Arabic), P.O.Box 51, Nazareth.

Alon Amidar, Ibn Gabirol St., Tel Aviv.

Alon Hamazkirut, P.O.Box 54, Netanya.

Alon Hayetzu, Ministry of Commerce and Industry, Jerusalem.

Aloneh, 1 Allenby Rd., Tel Aviv.

Azor On, 18 Brenner St., Tel Aviv.

Bemahane Hanahal, Ministry of Defence, Tel Aviv.

Bamivhan, 20, Levontin Street, Tel Aviv.

Barechev, P.O.Box 1723, Tel Aviv.

Bat Kol, 35 Nahmani St., Tel Aviv.

Beterem, 13, Disraeli St., Jerusalem.

Betochenu, P.O.B. 283, Jerusalem.

Bisnif Habirah, P.O.Box 1022, Jerusalem.

Bitui, P.O.Box 7065, Jerusalem.

B'telem, 6, Reines St., Tel Aviv.

Business Diary (English), 37, Harbour St., Haifa.

Chronicles (English), 10, Ibn Gabirol Street, Jerusalem.

Commerce (English), 30, Levontin Street, Tel Aviv.

Da et Haifa Ircha, Iriyat Haifa, Haifa.

Die Chronik (German), 10, Ibn Gabirol St., Jerusalem.

Die Stimme (German), 7, Frishman St., Tel Aviv.

Diglenu, 26, Ahad Haam Street, Tel Aviv.

Divrei Hayamim, 10, Ibn Gabirol Street, Jerusalem.

Doar, Government Printer, Jerusalem.

Dvar Hapoelet, 93, Arlosoroff Street, Tel Aviv.

Ecos de Israel (Spanish), P.O. Box 92, Jerusalem.

Eitanim, 64, Frishman Street Tel Aviv.

El-Al (Hebrew-English), 76, Maze St., Tel Aviv.

El Alam el Musawwar, (Arabic), P.O.Box 8511, Jaffa.

El Ekha (Arabic), P.O.Box 1376, Haifa.

Facts and Figures (English), Keren Hayesod Head Office, Jerusalem.

Gan Hahayot Hatenachi, Jerusalem Zoo, Jerusalem.

Gazit, P.O.Box 4190, Tel Aviv.

Habulai Ha'ivri (Hebrew-English), P.O.Box 1280, Tel Aviv.

Hahayal Hameshuhrar, P.O.Box 2420, Tel Aviv.

Hahodesh, P.O.B. 303, Tel Aviv.

Hakablan Vehaboneh, 19, Levontin Street, Tel Aviv.

Hameshek Hahaklai, 21, Melchett Street, Tel Aviv.

Hameshek Hazair (German), 21, Melchett St., Tel Aviv.

Hamifal, Citrus House, Tel Aviv.

Hamis'har (Hebrew-English), 30, Levontin Street, Tel Aviv.

Hamussach, 13 Petah Tikva St., Tel Aviv.

Ha'oved Hatzioni, 34, Allenby Road, Tel Aviv.

Harashut Hamkomit, Executive Committee Bldg., Arlosoroff Street, Tel Aviv.

Harofe Bahistadrut, 93, Arlosoroff St., Tel Aviv.

Hasechel, Esther Hamalka Street, Tel Aviv.

Hashilton Hamekomi, 45, Reines Street, Tel Aviv.

Hassadeh, 23, Lilienblum Street, Tel Aviv.

Hassadeh Lagan Velanoü, 23, Lilienblum St., Tel Aviv.

Hassadeh Lanoar, 23, Lilienblum Street, Tel Aviv.

Hassadeh Lemeshek Ha'ofot, 23, Lilienblum Street, Tel Aviv.

Hata'assiyah, 13, Montefiore St., Tel Aviv.

Hatevah ve Haaretz, 4, Mendele Street, Tel Aviv.

Ha'Uman, 16, Baale Melacha Street, Tel Aviv.

Hazon, P.O.B. 1743, Tel Aviv.

Hed Hanegev, P.O.B. 15, Beersheba.

Heimish (Yiddish), P.O.Box 9046, Tel Aviv.

Hu ve'Hee, P.O.Box 2760, Tel Aviv.

Iggeret Lagannenet, 6, Reines Street, Tel Aviv.

In the Field of Building (Hebrew-English), P.O.Box 4910, Haifa.

Israel au Travail (French), Histadrut Bldg., Arlosoroff St., Tel Aviv.

Israel Economic Indicators (Hebrew-English) Central Bureau of Statistics, Jerusalem.

Israel Economist (English), 16, King George Street, Jerusalem.

Israel Export Journal (English), 13, Montefiore Street, Tel Aviv.

Israel Vista (English), P.O.B. 283, Jerusalem.

Karnenu, P.O. Box 283, Jerusalem.

Kontress Bibliographi, 38, Yehuda Halevy Street, Tel Aviv.

Koor, P.O.Box 356, Tel Aviv.

La Koreh Hatzair, P.O.B. 80, Tel Aviv.

Layarkan Hamathil, P.O.Box 4, Tel Aviv.

Lebnsfragen (Yiddish), 25, Aaronsohn St., Tel Aviv.

Leket, Misrad Habitahon, Hakirya.

Lemitarim Bamahane Gadna, Ministry of Defence, Tel Aviv.

Leshonenu La'am, 32, King George Street, Jerusalem.

Likutim, Tel Aviv Municipality, Tel Aviv.

Maba, P.O.B. 28, Tel Aviv.

Maccabi World Review (English-Spanish), P.O.Box 76, Tel Aviv.

Mar'ot Hakalkala Beisrael, P.O.Box 3015, Jerusalem.

Massad, 10, Solomon St., Tel Aviv.

Mevo'ot, 52, Harakevet Street, Tel Aviv.

Misparim, K. H. Head Office, Jerusalem.

Molad, 52 Harakevet Street, Tel Aviv.

Moledet (Spanish), P.O.B. 92, Jerusalem.

Monthly Review of Labour and National Insurance (Hebrew-English), Ministry of Labour, Jerusalem.

Moznayim, P.O.Box 4151, Tel Aviv.

Ner, P.O.B. 451, Jerusalem.

Netiva, 112, Rothschild Boulevard, Tel Aviv.

Newsletter (English), Government Tourist Centre, P.O.Box 1018, Jerusalem.

Nivenu, Iriyat Haifa, Haifa.

Nivim, 123, Hayarkon Street, Tel Aviv.

Orot, P.O.Box 92, Jerusalem.

Pirsumim, 38, King George St., Tel Aviv.

Revivim (French), P.O.Box 92, Jerusalem.

Shedemot, 18a Brenner Street, Tel Aviv.

Shituf, 6 Mikve Israel Street, Tel Aviv.

Shluhot, P.O.B. 92, Jerusalem.

Shorashim, 99, Ben Yehuda St., Tel Aviv.

Shurot, Arlosoroff Street, Vaad Hapoel, Tel Aviv.

Sinai, P.O.B. 642, Jerusalem.

Statistical Bulletin of Israel (Hebrew-English), Central Bureau of Statistics, Jerusalem.

Sulam, Sansur Bldg., Room 246, Jerusalem.

Tashbetzon, P.O.Box 8117, Tel Aviv.

Tesha-Tesha-Tesha, 9 King George St., Tel Aviv.

Tlamim, 6, Reines Street, Tel Aviv.

The Holy Land Philatelist (English), 13, Montefiore St., Tel Aviv.

Toren, Dapim Leveith Zim, P.O.B. 1723, Haifa.

Traklin, 2, Pinsker Street, Tel Aviv.

Urim, 6, Reines Street, Tel Aviv.

Urim Lahorim, P.O.Box 77, Tel Aviv.

Visages d'Israel (French), P.O.Box 92, Jerusalem.

Weg und Ziel (German), P. O. Box 900, Tel Aviv.

Wizo Baaretz Uvatefuzot, 8, Beit Hashoeva Lane, Tel Aviv.

Wizo in Israel (English-German-French), 8, Beit Hashoeva Lane, Tel Aviv.

Yachdav, P.O.Box 2086, Tel Aviv.

Yarhon Brit Hacooperatzia Hazarchanit, P.O.B. 130, Tel Aviv.

Yam, P.O.B. 1917, Tel Aviv.

Yarhon Ha'Avoda, Ministry of Labour.

Yedidut Israel-USSR, 1, Aliyah St., Tel Aviv

Yediot Hakibbutz Hadati, P.O.Box 1921, Tel Aviv.

Yediot Iriat Ramat Gan.

Yediot Misrad Habriut, Ministry of Health, Jerusalem.

Yediot Tel Aviv-Yafo, 27, Bialik St., Tel Aviv.

Zra'im, P.O.B. 431, Tel Aviv.

Zu Haderech, P.O.Box 2675, Tel Aviv.

Bi-Monthlies

Al Hahoma, P.O.Box 2389, Tel Aviv.

Alumim, 79, Akiba Street, Bnei Brak.

Bamidgeh (Hebrew-English), Nir-David, P.O. Beit-Shean.

Bitahon Vehygiena ba'avoda, P.O.Box 1122, Tel Aviv.

Bitaon Heil Haavir, Israel Defence Forces.

Dapim Refuiyim (English-French-Hebrew), 64, Frishman Street, Tel Aviv.

Habonim (English), P.O.Box 4557, Tel Aviv.

Hahinuch, P.O.Box 303, Tel Aviv.

Hamitzpeh, P.O. Box 2389, Tel Aviv.

Harofeh La'Am, 72, Allenby Road, Tel Aviv.

Haroke'ah Ha'Ivri, 6, Rothschild Blvd., Tel Aviv.

Igeret la'Golah (English), P. O. Box 92, Jerusalem.

Israel Youth Horizon (English), P.O.Box 92, Jerusalem.

Iton Agudat Ha'ingenerim ve ha'architektim (Hebrew-English), 200, Dizengoff Street, Tel Aviv.

Kochav Hamizrah (Persian), P.O.Box 36, Tel Aviv.

Kol Nechei Milhama (Hebrew-Yiddish), P.O.Box 8052, Jaffa.

Maanit, 6, Reines Street, Tel Aviv.

Ma'arachot, Israel Defence Forces.

Ma'arachot Yam, Israel Defence Forces.

Roeh Haheshbon Hamusmach, 9, Shemarya Lewin Street, Tel Aviv.

Shalom (English), 35, Nahmani Street, Tel Aviv.

Shalom, 60, Rothschild Blvd., Tel Aviv.

Yedioth Beit Lohamei Hageta'ot, P.O.Box 520, Haifa.

Yediot Hahevra Hayisre'elit Lema'an Ha'ummot Hameuhadot (Hebrew-English), P.O.B. 628, Jerusalem.

Yediot Lehavrei Tnuat Moshavei Haovdim Beisrael, 6, Reines Street, Tel Aviv.

Quarterlies

Alim, P.O.Box 92, Jerusalem.

Am Vasefer, P.O.Box 1121, Tel Aviv.

Atidot, P.O.Box 92, Jerusalem.

Bamot, P.O.B. 298, Tel Aviv.

Behinot Bevikoret Hasafrut, P.O.B. 92, Jerusalem.

Bitahon Vehygiena Ba'Avoda, P.O.B. 1122, Tel Aviv.

Bulletin of the Research Council of Israel (English), Prime Minister's Office, Jerusalem.

Christian News from Israel (English-French-Spanish), Ministry for Religious Affairs, St. Julian's Way, Jerusalem.

Dapim, Live'ayot Hinnukhiyot Sotzialiyot, Misrad Hasaad, Jerusalem.

Di Goldene Keyt (Yiddish), P.O.Box 303, Tel Aviv.

Dmamah, 12, Yehezkiel Street, Haifa.

Gesher, 24, Montefiore Street, Tel Aviv.

Hama'ayan, P.O.Box 4346, Tel Aviv.

Hamin'hal, P.O. Box 2451, Tel Aviv.

Hamizrah Hehadash, Hebrew University, Jerusalem.

Hapraklit, P.O. Box 788, Tel Aviv.

Hate'ufa, 9, Montefiore Street, Tel Aviv.

Hayamai Hayisraeli, P.O.Box 1324, Haifa.

Hed Hagan, 49, Hovevei Zion Street, Tel Aviv.

Hedim, P.O.Box 92, Jerusalem.

Heye Nachon, 27 Hagra St., Tel Aviv.

Hikrei Avodah (Hebrew-English), Economic and Research Institute, P.O.Box 12, Tel Aviv.

Igereth Lahinuch, 123 Hayarkon Street, Tel Aviv.

Israel Economic Forum (English), Yehuda Halevy Street, Tel Aviv.

Israel Exploration Journal (English), P.O.B. 7010, Jerusalem.

Israel Tourist and Travel Bulletin (Hebrew-English), 68, Sheinkin Street, Tel Aviv.

Iyun, Hebrew University, Jerusalem.

Karnenu (French-German-Hebrew-Spanish-Yiddish), P.O.Box 283, Jerusalem.

Kiriat Sefer, P.O.B. 503, Jerusalem.

Korot (Hebrew-English), Dr. Muntner, Hanevi'im Street, Jerusalem.

Leshonenu, 32, King George St., Jerusalem.

Mada, 33, King George Street, Tel Aviv.

Mahbe'ret, P.O.Box 87, Jerusalem.

Meches Veta'avura, P.O.Box 2433, Tel Aviv.

Mehkarim Ufe'ullot, (Hebrew-English), P.O.Box 7007, Jerusalem.

Megamot, P.O.Box 7018, Jerusalem.

Meshek Habakar Vehehalav, 52a, Maza Street, Tel Aviv.

M'karkein Ve'erkam, (Hebrew-English), P.O.Box 4871, Haifa.

Niv, 33, King George Street, Tel Aviv.

Niv Hakvutza, 123, Hayarkon Street, Tel Aviv.

Niv Harofe, 93, Arlosoroff Street, Tel Aviv.

Orlogin, 73, Allenby Road, Tel Aviv.

Ort Bimdinat Yisrael, Migrashei Hata'arucha, Tel Aviv.

Refua Veterinarit, 126, Allenby Road, Tel Aviv.

Renaissance (French), P.O.Box 92, Jerusalem.

Review of Economic Conditions in Israel (English), Yehuda Halevy St., Tel Aviv.

Riv'on Le'khalkala, 113, Allenby Road, Tel Aviv.

Riv'on Le'matematika, Mr. Yarden, 11 Shikun Kiryat Moshe, Jerusalem.

Scopus (English), Hebrew University, Jerusalem.

Simon's Philatelic Magazine (Hebrew-English), P.O.B. 2926, Tel Aviv.

Tarbitz, P.O.B. 503, Jerusalem.

Tavruah, 26, King George Avenue, Jerusalem.

The Near East, P.O.B. 449, Tel Aviv.

Work (English), Histadrut Executive Committee, 93, Arlosoroff Street, Tel Aviv.

Yalkut Haigud Lemehkar Kerami, Ir Ganim, Doar Kfar Ata, Haifa.

Yediot Brit Pikuah Lacooperatzia Hahaklait, 5, Levontin Street, Tel Aviv.

Yediot Hafakultah Lirefua, P.O.Box 1255, Jerusalem.

Yediot Hahevra Lehakirat Eretz Israel ve-Atikoteha, P.O.Box 7010, Jerusalem.

Yediot Hauniversita Haivrit Biyrushalaim, Hebrew University, Jerusalem.

Ye'ul, Citrus House, Tel Aviv.

Yozma, 6, Rothschild Blvd., Tel Aviv.

Zion, P.O.B. 1062, Jerusalem.

Irregulars

Alon Havaad, c/o Bit'on Ovdei Misrad Hapnim, Jerusalem.

Alon Lefalha, Mispo Umechonot, P.O.B.1678 Haifa.

Alon Mahleket Ha'Atikot, Ministry of Education and Culture, P.O.B. 586, Jerusalem.

Anahnu, P.O.B. 1291, Jerusalem.

Bahinuch Uvatarbut, Ministry of Education and Culture, Jerusalem.

Bama Levituy Veinformatzia Lehavereinu Bamoshavim Uvikfarei Hahityashvut,, P.O.Box 1777, Tel Aviv.

Bamachon (French), P.O.Box 2092, Tel Aviv.

Beitenu, Moetzet Hapoalim, Hedera.

Bema'arechet Haklita, 99, Ben Yehuda Street Tel Aviv.

Bimat Hahovevim, 93, Arlosoroff Street, Tel Aviv.

Beyarketei Hatzafon, Moetzet Hapoalim, Kiryat Shmone.

Bulletin Economique d'Israel (French), Ministry of Commerce and Industry.

Bulletin Igud Oley Sin (Russian), 8, Rothschild Blvd., Tel Aviv.

Dapei Aliyah (English-Hebrew-Yiddish), P.O.Box 92, Jerusalem.

Dapim la'boker, Ministry of Agriculture, Jerusalem.

Divrei Haknesset, Knesset.

Eitanim Liladenu, P.O.B. 12, Tel Aviv.

Forum (English), P.O.B. 92, Jerusalem.

Habira, Iriyat Yerushalaym (Municipality), Jerusalem.

Haikar Haoved (English), 6 Reines Street, Tel Aviv.

Hane'eman, P.O.Box 413, Jerusalem.

Hasherut Habula'i, Ministry of Posts, Jerusalem.

He'avar, P.O.B. 118, Tel-Aviv.

Hed Hadfus, P.O.B. 303, Tel Aviv.

Hed Hamoatza Hadatit, P.O.Box 13, Jerusalem.

Hedim, Merhavya.

Hed Tikvatenu, Musrara, Jerusalem.

Igeret, P.O.Box 373, Jerusalem.

Israel and the Middle East (English), 57, Nahlat Binyamin, Tel Aviv.

Israel Bletter (Yiddish), 21, Aronson Street, Tel Aviv.

Israel Economic Bulletin (English), Ministry of Commerce and Industry, Jerusalem.

Kol Habirah, 6, Shamai Street, Jerusalem.

Kol Hanoar, P.O.Box 3095, Tel Aviv.

Kol Hastudent, Zecharya Street, Jerusalem.

Kol Zion Lagolah (Hebrew-English-French), P.O.B. 92, Jerusalem.

Lema'an Hayeled Vehano'ar, P.O.Box 7018, Jerusalem.

Ma'arachot Hapeles, Israel Defence Forces.

Machberot Lesifrut, 5, Gnessin Street, Tel Aviv.

Megilat Bnei Metzada, P.O.Box 2389, Tel Aviv.

Mibifnim, 98, Allenby Road, Tel Aviv.

Michlol-Histadrut Hastudentim shel Hauniversita Haivrit, P.O.Box 737, Tel Aviv.

Mikeren Zavit, Vaad Ovdei Misrad Mevaker Hamedina, Tel Aviv.

Min Ha'ir el Hakfar, Hahistadrut Haklalit, Arlosoroff Street, Tel Aviv.

Mishpat Vekhalkala, P.O.Box 788, Tel Aviv.

Netivot, P.O.B. 92, Tel Aviv.

Niv Hanegev, Moetzet Hapoalim, Beersheva.

Ofakim, 73 Allenby Street, Tel Aviv.

Olam Hasefer, 78, Ahad Haam Street, Tel Aviv.

Olamenu, Beth Haholim Leholei Nefesh, Kfar Shaul, Jerusalem.

Petah Tikva, P.O.Box 1, Petah Tikva.

Philatelic Services (English), 132, Allenby Rd., Tel Aviv.

Shikum, 6, Gruzenberg Street, Tel Aviv.

Thahar (French), P.O.Box 2092, Tel Aviv.

Torat Hayyim, P.O.B. 92, Jerusalem.

Tziklon, Israel Defense Forces.

Yalkut Magen, P.O.Box 4530, Tel Aviv.

Yalkut Techni, 22, Harakeveth Street, Tel Aviv.

Yeda Am, 23, Lilienblum Street, Tel Aviv.

Yediot Bahan, P.O.B. 622, Tel Aviv.

Yediot Hamahlaka ha'muslemit veha'druzit (Arabic), Ministry for Religious Affairs, Jerusalem.

Yediot Hitahdut ba'alei Kolnoa be'Israel, P.O.Box 4560, Tel Aviv.

Yediot Misrad Hahinuch veha'tarbut, Ministry of Education and Culture, Jerusalem.

Yediot Yad Vashem (Hebrew-Yiddish), 12, Ben Yehuda Street, Jerusalem.

Yovel, Ashkelon.

Annuals

Almanahul Alialei Romane (Rumanian), P.O.Box 2592, Tel Aviv.

Facts and Figures (English), Government Press Division.

Government Yearbook (English), Government Printer.

Israel Argosy (English), P.O.Box 92, Jerusalem.

Israel Economist Annual (English), P.O.B. 7052, Jerusalem.

Israel Industry (Hebrew-English), P.O.Box 2032, Tel Aviv.

Israel Science Bibliography (English), 33, King George Avenue, Jerusalem.

Israel Stock Exchange (English), 16, King George Street, Jerusalem.

Israel Year Book (English), 2 Bar Kokhba Street, Tel Aviv.

Journal d'Analyse Mathematique (Hebrew-English-French), 11b, Abrabanel Street, Jerusalem.

Kama-J.N.F. Year Book, P.O.B. 283, Jerusalem.

Karmelit, P.O.B. 6095, Haifa.

Ktavim (English), Agriculture Experimental Station, Rehovot.

Mitzpeh, 16, Herzl Street, Tel Aviv.

Oshiot, 97 Allenby Street, Tel Aviv.

Reshumot, Ministry of Justice, Jerusalem.

Sefer Hashana shel Ha'itonaim, 27, Rothschild Boulevard, Tel Aviv.

Shnaton Davar, 45, Sheinkin Street, Tel Aviv.

Shnaton Hamemshala, Government Printer,

Shnaton Herut, 38, King George Street, Tel Aviv.

Statistical Abstract of Israel (Hebrew-English), Central Bureau of Statistics, Jerusalem.

Yalkut Hakibutzim Vehakevutsot, 5, Levontin Street, Tel Aviv.

Yalkut Hamoshavim Hashitufiyim, 5, Levontin Street, Tel Aviv.

PHILIPPINE ISLANDS

Monthly

Information Bulletin, 1963, Taft Avenue, Manila.

SINGAPORE

Monthly

Jewish Welfare Board Bulletin, P.O. Box 474, Singapore.

Quarterly

Kadimah, P.O.B. 474, Singapore.

IV. AUSTRALIA AND NEW ZEALAND

Weeklies

Australian Jewish Herald, 94-96, Queensberry St., Carlton, North, 3.

Australian Jewish News (English-Yiddish), 306, Little Collins Street, Melbourne, Vic.

Australian Jewish Post (Yiddish), 94-96, Queensberry St., Carlton, North, 3.

Australian Jewish Times, 175, George Street, Sydney, N.S.W.

Sydney Jewish News (English-Yiddish), 147a, King Street, Sydney, N.S.W.

Monthlies

B'nai B'rith Monthly, 9 Darley Street, Darlinghurst, N.S.W.

Detail, 146, Darlinghurst Road, Darlinghurst, N.S.W.

Great Synagogue Journal, 164, Castlereagh Street, Sydney, N.S.W.

Maccabean, 27, Clifton Crescent, Mt. Lawley, W.A.

New Zealand Jewish Chronicle, P.O. Box 1423, Wellington.

Undzer Guedank (Yiddish), 341, Heidelberg Road, Northcote, N. 16, Melbourne.

Westralian Judean, 139 Stirling Street, Perth, W.A.

WIZO Ivriah, 147, Elizabeth Street, Sydney.

"Y" News, 3, Wentworth Street, Point Piper, N.S.W.

Quarterly

Australian Jewish Historical Society, 2, Castlereagh Street, Sydney.

V. AMERICA

(1. Canada — 2. United States — 3. Central and South America)

(1) CANADA

Dailies

Daily Hebrew Journal (Yiddish-English), 409 College St., Toronto.

Jewish Daily Eagle (Yiddish), 4075, St. Lawrence Blvd., Montreal.

Weeklies

Canadian Jewish Chronicle, 4075, St. Lawrence Blvd., Montreal.

Canadian Jewish Review, 265, Craig Street, Montreal.

Canadian Jewish Weekly (Yiddish-English), 556, Bathurst Street, Toronto.

Canadian News (Yiddish), 525, Dundas St., West, Toronto.

Israelite Press (Yiddish-English), 221 Flora Avenue, Winnipeg.

Jewish Post, 213, Selkirk Avenue, Winnipeg.

Jewish Western Bulletin, 2675, Oak Street, Vancouver.

Vochenblatt (Yiddish-English), 304, Brunswick Ave., Toronto.

Western Jewish News, 303, Times Building, Winnipeg.

Fortnightlies

Jewish Standard, 43 Yonge Street, Toronto.

Monthlies

Bulletin Du Cercle Juif (French), 493, Sherbrooke St., West Montreal.

Canadian Jewish Magazine, 1500 St. Catherine Street, West, Montreal.

Canadian Zionist, 2025, University Avenue, Montreal.

Congress Bulletin, 493, Sherbrooke Street, West, Montreal.

Dos Vort (English-Yiddish), 5101, Esplanade Avenue, Montreal.

Kanader Stimme (Yiddish), 130, Laurier W., Montreal.

Windsor Jewish Community Bulletin, 405, Pelissier St., Windsor.

(2) UNITED STATES

For American Jewish Periodicals see columns 299—313.

(3) CENTRAL AND SOUTH AMERICA

ARGENTINE

Dailies

Di Yidische Zaytung (Yiddish), Corrientes 2314, Buenos Aires.

Di Presse (Yiddish), Castelli 360, Buenos Aires.

Twice Weekly

Juedische Wochenschau — La Semana Israelita (German-Spanish), Hipolito Yrigoyen 2481, Buenos Aires.

Weeklies

Argentiner Lebn (Yiddish), Corrientes 2670, Buenos Aires.

Die Naie Zait (Yiddish), Ayacucho 352, Buenos Aires.

Hatikva-Esperanzo (Hungarian), Colombres 74, Buenos Aires.

Hatikva (Hungarian), Colombres 74, Buenos Aires.

Mundo Israelita, Sarmiento 2396, Buenos Aires.

Religiese Stimme (Yiddish), Ecuador 637, Buenos Aires.

Rosarier Lebn (Yiddish), Mitre 1546, Rosario.

Tribuna (Yiddish), Cangallo 2122, Buenos Aires.

Fortnightlies

Di Yiddishe Welt (Yiddish), Cangallo 2194, Buenos Aires.

Dos Naie Wort (Yiddish), Pueyrredon 667, Buenos Aires.

Landsmanschaften (Yiddish), Velasco 1165, Buenos Aires.

Nueva Sion, Viamonte 2296, Buenos Aires. Aires.

Renacimiento de Israel, Callao 257, Buenos

Undzer Welt (Yiddish), Corrientes 2791,
Buenos Aires.

Undzer Wort (Yiddish), Corrientes 4136,
Buenos Aires.

Monthlies

Argentiner Beimelej (Yiddish), Serrano 436,
Buenos Aires.

Argentiner Magazin (Yiddish), Jujuy 37,
Buenos Aires.

Campana unida pro Israel, Cangallo 1873,
Buenos Aires.

D.A.I.A., "Informa", Pasteur 633, Buenos
Aires.

Darom (Hebrew), Paraguay 2519, Buenos
Aires.

Der Shpigl (Yiddish), Sarmiento 2221,
Buenos Aires.

D.E.S.A., Pasteur 341, Buenos Aires.

Dos "Freie Wort" (Yiddish), Camargo 340,
Buenos Aires.

El Colono Cooperador (Yiddish-Spanish),
Corrientes 2387, Buenos Aires.

Eretz Israel, Pasteur 341, Buenos Aires.

Farn Folks Guezunt (Yiddish), Corrientes
2854, Beuenos Aires.

Hador, Ayacucho 352, Buenos Aires.

Iedies (Yiddish), Libertad 773, Buenos Aires.

Ilustrirte Literarishe Bleter (Yiddish-Spanish)
Remedios Escalada de San Martin 2670,
Dep. C., Buenos Aires.

Jazaq Veematz, Tucuman 3135, Buenos
Aires.

Jerusalem, Larrea 744, Buenos Aires.

Kol Hanoar, Larrea 746, Buenos Aires.

La Luz, Pasteur 359, Piso 2ºA, Buenos Aires.

O.S.F.A., Esparza 27, Buenos Aires.

Principios, Santa Fe 174, Parana.

Revista de la Cámara de Comercia Argentino-Israeli, Pasteur 341, piso 6°, Buenos
Aires.

S.H.A., Sarmiento 2223, Buenos Aires.

Shriftn (Yiddish), Viamonte 2534, Buenos
Aires.

Undzer Guedank (Yiddish), Viamonte 2296,
Buenos Aires.

Vida de Israel, Corrientes 2241, Buenos
Aires.

Yikuf (Yiddish), Valentin Gomez 3245,
Buenos Aires.

Bi-Monthly

Davar, Sarmiento 2223, Buenos Aires.

Periodicals

Aporte, Paso 481, Buenos Aires.

Argentiner Yivo Jedies (Yiddish), Pasteur
633, Buenos Aires.

Argentiner Yivo Schriften (Yiddish), Pasteur
633, Buenos Aires.

Congregacion, Libertad 785, Buenos Aires.

Di Yiddishe Froj (Yiddish-Spanish),
Valentin Gomez 3245, Buenos Aires.

Grodner Opklangen (Yiddish), Valentin Gomez 3243, Buenos Aires.

Israel, Sarmiento 2153, Buenos Aires.

Juventud Libre, Serrano 341, Buenos Aires.

Mizrachi Stimme (Yiddish), Sarmiento 2888,
Buenos Aires.

Naj Teater (Yiddish), Boulogne sur Mer
547/49, Buenos Aires.

Nuestra Palabra, Corrientes 4136, Buenos
Aires.

Shul Bleter (Yiddish), Serrano 341,
Buenos Aires.

Shul Shriften (Yiddish), Boulogne sur Mer,
671, Buenos Aires.

Quarterly

Comentario, Tucumán 2137, Buenos Aires.

Davke (Yiddish), Montes de Oca 1275,
Buenos Aires.

Annual

Holz-Industrial (Yiddish), Corrientes 2783,
Buenos Aires.

BOLIVIA

Fortnightlies

Die Zeit (German), Casilla 349, Cochabamba

Das Echo (German), Casilla 748, Cochabamba.

BRAZIL

Bi-Weekly

Nossa Voz (Portuguese-Yiddish), Rua Ribeiro de Lima 592, Sao Paulo.

Weeklies

Aonde Vamos, Av. 13 de Maio 23, sala 1538, Rio de Janeiro.

Diaro Israelita (Yiddish), Av. Presidente Vargas 417A, sala 904, Rio de Janeiro.

Imprensa Israelita (Yiddish), Av. Pres. Vargas 435, Rio de Janeiro.

Journal Israelita, Rua Buenos Aires 90, Rio de Janeiro.

O Novo Momento (Yiddish), Rua Jose Paulino 872, Sao Paulo.

Fortnightly

Cronica Israelita (Portuguese-German), Caixa Postal 4091, Sao Paulo.

Monthlies

Boletim de Associacao Religiosa Israelita (Portuguese-German), Rua Martins Ferreira 52, Botafogo, Rio de Janeiro.

Boletim de Centro Israelita Brasiliero "Bene Herzl," Rua Barata Ribeiro 489, Rio de Janeiro.

Boletim da Confederacao, Av. Pres. Vargas 446, grupo 1501, Rio de Janeiro.

Brasil-Israel, Av. Ipiranga 536, Sao Paulo.

Choshlim-Forjadores (Portuguese-Hebrew), Rua Real Grandeza 188, Rio de Janeiro.

Novo Noticiaro Israelita (German), Av. Rua Branca, 114-11, Rio de Janeiro.

O Reflexo, Rua Ribeiro de Lima 592, Sao Paulo.

Quarterly

Zionistishe Bleter (Portuguese-Yiddish), Av. Pres. Vargas 446, sala 1502, Rio de Janeiro.

CHILE

Twice Weekly

Dos Idische Wort (Yiddish), Serrano 871, Santiago.

Weekly

Mundo Judio, Serrano 202, 3° Piso, Santiago.

Monthly

Boletin Informativo de Sociedad Cultural Israelita "B'ne Jisrael" (German-Spanish), Avenita Portugal 810, Santiago.

COLOMBIA

Fortnightly

Das Blatt (German), Apartado Aereo 5490, Bogota.

Monthlies

El Amanecer, Apartado Aereo 20–90, Cali.

Kojavim, Apartado Aereo 5778, Bogota D.E.

Menorah, Apartado Aereo 5549, Bogota D.E.

Technion, Apartado Aereo 7542, Bogota D.E.

Irregulars

Artza, Avenida 4, No.4-66, Cali.

El Macabeo, Apartado Aereo 1691, Medellin.

CUBA

Bi-Weekly

Havaner Lebn (Yiddish-Spanish), Sol 153, Havana.

Annual

Almanaque Hebres Vida Habanera, Sol 153, Havana.

DUTCH GUIANA

Monthly

Teroenga, Heerenstraat 7, Paramaribo, Surinam.

ECUADOR

Fortnightly

Informaciones, Revista Israelita, Casilla 2552, Quito.

MEXICO

Weeklies

Der Veg (three times weekly—Yiddish), Apartado Postal 1686, Mexico, D.F.

Di Shtime (semi-weekly—Yiddish), Pedro Moreno 129, Mexico, D.F.

Prensa Israelita, Anaxagoras 556A, Depto. 1, Mexico, D.F.

Fortnightlies

Dos Vort (Yiddish), Insurgentes 180, Mexico, D.F.

Faroys (Yiddish), Laplace 26-2, Mexico, D.F.

Monthlies

Asi Es, Bolivar 36–107, Mexico, D.F.

Centro Deportivo Israelita (Spanish-Yiddish)

Juana Gutierrez de Mendoza 76, Col.
Periodista, Mexico, D.F.
Tribuna Israelita, Bolivar 36-505, Mexico,
D.F.

Bi-Monthly

Freeland (Spanish), Apartado Postal 181,
Mexico, D.F.

Irregulars

Avangard (Yiddish), Apartado Postal 25028,
Mexico, D.F.
Di Sionistiche Shtime (Yiddish), Chapul-
tepec 300, Mexico, D.F.
El Heraldo de Israel, Av. Amsterdam 229,
Mexico, D.F.
En Guardia, Apartado Postal 25028,
Mexico, D.F.
Frayvelt (Yiddish), Saltillo 70, Mexico, D.F.
Tribuna Sionista (Yiddish), Av. Amsterdam
229, Mexico, D.F.
Zionistishe Bleter (Yiddish), Chapultepec
300, Mexico, D.F.

Annuals

Kultur-Lebn (Yiddish), Cuba 81, Mexico
D.F.

NETHERLANDS WEST INDIES

Monthly

Mikve Israel, Pietermaai 29A, Willemstad,
Curacao.

PERU

Monthly

Nosotros, Calle Gallos 285-B, Lima.

URUGUAY

Dailies

Folksblat (Yiddish), Canelones 870,
Montevideo.
Unser Fraint (Yiddish), JHY Obes 1171,
Montevideo.

Weeklies

Der Moment (Yiddish), Andes 1146,
Montevideo.
Boletin Informativo (German), Rio Branco,
1168, Montevideo.
Gaceta Israelita, Cerrito 663, Montevideo.

Fortnightles

Amanecer, Buenos Aires 329. Montevideo.
Revista Familiar Israelita, Bartolome Mitre
1578, Montevideo.
Semanario Hebreo, Canelones 870, Montevideo.

Monthly

Unobhenigke Yiddishe Tribune (Yiddish),
Larranaga 1782, Moutevideo.

Quarterly

Sintesis, Florida 1418, Montevideo.

VENEZUELA

Weeklies

El Mundo Israelita, Sociedad a Troposos, 4
Altos-Oficina 26, Caracas.
Nuestro Camino, Avda. Francisco Javier
Ustariz, Ap. 3540, San Bernardino.

Monthly

Paginas Hebreas, Avenida Ustariz, Edif. San
Vicante, Apt. 10, San Bernardino.

ISRAEL

JEWISH POPULATION 1,800,000

(Non-Jewish Population 210,000)

Ancient Period

The ancient history of Eretz Israel, or Palestine, as it was called since the II century until the emergence of the State of Israel in 1948, is known from the Bible. The period of the Jewish Patriarchs, the exodus of the Israelites from Egypt, and their conquest of Palestine are recorded in the Pentateuch and in the Book of Joshua. After a period of 480 years when the people of Israel were ruled by the Judges, the Kingdom of Israel, the first Jewish State, was formed by Saul and David. It lasted 454 years, from 1040 to 586 B.C.E. when it was conquered by the Babylonians The period of the First Jewish Commonwealth is marked spiritually by the appearance of the Hebrew Bible and the Jewish Prophets.

The second Jewish Commonwealth, on the return from the Babylonian Exile in 538 B.C.E., lasted 420 years. It achieved complete independence after the heroic war of the Maccabees 175 B.C.E., and was destroyed by the Romans in 70 C.E. The prominent scholars and spiritual leaders of this period were the Sages of the Great Assembly (Knesseth Hagdola) and the early Tanaim whose teachings were compiled in the Mishna.

As to the Jewish population in ancient Eretz Israel (according to II Samuel: 24–9), David's census counted 800,000 Is-raelites and 500,000 Judeans of military age, which would amount to a total population of over 4,000,000. At the end of the Second Jewish State, the Jewish inhabitants approximated, according to Flavius, 3,000,000, a greater part of whom fell victims to the bloody war with Rome. Yet, a considerable population remained, about 1,200,000, as was shown by the Bar-Kochba revolt of 135. Even after the cruel suppression of this revolt, Galilee was still thickly populated, in addition to large Jewish communities in Judea.

Middle Ages

The persecution of the Byzantine Empire, which ruled over Palestine from 330 until 638, compelled many Palestine Jews to emigrate, reducing considerably the size of the Jewish community. Even in this oppressive period, the spiritual life in Palestine continued unabated. The Palestine Talmud, including the teachings of the Palestinian sages of the 4th–5th century called Amoraim, was compiled there in the 5th century. The conquest of Palestine by the Arabs in 638 improved the situation of the Jews. Palestine became again a center of Jewish learning in newly restored Yeshivoth and especially in the field of Haggadah and Midrashic literature. The synagogue poetry was greatly enriched by the composers Yannai, Eleazar Hakalir, and others. Outstanding scholars worked in Palestine in the period 700–900 C.E. to give final, correct form to the Bible text (Masorah) and the system of Hebrew vocalization (Nikkud).

The rule of the Crusaders for 88 years (1098–1186) almost annihilated Palestinian Jewry. The traveler Benjamin of Tudela then found scarcely 1,500 Jews in the entire country. As Saladin reconquered Palestine from the Crusaders and alleviated the plight of the Jews, Jews began to emigrate to Palestine from western Europe where they had been hard pressed since the beginning of the Crusades. Three hundred rabbis of France and England made a pilgrimage to Palestine in 1211, and many stayed there. Saladin welcomed the return of the Jews to their ancient homeland.

A short time after the invasion of the Mongols (1259–60), the *Mamelukes* who also ruled over Palestine came to power in Egypt (1260). Under them, the conditions for Jewish immigration to Palestine improved. The Jewish community in Jerusalem was soon reorganized by Nahmanides (Ramban) who came to the country in 1267. Since that time, the Jewish community in Jerusalem has had an uninterrupted existence. The 14th century was the most tragic period of the entire Middle Ages for the Jews of western Europe and many of them emigrated from there to Palestine where, under the Mamelukes, Jews enjoyed security and economic freedom.

During the rule of the Turks, which began 1517, many Jews, especially the Spanish exiles, found refuge in Palestine. Safed became an important Jewish center with famous religious scholars as Jacob Berab, Joseph Caro, the compiler of the Shulhan Aruch, and Yitzhak Luria, founder of a new Cabbalistic school. Joseph Nasi unsuccessfully attempted to establish an autonomous Jewish settlement in and around Tiberias in 1571. But the corrupt Turkish administration impoverished the country and the taxes became unbearable. The Pasha of Jerusalem, Ibn Farukh (1625–27), imprisoned Jewish leaders in order to extort ransom from the community. One of these prisoners was the famous former Rabbi of Prague, Isaiah Horovitz (Shelah Hakadosh).

After the fearful pogroms of Chmielnicki (1648–49), numerous families escaped to Palestine. A group of a few hundred Polish Jews emigrated to Palestine under the leadership of Rabbi Yehuda Hasid of Siedlce at the end of 1700. An important immigration was that of the Hasidim from Poland and Russia in the 1750's, mainly to Safed and Tiberias. Another group of 300 Hasidim from Russia came under the leadership of Mendel of Vitebsk. In 1810, the disciple of the Gaon, Rabbi Eliahu of Vilna, Israel Shklover, came with a group of Jews who formed the community of Perushim.

Modern Period

During the conflict between Sultan Abdul Mejid and the Pasha of Egypt and the disorders in Syria and Palestine (1820–1838), the European powers intervened. Projects were advanced at the time to restore Palestine to the Jews in order to create a buffer state beween Turkey and

Egypt. In 1840, Turkey regained Palestine through the influence of the European powers which then established their consulates in the country. Jews could place themselves under the protection of the various consulates, thus acquiring special protection. This made Jewish immigration on a larger scale possible.

The pogroms in Russia (1881–82) revived the old latent desire to return to Zion and a movement for the formation of Jewish agricultural settlements in Palestine arose. Montefiore and, later, the generous assistance of Baron Edmund de Rothschild of Paris came to the aid of Jewish colonization beginning with 1882. The urge to return to Palestine was also strong among the Jews of Yemen, Persia, the Caucasus, and North Africa. The number of Jews rose from 12,000 in 1850 to 35,000 in 1882 and to 85,000 in 1914. Palestine again became a Jewish spiritual center with its greatest accomplishment, the rebirth of the Hebrew language.

In 1897, Theodor Herzl convened the first Zionist Congress, thus initiating the World Zionist movement. The Zionist Organization had a decisive impact upon the upbuilding of Palestine and the issuance of the Balfour Declaration. Ultimately, it brought about the establishment of the State of Israel.

The Period Between the Two World Wars

The First World War brought great suffering to Palestinian Jewry. Jews who were citizens of the Entente Powers were compelled to flee the country. Jemal Pasha, commander of the Turkish forces, cruelly persecuted the Jewish population and deported its leaders. On November 2, 1917, the British Government issued the Balfour Declaration, promising to help establish a Jewish Homeland in Palestine. Jewish youth hastened to enroll in the Jewish Legion to participate in the liberation of Palestine. The British army defeated the Turks and, in 1922, Britain was granted a mandate over Palestine by the League of Nations with the obligation to carry out the promises in the Balfour Declaration. As a result of Arab opposition which reached the dimensions of rioting, the British Government limited considerably the implementation of the Balfour Declaration and curtailed Jewish immigration. The British Shaw Commission of 1929 and the Simpson report of 1930 recommended severe restrictions on immigration, and the Passfield White Paper practically annulled the provisions of the Balfour Declaration in 1930. In 1936, the Peel Commission proposed the partition of Palestine into an Arab State and a smaller Jewish State, but the Woodhead Commission of 1938 rejected the proposed partition plan. In 1939, the MacDonald White Paper called for admission of only 75,000 Jews to the country during the next five years, whereupon Jewish immigration would be permanently prohibited, and in addition, forbade purchase of land in most of the country and envisaged the formation of an independent Palestinian government with an Arab majority at the end of a ten-year period. The Mandates Commission of the League of Nations, however, rejected the terms of the British White Paper, considering the restrictions on Jewish immigration and land purchase a violation of the terms of the Mandate.

Despite all restrictions, immigration was maintained, thanks to the increasing efforts of the Zionist Movement and the Jewish Agency. At the close of the first World War, there were 55,000 Jews in Palestine. In 1922, their number increased to 84,000, 1931 to 175,000, 1936 to 410,000, and in 1942 to 550,000, comprising 35% of the total population of the country.

Palestine Jewry's contribution to the Allies during the second World War was very substantial. One hundred and thirty-six thousand Jews registered to participate in the war effort. About 40,000 Jewish volunteers served in the British forces and the Home Guard during the war. In 1944, the formation of the Jewish Brigade was officially announced by the British government.

The Mandatory Power closed the gates of Palestine to Europe's Jews who were victims of the Nazis. The English Foreign Secretary, Ernest Bevin, issued a statement in 1945 limiting Jewish immigration to Palestine to 1,500 monthly, making even this insignificant number contingent upon Arab consent which was certain to be withheld. The Anglo-American Inquiry Committee went to Europe and Palestine, and recommended the admission of 100,000 Jewish refugees to Palestine, but the British Labour government rejected its findings. As a result of barring the immigration of refugees, an "illegal," i.e. unauthorized by England, immigration of Jewish Nazi victims began. Tens of thousands succeeded in arriving in the country

after heroic suffering, and many thousands were intercepted by the British fleet and interned in Cyprus. The underground defense force (Hagana, which had been organized by the Jews of Palestine to protect the Jewish population against Arab terrorism) took up the fight to combat the restrictions of British policy.

Establishment of the State of Israel

On November 29, 1947, the General Assembly of the United Nations resolved by a vote of 33 to 13 upon the partition of Palestine into a *Jewish State* and an Arab State with economic union of both. Arab attacks flared up throughout the country with the assistance of thousands of irregular Arab soldiers from neighboring countries. Jerusalem was besieged by Arab forces. In April, 1948, the Hagana defeated the Kawukji army in the Valley of Esdraelon and brought Haifa under Jewish control.

On May 14, upon the termination of the British Mandate, the Vaad Leumi, representing Palestine Jewry and the World Zionist Organization, proclaimed the *re-establishment of Medinat Israel— the State of Israel.*

A provisional government headed by David Ben Gurion was sworn in. The U.S.A recognized Israel *de facto* the same day, and the Soviet Union granted *de jure* recognition three days later. On May 15, the regular armies of Egypt, Iraq, Trans-Jordan, Lebanon, and Syria attacked Israel. Chaim Weizmann was elected first President of the Jewish State. The Arabs' attempt to achieve a quick victory failed. The Arabs were fought to a standstill in

June. After a shaky cease-fire lasting from June 11 to July 9, the Israel forces swung over to counterattack, capturing Lod, Ramle, and Nazareth. In October, Israel troops broke through the Egyptian front in the Negev and liberated Beersheba. At the same time the Galilee was cleared of Kawukji's Arab Army. Free immigration had been announced, and 102,000 Jews arrived in Israel in the period from May to December 1948.

Premier David Ben Gurion's Mapai Party won a sizable plurality January 25, 1949 in Israel's first election, held to select a 120-member constituent assembly (Knesset).

In 1949, Egyptian invading forces were routed and an armistice agreement with Egypt was signed at Rhodes in February, followed by similar agreements with Lebanon, Jordan, and Syria. During 1949, 240,000 immigrants arrived in the newly formed Jewish State. In 1950, Yemen's 47,000 Jews were flown to Israel. The total immigration this year amounted to 170,000. In 1951, the immigration of 110,000 Iraqi Jews was completed. In all, 174,000 immigrants entered the country in 1951. The Knesset re-elected Weizmann as President of Israel for a second term. In September, the Israel-German indemnity agreement was signed, through the negotiations of Dr. N. Goldmann with the German Government, according to which West Germany would pay to Israel in 12–14 annual instalments $715 million, beside $107 million to be used for Jewish Nazi victims outside Israel. In November, President Weizmann passed away at

76, and Itzhak Ben-Zvi was elected his successor the following month.

The neighboring Arab states have constantly been violating the terms of the Armistice agreement by boycotts and raids into Israel territory, killing and wounding soldiers and civilians and pillaging settlements. Israel retaliated for these hostile acts by counterraids. The Mixed Armistice Commissions and the U.N. Security Council condemned both the Arabs and Israel for such acts, but border incidents are continuously being provoked by the Arabs with threats to wipe Israel off the map. Israel's repeated proposals for final peace negotiations are rejected by the Arab countries. The acquisition in 1955 of great amounts of modern weapons by Egypt from the communist countries further increased tension and the menace of war and compelled Israel to strike against Egyptian bases in Sinai in October, 1956. Yielding to UN pressure, she withdrew from Sinai and the Gaza Strip by March 1957, to find herself facing a similar situation on the Syrian border later on in the year.

HIGHLIGHTS OF EVENTS
(1948–1957)

1947

On November 29, the United Nations General Assembly by a vote of 33 to 13 with 10 abstentions, resolved upon the partition of Palestine into a Jewish State, an Arab State and an International Zone of Jerusalem, with economic union of the three parts. This settlement was to come into being upon the termination of the British Mandate on May 15, 1948. "Any attempt to alter by force the settlement envisaged" was to be regarded as "a threat to the peace," according to the General Assembly's resolution.

Nov. 30—Arab attacks on Jews begin throughout the country with the assistance of thousands of irregular Arab soldiers from neighboring countries infiltrating into Palestine as "volunteers."

1948

March 1—The National Council of Palestine Jews (Vaad Leumi) decides to set up a Provisional Governing Council which is to constitute, upon termination of the Mandate, the provisional organs of the State in accordance with the United Nations resolution.

March—Jerusalem is besieged by Arab forces and cut off from the coast.

April 1-20—"Operation Nakshon": Three great convoys break through to Jerusalem providing the besieged and starving population with food, arms, and ammunition.

April 15-17—Battle of Mishmar Ha'emek (settlement in the Valley of Esdraelon). The defeated Arab "Yarmuk Army," under the command of Fawzi el Kawukji, flees towards Jenin, in the Arab "Triangle" (Nablus, Jenin, Tulkarm).

April 21-22—After a twenty-four hour battle, Haifa is brought under the control of the Haganah (Jewish Defense Force).

April 26-28 — Haifa District British Police Headquarters reports that "every effort is being made by the Jews to persuade the Arab populace to stay and carry on with their normal lives, to get their shops and businesses open and assure them that their lives and interests will be saved." However, "Arab leaders reiterated their determination to evacuate the entire Arab population."

May—At its special session, the United Nations General Assembly considers and rejects a proposal for establishing United Nations control over Jerusalem upon termination of the Mandate on May 15, 1948. Thus, when the Mandatory Government withdrew, Jerusalem found the United Nations unable or unwilling to provide for its administration and security. This inaction on the part of the United Nations, followed by the siege and horrors of the war, brought about the integration of Jerusalem into the system of order and defense of Israel and Jordan, respectively.

May 14—The Provisional People's Council, representing the Jews of Palestine and the World Zionist Organization, proclaims the *re-establishment of Medinat Israel — the State of Israel.*

Provisional Government sworn in, with David Ben-Gurion as Prime Minister.

United States of America recognizes Israel *de facto.*

May 15—Regular armies of Egypt, Iraq, Jordan, Lebanon, and Syria attack Israel.

May 16—Dr. Chaim Weizmann elected President of the Provisional Council of State.

May 18—U.S.S.R. recognizes Israel *de jure.*

May 23—Israel accepts Security Council's request for a cease-fire.

May 26—Israel Defence Forces Ordinance promulgated, establishing the Israel Defense Army.

May 26—Arab States reject Security Council's request for a cease-fire.

June 11—After delays caused by the Arab States, first truce begins. The Arab attempt to achieve a quick victory has failed. No major Israel position has been surrendered. The armies of the Arab States have been forced back on the defensive. Truce comes when the Israel forces have just reached top form and begin to swing over to counterattack. During the fighting, the 'Burma Road,' an alternate route to Jerusalem, has been constructed. Never again is Jerusalem to be cut off from other parts of the State.

The new State has succeeded in establishing its administration and organizing the services essential to a modern community.

July 9—Truce ends when Mediator's appeal for an extension is rejected by the Arab States. Israel agrees to the extension. Fighting lasts ten days. Israel forces capture among other places Lod, Ramle, and Nazareth and break through the Egyptian barrier to the Negev.

July 18—Second truce begins.

October 21—Negev fighting ends with liberation of Beersheva by Israel Defence Forces;

isolation of Egyptian troops in Hebron from their main base; encirclement of Egyptian troops in Faluja pocket and the opening of free land communications with the Negev settlements.

October 30-31—Israel Defence Forces clear all Galilee in fifty-hour operation against Kawukji's irregulars.

December—Persistent Egyptian attacks on Israel settlements in the Negev lead to second Negev flare-up on December 23.

December 31—102,000 immigrants have arrived in Israel since the establishment of the State.

1949

January 7—End of hostilities in southern Israel with the defeat of Egyptian invading forces.

January 13—Israel-Egyptian negotiations for an armistice open in Rhodes.

February 14—Israel's First Knesset opened in Jerusalem by Dr. Chaim Weizmann.

February 17—Dr. Chaim Weizmann elected First President of Israel.

February 24—Armistice Agreement with Egypt signed in Rhodes.

March 12—Israel flag hoisted at Eilat on the Red Sea.

March 23—Israel-Lebanon Armistice Agreement signed at Rosh Hanikra (Ras en Naqura).

April 3 — Israel-Jordan Armistice Agreement signed at Rhodes.

May 11—Israel admitted to membership in the United Nations.

July 20—Israel-Syria Armistice Agreement signed in no-man's land near Mahanayim.

December 31—239,141 immigrants arrived during 1949.

1950

January 23—Knesset proclaims that Jerusalem had resumed its status as the Capital of the State with the proclamation of Israel's independence on May 14, 1948.

1951

November 19—Knesset re-elects Dr. Chaim Weizmann as President of Israel for a second term.

December 31—173,901 immigrants arrived in Israel in 1951, and 67 new settlements were established.

1952

September 10—Israel-West Germany Indemnity agreement signed at Luxembourg. Under the agreement, West Germany shall pay to Israel and the Conference on Jewish Material Claims against Germany 3,450 million D.M. ($822,000,000) mostly in goods in twelve to fourteen annual instalments. Of this amount $715,000,000 is earmarked for Israel.

November 9—Dr. Chaim Weizmann, first President of Israel, passes away at his residence in Rehovot at 5:55 a.m. on 21 Heshvan 5713, at the age of 76.

December 8—Knesset elects Mr. Itzhak Ben-Zvi President of Israel.

1953

February 12—Soviet Union severs diplomatic relations with Israel, following a bomb explosion at the Soviet Legation in Tel Aviv (February 9).

July 20—Diplomatic relations between the Soviet Union and Israel resumed.

December 6—David Ben-Gurion, Prime Minister and Minister of Defence since the establishment of the State of Israel, resigns because of "extreme weariness" and retires to Sde Boker, agricultural settlement in the Negev.

December 9—President Ben-Zvi entrusts Foreign Minister and Acting Prime Minister Moshe Sharett with the task of forming a new Government.

1954

January 25—Mr. Sharett's new coalition Government, composed of the same parties (except Progressives who joined January 31) and carrying on the same policies as Mr. Ben-

Gurion's Cabinet, is formally constituted by a vote of confidence in the Knesset. Following the resignation of the Minister of Defense, Mr Pinhas Lavon, Mr. Ben-Gurion joined Mr. Sharett's Government resuming his duties in this capacity on February 20, 1955.

February 16—Knesset abolishes capital punishment for murder, retaining the death penalty only for persons convicted of aiding the Nazis.

THE DEAD SEA SCROLLS

1955

February 13—Prime Minister Moshe Sharett announced that four of the seven scrolls discovered by Bedouin shepherds near the northwestern end of the Dead Sea in 1947 were acquired in the United States and brought back to Jerusalem through the efforts of Israel's archaeologist and former Chief of Staff, General Yigael Yadin, The American Fund for Israel Institutions, and the generosity of the D. S. and R. H. Gottesman Foundation of New York. The Scrolls acquired consist of: 1. Isaiah—Manuscript A, the earliest known complete manuscript of the Book of Isaiah; 2, a commentary on the Book of Habbakuk; 3. "The Manual of Discipline" of a Jewish religious sect or community; 4. the Aramaic "Lemech Apocalypse," referred to in several ancient texts, no copy of which was previously known. The scrolls were in the possession of the Syrian Orthodox Metropolitan at St. Mark's Monastery in the Old City of Jerusalem and were offered for sale in New York. The other three scrolls were acquired in 1947 for the Hebrew University of Jerusalem by its Professor of Archaeology, the late Eliezer L. Sukenik, father of General Yadin, the first scholar to identify the scrolls and evaluate their importance. These consist of: 1. Manuscript B of the Book of Isaiah; 2. "The War of the Sons of Light with the Sons of Darkness"; 3. The Psalms of Thanksgiving. Tests showed that all the scrolls were laid away between

200 B.C.E. and 200 C.E. The President of the Hebrew University, the noted archaeologist and historian of ancient Israel, Dr. Benjamin Mazar, declared: "With the acquisition of these scrolls we now have one of the greatest historical treasures in the world."

The Israel Government has established a national trust to be known as the "Keren Hekhal Hasefer," or the "Shrine of the Book," which will hold in perpetual trust the Dead Sea Scrolls and other manuscripts and documents relating to the Bible. The Chairman of the Board of Trustees of Hekhal Hasefer will be the President of the State of Israel.

June 1955—Completion of the 65-mile Yarkon-Negev water pipe-line diverting the waters from the River Yarkon north of Tel Aviv to the parched land of the Negev. The pipeline will supply the Negev with 100,000,000 cubic meters of water annually.

1956

October 29—Israel invaded the Sinai Peninsula to eliminate the Egyptian Fedayeen (commando) bases.

Within four days Israel won an unprecedented victory, routed the Egyptian Army, occupied almost the entire Sinai Peninsula and the Gaza Strip, took over 5,000 prisoners of war, and captured enormous quantities of weapons and supplies at the cost of 171 dead, and 700 wounded.

October 30—Britain and France called on Israel and Egypt to end hostilities and withdraw to a line 10 miles on either side of the Suez Canal. Britain and France vetoed a Security Council resolution calling on Israel to withdraw and appealing to all United Nations members to refrain from force.

November 2—the General Assembly called for a cease-fire.

November 5—British-French paratroops landed in Egypt. The General Assembly created a United Nations Emergency Force to supervise a cease-fire. Egypt and Israel accepted the cease-fire.

November 7—the General Assembly called on Britain, France, and Israel to withdraw from the territory they occupied. Prime Minister David Ben-Gurion announced in the Knesset that the armistice agreement with Egypt no longer existed, having been destroyed by Egyptian belligerency. He declared that Israel would permit no foreign troops in territory held by her.

November 9—in an unprecedented midnight radio talk, Prime Minister David Ben-Gurion announced that Israel was yielding to American and Soviet pressure and would withdraw from Sinai.

November 24—the General Assembly called for withdrawal of Britain, France, and Israel from Egypt "forthwith" and authorized the United Nations to clear the blocked canal.

December 2—Israel pulled back to more than thirty miles east of the canal.

December 3—Britain and France agreed to withdraw.

1957

January 19—the General Assembly again called for Israeli withdrawal.

January 22—Israel completed withdrawal from all occupied territory except the Gaza Strip and the Gulf of Aqaba area.

February 2—the General Assembly called for complete Israeli withdrawal and proposed thereafter to station the United Nations Emergency Force in the Gaza Strip.

February 20—President Eisenhower said that the United Nations had no choice but to "exert pressure on Israel to withdraw from Egypt."

March 4—Israel ordered complete withdrawal from all occupied territory.

March 6—the United Nations Force entered the Gaza Strip.

March 7—Israel withdrew from the Gaza Strip.

March 10—Israel began evacuating the Straits of Tiran area.

March 11—Egypt named a Governor to take over the Gaza Strip administration.

April 6—the American tanker *Kern Hills* arrived in Elath with a cargo of crude oil from the Persian Gulf subsequently piped to Beersheba in an 8" pipeline constructed in four months.

April 13—increased vigilance along Israel's frontier with Jordan as pro-Western coup gets under way. Foreign Minister Golda Meir announces in Knesset that Israel is interested in status quo in Jordan.

May 6—half million persons watch gigantic military parade in Tel Aviv in honor of Independence Day featuring new equipment and Soviet Bloc arms captured in Sinai.

May 14—U.S. Secretary of State John F. Dulles announces his government will not oppose Israeli testship in Suez Canal but would not sanction use of force to secure her passage.

May 21—Israel announces support of "Eisenhower Doctrine."

June 2—Israel warns Egypt against aggressive acts on Gaza Strip border.

July 4—British complete evacuation of Jordan bases. U.S. lifts embargo on sending military equipment to Israel.

July 8—Unofficial talks with Arab representatives in Europe to discuss Arab refugee problem.

July 9—One killed, 7 wounded in Syrian attack on border police. Both sides use artillery.

July 10—400 Bulgarian soldiers reach Syria in capacity of technicians and military instructors.

July 13—Soviet Russia sent $140,000,000 worth of arms to Syria accompanied by 250 experts.
—State Department official announces U.S. will not sell arms to Israel.
—four UN observation posts established on Israel side of Syrian border and four on Syrian side.

July 16—Shell company announces intention to liquidate its enterprises in Israel, yielding to Arab pressure.

July 28—Second World Congress for Jewish Studies opens in Jerusalem.

August 18—103 day strike at "Atta" textile works settled.

August 28—Communist and non-Communist delegations return from Moscow Youth Festival. Russian Jews displayed strong interest in Israel in public demonstrations.

POPULATION

The growth of the population since the emergence of the State of Israel was as follows: 1948—758,701; 1949—1,173,871; 1950—1,370,094; 1951—1,577,825; 1952—1,629,519; 1953—1,669,417; 1954—1,717,834; 1955—1,789,000. The composition of the 210,000 non-Jewish population by religion is approximately 141,400 Moslems, 44,500 Christians and 19,800 Druzes.

The birth-rate per 1,000 was: 1951—33.8; 1952 — 33.00; 1953—32.11; 1954 — 29.22, against the following death rates: 1951—6.60; 1952—7.32; 1953—6.67; 1954—6.76.

In 1956 the urban population was 1,337,046, the rural population 535,344. The number of cities and towns is 60, rural settlements 846 of which 103 are Arab villages.

The immigration was in May-December, 1948—102,000; 1949—240,000; 1950—170,000; 1951—174,000; 1952—23,000; 1953—10,000; 1954—17,000; 1955—36,000; 1956—55,000; 1957 (to July 1)—50,120.

GROWTH OF POPULATION

Population at end of period	Total	Jews	Non-Jews
1948	—*	758,701	—*
1949	1,173,871	1,013,871	160,000
1950	1,370,094	1,202,993	167,101
1951	1,577,825	1,404,392	173,433
1952	1,629,519	1,450,217	179,302
1953	1,669,417	1,483,641	185,761
1954	1,717,834	1,526,016	191,818
1955	1,789,000	1,591,000	198,000
1956	1,872,000	1,667,000	205,000
1957			
(May)	1,930,000	1,720,000	210,000

* No figures available.

POPULATION OF CITIES AND TOWNS

Having 10,000 Inhabitants or More
as of December 31, 1956

Tel Aviv–Yafo	365,000
Haifa	154,500
Jerusalem	148,000
Ramat Gan	65,150
Petah Tikva	46,000
Natanya	33,100
Holon	32,200
Bnei Brak	30,000
Rehovot	29,500
Hadera	23,000
Nazareth	23,000
Ramle	20,650
Rishon LeZion	22,300
Givatayim	20,350
Lod (Lydda)	17,600
Acco (Acre)	15,200
Herzlia	21,000
Tveria (Tiberias)	17,400
Beersheba	25,550
Kfar Saba	16,100
Migdal Ashkelon	19,200
Tirat HaCarmel	13,000
Bat Yam	15,000
Kfar Ata	11,800
Nes Ziona	10,800

GOVERNMENT

The State of Israel is a Republic headed by a President who is elected by the Knesset (Parliament) for a five-year term.

The President of Israel is Itzhak Ben-Zvi. Mr. Ben-Zvi succeeded Dr. Chaim Weizmann who passed away on November 9, 1952.

THE LEGISLATURE

The Legislature consists of a unicameral 120-member house called Knesset. The Knesset is elected by secret ballot and universal suffrage for a four-year term.

The following is the party composition of the Third Knesset as a result of the 1955 elections:

Mapai 40
Herut 15
General Zionists 13
Hapoel Hamizrahi–Mizrahi 11
Ahdut Ha'avoda–Poale Zion 10
Mapam 9
Israel Communist Party 6
Progressives 5
Agudat Israel 3
Poalei Agudat Israel 3
Israel Arab Democrats 2
Progress and Work (Arab) 2
Agriculture and Development (Arab) . . 1

POLITICAL PARTIES REPRESENTED IN THE KNESSET

In their platforms the parties represented in the Second Knesset defined their programs as follows:

Mapai (Mifleget Poalei Eretz Israel— Israel Labor Party).

"A Zionist Socialist party whose aims are the ingathering of the Jewish People from the Diaspora, the upbuilding of the State of Israel, and a socialist regime founded on spiritual and political freedom. Its internal policy stands for democracy and state-planned economy based on the development of constructive private enterprises. Its foreign policy stands for non-identification with any bloc and is based on the strengthening of the political and moral authority of the United Nations Organization."

General Zionists

"Freedom of the individual is the basis of national welfare and progress. Freedom of religion, of initiative and expression, and of lawful organizations are essential."

Mapam (Mifleget Poalim Meuhedet — United Workers Party)

"A left-wing Zionist Socialist party, aiming at the ingathering of the Jewish people within a Socialist Jewish State. Its program postulates a Government based on a united Socialist front, Jewish-Arab working-class solidarity, an active anti-fascist policy aiming at permanent international peace, and friendship between Israel and the Soviet Union as well as other progressive forces of the world."

Mizrahi

"The party demands that legislation be based on Jewish jurisprudence and that the cultural climate of the country be determined by the tradition of the Torah. The party stands for private enterprise and competition."

Hapoel Hamizrahi (Mizrahi Workers)

"Both the laws and the planned development of the State should be based on the Torah. The party stands for the social and economic quality of men and women, but demands strict observance of the laws of personal status contained in the Torah. The party also stands for maximum development of Israel's agriculture and equal treatment of the private and cooperative economic sectors."

Herut (Freedom)

"A party founded by the Irgun Zvai Leumi, in opposition to the present regime in Israel. It calls for the territorial integrity of Eretz Israel (Land of Israel) within its historic boundaries on both sides of the Jordan, for private initiative in the economic and social structure of the State, and for the institution of reforms towards the attainment of social justice and the inalienable individual freedom of man."

Israel Communist Party

"Its aim—Socialism. Basing itself on the Marxist theory of class struggle and guided by the theory of Marx-Engels-Lenin-Stalin, the party fights for peace, the real independence of Israel, genuine democracy, civil and national equality of rights, and for the interests of the toiling masses."

Progressives

"A non-socialist party with progressive liberal tendencies comprising both middle and working-class memberships."

Agudat Israel

"The party stands for the strictest observance of the Torah in the administration of the State, with jurisdiction entrusted to rabbinical authorities."

Poalei Agudat Israel (Agudat Israel Workers)

"No legal code other than that of the Torah is acceptable for the State of Israel. An eight-hour workday, fair wages, adequate protection against the exploitation of workers, and full employment are to be safeguarded. The party opposes the formal equality of men and women.'

Leahdut Ha'avoda–Poalei Zion

"We see our mission in the struggle for the genera! historical interests of the Jewish working class; the rescue of the people, the ingathering of the exiles, and a socialist State of Israel in the entire homeland."

THE PRESENT GOVERNMENT

The present Government (1956) is based on a coalition which was formed in 1955 and comprises the following parties: Mapai, Hapoel Hamizrahi-Mizrahi, Leahdut Ha'avoda, Mapam, and Progressives.

Prime Minister and Minister of Defence	David Ben-Gurion (Mapai)
Minister for Foreign Affairs	Mrs. Golda Meir (Mapai)
Minister of Finance	Levi Eshkol (Mapai)
Minister of Commerce and Industry	Pinhas Sapir (Mapai)
Minister of Agriculture	Kadish Luz (Mapai)
Minister of Labor	Mordecai Namir (Mapai)
Minister of Development	Mordecai Bentov (Mapam)
Minister of Education and Culture	Zalman Aranne (Mapai)
Minister for Religious Affairs and Social Welfare	Moshe Shapira (Hapoel Hamizrahi)
Minister of Health	Israel Barzilai (Mapam)
Minister of the Interior	I. Bar-Yehuda (Ahdut Ha'avoda)
Minister of Justice	Pinhas Rosen (Progressives)
Minister of Police	Behor Shalom Shitreet (Mapai)
Minister of Communications	Moshe Carmel (Ahdut Ha'avoda)
Minister of Posts	Joseph Burg (Hapoel Hamizrahi)

ISRAEL DEFENSE FORCES

The Israel Defense Forces comprise the Army, the Navy, and the Air Force. The General Staff of the Israel Defense Forces commands all the three services. The ranks in all the services are uniform.

Men and unmarried women, on reaching the age of 18, are drafted for military service. The women are organized in a separate formation called *Khen* (for Kheyl Nashim—women's corps). Men of the age groups 18–26 serve for thirty months, from 27–29, for two years. Women of the age group 18–26 serve for two years.

Women may be exempted from military service on religious grounds.

The Regular Army is the basic nucleus of the armed forces. All its ranks are volunteers who have completed their military service and are ready to serve for an additional number of years under contract.

The Reserves: Men up to the age of 45 and women without children between the ages of 18 and 34 are called up for reserve service for periods from 14 to 38 consecutive days a year according to rank and age, in addition to one day's service per month.

Nahal. A unique feature of Israel's Army is its agricultural training in a special formation called Nahal (Noar Halutzi Lohem—Pioneer Fighting Youth). After basic military training for a period of three months, the rest of the first year of service is devoted to agricultural training.

The following are the ranks in the Israel Defense Army and their American equivalents:

Rav-Aloof	Major General
Aloof	Brigadier General
Aloof Mishneh	Colonel
Sgan-Aloof	Lieut. Colonel
Rav-Seren	Major
Seren	Captain
Segen	Lieutenant
Segen Mishneh	Second Lieutenant
Rav-Samal Gdudi	Battalion First Sgt.
Rav-Samal Plugati	Company First Sgt.
Samal Rishon	Sergeant First Class
Samal	Sergeant
Rav-Turai	Corporal
Turai Rishon	Private First Class
Turai	Private

RELIGIONS

The Government of Israel through the Ministry for Religious Affairs assists the various religious communities in their activities. The Ministry has special departments for Jewish, Moslem, Christian, Druze, and Bahai communities. They carry out their functions according to the principle of non-intervention in the internal religious affairs of the communities. The religious courts of the respective communities are autonomous. Under the law, they have jurisdiction in matters of marriage and divorce of members of their respective communities.

Jewish Religious Life

The rapidly increasing Jewish population and the establishment of about 400 new settlements necessitated the expansion of facilities for religious services and activities. The number of Rabbis and Dayanim (judges in Rabbinical Courts) increased from 130 in 1948 to more than 400 in 1955. The number of synagogues rose from about 600 in 1948 to 2,553 in

1953. In 1954, 377 synagogues were erected, extended, or repaired. Most of the new synagogues were established with the assistance of the Ministry for Religious Affairs.

The Chief Rabbinate is the highest Rabbinical authority in the country and serves as a Court of Appeal from the local Rabbinical Courts. There are two Chief Rabbis: an Ashkenazi, Rabbi Yitzhak Halevi Herzog, and a Sephardi, Rabbi Yitzhak Nissim.

The Military Rabbinate appoints chaplains, supervises Kashrut, and provides religious services and rituals for religious soldiers in the Israel Defense Forces. The serving of non-kosher food is prohibited in all military as well as in other government establishments.

The Religious Council, a representative body of the local religious community, appoints and pays the rabbis, assists in the establishment and maintenance of synagogues, supervises Kashrut, etc. The number of Religious Councils increased from ten in 1948 to about 200 in 1954. The bulk of their expenditures is covered by the Government Treasury.

Kara'im (Karaites)

The Kara'im are a Jewish sect which rejects the post-biblical rabbinic traditions and claims to base its teaching on a literalistic interpretation of the Bible (Mikra). Among the arrivals in Israel during the period of mass immigration were also members of the Karaite community in Egypt and some from Iraq. At present there are 1,500 Kara'im in Israel, or over one-third of the Kara'im population of the world. Before the establishment of the State, there were only two Kara'im families in the whole country, resident in Jerusalem. About 500 now live in their new settlement, Rannen, Negev, 200 in Matsliah near Ramle, and 250 in the Ma'abara Ramle Gimmel. The Ministry for Religious Affairs provides for the religious requirements of the two Kara'im settlements of Matsliah and Rannen.

Shomronim (Samaritans)

The Shomronim are a Jewish sect which claims to be a remnant of the Kingdom of Israel that fell in 722 B.C.E. Their religion is based on the Pentateuch, and no other books of the Bible are recognized. The Shomronim community in Israel numbers about 90 souls, about one-third of the whole sect, residing chiefly in Jaffa and Holon. The other 200 live in Shechem (Nablus) which is under Jordanian control.

Moslem Religious Life

The Ministry for Religious Affairs takes an active part in promoting Moslem religious life within the Moslem community of 125,000. Its activities in this field include: 1. establishment of the Shar'ia (religious courts); 2. assistance to the community in conducting its religious affairs; and 3. repair and safeguarding of places of worship and cemeteries.

Moslem religious committees function in Jaffa, Haifa, and Acco. Their task is to advise the Ministry and to look after the religious education and needs of the orphans and aged. On their recommendation, allocations for destitute widows and orphans are made from Moslem charity funds (Waqf).

The Moslem religious officials are paid by the Government. The State radio, "Kol Israel" (Voice of Israel) regularly broadcasts Moslem prayers and readings from the Koran. The Ministry for Religious Affairs publishes an information Bulletin dealing with the religious affairs of the Moslem community.

Christian Religious Life

The more than 44,000 members of the Christian communities are served by about 1,000 religious functionaries. There are over 160 places of worship for Christians in addition to about 50 religious schools and a score of charitable institutions and hospices.

Special care has been taken to preserve the integrity of Christian Holy Places and the free approach to them. Roads leading to some of them have been improved and new roads are being constructed. In the course of the Arab war against Israel in 1948, a number of Christian religious buildings was damaged. The Israel Government has, of its own accord, incurred the expenses of considerable repairs.

Facilities are accorded to church organizations for the construction of new churches. A new Church of the Annunciation is now being built by the Franciscan Order in Nazareth and, when completed, will be the largest Christian Church in the Middle East.

Christian services are broadcast over the State Radio "Kol Israel" (Voice of Israel). The Ministry for Religious Affairs publishes a bulletin, "Christian News from Israel," in separate English, French, and Spanish editions. The religious leaders of all the Christian denominations discuss the affairs of their communities in this periodical.

MAIN CHRISTIAN COMMUNITIES

Greek Catholic (Melkites)	17,500
Greek Orthodox	13,400
Roman Catholics (Latins)	4,100
Armenians	1,030
Maronites	1,030
Anglicans	1,040

Other Christian Communities include:

Copts, Syrian Jacobites, Ethiopians, Assyrians (Chaldeans), Church of Scotland, Baptists, various other Protestant churches.

The Druze Community

The religion of the 19,800 Druzes is believed to embody elements of Jewish, Christian, and Moslem traditions. Their rites and dogmas are a close secret. They speak Arabic, but have always retained their identity as a separate community. The British Mandatory Government did not recognize their community identity and considered them part of the Moslem religious community, an arrangement which was opposed by the Druzes and brought about conflicts between the two communities. With the establishment of Israel, the Druzes were granted the status of a separate religious community with autonomy in their religious affairs as in the case of all other religious groups. The buildings of the tomb of Jethro (Nebi Shu'eib), a central Druze shrine at Hittin, have been extended to provide accommodations for the annual pilgrimages of the faithful.

The Bahais

Although the number of Bahai adherents in Israel is not large, a special Department in the Ministry for Religious Affairs was established for this community, since the Bahai faith has its world religious center in Haifa. During 1953, the Bahais completed the splendid Bahai Mausoleum on the slopes of Mount Carmel.

ECONOMY

	1952	1953	1954
*National Income (IL. million)	829	1,100	1,426
Per Capita Income (IL.)	516	666	843
Index of Prices	100	128	144
Real National Income in 1952 prices (IL. million) .	829	859	990
Real Per Capita Income in 1952 prices (IL.) . . .	516	520	585
Index of Real National Income	100	104	120
Index of Real Per Capita Income	100	101	113

* The national income was estimated at IL.2,090,000 at the end of 1956, a rise of 19% over 1955 (IL.1,751,000), a real rise of about 8%.

In real terms, national income in 1953 just kept pace with the increase in population. In 1954, however, real per capita income increased by 12% as compared with the previous year. This increase may serve as an indicator of the increase in the average level of productivity.

NATIONAL INCOME BY ECONOMIC SECTORS

	1955		1956	
	(IL. Million)	%	(IL. Million)	%
Agriculture	213.0	11.9	281.0	13.1
Mining & Industry	372.0	20.8	437.6	20.5
Construction	128.9	7.2	129.5	6.1
Public Services, Water & Electricity	30.2	1.7	36.3	1.7
Transportation	139.7	7.8	164.1	7.7
Commerce	207.7	11.6	248.3	11.6
Banking, Finance, Insurance, Real Estate	151.6	8.5	187.5	8.8
Other Services	206.9	11.6	230.7	10.8
Government & Public Institutions	338.3	18.9	420.2	19.7
Net total of local production	1,788.3	100.0	2,135.2	100.0
Minus net payments to factors of production abroad	37.2		44.9	
National Income	1,751.1		2,090.3	

OCCUPATIONAL DISTRIBUTION OF ACTIVE POPULATION
June 1954

Economic Branch	Total Thousands	%	Men %	Women %
Total	561.4	100.0	100.0	100.0
Agriculture, Forestry, and Fishing	102.2	18.2	18.7	15.8
Manufacturing (Industry and Handicrafts) . .	135.9	24.2	26.4	16.1
Building and Public Works	53.9	9.6	11.9	0.5
Transport and Communications	35.9	6.4	7.6	1.5
Commerce and Banking	68.5	12.2	12.6	11.4
Health, Education, Welfare, etc.	55.0	9.8	6.0	24.3
Other Public and Private Services	110.0	19.6	16.8	30.4

GROSS NATIONAL INVESTMENT

	1953 IL. Million	%	1954 IL. Million	%	1949–54 %
Agriculture	75	23.1	135	31.2	23.0
Industry	62	19.1	65	15.0	14.0
Housing	115	35.4	142	32.0	39.4
Public Buildings and Public Works	28	8.6	32	7.5	7.2
Transportation	33	10.1	38	8.8	8.0
Commerce and Services (incl. Government) .	12	3.7	20	4.6	7.5
Gross National Investment	325	100.0	432	100.0	100.0
Depreciation	105		140		
Net Capital Formation	220		292		

Encouragement of Capital Investment

A Law for the Encouragement of Capital Investment was passed by the Knesset on March 29, 1950.

Under this law, substantial facilities and privileges are granted to both foreign and local investors. These include relief from property tax in the first five years after an enterprise has been established— in some cases up to ten years, an increased allowance for depreciation, and considerable reductions in the rates of income taxes both for companies and individuals. The Law also provides that a non-resident foreign investor may transfer his profits, in the same currency in which his investment was originally made, in the amount of up to 10% of his investment annually. The Treasury may permit the 10% to be exceeded in the case of export enterprises in proportion to additional foreign currency earned by such enterprises.

Under an amendment passed by the Knesset in February 1955, the investment of foreign capital in Israel was further encouraged: a higher tax exemption was granted for a longer period of time; faster depreciation rates were allowed; and the definition of "Approved Capital Investment" was broadened to include foreign currency loans.

Investment Center

An "Investment Center" was established in order to:

(a) furnish information on problems connected with the investment of capital in Israel;

(b) decide whether any enterprise in which it is proposed to invest is an "approved enterprise" within the meaning of the Law and therefore entitled to the special benefits provided by the Law;

(c) maintain contact between investors and government departments on all matters connected with capital investment.

Since the establishment of the Investment Center in May, 1950, a total of 1,271 enterprises involving an investment of IL.164.2 million in local capital and $220 million in foreign capital have been approved or recommended by the Center. Fifty-five per cent of these were accepted as fully approved enterprises and the other 45% received various kinds of facilities and recommendations.

Approved Enterprises Operating More Than One Year—1956

No.—248; Investments—IL.99,476,000; $38,915,000. Value of products — IL.-197,300,000. No. of workers—14,555; Wages—IL.3,827,800; Expenses for raw materials, fuel, and electricity—IL.- 113,919,000; Export—$2,442,100.

Foreign investors in Israel enterprises received a total of $4,538,000 in dividend payments and other transfers of earnings during the three past fiscal years ending March 31, 1955. Nearly $2,000,000 of the total was paid out during the last fiscal year. The $4,500,000 does not represent the net profits made by foreign investors in Israel. Because of widening marketing opportunities and subsequent expanding production, many preferred to reinvest their profits.

BALANCE OF TRADE 1949-1956
In Current Value

	Imports	Exports	Exports as %	Imports per	Exports per
	$ million		of imports	Capita-$	Capita-$
1949	253.1	29.7	11.7	243	28
1950	298.8	36.9	12.3	236	29
1951	379.8	46.8	12.3	254	31
1952	321.1	43.4	13.8	200	28
1953	282.1	59.6	21.1	171	36
1954	289.7	88.1	30.4	171	52
1955	426.7	143.9			
1956	529.3	178.3			

COMPOSITION OF IMPORTS BY ECONOMIC DESTINATION
In Percentage of Total

	1949	1953	1954
Consumers' Goods	35	21.2	18.5
Production Goods	32	45.4	51.5
Investment Goods	29	22.6	20.3
Fuel and Lubricants	4	10.8	9.7
TOTAL	100	100.0	100.0
	($ 253.1 million)	($ 282.1 million)	($ 289.7 million)

COMPOSITION OF EXPORTS BY MAIN COMMODITIES
In Percentage of Total

	1953	1954
Citrus Fruit (exc. gift parcels)	37.6	39.3
Diamonds	22.1	18.5
Motor Cars	8.8	7.6
Textiles	6.4	4.0
Cement	2.2	2.9
Rubber Tires and Tubes	1.6	2.7
Fruit Juices	3.5	2.5
Plywood	0.9	1.7
Groundnuts in Shell	—	1.6
Watches and Clocks	0.4	1.0
Parts of Motor Cars and other Vehicles	0.4	1.0
Raincoats	2.5	0.9
Pharmaceuticals	1.0	0.9

IMPORTS BY COUNTRIES OF ORIGIN

The main suppliers of Israel's imports, in percentages of the total were:

	1956
United States	31.7
German Federal Republic*	17.8
United Kingdom	9.9
Holland	3.3
Finland	2.8
France	2.5
Switzerland	2.4

* Under the West Germany-Israel Indemnity Agreement of September 10, 1952.

EXPORTS BY COUNTRIES OF DESTINATION

The main customers for Israel's exports, in percentages of the total were:

	1953	1954	1956
United Kingdom	25.9	22.9	22.1
United States	21.3	16.9	18.1
Turkey	13.7	14.9	5.0
Finland	10.2	8.0	5.8
U.S.S.R.	1.9	3.7	—
Belgium	2.2	3.3	6.2
Sweden	1.9	3.1	3.1
France	—	—	4.0
Germany	—	—	3.9
Switzerland	—	—	3.4

The Tourist Trade

In 1956/57, 40,000 tourists visited Israel, as compared with 48,720 tourists in 1954/55. American tourists constituted 36% of the total; the others came from nearly 50 countries on all five continents. From May 1948 to the end of March, 1957, 300,000 tourists visited Israel.

The tourist trade brought in $5.5 million in foreign currency in 1956/57.

There are Government Tourist Information Centers in Jerusalem, Tel Aviv, Haifa, Tiberias, Natanya, Nazareth, and Lod (Lydda) airport. Israel Government tourist centers are maintained in New York, London, Paris, and Rome.

As of March 1955, there were 115 luxurious hotels with 3,500 rooms available for foreign visitors.

MAJOR BRANCHES OF INDUSTRY BY EMPLOYMENT AND VALUE ADDED 1953

	Number of Employees (1,000's)	Value added (IL. 1,000's)
Food	16.0	53,006
Metals	13.0	29,863
Textiles	10.3	24,570
Clothing and Footwear	8.1	14,078
Stone, Cement and Minerals	6.8	17,949
Wood	6.1	23,238
Chemicals	4.5	14,026
Paper and Printing	3.3	9,747
Machinery	3.3	8,777
Electrical Appliances	3.0	7,486
Diamonds	2.5	6,220
Leather	1.1	3,726
Miscellaneous (excl. Power)	3.3	8,508
TOTAL	81.3	221,194

INDUSTRIAL AND TRADE ORGANIZATIONS

Manufacturers' Association of Israel

The Association is organized in the following industrial sections:

Textiles
Metal and Electrical Goods
Foodstuffs
Tobacco and Cigarettes
Chemicals
Pharmaceuticals
Glassware
Ceramics
Cosmetics
Building Materials
Furniture
Stationery and Office Equipment
Diamonds
Union of Israel Fashion Industries
Plastics
Cardboard Products

The Association maintains a permanent Exhibition of Israel Industrial Products and an industrial library. It publishes a monthly review of industry and economics, "Hatasiya" (Industry), in Hebrew and the "Israel Export Journal" in English.

The association maintains a branch office in New York.

WORKSHOP OWNERS' AND SMALL MANUFACTURER'S ASSOCIATION

The Association is organized in three sections:

(a) Artisans in self-owned workshops: watchmakers, shoemakers, etc.

(b) Services: laundries, cleaners and dyers, etc.

(c) Small industrial workshops employing from 3 to 6 workers.

The Workshop Owners' Association publishes a monthly paper for internal circulation, "Ha'uman" (The Artisan).

CHAMBERS OF COMMERCE

There are three Chambers of Commerce:

(a) The Jerusalem Chamber of Commerce;

(b) The Tel Aviv-Jaffa Chamber of Commerce;

(c) The Haifa Chamber of Commerce and Industry.

Their activities are coordinated through a "Joint Representation of the Chambers of Commerce."

The Tel Aviv-Jaffa Chamber of Commerce publishes a monthly journal in Hebrew and English called "Commerce."

The Haifa Chamber of Commerce and Industry issues a monthly news circular and a yearbook.

LABOR ORGANIZATION

There are four labor organizations in Israel:

Histadrut Haklalit Shel Haovdim Ha-ivrim B'eretz Israel (General Federation of Jewish Labor in Israel);

Hapoel Hamizrahi (Mizrahi Workers' Organization);

Poalei Agudat Israel (Agudat Israel Workers' Organization);

Histadrut Haovdim Haleumit (National Workers' Organization).

HISTADRUT HAKLALIT SHEL HAOVDIM HAIVRIM B'ERETZ ISRAEL
(General Federation of Jewish Labor in Israel)

The Histadrut was founded in 1920. At the beginning of 1955, direct paid-up membership was 509,917, compared with 175,000 in 1948. In October 1952 and April 1953, respectively, Hapoel Hamizrahi, with 35,000 of its members, and Poalei Agudat Israel with 15,000 of its members, became affiliated with the Trade Union Department of the Histadru.t

The membership of the Histadrut is distributed among 27 individual unions, the major ones being the Agricultural Workers, Clerks and Office Workers, Teachers, Textile Workers, Nurses, Food Workers and Diamond Workers.

The Histadrut maintains a separate organization for youth workers up to the age of 18 (Hanoar Haoved). The Histadrut's Women Workers' Council (Moetzet Hapoalot) represents all the women members of the Histadrut—women workers and wives of members working in their own households. The Agricultural Center (Merkaz Haklai) represents the members of collective and cooperative settlements as well as hired agricultural workers.

Membership in the Histadrut is individual and membership dues are levied on a progressive scale based on earnings. The dues include the members' contribution for health insurance for himself and his family with Kupat Holim (Sick Fund).

In addition to normal trade union activities, the Histadrut maintains extensive social, cultural, and educational institutions and has created large cooperative, industrial and commercial enterprises of its own.

Social Services

The Histadrut social services and mutual aid institutions include its Sick Fund (Kupat Holim), the largest medical organization in the country in which about two thirds of the population are voluntarily insured. Kupat Holim maintains 14 major hospitals (2,000 bed capacity) and 860 medical centers, 12 convalescent homes, over 182 infant welfare centers, over 60 dental clinics, 20 X-ray institutes, and 150 institutes for electrotherapy.

Cultural and Educational Activities

The Histadrut publishes two daily papers — *Davar*, the official organ of the Histadrut, and *Omer* which is printed in vowelled Hebrew for new immigrants — and a number of subsidiary periodicals. These include a children's weekly (Davar Liladim), a women's journal, a weekly in Arabic, an illustrated weekly (Dvar Hashavua) and journals for immigrants in various languages.

Arab Workers

In May 1953, the Histadrut invited Arab workers to join its trade unions. By the end of 1954, approximately 11,000 Arab workers had joined the Histadrut.

The Histadrut has an Arab Affairs Department which has set up an economic section to assist Arab workers and peasants to form cooperatives, both for production and for the marketing of agricultural produce.

International Affiliation

The Histadrut is a member of the International Confederation of Free Trade Unions.

THE HAPOEL HAMIZRAHI ORGANIZATION
(Mizrahi Workers' Organization)

The Hapoel Hamizrahi Organization has a membership of about 50,000. At the beginning of 1954, Hapoel Hamizrahi had 62 agricultural settlements (11 kibbutzim of the Kibbutz Hadati Movement, 50 Moshvei Ovdim, and 11 Moshavim Shitufiyim). It maintains central organizations for settlement, education, absorption of new immigrants, etc. The settlements are members of the Agricultural Workers' Center. They market their products through the Histadrut's Tnuva and buy their supplies through the Histadrut's Hamashbir Hamerkazi. The Hapoel Hamizrahi Organization is affiliated with the Trade Union Department of the Histadrut. Its members are insured with the Histadrut Sick Fund, Kupat Holim.

POALEI AGUDAT ISRAEL
(Agudat Israel Workers' Organization)

The Poalei Agudat Israel Organization has a membership of about 19,000. The ten Poalei Agudat Israel settlements are organized within the Agricultural Work-ers' Center and use the Histadrut Central Marketing and Purchasing cooperatives, Tnuva and Hamashbir Hamerkazi, for the marketing of their products and the purchase of their supplies. The Organiza-tion maintains its own central organization for settlement, education, etc. Poalei Agu-dat Israel is affiliated with the Trade Union Department of the Histadrut, and its members are insured with the Histad-rut Sick Fund, Kupat Holim.

HISTADRUT HAOVDIM HALEUMIT
(National Workers' Organization)

The Histadrut Haovdim Haleumit, which was founded by the Revisionist Or-ganization, has about 18,000 members who are also covered by its National Workers' Sick Fund. It participates in the General Labor Exchange. The members of eleven agricultural settlements (3 Moshavim Shi-tufiyim and 8 Moshvei Ovdim), establish-ed by the Betar and Herut Movements, are members of the Histadrut Haovdim Haleumit. These settlements market most of their produce through Tenne (see page 51), and partly through the Histadrut's Tnuva.

RURAL SETTLEMENT

On December 31, 1956, there were 846 settlements throughout the country. There are six specific types of settlements, and the pattern of some of these types reflects various social philosophies and the need to meet the special conditions of the coun-try. Except for the Moshavot (farm vil-lages), all other types of settlements are established on Keren Kayemet Le'Israel (Jewish National Fund) lands. The settle-ment as a whole or the individual farmer holds a 49-year lease (Levit. 25) which is renewable after the expiration of that period and may be inherited.

At the end of 1956 there were 27 Mo-shavot with a population of 59,974.

Moshvei Ovdim (singular, Moshav Ov-dim) are workers' cooperative smallhold-ers' settlements. These settlements are founded on the principles of mutual aid and equality of opportunity among the members, all farms being equal in size; hired labor is prohibited. Each individual farm is worked by the member and his family, but the settlement is completely cooperative in that all the produce of the farms is sold through a central coopera-tive, and all purchases for the require-ments of the village are undertaken co-operatively.

The population of the Moshav Ovdim ranges from 100 to 1,000, and at the end of 1956, the 289 Moshvei Ovdim had a population of 101,777.

These settlements are predominantly agricultural in character.

Kibbutzim or Kvutzot (singular, Kib-butz or Kvutza) are collective settlements. All property is collectively owned and work in the settlement organized on a collective basis.

The population of the Kibbutz ranges from 60 in the smallest to approximately 2,000 in the largest. At the end of 1956, the 228 Kibbutzim and Kvutzot had a population of 79,688.

Moshavim Shittufiyim (singular, Mo-shav Shittufi) are settlements based on collective ownership of property and collective work as in the Kibbutz. Each family, however, as in the Moshav Ovdim, has its own house and is responsible for its own domestic services, such as feeding, laundry, and care of the children. The population of the Moshav Shittufi ranges in size from 60 to 300. At the end of 1956, there was a total population of 4,218 in 25 Moshavim Shittufiyim.

Settlements of new immigrants: Ma'a-barot (singular, Ma'bara, meaning "transition" village) ; Kfarei Avoda (singular, Kfar Avoda, meaning "work village"). The independent Ma'abarot and work villages established for the absorption of new immigrants are intended to become permanent agricultural settlements and will, in time, conform to the pattern of one or another type of established settlement.

At the end of 1956, there were 34 independent Ma'abarot and Kfarei Avoda with a total population of 32,607.

EDUCATION AND CULTURE

According to the Compulsory Education Law of 1949, school attendance is compulsory and free between the ages of 5 and 13. Youth between the ages of 14 and 17 who have not completed an 8-year elementary school education must attend classes until they either complete the required curriculum or reach the age of 17.

During the Mandatory period, education for the Jewish population was organized on a voluntary community basis which had resulted in the establishment of four networks or "trends": "General," "Labor," "Mizrahi," and 'Agudat Israel." The Compulsory Education Law recognized this trend system. In August 1953,

the Knesset passed the State Education Law which abolished the "trend" system and set up a unified system of state education. In addition, the Government provides for state religious education. These institutions are religious with respect to curriculum, way of life, teachers, and inspectors.

Structure of Educational System

A total of 425,000 persons are attending educational institutions in Israel ranging from kindergarten through university.

Kindergartens and Nursery Schools

About 70 per cent of all children between the ages of 3 and 6 attend kindergartens and nursery schools. This percentage is among the highest in the world and is far higher than in most European countries. Kindergarten for 5-year olds is compulsory.

Since 1948, there has been an almost fourfold increase in the number of children attending kindergartens and nursery schools.

> *1948–49*
> 16,695 children
> 426 kindergartens and nursery schools
> *1955–56*
> 65,000 children
> 1,340 kindergartens and nursery schools

Elementary Schools

Elementary School provides an 8-year course of study. Attendance has more than trebled in the past seven years:

> *1948–49*
> 71,542 pupils
> 342 schools

1956-57
350,000 pupils
929 schools

In 1956-57, 65.3% of the number of pupils in elementary schools attended State Schools, 27.3% attended State Religious Schools and 7.4% recognized Religious Schools of the Agudat Israel.

In 1955-56, 83.7% of the IL.36,165,000 allocated by the budget for education was spent on elementary schools.

High Schools

There are General, Technical and Agricultural high schools. The curriculum consists of a 4-year course of studies. Some vocational high schools have a 3-year course of studies.

High schools are either private institutions or maintained by municipalities under the supervision of the Ministry of Education and Culture. Both the State and local authorities provide scholarships for high school education. In 1955-56, 4,687 scholarships were distributed to high school students.

In the 1956–57 school year, some 24,351 pupils attended high schools. Twenty-five thousand of the pupils attended general high schools which some 11,000 others were enrolled in technical or agricultural high schools. Four thousand five-hundred were enrolled in Hadarim and Yeshivoth.

Teachers' Colleges

There are 26 teachers' colleges throughout the country. The total enrollment in these colleges in 1956-57 was 2,742 men and women.

The School of Education at the Hebrew University contains four departments: the Department for Secondary and Higher Education; the Department for Primary Education; the Department for Adult Education and the Department for Post-Graduate Study.

Hebrew University

The Hebrew University of Jerusalem has six faculties with the following enrollment in the academic year 1956–57:

	No. of Students
Humanities and Social Sciences . .	1,491
Mathematics and Sciences . . .	741
Agriculture	251
Law	397
Medicine, Dentistry, and Pharmacology	492
Librarians' School	26
TOTAL	3,398

In addition, there were 306 graduate students doing research for their Ph.D. degrees.

The academic staff of the Hebrew University consisted in 1956–57 of 658 professors, lecturers, and instructors.

The University awards Bachelor, Master, and Doctor degrees in all the above faculties.

Israel Institute of Technology–Technion

The Israel Institute of Technology in Haifa has seven faculties with the following enrollment in the academic year 1956–1957:

	No. of Students
Civil Engineering	309
Architecture	149
Mechanical Engineering	379
Electrical Engineering	338
Sciences	111
Chemical Engineering	164
Agricultural Engineering	104
Aeronautics	62
Others	405
TOTAL	2,021

The Technion awards advanced degrees: Master of Science and Doctor of Technical Science.

The Weizmann Institute of Science

The Weizmann Institute of Science in Rehovot is devoted primarily to pure scientific research. Since the establishment of its first unit, the Daniel Sieff Research Institute, in 1933, applied science, mainly in the fields of agriculture and chemical industry, has been included in its research activities.

The scientific staff of the Institute is composed of 500 research workers.

The Institute comprises the following departments:

Department of Applied Mathematics
Department of Biophysics
Department of Experimental Biology
Department of Isotope Research
Department of Nuclear Physics
Department of Optics
Department of Organic Chemistry
Department of Polymer Research
Department of Electronics
Physics
Plant Genetics Section
Microbiology Section

THEATER

Israel theater consists of a number of self-supporting theatrical companies constituted as cooperatives with a more or less permanent staff of actors and directors, occasionally hiring directors from abroad. There are three dramatic companies: Habimah, founded in 1918 in Russia and transferred to Israel in 1928; Ohel, founded in 1925 and associated with the Histadrut; and the Chamber Theater, founded in 1945. Telem, established in 1952, specializes in performances in new immigrants' centers and settlements.

There are also over 50 permanent amateur theater groups, most of them in agricultural settlements.

MUSIC

The three leading orchestras in Israel are:

(a) The Israel Philharmonic Orchestra, founded in 1936 by Bronislav Huberman. It consists of some 80 players.

(b) The Haifa Orchestra, founded in 1950.

(c) Israel Radio Orchestra, founded in 1936 (as Jerusalem Radio Orchestra).

Opera and Choral Music

The Hebrew National Opera Company was founded in 1948.

There are some 100 permanent choirs of varying sizes throughout the country.

Music Education

There are 18 Music Conservatoires in Israel. Israel. The Music Division of the

Ministry of Education and Culture supervises the musical education in recognized conservatoires and awards diplomas to graduates of these conservatoires.

MUSEUMS, ART GALLERIES, AND EXHIBITIONS

Israel's oldest museum is the Bezalel Museum in Jerusalem, named after the biblical craftsman, and founded in 1906 by Professor Boris Schatz. Other museums include the Tel Aviv Museum founded in 1926, the Ha'aretz Museum of Archaeology in Tel Aviv, the Museum of Antiquities in Jerusalem, the Archaeological Museum in Tel Aviv, the Mishkan Le'omanut (Temple of Art) in Ein Harod as well as the Sturman Collection of Natural Sciences there.

LIBRARIES AND BOOK PUBLISHING

The largest library is the Jewish National Library in Jerusalem. Others include the Municipal Library and the Rambam Library of Tel Aviv, the Knesset (Parliament) Library and the nationwide library chain of the Histadrut (General Federation of Labor). "Bookmobiles" have been organized to cater to immigrants and settlers living in outlying districts.

During 1956, about 1,200 Hebrew books were published. Of these, 205 were fiction —including drama and poetry (70 being originals and 135 translations of both classics and modern writers); 108 (49 originals and 59 translations) were for children and young people; 63 books (of which only two were translations) dealt with Jewish scholarship; 20 books (one translation) were on the history of the Land of Israel; 19 works were devoted to general history and 11 to Jewish history.

THE PRESS

Twenty-one morning and two afternoon newspapers appear daily in Israel. Fifteen of these are Hebrew-language papers. The others appear in Arabic (1), English (1), French (1), German (2), Hungarian (1), Bulgarian (1), and Yiddish (1).

Other journals include 41 newspapers which appear more than once a week (2 in Hebrew and 39 in other languages), 117 weeklies and bi-weeklies (64 in Hebrew, 53 in other languages), 76 monthlies (50 in Hebrew) and 24 quarterlies (7 in Hebrew). In all, there are 154 journals and periodicals published in Hebrew and 136 in foreign languages including illustrated, technical and scientific, literary, art, and religious publications. The above figures do not include various Government publications.

The following are the daily newspapers with their affiliations:

Name	Founded	Affiliation	Language	Description
Ha'aretz	1918	Independent	Hebrew	Morning Paper
Davar	1925	Histadrut	Hebrew	Morning Paper
Haboker	1934	General Zionist	Hebrew	Morning Paper
Hatzofe	1938	Mizrahi	Hebrew	Morning Paper
Al Hamishmar	1943	Mapam	Hebrew	Morning Paper

Name	Founded	Affiliation	Language	Description
Kol Ha'am	1947	Communist	Hebrew	Morning Paper
Herut	1948	Herut Party	Hebrew	Morning Paper
Hakol	1949	Agudat Israel	Hebrew	Morning Paper
Hammodia	1950	World Agudat Israel	Hebrew	Morning Paper
Omer	1950	Histadrut	Vowelled-Hebrew	Morning Paper
She'arim	1951	Poalei Agudat Israel	Hebrew	Morning Paper
Lamerhav	1954	Ahdut Ha'avoda	Hebrew	Morning Paper
Yediot Aharonot	1939	Independent	Hebrew	Afternoon Paper
Ma'ariv	1948	Independent	Hebrew	Afternoon Paper
El Yom	1948	Independent	Arabic	Morning Paper
Jerusalem Post	1932	Independent	English	Morning Paper
Yediot Hadashot	1936	Independent	German	Morning Paper
Yediot Hayom	1936	Independent	German	Morning Paper
L'Echo d'Israel	1948	Independent	French	Morning Paper
Uj Kelet	1948	Independent	Hungarian	Morning Paper
Israelski Far	1952	Independent	Bulgarian	Morning Paper
Letzte Neies—				
Haintige Neies	1949	Independent	Yiddish	Morning Paper

HEALTH PERSONNEL
(December 31, 1954)

Physicians	3,987
Dentists and Dental Surgeons	1,313
Midwives	220
Pharmacists	938

Israel has one doctor per 450 inhabitants, which is the highest rate in the world. Almost 50 per cent of the doctors, however, are over 50 years of age.

Hospitals

By the end of 1948, Israel had 63 hospitals with a total of 4,626 beds. By the beginning of 1956, the number of hospitals had risen to 87 with 12,200 beds. In spite of the large increase in population, the number of hospital beds per 1,000 of the population rose from 5.33 in 1949 to 6.50 in 1954.

ISRAEL MISSIONS ABROAD
Israel Delegation to the United Nations

New York: 11 East 70th St., New York 21. Abba S. Eban, Permanent Representative to the United Nations.

Geneva: 1 Rue Hoffmann. Menahem Kahany, Permanent Israel Delegate to the European Office of the United Nations.

Argentina: Legation: Buenos Aires, Arroyo 910. Aryeh L. Kubovy, Envoy Extraordinary and Minister Plenipotentiary.

Australia: Legation: Sydney, N.S.W., 84 Pitt St., Box 4414 G.P.O. Mordecai Nurock, Envoy Extraordinary and Minister Plenipotentiary.

Austria: Consulate: Vienna XIX, Peter Jordanstrasse 66. S. Bentsur, Consul.

Belgian Congo: Consulate: Leopoldville, Avenue des Congolias, P.O.B. 52. M. Alhadeff, Consul (honorary).

Belgium: Legation: Brussels, 35 rue Washington. Gideon Rafael, Envoy Extraordinary and Minister Plenipotentiary.

Bolivia: Tuvia Arazi, Lima, Peru.

Brazil: Legation: Rio de Janeiro 134, rue Paissandu, Caixa Postal 5126. A. Aroch, Envoy Extraordinary and Minister Plenipotentiary.

Bulgaria: Legation: Sofia, Luben Karavelov 34. Reuven Nall, Charge d'Affaires.

Burma: Legation: Rangoon, 97, 36th St. Y. Shimoni, Envoy Extraordinary and Minister Plenipotentiary.

Canada: Embassy: Ottawa, 45 Powell Ave. Michael Simon, Ambassador Extraordinary and Plenipotentiary. Consulate-General: Montreal, 1555 McGregor St. Yehuda Gaulan, Consul-General.

Chile: Legation: Santiago de Chile, Ahumada 131, Oficina 311, Casilla 1224. Aryeh L. Kubovy, Envoy Extraordinary and Minister Plenipotentiary.

Colombia: Bogota, Apartado Aereo 4215. Tuvia Arazi, Lima, Peru.

Costa Rica: Consulate: San Jose, Apartado 3075. A. Meltzer, Consul (honorary).

Cuba: Consulate: Havana, Vedado, Calle 23, No. 309. S. Kaplan, Consul (honorary).

Curacao: Consulate: Willemstad, Clement Cohen Inc., Heerenstraat 13, P.O.B. 155. W. Cohen, Consul (honorary).

Cyprus: Consulate: Nicosia, 27 Androcleus St., P.O.B. 626. Peretz Leshem, Consul.

Czechoslovakia: Legation: Prague II, Vorsilka 10. Shmuel Bendor, Envoy Extraordinary and Minister Plenipotentiary.

Denmark: Legation: Copenhagen, 2 Brodervens Alle, Hellerup. Zvi Avnon, Envoy Extraordinary and Minister Plenipotentiary.

Dominican Republic: Consulate: Ciudad Trujillo, Avenida Mella No.29, Bruno Phillip, Consul (honorary).

Ecuador: Consulate: Quito, Calle Venezuela No.1231, Casilla 554. M. Weiser, Consul (honorary).

El Salvador: Consulate: San Salvador, Apartado 195. Ernesto Liebes, Consul (honorary).

Ethiopia: Consulate General: Addis Ababa, P.O.B. 390. R. Pilpoul, Consul General.

Finland: Legation: Helsinki, 1A Laivurinrinne, A. Shoham, Envoy Extraordinary and Minister Plenipotentiary.

France: Embassy: Paris XVIIe, 143 Avenue du Wagram. Jacob Tsur, Ambassador Extraordinary and Plenipotentiary. Consulate: Marseilles, 454 Rue Paradis. H. Diskan, Consul.

Germany (Federal Republic): Israel Mission: Koeln Ehrenfeld I, Subbelrather Strasse 15, E. Shinnar, Chairman.

Ghana: Legation: Accra, P.O.B. 3275, Ehud Avriel, Envoy Extraordinary and Plenipotentiary.

Gibraltar: Consulate: Gibraltar, P.O.B. 141, 186 Main St. David Benaim, Consul (honorary).

Great Britain: Embassy: London W.8, 2, Palace Green. Eliahu Elath, Ambassador Extraordinary and Plenipotentiary. Consulate: London W.1. 18 Manchester Square. Rehaveam Amir, First Secretary, Consul.

Greece: Diplomatic Representation: Athens, 4, Rue Koumbari, Kolonaki. Jeonathan Prato. Diplomatic Representative.

Guatemala: Consulate: Guatemala City, Apartado 614. Eric W. Heinemann, Consul (honorary).

Honduras: Consulate: San Pedro Sula. Jacobo Weizenblut, Consul (hororary).

Hungary: Legation: Budapest. Gorkij Fasor 37. Meir Touval, Envoy Extraordinary and Minister Plenipotentiary.

Iceland: Legation: Stockholm. C. Yahil, Envoy Extraordinary and Minister Plenipotentiary.

India: Consulate: Bombay 26, 50, Pedder Road, Cumballa Hill. Avshalom Caspi, Consul.

Italy: Legation: Rome, Via Bertoloni 11. Eliahu Sasson, Envoy Extraordinary and Minister Plenipotentiary. Consulate: Milan, Via Monte Napoleone 9. Astorre Mayer, Consul (honorary). Consulate: Genoa, Piazza della Vittoria 4. Lellio Valobra, Consul (honorary).

Japan: Legation: Tokyo, 49, Shotomachi Shibuya-Ku. Avigdor Dagan, First Secretary.

Kenya: Consulate: Nairobi. P.O.B. 1334. Israel Somen, Consul (honorary).

Laos: Legation: Rangoon. Ya'acov Shimoni.

Liberia: Ehud Avriel, Envoy Extraordinary and Plenipotentiary, Accra. Consulate: Monrovia. Simon's Trading House. S. Simonovich, Consul (honorary).

Luxemburg: Legation: Brussels. Gideon Rafael, Envoy Extraordinary and Minister Plenipotentiary.

Mexico: Legation: Mexico City, Avenida Alejandro Dumas 231. Brigadier-General David Shaltiel, Envoy Extraordinary and Minister Plenipotentiary.

Netherlands: Legation: The Hague. Alexander Gogelweg 20. Ezra Yoran, Envoy Extraordinary and Minister Plenipotentiary. Consulate: Amsterdam, 26 John Vermeerstraat. R. G. Ginthon, Consul.

New Zealand: Legation: Sydney. Mordecai Nurock, Envoy Extraordinary and Minister Plenipotentiary.

Nicaragua: Consulate: Managua, Apartado Postal No. 1607. Jose Retelny, Consul (honorary).

Norway: Legation: Oslo, Gange Rolvsgate. C. Yahil, Envoy Extraordinary and Minister Plenipotentiary (resides in Stockholm).

Panama: Consulate: Panama, Via Espana y 2a Calle, Parque Lefevre, Apartado Postal No. 3255. Aaron Eisen, Consul (honorarary).

Paraguay: Legation: Asuncion, Calle Rio de Janeiro 333. B. Sapira, Consul (honorary).

Peru: Legation. Lima, Colemna 672, Dept. 407. Tuvia Arazi, Envoy Extraordinary and Minister Plenipotentiary.

Philippines: Consulate: Manila, 26–28, Plaza Moraga, P.O.B. 3150. Ernest E. Simke, Consul (honorary).

Poland: Legation: Warsaw, Ul. Ludwika Krzywickiego 24. Katriel Katz, Envoy Extraordinary and Minister Plenipotentiary.

Rumania: Legation: Bucharest, 5, Rue Burghelea. Arie Harel, Envoy Extraordinary and Minister Plenipotentiary.

Sweden: Legation: Stockholm, Ö. Torstenssonsgatan 4. C. Yahil, Envoy Extraordinary and Minister Plenipotentiary.

Switzerland: Legation: Berne, Marienstrasse 27. Eliahu Tavor, Charge d'Affaires. Consulate General: Zurich, Stampfenbachstrasse 3. Y. Ilsar, Consul, in charge of Consulate-General.

Thailand: Consulate: Bangkok, 295 Suriwongse Road. P. B. Jacobsohn, Consul-General (honorary).

Turkey: Legation: Ankara, Ozdemir Caddesi No. 6, Kavalklidere. Moshe Alon, Counsel, Charge d'Affaires. Consulate: Istanbul, Cinar Caddesi No. 53, Nisantas. A. Gilboa, Consul General.

Union of South Africa: Legation: Pretoria, 496 Lanham St., Bailey's Muckleneuk. I. Bavly, Envoy Extraordinary and Minister Plenipotentiary. Consulate General: Johannesburg, 906–912 South African Centre, 253 Bree St. G. Doron, Consul General.

Union of Soviet Socialist Republics: Embassy: Moscow, Ulitza Vesnina 16. Brigadier-General J. Avidar, Ambassador Extraordinary and Plenipotentiary.

United States of America: Embassy: Washington 8, D.C., 1621 22nd St., N.W. Abba S. Eban, Ambassador Extraordinary and Plenipotentiary. Consulate General: New York 21, 11 E. 70th St., Semah C. Hyman, Consul General. Consulate: Los Angeles, California, 659 South Highland Ave., Avraham Biran, Consul General. Consulate: Chicago, Illinois, 936 North Michigan Ave. Simha Pratt, Consul. Consulate: Atlanta, Georgia, 795 Peachtree St., N.E. N. Astar, Consul.

Uruguay: Legation: Montevideo, Ellauri 597. Joel Barromi, Charge d'Affaires.

Venezuela: Consulate: Caracas, Bolsa A. Mercaderes 19. E. Sonneschein, Consul (honorary).

Yugoslavia: Legation: Belgrade, Rue Zmaj Jovina 34. Avraham Darom, Envoy Extraordinary and Minister Plenipotentiary.

THE COMMUNITIES IN ISRAEL

Roman numerals at the top of each column refer to the following:

I   Name of settlement
II   Date of foundation
III   Geographical region
IV   Form of settlement
V   National organization with which affiliated
VI   Settlers' country of origin
VII   Population on December 31, 1956

I	II	III	IV	V	VI	VII
Abba Hillel (Kephar Silver)	1951	S. Coastal Plain	Agricultural Institution	—	—	—
Acre (Akko)	—	Upper Galilee Coast	Town	—	Various	15,200
Adanim	1950	S. Sharon	Smallholders' Settlement	Tenuat Hamoshavim	—	—
Addirim	1956	Jezreel Valley	Smallholders' Settlement	Tenuat Hamoshavim	—	—
Afula	1925	Jezreel Valley	Town	—	Various	11,900
Agur	1950	Judean Foothills	Immigrant Smallholders' Settlement	Tenuat Hamoshavim	Iraq, Yemen	—
Ahiezer	1950	Judean Plain	Immigrant Smallholders' Settlement	Hapoel Hamizrahi	Yemen	—
Ahihud	1950	W. Lower Galilee	Immigrant Smallholders' Settlement	Tenuat Hamoshavim	—	472
Ahisamakh	1950	Judean Plain	Immigrant Smallholders' Settlement	Tenuat Hamoshavim	Tripolitania	—
Ahituv	1951	N. Sharon	Immigrant Smallholders' Settlement	Tenuat Hamoshavim	Iraq, India	—
Ahuzam	1950	S. Coastal Plain	Immigrant Smallholders' Settlement	Ha'oved Hatziyyoni	Tripolitania Morocco, Algeria, Tunisia	—
Ahuzat Naphtali	1949	E. Lower Galilee	Cooperative Settlement	Poalei Agudat Yisrael	Western Europe, Israel	7
Alma	1949	Central Upper Galilee	Immigrant Smallholders' Settlement	Hapoel Hamizrahi	Tripolitania, Italy, N. Africa	—
Allonei Abba	1948	Jezreel Valley	Cooperative Settlement	Ha'oved Hatziyyoni	—	193

I	II	III	IV	V	VI	VII
Allonei Yitzhak	1950	N. Sharon	Youth Training Farm	Ha'oved Hatziyyoni	Eastern and Western Europe	243
Allonim	1938	Jezreel Valley	Kibbutz	Hakibbutz Hameuhad	Israel, Eastern and Western Europe	564
Amatzya	1955	S. Coastal Plain	Kibbutz	Ihud Hakibbutzim	Israel	—
Amir	1939	Huleh Valley	Kibbutz	Hashomer Hatzair	Israel, Western Europe	—
Amitim (Parod Illit)	1950	C. Upper Galilee	Work Village	Hapoel Hamizrahi	Yemen	—
Amka	1949	W. Upper Galilee	Immigrant Smallholders' Settlement	Tenuat Hamoshavim	Yemen	487
Ammiad (Hahoshelim)	1946	E. Upper Galilee	Kibbutz	Ihud Hakibbutzim	Israel, various	—
Amminadav	1950	Judean Hills	Immigrant Smallholders' Settlement	Tenuat Hamoshavim	Yemen	—
Ammikam	1950	Samaritan Hills	Immigrant Smallholders' Settlement	Herut Movement	Eastern Europe, Harbin (China)	230
Ammi Oz	1957	N. Negev	Smallholders' Settlement	Tenuat Hamoshavim	Egypt	—
Aphek	1939	Plain of Zebulun	Kibbutz	Hakibbutz Hameuhad	Israel and Eastern and Central Europe	517
Aphikim	1932	Kinnarot Valley	Kibbutz	Ihud Hakibbutzim	Russia, Israel	—
Araba	—	W. Upper Galilee	Arab village	—	Israel	2,700
Arbel	1949	E. Lower Galilee	Cooperative Settlement	Tenuat Hamoshavim	Israel, Western Europe	—
Arugot	1949	S. Coastal Plain	Immigrant Smallholders' Settlement	Tenuat Hamoshavim	Poland, Rumania	301
Arza	1920	Judean Hills	Convalescent Home	—	Israel	—
Aseret	1954	Judean Foothills	Regional Center	—	—	—
Ashalim	1956	N. Negev	Kibbutz	Hakibbutz Hameuhad	—	—
Ashdod Yam	1956	S. Coastal Plain	Urban Settlement	—	—	219
Ashdot Yaakov (Aleph)	1933	Kinnarot Valley	Kibbutz	Ihud Hakibbutzim	Various	—
Ashdot Yaakov (Beit)	1933	Kinnarot Valley	Kibbutz	Hakibbutz Hameuhad	Various	—

I	II	III	IV	V	VI	VII
Ashmurah	1952	Huleh Valley	Kibbutz	—	Israel	—
Ashkelon (Afridar)	1950	S. Coastal Plain	Municipality	—	S. Africa, Various	19,200
Ashrat	1951	W. Upper Galilee	Ma'bara	—	Iraq, Rumania	—
Atlit	1903	Carmel Coast	Village	—	Various	1,300
Aviel	1949	Samaritan Foothills	Smallholders' Village	Herut Movement	Poland, Rumania	322
Avital	1953	Jezreel Valley	Immigrant Smallholders' Settlement	Tenuat Hamoshavim	Iran	—
Avigdor	1950	S. Coastal Plain	Smallholders' Settlement	Tenuat Hamoshavim	Israel, Poland, Rumania	—
Avihayil	1932	Plain of Hepher	Smallholders' Settlement	Tenuat Hamoshavim	Russia, U.S.A., Israel	627
Avuka	1941	Beit She'an Valley	Youth Training Farm	—	—	—
Ayanot	1930	Judean Plain	Youth Training Farm	Histadrut	Various	407
Ayyelet Hashahar	1918	Huleh Valley	Kibbutz	Ihud Hakibbutzim	Eastern and Central Europe, Israel	—
Azarya	1949	Judean Foothills	Immigrant Smallholders' Settlement	Tenuat Hamoshavim	—	—
Azor	1948	Judean Plain	Suburban Village	—	Eastern Europe, Balkans	3,650
Azriel	1951	S. Sharon	Immigrant Smallholders' Settlement	Hapoel Hamizrahi	Yemen	—
Azrikam	1950	S. Coastal Plain	Immigrant Smallholders' Settlement	Tenuat Hamoshavim	Tunisia	465
Azzata	1956	N. Negev	Rural Settlement	—	—	—
Bahan	1953	N. Sharon	Kibbutz	—	Israel	—
Balfouriya	1922	Jezreel Valley	Smallholders' Settlement	Tenuat Hamoshavim	Israel, Eastern Europe	302
Barak	1956	Jezreel Valley	Smallholders' Settlement	Tenuat Hamoshavim	—	—
Baram	1949	Central Upper Galilee	Kibbutz	Hashomer Hatzair	Israel Central Europe, various	—
Bareket	1952	Judean Foothills	Immigrant Smallholders' Settlement	Hapoel Hamizrahi	Yemen	—

I	II	III	IV	V	VI	VII
Bar Giora	1950	Judean Hills	Immigrant Smallholders' Settlement	Herut Movement	Morocco, Iraq	—
Barkai	1949	Samaritan Foothills	Kibbutz	Hashomer Hatzair	Eastern and Central Europe, English-speaking countries	—
Bat Shelomo	1889	Samaritan Foothills	Village	—	Eastern and Central Europe, Israel	—
Bat Yam	1926	Tel Aviv-Jaffa	Municipality	—	Various	15,000
Be'er Ora	1950	Arava	Experimental Farm	Gadna Military Youth	Various	—
Beersheba	1948	N. Negev	Town	—	Rumania, Iraq, Israel, various	25,550
Be'er Tuvya	1930	S. Coastal Plain	Smallholders' Settlement	Tenuat Hamoshavim	Rumania, Russia, Germany, Israel	570
Be'er Yaakov	1907	Judean Plain	Village		Tripolitania, various	3,000
Be'eri	1946	N. Negev	Kibbutz	Hakibbutz Hameuhad	Israel, Iraq, Various	—
Be'erot Yitzhak	1948	Judean Plain	Kibbutz	Hapoel Hamizrahi	Central Europe, N. Africa	283
Be'erotayim	1949	Plain of Hepher	Immigrant Smallholders' Settlement	Tenuat Hamoshavim	Czechoslovakia, Central Europe	341
Beit Alpha	1922	Jezreel Valley	Kibbutz	Hashomer Hatzair	Israel, Eastern Europe	—
Beit Ariph	1949	Judean Foothills	Immigrant Smallholders' Settlement	Tenuat Hamoshavim	Yemen	—
Beit Dagan	1948	Judean Plain	Suburban Village	—	Various	2,900
Beit Elazari	1948	Judean Plain	Immigrant Smallholders' Settlement	Tenuat Hamoshavim	Eastern Europe	561
Beit Ezra	1950	S. Coastal Plain	Immigrant Smallholders' Settlement	Tenuat Hamoshavim	Iraq	457
Beit Gamliel	1949	S. Coastal Plain	Immigrant Smallholders' Settlement	Hapoel Hamizrahi	Central and Eastern Europe	452
Beit Gan	1904	District of Kinneret	Rural Settlement	—	Israel	350
Beit Guvrin	1949	Judean Foothills	Kibbutz	Hakibbutz Hameuhad	N. Africa, Rumania, Israel	—
Beit Ha'emek	1949	N. Upper Galilee	Kibbutz	Ihud Hakibbutzim	Hungary, England, Holland	155

I	II	III	IV	V	VI	VII
Beit Hagaddi	1949	N. Negev	Immigrant Smallholders' Settlement	Hapoel Hamizrahi	Tunisia	—
Beit Halevi	1945	Plain of Hepher	Smallholders' Settlement	Tenuat Hamoshavim	Bulgaria, Israel	238
Beit Hanan	1930	Judean Plain	Smallholders' Settlement	Tenuat Hamoshavim	Bulgaria, Israel	500
Beit Hananya	1950	N. Sharon	Immigrant Smallholders' Settlement	Tenuat Hamoshavim	Central and E. Europe, Israel	257
Beit Hashitta	1935	Jezreel Valley	Kibbutz	Hakibbutz Hameuhad	Israel, Eastern and Central Europe	—
Beit Herut	1933	Plain of Hepher	Smallholders' Settlement	Tenuat Hamoshavim	Various	274
Beit Hillel	1940	Huleh Valley	Smallholders' Settlement	Tenuat Hamoshavim	Russia, Rumania	—
Beit Hilkiya	1953	S. Coastal Plain	Immigrant Smallholders' Settlement	Poalei Agudat Yisrael	Hungary, Rumania	—
Beit Kama	1949	N. Negev	Kibbutz	Hashomer Hatzair	Hungary, Israel	—
Beit Katzir	1949	Kinnarot Valley	Kibbutz	Ihud Hakibbutzim	Israel, Asia W. Europe	—
Beit Keshet	1944	E. Lower Galilee	Kibbutz	Hakibbutz Hameuhad	Israel	—
Beit Lehem Hagelilit	1948	W. Lower Galilee	Smallholders' Settlement	Tenuat Hamoshavim	Poland, Israel, Central Europe	—
Beit Meir	1950	Judean Hills	Immigrant Smallholders' Settlement	Mizrahi	Hungary, Czechoslovakia	—
Beit Nehemya	1950	Judean Foothills	Immigrant Smallholders' Settlement	Ha'oved Hatziyyoni	Iran	—
Beit Nekopha	1949	Judean Hills	Immigrant Smallholders' Settlement	Tenuat Hamoshavim	Yugoslavia	—
Beit Nir	1955	S. Coastal Plain	Cooperative Settlement		Israel	—
Beit Oren	1939	Carmel	Kibbutz	Hakibbutz Hameuhad	Israel, Rumania, N. Africa	355
Beit Oved	1933	Judean Plain	Smallholders' Settlement	Tenuat Hamoshavim	Russia	196
Beit Rabban	1946	Judean Plain	Farm	—	—	106
Beit Re'im	1949	N. Negev	Kibbutz	Hakibbutz Hameuhad	Israel, N.Africa, Western Europe	—
Beit She'an	1948	Beit She'an Valley	Town	—	Various	7,900

I	II	III	IV	V	VI	VII
Beit She'arim	1936	Jezreel Valley	Smallholders' Settlement	Tenuat Hamoshavim	Israel, E. Europe	426
Beit Shemesh	1950	Judean Hills	Urban Settlement	—	—	3,830
Beit Shemuel	1951	Judean Plain	—	—	Israel	—
Beit Shikma	1950	S. Coastal Plain	Immigrant Smallholders' Settlement	Tenuat Hamoshavim	Tripolitania	—
Beit Uzziel	1956	Judean Plain	Smallholders' Settlement	Hapoel Hamizrahi	—	59
Beit Yannai	1933	Plain of Hepher	Smallholders' Settlement	Hamo'etza Hahaklait	Poland, Lithuania, America	160
Beit Yehoshua	1938	S. Sharon	Smallholders' Settlement	Ha'oved Hatziyyoni	Poland	262
Beit Yerah	—	District of Kinneret	Agricultural School	—	Israel	—
Beit Yitzhak	1940	Plain of Hepher	Smallholders' Settlement	Hamo'etza Hahaklait	Germany, Israel	970
Beit Yoseph	1937	Beit She'an Valley	Smallholders' Settlement	Tenuat Hamoshavim	Russia, Rumania	—
Beit Zayit	1949	Judean Hills	Immigrant Smallholders' Settlement	Hamo'etza Hahaklait	Yugoslavia, Tripolitania	—
Beit Zera	1927	Kinnarot Valley	Kibbutz	Hashomer Hatzair	Israel Eastern Europe,	—
Bekoa	1951	Judean Foothills	Immigrant Smallholders' Settlement	Tenuat Hamoshavim	Yemen, Israel	—
Ben Ammi	1949	W. Upper Galilee	Smallholders' Settlement	Tenuat Hamoshavim	Israel, Eastern Europe	268
Benaya	1949	S. Coastal Plain	Immigrant Smallholders' Settlement	Tenuat Hamoshavim	Rumania, Poland	320
Benei Atarot	1948	Judean Plain	Smallholders' Settlement	Tenuat Hamoshavim	Eastern and Central Europe, Israel	281
Benei Berak	1924	Tel Aviv-Jaffa	Town	—	Various	30,000
Benei Berit (Moledet)	1937	E. Lower Galilee	Cooperative Settlement	Tenuat Hamoshavim	Central Europe, Israel	349
Benei Darom	1949	S. Coastal Plain	Kibbutz	Hapoel Hamizrahi	America, Germany, various	—
Benei Deror	1946	S. Sharon	Cooperative Settlement	Tenuat Hamoshavim	Various	180
Benei Re'em	1949	S. Coastal Plain	Immigrant Smallholders' Settlement	Poalei Agudat Yisrael	Rumania	364

I	II	III	IV	V	VI	VII
Ben Shemen	1921	Judean Foothills	Youth Training Farm	Youth Aliya	Various	—
Ben Shemen	1952	Judean Foothills	Immigrant Smallholders' Settlement	Tenuat Hamoshavim	Rumania	—
Benei Zion	1947	S. Sharon	Smallholders' Settlement	Hamo'etza Hahaklait	Russia, Central Europe, Israel	387
Ben Zakkai	1950	Judean Plain	Immigrant Smallholders' Settlement	Hapoel Hamizrahi	Tripolitania	452
Berekhyah	1950	S. Coastal Plain	Immigrant Smallholders' Settlement	Tenuat Hamoshavim	Tunisia (Jerba Island)	521
Beror Hayil	1948	S. Coastal Plain	Kibbutz	Ihud Hakibbutzim	Egypt, Various	—
Berosh	1953	N. Negev	Immigrant Smallholders' Settlement	Tenuat Hamoshavim	N. Africa	—
Berurim	1951	S. Coastal Plain	Seed Farm	—	—	32
Betzet	1949	W. Upper Galilee	Immigrant Smallholders' Settlement	Tenuat Hamoshavim	Yugoslavia Rumania	—
Binyamina	1922	N. Sharon	Village	—	Various	2,550
Biriya	1945/49	E. Upper Galilee	Work Village	—	Tripolitania	272
Bitan Aharon	1936	Plain of Hepher	Smallholders' Settlement	Hamo'etza Hahaklait	Eastern Europe, Israel	—
Bitanya	1941	Kinnarot Valley	Kibbutz	Ihud Hakibbutzim	Various	168
Bit'ha	1950	N. Negev	Immigrant Smallholders' Settlement	Tenuat Hamoshavim	Yemen	—
Bitzaron	1935	S. Coastal Plain	Smallholders' Settlement	Tenuat Hamoshavim	Russia, Balkans, Israel	520
Borgata	1949	Plain of Hepher	Immigrant Smallholders' Settlement	Tenuat Hamoshavim	Turkey	—
Botzra	1946	S. Sharon	Smallolders' Settlement	Hamo'etza Hahaklait	Israel, Central and Eastern Europe	399
Bustan Hagalil	1948	W. Upper Galilee	Smallholders' Settlement	Hamo'etza Hahaklait	Israel, Central and Eastern Europe	332
Daliya	1939	Samaritan Foothills	Kibbutz	Hashomer Hatzair	Germany, Rumania, various	—
Dalton	1950	Central Upper Galilee	Immigrant Smallholders' Settlement	Hapoel Hamizrahi	Tripolitania	—

I	II	III	IV	V	VI	VII
Dan	1939	Huleh Valley	Kibbutz	Hashomer Hatzair	Eastern Europe, Israel	—
Daphna	1939	Huleh Valley	Kibbutz	Hakibbutz Hameuhad	Eastern Europe, Israel	—
Daverat	1946	Jezreel Valley	Kibbutz	Ihud Hakibbutzim	Central Europe, Israel	321
Deganim	1952	S. Coastal Plain	Administrative Farm	Jewish Agency	Various	28
Degania Aleph	1909	Kinnarot Valley	Kibbutz	Ihud Hakibbutzim	Israel, Eastern Europe	—
Degania Beit	1920	Kinnarot Valley	Kibbutz	Ihud Hakibbutzim	Israel, Eastern Europe	—
Devira	1951	Kinnarot Valley	Kibbutz	Hashomer Hatzair	Hungary, Central Europe	—
Devora	1956	Jezreel Valley	Smallholders' Settlement	Tenuat Hamoshavim	—	—
Dimona	1955	N. Negev	Suburban Settlement	—	Israel	1,750
Dishon	1953	E. Upper Galilee	Immigrant Smallholders' Settlement	Hamo'etza Hahaklait	—	—
Dor	1949	Carmel Coast	Immigrant Smallholders' Settlement	Tenuat Hamoshavim	Greece	211
Dorot	1941	S. Coastal Plain	Kibbutz	Ihud Hakibbutzim	Central Europe, Israel	—
Doshen	1955	Jezreel Valley	Agricultural Farm	Ihud Hakibbutzim	Israel	10
Dove	1950	W. Upper Galilee	Immigrant Smallholders' Settlement	Tenuat Hamoshavim	Iraq	352
Eilat	1949	S. Arava	Municipality	—	Various	2,600
Eilon	1938	W. Upper Galilee	Kibbutz	Hashomer Hatzair	Poland, Israel, various	—
Einat (Givat Hashlosha B)	1925/54	Judean Foothills	Kibbutz	Ihud Hakibbutzim	Various	—
Ein Ayyala	1949	Carmel Coast	Immigrant Smallholders' Settlement	Tenuat Hamoshavim	Czechoslovakia	321
Ein Dor	1948	E. Lower Galilee	Kibbutz	Hashomer Hatzair	Israel, Western Europe, various	437
Ein Gedi	1953	Dead Sea Coast	Kibbutz	Ihud Hakibbutzim	Various	—
Ein Gev	1937	Kinnarot Valley	Kibbutz	Ihud Hakibbutzim	Various	—
Ein Ha'emek	1944	Samaritan Foothills	Smallholders' Settlement	—	Kurdistan	295

I	II	III	IV	V	VI	VII
Ein Hahoresh	1931	Plain of Hepher	Kibbutz	Hashomer Hatzair	E. Europe, Israel	—
Ein Hamiphratz	1938	Plain of Zebulun	Kibbutz	Hashomer Hatzair	E. Europe, Israel	542
Ein Hanatziv	1946	Beit She'an Valley	Kibbutz	Hapoel Hamizrahi	Germany	—
Ein Harod Aleph	1921	Jezreel Valley	Kibbutz	Hakibbutz Hameuhad	Various	—
Ein Harod Beit	—	Jezreel Valley	Kibbutz	Ihud Hakibbutzim	Various	—
Ein Hashelosha	1950	Negev	Kibbutz	Ha'oved Hatziyyoni	S. America	—
Ein Hashophet	1937	Samaritan Foothills	Kibbutz	Hashomer Hatzair	America, Eastern Europe, Israel	—
Ein Hod	1949	Carmel	Artists' Village	—	Various	32
Ein 'Iron	1934	Samaritan Foothills	Smallholders' Settlement	Tenuat Hamoshavim	—	—
Ein Karmel	1947	Carmel Coast	Kibbutz	Hakibbutz Hameuhad	Israel, Eastern Europe	438
Ein Kerem	—	Judean Hills	Suburban Settlement	—	Israel	—
Ein Kerem	1953	Judean Hills	Agricultural High School	—	Israel	—
Ein Na'aman	1950	Plain of Zebulun	Suburban Settlement	—	Various	1,500
Ein Netafim	1950	N. Negev	Kibbutz	—	Israel	—
Ein Sarid	1950	S. Sharon	Rural Settlement	—	Turkey, Rumania	669
Ein Shemer	1927	N. Sharon	Kibbutz	Hashomer Hatzair	E. Europe, Israel	—
Ein Tzurim	1949	S. Coastal Plain	Kibbutz	Hapoel Hamizrahi	Israel, Western Europe	202
Ein Vered	1930	E. Sharon	Smallholders' Settlement	Tenuat Hamoshavim	E. Europe, Israel	504
Ein Yahav	1953	Central Arava	Work Village	—	Various	—
Ein Ya'akov	1950	Central Upper Galilee	Work Village	—	Iraq	—
Ein Zeitim	1946/54	E. Upper Galilee	Youth Training Farm	Jewish Agency	Various	—
Eitan	1955	S. Coastal Plain	Smallholders' Settlement	Hapoel Hamizrahi	Israel	—
Eitanim	1952	Judea Hills	Hospital	—	Various, Israel	125
Eliphelet	1949	E. Upper Galilee	Village Work	—	India	—

I	II	III	IV	V	VI	VII
Elishama	1951	S. Sharon	Immigrant Smallholders' Settlement	Tenuat Hamoshavim	Israel, Tripolitania	—
Elkosh	1949	Central Upper Galilee	Immigrant Smallholders' Settlement	Tenuat Hamoshavim	Iraq	—
Elro'i	1935	Plain of Zebulun	Smallholders' Settlement	—	Israel, Kurdistan	561
Elyakhin	1950	Plain of Hepher	Village	—	Yemen, Iraq	1,490
Elyakim	1949	Samaritan Foothills	Immigrant Smallholders' Settlement	Tenuat Hamoshavim	Yemen	500
Elyashiv	1953	Plain of Hepher	Smallholders' Settlement	Hitahdut Ha'ikkarim	Yemen	418
Emunim	1950	S. Coastal Plain	Immigrant Smallholders' Settlement	Tenuat Hamoshavim	Egypt	375
Ephal	1952	Judean Plain	Seminary	—	Israel	—
Erez	1949	S. Coastal Plain	Kibbutz	Ihud Hakibbutzim	Israel, Central Europe	—
Eshel Hanasi	1952	N. Negev	Agricultural School	—	—	277
Eshbol	1955	N. Negev	Smallholders' Settlement	Tenuat Hamoshavim	—	—
Eshkolot	1955	S. Coastal Plain	Plantation	—	—	277
Eshta'ol	1949	Judean Foothills	Immigrant Smallholders' Settlement	Tenuat Hamoshavim	Yemen	—
Even Sappir	1950	Judean Hills	Immigrant Smallholders' Settlement	Tenuat Hamoshavim	Iraq	—
Even Shemuel	—	S. Coastal Plain	Village Center	—	—	50
Even Yehuda	1952	S. Sharon	Village Council	—	Israel, Eastern Europe	2,555
Even Yitzhak	1945	Samaritan Foothills	Kibbutz	Ihud Hakibbutzim	Central Europe	—
Evron	1945	W. Upper Galilee	Kibbutz	Hashomer Hatzair	Rumania, Poland, Israel	401
Eyal	1949	S. Sharon	Kibbutz	Hakibbutz Hameuhad	Balkans, various	—
Ezuz	1956	C. Negev	Kibbutz	Ihud Hakibbutzim	—	—
Ga'ash	1951	S. Sharon	Kibbutz	Hashomer Hatzair	S. America, Eastern and Central Europe	214

I	II	III	IV	V	VI	VII
Gaaton	1948	W. Upper Galilee	Kibbutz	Hashomer Hatzair	Israel, Western Europe	—
Gadish	1956	Jezreel Valley	Smallholders' Settlement	Tenuat Hamoshavim	—	—
Gadot	1949	E. Upper Galilee	Kibbutz	Hakibbutz Hameuhad	Israel	—
Gal On	1946	S. Coastal Plain	Kibbutz	Hashomer Hatzair	Poland, Israel	—
Gan Hasharon		S. Sharon	Farm	—	—	—
Gan Hayyim	1935	S. Sharon	Smallholders' Settlement	Tenuat Hamoshavim	Russia	—
Gannei'am	1934	S. Sharon	Smallholders' Settlement	Tenuat Hamoshavim	E. Europe, Israel	208
Gannei Tikva	1953	Judean Plain	Suburban Village	—	Israel	2,700
Gannei Yehuda	1950	Judean Plain	Smallholders' Settlement	Hamo'etza Hahaklait	S. Africa	230
Gannei Yona	1949	Judean Plain	Immigrant Smallholders' Settlement	Tenuat Hamoshavim	Israel, Poland	285
Gannot	1953	Judean Plain	Smallholders' Settlement	Hamo'etza Hahaklait	—	118
Gannot Hadar	1953	S. Sharon	Smallholders' Settlement	Hamo'etza Hahaklait	America	62
Gan Shelomo	1927	Judean Plain	Kibbutz	Ihud Hakibbutzim	Poland, Israel	347
Gan Shemuel	1913/21	N. Sharon	Kibbutz	Hashomer Hatzair	E. Europe, Israel	664
Gan Shomron	1934	N. Sharon	Smallholders' Settlement	Hamo'etza Hahaklait	Central Europe, Israel	—
Gan Sorek	1956	Judean Plain	Smallholders' Settlement	Tenuat Hamoshavim	—	115
Gan Yavne	1931	Judean Plain	Village Council	—	Various	2,655
Gan Yoshiya	1949	N. Sharon	Smallholders' Settlement	Tenuat Hamoshavim	Rumania	—
Gat	1942	S. Coastal Plain	Kibbutz	Hashomer Hatzair	E. Europe, Israel	—
Gat Rimmon	1926	Judean Plain	Smallholders' Settlement	—	E. Europe	238
Gazit	1948	E. Lower Galilee	Kibbutz	Hashomer Hatzair	Eastern and Central Europe	—
Ge'alya	1948	S. Coastal Plain	Immigrant Smallholders' Settlement	Tenuat Hamoshavim	Bulgaria	390
Gedera	1884	Judean Plain	Municipal Settlement	—	Various, Israel	4,000

I	II	III	IV	V	VI	VII
Gefen	1955	Judean Hills	Smallholders' Settlement	Hapoel Hamizrahi	Israel	—
Gelil Yam	1943	S. Sharon	Kibbutz	Hakibbutz Hameuhad	Various	386
Gesher	1939	Kinnarot Valley	Kibbutz	Hakibbutz Hameuhad	Various	—
Gesher Haziv	1949	W. Upper Galilee	Kibbutz	Ihud Hakibbutzim	Israel, English-speaking countries	—
Geulei Teiman	1947	Plain of Hepher	Smallholders' Settlement	Hapoel Hamizrahi	Yemen	314
Geulim	1945	S. Sharon	Smallholders' Settlement	Tenuat Hamoshavim	Yemen	422
Geva	1921	Jezreel Valley	Kibbutz	Ihud Hakibbutzim	Israel, Eastern Europe	—
Geva Karmel	1949	Carmel Coast	Immigrant Smallholders' Settlement	Tenuat Hamoshavim	Turkey	400
Gevaram	1942	S. Coastal Plain	Kibbutz	Hakibbutz Hameuhad	Central Europe, Israel	—
Gevat	1926	Jezreel Valley	Kibbutz	Hakibbutz Hameuhad	Various	604
Gevim	1947	N. Negev	Kibbutz	Ihud Hakibbutzim	—	—
Gevulot	1943	N. Negev	Kibbutz	Hashomer Hatzair	Tukey, Western Europe, various	—
Geya	1949	S. Coastal Plain	Immigrant Smallholders' Settlement	Tenuat Hamoshavim	Czechoslovakia	—
Gezer	1945	Judeean Foothills	Kibbutz	Ihud Hakibbutzim	Central Europe, Israel	—
Gibbeton	1933	Judean Plain	Smallholders' Settlement	Tenuat Hamoshavim	Israel	200
Gidona	1948	Jezreel Valley	Work Village	—	Yemen	—
Gilam	1951	W. Upper Galilee	Suburban Village	—	—	556
Gilat	1949	N. Negev	Immigrant Smallholders' Settlement	Tenuat Hamoshavim	Tunisia	—
Gimzo	1950	Judean Foothills	Immigrant Smallholders' Settlement	Poalei Agudat Yisrael	Rumania	—
Ginnaton	1952	Judean Plain	Immigrant Smallholders' Settlement	Tenuat Hamoshavim	Eastern Europe	282
Ginnegar	1922	Jezreel Valley	Kibbutz	Ihud Hakibbutzim	Israel, Eastern Europe	483

I	II	III	IV	V	VI	VII
Ginnosar	1937	Kinnarot Valley	Kibbutz	Hakibbutz Hameuhad	Israel, various	—
Givat Ada	1903	Samaritan Foothills	Rural Settlement	—	Rumania, Israel	1,200
Givatayim	1922	Judean Plain	Urban Settlement	—	Israel, Eastern Europe	20,350
Givat Berakha	1952	Judean Plain	Rural Settlement	—	Various	—
Givat Brenner	1928	Judean Plain	Kibbutz	Hakibbutz Hameuhad	Israel, Eastern and Central Europe	1,678
Givat Hasharon	1952	W. Lower Galilee	Kibbutz	Ihud Hakibbutzim	Various	625
Givat Hashlosha A	1925	Judean Plain	Kibbutz	Hakibbutz Hameuhad	Israel, Eastern Europe	—
Givat Haviva	1951	N. Sharon	Seminary	Hashomer Hatzair	Eastern and Central Europe	—
Givat Hayyim A	1932	Plain of Hepher	Kibbutz	Hakibbutz Hameuhad	Various	787
Givat Hayyim B	1952	Plain of Hepher	Kibbutz	Ihud Hakibbutzim	Central Europe, Israel	792
Givat Hen	1933	S. Sharon	Smallholders' Settlement	Tenuat Hamoshavim	E. Europe, Israel	220
Givat Koah	1950	Judean Foothills	Immigrant Smallholders' Settlement	Tenuat Hamoshavim	Yemen	—
Givat Mordekhai	1952	Judean Foothills	Smallholders' Settlement	Mizrahi	—	—
Givat Nili	1953	Samaritan Foothills	Smallholders' Settlement	Herut Movement	Israel, Turkey	—
Givat Oz	1949	Samaritan Foothills	Kibbutz	Hashomer Hatzair	Western Europe	—
Givat Shemuel	1942	Judean Plain	Suburban Settlement	—	Eastern Europe	3,150
Givat Washington	1950	Judean Plain	Seminary (Yeshiva)	Hapoel Hamizrahi	N. Africa	—
Givat Ye'arim	1950	Judean Hills	Immigrant Smallholders' Settlement	Tenuat Hamoshavim	Yemen	—
Givati	1950	S. Coastal Plain	Smallholders' Settlement	Tenuat Hamoshavim	Egypt, Iraq	350
Givolim	1952	N. Negev	Immigrant Smallholders' Village	Hapoel Hamizrahi	Iraq	—
Givot Zayd	1943	Jezreel Valley	Kibbutz	Ihud Hakibbutzim	Central Europe, Israel	142
Gonen	1951	Huleh Valley	Kibbutz	Ihud Hakibbutzim	Israel	—

I	II	III	IV	V	VI	VII
Goren	1950	W. Upper Galilee	Work Village	—	Iran	—
Habonim	1949	N. Sharon	Cooperative Settlement	Tenuat Hamoshavim	—	226
Hadar Am	1933	Plain of Hepher	Smallholders' Settlement	Hamo'etza Hahaklait	—	203
Hadar-Ramatayim	1925	S. Sharon	Municipality	—	Various	6,400
Hadassim	1947	S. Sharon	Youth Training Farm	Canadian Hadassah (Wizo), YouthAliya	Israel	481
Hadera	1890	N. Sharon	Municipality	—	Various	23,000
Hadid	1949/52	Judean Foothills	Immigrant Smallholders' Settlement	Hapoel Hamizrahi	Yemen	—
Hadid Illit	1952	Judean Foothills	Work Village	Hapoel Hamizrahi	Yemen	—
Hagor	1949	S. Sharon	Immigrant Smallholders' Settlement	Tenuat Hamoshavim	Bulgaria	—
Hagoshrim	1943/8	Huleh Valley	Kibbutz	Hakibbutz Hameuhad	Turkey, Israel various	—
Hagovrim	1949	Huleh Valley	Kibbutz	Hakibbutz Hameuhad	Israel	—
Hahotrim	1948	Carmel Coast	Kibbutz	Hakibbutz Hameuhad	Israel, Central Europe	331
Haifa	—	Carmel	Town	—	Various	153,000
Hamapil	1945	Plain of Hepher	Kibbutz	Hashomer Hatzair	Eastern and Central Europe, Israel	—
Hamadya	1942	Beit She'an Valley	Kibbutz	Ihud Hakibbutzim	Various, Israel, Central Europe	—
Hanniel	1950	Plain of Hepher	Immigrant Smallholders' Settlement	Tenuat Hamoshavim	Rumania	—
Hanita	1938	W. Upper Galilee	Kibbutz	Ihud Hakibbutzim	Israel, Eastern and Central Europe	—
Ha'ogen	1947	Plain of Hepher	Kibbutz	Hashomer Hatzair	Central Europe	508
Ha'on	1949	Kinnarot Valley	Kibbutz	Ihud Hakibbutzim	Rumania, various	—
Haphetz Hayyim	1944	Judean Plain	Kibbutz	Poalei Agudat Yisrael	Israel, Central Europe	427
Harel	1948	Judean Foothills	Kibbutz	Hashomer Hatzair	Israel	—
Hartuv (Beit Shemesh)	1895	Judean Foothills	Municipality	—	Various	—

I	II	III	IV	V	VI	VII
Haruvit	1955	S. Coastal Plain	Training Settlement	—	Israel	—
Harutzim (Maaberet Hoph Hasharon)	1951	S. Sharon	Maabara	—	Iraq, various	448
Hasolelim	1949	W. Lower Galilee	Kibbutz	Ha'oved Hatziyyoni	Israel, America	—
Hatzav	1949	S. Coastal Plain	Immigrant Smallholders' Settlement	Tenuat Hamoshavim	Tripolitania	—
Hatzerim	1946	N. Negev	Kibbutz	Ihud Hakibbutzim	C. Europe, Israel, N. Africa	—
Hatzeva	1948	N. Negev	Workers' Camp	—	Israel	—
Hatzor (A & B)	1953	C. Upper Galilee	Rural Settlement	—	—	2,937
Hatzor-Ashdod	1947	S. Coastal Plain	Kibbutz	Hashomer Hatzair	Israel, Germany, Poland, U.S.A.	—
Havvat Akko	—	W. Upper Galilee	Experimental Farm	—	—	—
Havvat Eden	1955	Beit She'an Valley	Experimental Farm	—	—	—
Havvat Farwana	—	Beit She'an Valley	Experimental Farm	—	—	—
Havvat Hashomer	1956	Kinnarot Valley	Agricultural School	Hapoel Hamizrahi	—	101
Havvat "Hatzera"	1955	S. Coastal Plain	Seed-growing Farm	—	Israel	—
Havvat Mordekhai	—	Judean Plain	Experimental Farm	—	—	24
Havvat Nevei Yaar	1949	W. Lower Galilee	Experiment Farm	—	—	—
Havvat Noi	1955	Plain of Hepher	Experimental Farm	—	—	—
Havvat Shemuel	1952	Jezreel Valley	Agricultural Farm	—	Israel	—
Havatzelet Hasharon	1935	Plain of Hepher	Smallholders' Settlement	Hamo'etza Hahaklait	Eastern Europe, Israel	179
Hayogev	1949	Jezreel Valley	Smallholders' Settlement	Tenuat Hamoshavim	Eastern and Central Europe, Israel	—
Hazore'a	1936	Jezreel Valley	Kibbutz	Hashomer Hatzair	Central Europe, Various, Israel	583
Hazor'im	1939	Kinnarot Valley	Settlement Smallholders'	Hapoel Hamizrahi	—	332
Heila	1949	E. Lower Galilee	Farm	—	Israel	—

I	II	III	IV	V	VI	VII
Heletz	1950	S. Coastal Plain	Immigrant Smallholders' Settlement	Tenuat Hamoshavim	Yemen	—
Hemed	1950	Judean Plain	Smallholders' Settlement	Hapoel Hamizrahi	Rumania, Czechoslovakia	375
Hephzibah	1922	Jezreel Valley	Kibbutz	Hakibbutz Hameuhad	Israel, Eastern and Central Europe	500
Herev Le'et	1947	Plain of Hepher	Smallholders' Settlement	Hamo'etza Hahaklait	Various, Eastern Europe	250
Herut	1930	S. Sharon	Smallholders' Settlement	Tenuat Hamoshavim	Israel, Eastern Europe	—
Hertzliya	1924	S. Sharon	Municipality	—	Various	21,000
Hibbat Zion	1933	Plain of Hepher	Smallholders' Settlement	Hitahdut Ha'ikkarim	Russia	355
Hodiya	1949	S. Coastal Plain	Immigrant Smallholders' Settlement	Tenuat Hamoshavim	India	455
Hogla	1933	Plain of Hepher	Smallholders' Settlement	Tenuat Hamoshavim	Israel, Eastern Europe	211
Holon	1931	Judean Plain	Municipality	—	Various	32,200
Hophit	1956	N. Sharon	Urban Settlement	—	—	—
Horshim	1955	Judean Plain	Kibbutz	Hashomer Hatzir	Israel	—
Hosen	1949	Central Upper Galilee	Immigrant Smallholders' Settlement	Herut Movement	Rumania, Israel	—
Hoter	1950	Judean Plain	Maabara	—	Israel	3,000
Hulata	1936	Huleh Valley	Kibbutz	Hakibbutz Hameuhad	Various, Israel	—
Hulda	1907/30	Judean Foothills	Kibbutz	Ihud Hakibbutzim	Israel, Eastern Europe	—
Hukkok	1945	E. Lower Galilee	Kibbutz	Hakibbutz Hameuhad	Israel, various	—
Ibbim	1953	N. Negev	Agricultural Farm	—	Israel	—
Iddit	1954	Judean Foothills	Agricultural Association	—	—	—
Ilaniya (Sejera)	1902	E. Lower Galilee	Farm Village	—	Israel, North Africa, Western Europe	243
Ilanot	1950	S. Sharon	Tree Nursery	—	Various	25
Ir Hamiphratz	1952	Plain of Zebulun	Maabara	—	Various	—
Iron	1934	N. Sharon	Smallholders' Settlement	Tenuat Hamoshavim	Russia, Poland, Germany	370

I	II	III	IV	V	VI	VII
Jerusalem	—	Judean Hills	Capital Town	—	Various	148,000
Kabri	1949	W. Upper Galilee	Kibbutz	Hakibbutz Hameuhad	Israel, Central Europe	—
Kadima	1933	S. Sharon	Smallholders' Settlement	Hitahdut Ha'ikkarim	Various	650
Kadduri	1931	E. Lower Galilee	Youth Training Farm	—	Israel	236
Kannot	1952	S. Coastal Plain	Youth Training Farm	—	Various	—
Karei Deshe	1954	Upper Galilee	Cattle Farm	—	Israel	30
Karei Naaman	1955	Plain of Zebulun	Cattle Farm	—	—	—
Karkur	1913	N. Sharon	Rural Settlement	—	Various	3,000
Karmiya	1950	S. Coastal Plain	Kibbutz	Hashomer Hatzair	Tunisia, France	—
Karmon	1952	S. Coastal Plain	Smallholders' Settlement	Tenuat Hamoshavim	Rumania	103
Kedma	1946	S. Coastal Plain	Kibbutz	Hakibbutz Hameuhad	Various, Israel	246
Kelahim (Shoval 4)	1954	N. Negev	Smallholders' Settlement	Ha'oved Hatziyyoni	—	—
Ketziot	1953	Central Negev	Kibbutz	Hakibbutz Hameuhad	Israel	—
Kephar Ahim	1949	S. Coastal Plain	Immigrant Smallholders' Settlement	Tenuat Hamoshavim	Central Europe, Rumania	279
Kephar Atta	1925	Zebulun Valley	Suburban Settlement	—	Various	11,800
Kephar Avdon	1952	W. Upper Galilee	Work Village	—	Iran	—
Kephar Aviv	1951	S. Coastal Plain	Smallholders' Settlement	Hamo'etza Hahaklait	Egypt	211
Kephar Avoda	1942	S. Sharon	Educational Institution	—	Various	81
Kephar Avraham	1932	Judean Plain	Smallholders' Setttlement	Hapoel Hamizrahi	Israel	—
Kephar Azar	1932	Judean Plain	Smallholders' Settlement	Tenuat Hamoshavim	E. Europe, Israel	305
Kephar Azza	1951	N. Negev	Kibbutz	Ihud Hakibbutzim	N. Africa	—
Kephar Barukh	1926	Jezreel Valley	Smallholders' Settlement	Tenuat Hamoshavim	Various, Israel	253
Kephar Bialik	1934	Plain of Zebulun	Smallholders' Settlement	Hamo'etza Hahaklait	Germany	308

I	II	III	IV	V	VI	VII
Kephar Bilu	1932	Judean Plain	Smallholders' Settlement	Tenuat Hamoshavim	E. Europe, Poland, Rumania, Israel	398
Kephar Bin-Nun	1952	Judean Foothills	Smallholders' Settlement	Ha'oved Hatziyyoni	Rumania	—
Kephar Blum	1943	Huleh Valley	Kibbutz	Ihud Hakibbutzim	Israel, Baltic and English-speaking countries	—
Kephar Daniel	1949	Judean Foothills	Cooperative Settlement	Tenuat Hamoshavim	English-speaking countries, India	—
Kephar Ekron	1948	Judean Plain	Rural Settlement	—	Yemen, Various	3,800
Kephar Gallim	1952	Carmel Range	Educational Institution	—	Israel	307
Kephar Gannim	1926	Judean Plain	Rural Settlement	—	Israel, Eastern Europe	2,000
Kephar Gevirol	1949	Judean Plain	Rural Settlement	—	Iraq, Various	—
Kephar Gid'on	1923	Jezreel Valley	Smallholders' Settlement	Agudat Yisrael	Rumania, various	244
Kephar Giladi	1916	E. Upper Galilee	Kibbutz	Ihud Hakibbutzim	Various, Israel	—
Kephar Glickson	1939	Samaritan Foothills	Kibbutz	Ha'oved Hatziyyoni	Rumania, Israel	—
Kephar Habad	1949	Judean Plain	Smallholders' Settlement	Habad Hasidim	—	560
Kephar Habonim	1949	Carmel Coast	Cooperative Settlement	Tenuat Hamoshavim	English-speaking countries	—
Kephar Hahoresh	1933	N. Lower Galilee	Kibbutz	Ihud Hakibbutzim	Israel, Western Europe	—
Kephar Hamakabbi	1936	Plain of Zebulun	Kibbutz	Ihud Hakibbutzim	Israel, Central Europe	340
Kephar Hamesubbim	1951	Judean Plain	Maabara	—	Iraq	538
Kephar Hanagid	1949	Judean Plain	Immigrant Smallholders' Settlement	Tenuat Hamoshavim	Bulgaria	360
Kephar Hanasi	1948	E. Uppeer Galilee	Kibbutz	Ihud Hakibbutzim	Britain, Israel	—
Kephar Hanoar Hadati	1937	Plain of Zebulun	Youth Training Farm	—	N. Africa, various	410
Kephar Hariph	1956	S. Coastal Plain	Farm Settlement	—	—	—
Kephar Haro'e	1934	Plain of Hepher	Smallholders' Settlement	Hapoel Hamizrahi	Central and E. Europe, Israel	850
Kephar Hasidim A	1924	Jezreel Valley	Smallholders' Settlement	Hapoel Hamizrahi	Poland, various	480

I	II	III	IV	V	VI	VII
Kephar Hasidim B	1950	Jezreel Valley	Rural Settlement	—	—	600
Kephar Hasidim (Maabara)	1950	Jezreel Valley	Maabara	—	—	405
Kephar Hayarok	1950	S. Sharon	Youth Training Farm	—	Israel, various	300
Kephar Hayyim	1933	Plain of Hepher	Smallholders' Settlement	Tenuat Hamoshavim	Russia, Israel	354
Kephar Hess	1933	S. Sharon	Smallholders' Settlement	Tenuat Hamoshavim	Israel, Eastern Europe	—
Kephar Hittim	1907/36	E. Lower Galilee	Cooperative Settlement	Tenuat Hamoshavim	Bulgaria, Israel	—
Kephar Kisch	1946	E. Lower Galilee	Smallholders' Settlement	Tenuat Hamoshavim	Israel, Eastern Europe	—
Kephar Malal	1922	S. Sharon	Smallholders' Settlement	Tenuat Hamoshavim	Eastern Europe, various	339
Kephar Masaryk	1938	Plain of Zebulun	Kibbutz	Hashomer Hatzair	Czechoslovakia, various	557
Kephar Menahem	1937	S. Coastal Plain	Kibbutz	Hashomer Hatzair	Poland, U.S.A., Germany, Israel	—
Kephar Monash	1946	Plain of Hepher	Smallholders' Settlement	Tenuat Hamoshavim	Israel, Western Europe	293
Kephar Mordekhai	1950	S. Coastal Plain	Smallholders' Settlement	Hamo'etza Hahaklait	England, Israel	216
Kephar Nahman	1951	Judean Plain	Maabara	—	Iraq, Iran	1,470
Kephar Netter	1939	S. Sharon	Smallholders' Settlement	Tenuat Hamoshavim	Israel, Eastern Europe	284
Kephar Pines	1933	N. Sharon	Smallholders' Settlement	Hapoel Hamizrahi	Israel, Eastern Europe	—
Kephar Rosh Hanikra	1949	W. Upper Galilee	Kibbutz	Ihud Hakibbutzim	Israel	—
Kephar Ruppin	1938	Beit She'an Valley	Kibbutz	Ihud Hakibbutzim	Western Europe, Israel	—
Kephar Saphariya	1951	Judean Plain	Rural Settlement	—	Various	—
Kephar Sava	1903	S. Sharon	Municipality	—	Various	16,100
Kephar Shammai	1949	C. Upper Galilee	Immigrant Smallholders' Settlement	Hapoel Hamizrahi	Yemen	282
Kephar Shemuel	1950	Judean Foothills	Smallholders' Settlement	Ha'oved Hatziyyoni	Rumania	—
Kephar Shemaryahu	1937	S. Sharon	Smallholders' Settlement	Hamo'etza Hahaklait	Germany	745
Kephar Syrkin	1936	Judean Plain	Smallholders' Settlement	Tenuat Hamoshavim	Israel, Eastern Europe	613

I	II	III	IV	V	VI	VII
Kephar Szold	1942	Huleh Valley	Kibbutz	Hakibbutz Hameuhad	Hungary, various	—
Kephar Tavor	1901	E. Lower Galilee	Farm Village	—	Israel, Eastern Europe	287
Kephar Truman	1949	Judean Foothills	Smallholders' Settlement	Tenuat Hamoshavim	Israel, Rumania, various	—
Kephar Tzevi (Sitrin	1953	N. Sharon	Agricultural School	—	—	149
Kephar Uriya	1912/44	Judean Foothills	Smallholders' Settlement	Tenuat Hamoshavim	Bulgaria, Israel	—
Kephar Vitkin	1933	Plain of Hepher	Smallholders' Settlement	Tenuat Hamoshavim	E. Europe, Israel	903
Kephar Warburg	1939	S. Coastal Plain	Smallholders' Settlement	Tenuat Hamoshavim	Central and Eastern Europe, Israel	501
Kephar Yabetz	1932/48/53	S. Sharon	Immigrant Smallholders' Settlement	Hapoel Hamizrahi	Rumania	—
Kephar Yehezkel	1921	Jezreel Valley	Smallholders' Settlement	Tenuat Hamoshavim	E. Europe, Israel	—
Kephar Yehoshua	1927	Jezreel Valley	Smallholders' Settlement	Tenuat Hamoshavim	Russia, Israel Tripolitania	652
Kephar Yeladim	1922	Jezreel Valley	Educational Institution	—	Israel	—
Kephar Yeruham	1951	C. Negev	Maabara	—	Rumania	—
Kephar Yona	1932	Sharon	Rural Settlement	—	Various	2,705
Kephar Yuval	1952	S. Sharon	Smallholders' Settlement	Tenuat Hamoshavim	Israel, Iraq	—
Kephar Zeitim	1950	E. Lower Galilee	Immigrant Smallholders' Settlement	Tenuat Hamoshavim	Yemen	218
Kephar Zekharya	1950	Judean Foothills	Immigrant Smallholders' Settlement	Tenuat Hamoshavim	Iraq, Israel	—
Kephar Ziv	—	S. Sharon	Rural Settlement	—	Various	—
Kerem Ben Zimra	1949	C. Upper Galilee	Immigrant Smallholders' Settlement	Hapoel Hamizrahi	Turkey, Rumania	—
Kerem Maharal	1949	Mt. Carmel	Immigrant Smallholders' Settlement	Tenuat Hamoshavim	Czechoslovakia	329
Kerem Shalom	1956	N. Negev	Kibbutz	Hapoel Hamizrahi	—	—
Kerem Yavne	1941	Judean Plain	Kibbutz	Hapoel Hamizrahi	C. Europe, Israel	589

I	II	III	IV	V	VI	VII
Kesalon	1950/52	Judean Hills	Smallholders' Settlement	Hamo'etza Hahaklait	Rumania, Brazil	—
Kidron	1949	Judean Plain	Immigrant Smallholders' Settlement	Tenuat Hamoshavim	Yugoslavia	570
Kinneret	1909	Kinnarot Valley	Village	—	E. Europe, various, Israel	—
Kinneret	1908	Kinnarot Valley	Kibbutz	Ihud Hakibbutzim	Eastern Europe, Israel	—
Kiryat Amal	1937	Jezreel Valley	Suburban Settlement	—	Various	3,375
Kiryat Anavim	1920	Judean Hills	Kibbutz	Ihud Hakibbutzim	Eastern Europe, Israel	—
Kiryat Bialik	1934	Plain of Zebulun	Suburban Settlement	—	Various	7,500
Kiryat Binyamin	1937	Plain of Zebulun	Suburban Settlement	—	Various	4,830
Kiryat Gat	1954	S. Coastal Plain	Town	—	Israel	1,804
Kiryat Haroshet	1935	Plain of Zebulun	Suburban Settlement	—	Various, Israel	170
Kiryat Hayyim	1933	Haifa Bay	Town	—	Israel	12,500
Kiryat Malakhi	1951	S. Coastal Plain	Rural Settlement	--	Iraq, various	3,050
Kiryat Motzkin	1934	Plain of Zebulun	Suburban Settlement	—	Various	8,800
Kiryat Ono	1939	Judean Plain	Rural Settlement	—	Iraq	8,800
Kiryat Shaul	1924	S. Sharon	Rural Settlement	—	Greece, various	220
Kiryat Shemona	1949	Huleh Valley	Suburban Settlement	—	Various	8,500
Kiryat Yam	1946	Plain of Zebulun	Suburban Settlement	—	Various	9,105
Kiryat Ye'arim	1952	Judean Hills	Youth Training Farm	—	Various	—
Kissuphim	1951	N. Negev	Kibbutz	Hakibbutz Hameuhad	S. America	—
Kokhav	1950	S. Coastal Plain	Immigrant Smallholders' Settlement	Tenuat Hamoshavim	Iraq	—
Komemiyut	1950	S. Coastal Plain	Smallholders' Settlement	Poalei Agudat Yisrael	Hungary, Czecho-slovakia, Poland, Israel, Rumania	436
Lachish	1955	S. Coastal Plain	Smallholders' Settlement	Tenuat Hamoshavim	Israel	--

I	II	III	IV	V	VI	VII
Lahavot Habashan	1945	Upper Galilee	Kibbutz	Hashomer Hatzair	Israel, Western Europe	—
Lahavot Haviva	1949	N. Sharon	Kibbutz	Hashomer Hatzair	Israel, Western Europe	—
Lavi	1949	E. Lower Galilee	Kibbutz	Hapoel Hamizrahi	Britain, U.S.	—
Lohamei Hageta'ot	1949	W. Upper Galilee	Kibbutz	Hakibbutz Hameuhad	Poland	402
Luzit	1955	Judean Foothills	Smallholders' Settlement	Tenuat Hamoshavim	—	—
Lydda (Lod)	1948	Judean Plain	Town	—	Various	16,125
Maabarot	1933	Plain of Hepher	Kibbutz	Hashomer Hatzair	Various	629
Maaberet Amishav	1950	Judean Plain	Maabara	—	Various	—
Maaberet Be'er Yaakov	1950	Judean Plain	Maabara	—	Tripolitania, Iraq	—
Maaberet Ein Hanatziv	1950	Bet She'an Valley	Maabara	—	Various	—
Maaberet Gelilot	1950	S. Sharon	Maabara	—	Various	—
Maaberet Gevim-Dorot	1950	S. Coastal Plain	Maabara	—	Asia	190
Maaberet Gilam	1951	Plain of Zebulun	Maabara	—	Various	—
Maaberet Givat Brenner	1951	Judean Plain	Maabara	—	Iraq	—
Maaberet Hakarmel	1951	Carmel Coast	Maabara	—	Iraq, Rumania	—
Maaberet Kadduri	1950	E. Lower Galilee	Maabara	—	Iraq, Iran	—
Maaberet Kephar Hasidim	1950	Plain of Zebulun	Maabara	—	Various	—
Maaberet Kephar Nahum	1951	Judean Plain	Maabara	—	Various	—
Maaberet Kiryat Ono	1950	Judean Plain	Maabara	—	Various	—
Maaberet Midrash	1951	Jezreel Valley	Maabara	—	Various	—
Maaberet Nahal Sorek	1951	S. Coastal Plain	Maabara	—	Various	—
Maaberet Ramat Hasharon	1950	S. Sharon	Maabara	—	Iraq	—
Maaberet Shimron	1951	W. Lower Galilee	Maabara	—	Rumania, N. Africa	—
Maaberet Tel Mond	1950	S. Sharon	Maabara	—	Various	—

I	II	III	IV	V	VI	VII
Maaberet Tel Adashim	1951	Jesreel Valley	Maabara	—	Various	—
Maaberet Tirah	1950	Carmel Coast	Maabara	—	Iraq, Eastern Europe	—
Maaberet Tzemah	1950	Kinnarot Valley	Maabara	—	N. Africa, Iraq	—
Maaberet Yavneh-Yohanan	1949/1950	Judean Plain	Maabara	—	Iraq, Iran	—
Maaberet Zarnoka	1950	Judean Plain	Maabara	—	Iraq	—
Maagan	1949	Kinnarot Valley	Kibbutz	Ihud Hakibbutzim	Various	—
Maagan Mikhael	1949	N. Sharon	Kibbutz	Hakibbutz Hameuhad	Israel, Central Europe	354
Maale Habashan	1945	Huleh Valley	Kibbutz	Hashomer Hatzair	Israel	—
Maale Hahamisha	1938	Judean Hills	Kibbutz	Ihud Hakibbutzim	Poland, various	—
Maanit	1942	Samaritan Foothills	Kibbutz	Hashomer Hatzair	Czechoslovakia, various	—
Maas	1935	Judean Plain	Smallholders' Settlement	Tenuat Hamoshavim	Various	412
Maavak	1948	W. Lower Galilee	Collective Smallholders' Settlement	Ha'oved Hatziyyoni	Rumania, Israel	193
Maayan Barukh	1947	Huleh Valley	Kibbutz	Ihud Hakibbutzim	S. Africa, Israel, various	500
Maayan Tzevi	1938	Mount Carmel	Kibbutz	Ihud Hakibbutzim	Central Europe, Israel	499
Maggal	1953	N. Sharon	Kibbutz	Ihud Hakibbutzim	Israel	—
Magen	1949	N. Negev	Kibbutz	Hashomer Hatzair	Rumania	—
Magdiel	1924	S. Sharon	Rural Settlement	—	Various	4,950
Magshimim	1949	Judean Plain	Smallholders' Settlement	Hamo'etza Hahaklait	Israel	275
Mahanayim	1939	E. Upper Galilee	Kibbutz	Hakibbutz Hameuhad	Israel	—
Mahane Yisrael	1950	Judean Plain	Work Camp	—	Various	4,070
Mahaseyah	1950	Judean Foothills	Immigrant Smallholders' Settlement	Hapoel Hamizrahi	Yemen, Israel	—
Malkiyah	1949	E. Upper Galilee	Kibbutz	Hakibbutz Hameuhad	Israel, various	—
Mamshit	1955	N. Negev	Suburban Settlement	—	Israel	—

I	II	III	IV	V	VI	VII
Manahat	1950	Judean Hills	Suburban Settlement	—	Israel	—
Ma'or	1953	N. Sharon	Smallholders' Settlement	Tenuat Hamoshavim	Poland, Rumania	—
Ma'oz Hayyim	1937	Beit She'an Valley	Kibbutz	Hakibbutz Hameuhad	Iraq, Iran	—
Ma'oz Tziyyon	1951	Judean Hills	Suburban Settlement	—	Iraq	—
Margaliyyot	1951	E. Upper Galilee	Immigrant Smallholders' Settlement	Tenuat Hamoshavim	Iraq	—
Mar'it (Havvat Goldberg)	1954	N. Negev	Farm	—	—	—
Massada	1937	Kinnarot Valley	Kibbutz	Ihud Hakibbutzim	Israel, Rumania, Poland, various	—
Mashabe-Sade	1949	C. Negev	Kibbutz	Hakibbutz Hameuhad	Israel, various	—
Mashen	1950	S. Coastal Plain	Immigrant Smallholders' Settlement	Tenuat Hamoshavim	Yemen	—
Mashmia Shalom	1949	S. Coastal Plain	Rural Settlement	—	Various	619
Maslul	1950	N. Negev	Immigrant Smallholders' Settlement	Tenuat Hamoshavim	Iran	—
Massua	1955	Judean Plain	Training Camp	—	Israel	—
Massuot Yitzhak	1949	S. Coastal Plain	Cooperative Settlement	Hapoel Hamizrahi	Hungary, various	250
Matta	1950	Judean Hills	Immigrant Smallholders' Settlement	Tenuat Hamoshavim	N. Africa	—
Matzliah	1950	Judean Plain	Immigrant Smallholders' Settlement	Tenuat Hamoshavim	Egypt (Karaite Sect)	620
Matsuva	1940	W. Upper Galilee	Kibbutz	Ihud Hakibbutzim	Central Europe, Israel	—
Mavki'im	1949	S. Coastal Plain	Cooperative Settlement	Ha'oved Hatziyyoni	Hungary, Rumania	—
Mazkeret Batya	1883	Judean Plain	Rural Settlement	—	Israel, Eastern Europe	375
Mazor	1949	Judean Foothills	Immigrant Smallholders' Settlement	Tenuat Hamoshavim	Czechoslovakia, Hungary	—
Megadim	1949	Carmel Coast	Immigrant Smallholders' Settlement	Tenuat Hamoshavim	Morocco	500

I	II	III	IV	V	VI	VII
Megiddo	1949	Jezreel Valley	Kibbutz	Hashomer Hatzair	Poland	—
Mele'a	—	Jezreel Valley	Smallholders' Settlement	Tenuat Hamoshavim	—	—
Melilot	1953	N. Negev	Immigrant Smallholders' Settlement	Hapoel Hamizrahi	Iran	—
Menahemya	1902	Kinnarot Valley	Smallholders' Settlement	Hamo'etza Hahaklait	Various	—
Menuha	1953	S. Coastal Plain	Immigrant Smallholders' Settlement	Tenuat Hamoshavim	Iraq	362
Me'ona	1949	C. Upper Galilee	Smallholders' Settlement	Tenuat Hamoshavim	Rumania	—
Me'ona (Tarshiha)	1949	C. Upper Galilee	Suburban Settlement	—	Various	—
Mephalsim	1949	S. Coastal Plain	Kibbutz	Ihud Hakibbutzim	S. America	—
Merhavyah	1922	Jezreel Valley	Smallholders' Settlement	Tenuat Hamoshavim	Eastern Europe, Israel	—
Merhavyah	1911	Jezreel Valley	Kibbutz	Hashomer Hatzair	Eastern Europe, Israel, various	—
Meron	1949	C. Upper Galilee	Smallholders' Settlement	Hapoel Hamizrahi	Balkans, Israel	—
Meshar	1950	S. Coastal Plain	Smallholders' Settlement	Hamo'etza Hahaklait	Poland, Israel	204
Meshek Schwartz (Naama)	1940	E. Upper Galilee	Farm	—	Eastern Europe, Balkans, Israel	3
Meshullam	1952	S. Coastal Plain	Immigrant Smallholders' Settlement	—	Iraq	—
Mesillat Tziyyon	1950	Judean Foothills	Immigrant Smallholders' Settlement	Tenuat Hamoshavim	Yemen	—
Mesillot	1938	Bet She'an Valley	Kibbutz	Hashomer Hatzair	Eastern Europe, Israel, Bulgaria, various	—
Metav (Taanakh)	1953	Jezreel Valley	Immigrant Smallholders' Settlement	Tenuat Hamoshavim	Iraq	—
Metzer	1953	N. Sharon	Kibbutz	Hashomer Hatzair	S. America	—
Metula	1896	E. Upper Galilee	Rural Settlement	—	Eastern Europe	—
Mevaseret Yerushalayim	1956	Judean Hills	Rural Settlement	—	—	—
Mevo Betar	1950	Judean Hills	Cooperative Settlement	Herut Movement	S. America, English speaking countries	—

I	II	III	IV	V	VI	VII
Mevo'ot Yam	1955	Sharon	Naval School	—	Israel	63
Midrakh Oz	1952	Jezreel Valley	Immigrant Smallholders' Settlement	Tenuat Hamoshavim	Turkey	—
Midrakh Oz (Maabara)	1951	Jezreel Valley	Maabara	—	—	1,170
Midreshet Ruppin	1948	Sharon	Agricultural School	—	Israel	16
Migda	1956	N. Negev	—	—	—	—
Migdal	1910	Kinnarot Valley	Smallholders' Settlement	Hamo'etza Hahaklait	Various	681
Migdal Ashkelon	1950	S. Coastal Plain	Town	—	Various	19,200
Migdal Ha'emek	1952	W. Lower Galilee	Rural Settlement	—	Israel, various	3,025
Mikhmoret	1945	Plain of Hepher	Smallholders' Settlement	Tenuat Hamoshavim	Israel, various	115
Mikhmoret Beit	1954	Plain of Hepher	Smallholders' Settlement	Tenuat Hamoshavim	Israel, various	—
Mikhrot Timna	1952	N. Negev	Workers' Camp	—	Israel	—
Mikve Yisrael	1870	Judean Plain	Youth Training Farm	—	Various	886
Misgav Am	1945	E. Upper Galilee	Kibbutz	Hakibbutz Hameuhad	Israel, various	—
Mishmar Ayyalon	1949	Judean Foothills	Immigrant Smallholders' Settlement	Tenuat Hamoshavim	Czechoslovakia	—
Mishmar David	1948	Judean Foothills	Kibbutz	Ihud Hakibbutzim	Israel, Rumania	—
Mishmar Ha'emek	1926	Jezreel Valley	Kibbutz	Hashomer Hatzair	Eastern Europe, Israel	—
Mishmar Hanegev	1946	N. Negev	Kibbutz	Hakibbutz Hameuhad	Western Europe, Israel	—
Mishmar Hasharon	1933	Plain of Hepher	Kibbutz	Ihud Hakibbutzim	E. Europe, Israel	454
Mishmar Hashiva	1949	Judean Plain	Smallholders' Settlement	Tenuat Hamoshavim	Israel	362
Mishmar Hashelosha	1933	S. Lower Galilee	Smallholders' Settlement	Tenuat Hamoshavim	Israel	—
Mishmar Hayarden (Benei Tzephat)	1949	E. Upper Galilee	Smallholders' Settlement	Herut Movement	Various	—
Mishmarot	1933	N. Sharon	Kibbutz	Ihud Hakibbutzim	East Europe, Israel	308
Mishmeret	1947	S. Sharon	Smallholders' Settlement	Tenuat Hamoshavim	Israel, various	—

I	II	III	IV	V	VI	VII
Mitzpa	1908	E. Lower Galilee	Rural Settlement	—	E. Europe, Israel	—
Mitzpe Ramon	1956	C. Negev	Work Camp	—	—	—
Mivhor	1955	S. Coastal Plain	Farm	—	—	—
Mivtahim	1950	W. Negev	Immigrant Smallholders' Settlement	Tenuat Hamoshavim	Kurdistan	—
Mizra	1923	Jezreel Valley	Kibbutz	Hashomer Hatzair	Israel, Eastern and Central Europe	664
Motza Tahtit (Lower)	1894	Judean Hills	Rural Settlement	—	Various	—
Motza Illit (Upper)	1933	Judean Hills	Rural Settlement	—	—	—
Naamanim	1953	Sharon	Plantations	—	—	—
Naan	1930	Judean Hills	Kibbutz	Hakibbutz Hameuhad	Israel	902
Nahal Oz	1951	N. Negev	Kibbutz	Ihud Hakibbutzim	Israel	—
Nahala	1953	S. Coastal Plain	Immigrant Smallholders' Settlement	Tenuat Hamoshavim	Yemen	—
Nahalal	1921	Jezreel Valley	Smallholders' Settlement	Tenuat Hamoshavim	E. Europe, Israel	658
Nahala'ot	1954	Jezreel Valley	Agricultural Association	—	—	—
Nahalat Yehuda	1914	Judean Plain	Suburban Settlement	—	Iraq	3,800
Naham	1950	Judean Foothills	Smallholders' Settlement	Hapoel Hamizrahi	Yemen	—
Nahariya	1934	W. Upper Galilee	Municipality	—	Rumania, Central and Eastern Europe	11,100
Nahsholim	1948	Carmel Coast	Kibbutz	Hakibbutz Hameuhad	Israel, America, Poland	245
Nahshon	1950	Judean Foothills	Kibbutz	Hashomer Hatzair	Israel, Eastern Europe	—
Nahshonim	1949	Judean Foothills	Kibbutz	Hashomer Hatzair	Egypt, Belgium, Israel	—
Nazareth	—	Jezreel Valley	Town (Arab)	—	Israel	23,000
Negba	1939	S. Coastal Plain	Kibbutz	Hashomer Hatzair	Poland, various	—
Nehalim	1948	Judean Plain	Smallholders' Settlement	Hapoel Hamizrahi	Hungary, Eastern Europe, Israel	410
Nehora	1956	Judean Foothills	Village Center	—	—	—

I	II	III	IV	V	VI	VII
Nehusha	1955	S. Coastal Plain	Cooperative Settlement	Hapoel Hamizrahi	—	—
Ne'ot Mordekhai	1946	Huleh Valley	Kibbutz	—	Central Europe, Israel	—
Nes Harim	1950	Judean Hills	Immigrant Smallholders' Settlement	Tenuat Hamoshavim	Kurdistan	—
Nes Tziyyona	1883	Judean Plain	Municipality	—	Various	10,800
Nesher-Tel Hanan	1925	Plain of Zebulun	Suburban Settlement	—	Various	7,150
Neta	1955	S. Coastal Plain	Plantations	—	—	—
Neta'im	1932	Judean Plain	Smallholders' Settlement	Tenuat Hamoshavim	E. Europe	196
Netanya	1929	S. Sharon	Town	—	Various	33,100
Netiv Halamed He	1949	Judean Foothills	Kibbutz	Hakibbutz Hame'uad	Israel, various	—
Netiva	1949	S. Coastal Plain	Smallholders' Settlement	Poalei Agudat Yisrael	Poland	132
Netzer Sereni	1948	Judean Plain	Kibbutz	Ihud Hakibbutzim	Poland, various	602
Neurim	1953	Sharon	—	Educational Institution	—	81
Nevatim	1946/49	N. Negev	Immigrant Smallholders' Settlement	Tenuat Hamoshavim	India	—
Neve Amiel	1948	Jezreel Valley	Youth Training Farm	Hapoel Hamizrahi	N. Africa	119
Neve Avot	1948	N. Sharon	Immigrant Reception Center	—	—	1,087
Neve Eitan	1938	Beit She'an Valley	Kibbutz	Ihud Hakibbutzim	Israel, Eastern Europe	—
Neve Hadassah	1948	W. Lower Galilee	Youth Training Farm	Ha'oved Hatziyyoni	Various	246
Neve Ilan	1946	Judean Hills	Agricultural School	—	—	—
Neve Mivtah	1950	S. Coastal Plain	Immigrant Smallholders' Settlement	Tenuat Hamoshavim	Poland	—
Neve Ur	1949	Beit She'an Valley	Kibbutz	Hakibbutz Hameuhad	Iraq, various	—
Neve Yam	1939	Carmel	Kibbutz	Ihud Hakibbutzim	Israel, Central and Eastern Europe	218
Neve Yamin	1949	S. Sharon	Immigrant Smallholders' Settlement	Tenuat Hamoshavim	Greece, N. Africa, Iraq	—

I	II	III	IV	V	VI	VII
Neve Yarak	1951		Immigrant Smallholders' Settlement	Tenuat Hamoshavim	Rumania	415
Nir Akiva	1953	N. Negev	Smallholders' Settlement	Tenuat Hamoshavim	—	—
Nir Am	1943	S. Coastal Plain	Kibbutz	Ihud Hakibbutzim	Israel, Central and East Europe	—
Nir Banim (Tzur Ma'on)	1954	N. Negev	Smallholders' Settlement	Tenuat Hamoshavim	Israel, Western Europe	143
Nir David	1936	Beit She'an Valley	Kibbutz	Hashomer Hatzair	Poland, Israel	—
Nir Eliyahu	1950	S. Sharon	Kibbutz	Ihud Hakibbutzim	Rumania, Poland, Turkey	—
Nir Etzyon	1950	Mt. Carmel	Cooperative Settlement	Hapoel Hamizrahi	Central Europe, various	214
Nir Gallim	1949	S. Coastal Plain	Cooperative Settlement	Hapoel Hamizrahi	Western Europe, Israel	—
Nir Hen	1955	S. Coastal Plain	Cooperative Settlement	Tenuat Hamoshavim	—	—
Nir Moshe	1953	N. Negev	Smallholders' Settlement	Tenuat Hamoshavim	Israel, E. Europe	—
Nir Oz	1955	N. Negev	Kibbutz	Hashomer Hatzair	—	—
Nir Yafe	1956	Jezreel Valley	Smallholders' Settlement	Tenuat Hamoshavim	—	254
Nir Yisrael	1949	S. Coastal Plain	Immigrant Smallholders' Settlement	Ha'oved Hatziyyoni	Czechoslovakia	242
Nir Yitzhak	1940/49	N. Negev	Kibbutz	Hashomer Hatzair	Rumania, various	—
Nir Tzevi (Kephar Argentina)	1954	Judean Plain	Smallholders' Settlement	Hamo'etza Hahaklait	—	170
Nirim	1949	N. Negev	Kibbutz	Hashomer Hatzair	Israel, various	—
Nitzanei Oz	1951	Plain of Hepher	Smallholders' Settlement	Tenuat Hamoshavim	E. Europe, Syria	—
Nitzanim	1943	S. Coastal Plain	Kibbutz	Ha'oved Hatziyyoni	Rumania	—
Nitzanim	1949	S. Coastal Plain	Youth Training Farm	Ha'oved Hatziyyoni	Various	—
No'am	1955	S. Coastal Plain	Smallholders' Settlement	Hapoel Hamizrahi	—	—
Noga	1955	S. Coastal Plain	Smallholders' Settlement	Tenuat Hamoshavim	—	—
Nophekh	1949	S. Coastal Plain	Work Camp	—	—	—

I	II	III	IV	V	VI	VII
Nordiya	1948	S. Sharon	Cooperative Settlement	Herut Movement	Israel, Eastern and Central Europe	226
Nurit	1950	Jezreel Valley	Smallholders' Settlement	Tenuat Hamoshavim	Yemen	—
Olesh	1949	Hepher Valley	Immigrant Smallholders' Settlement	Tenuat Hamoshavim	Rumania	—
Omer	1949	N. Negev	Immigrant Smallholders' Settlement	Tenuat Hamoshavim	Central and Eastern Furope	—
Ometz	1949	Hepher Valley	Smallholders' Settlement	Tenuat Hamoshavim	Rumania, Israel	—
Ono	1949	Judean Plain	Rural (Suburban) Settlement	—	Iraq	—
Ophakim	1955	N. Negev	Urban Settlement	—	—	1,875
Opher	1950	Carmel Coast	Immigrants Smallholders' Settlement	Tenuat Hamoshavim	India	313
Or Akiva	1951	N. Sharon	Smallholders' Settlement	—	Various	1,838
Ora	1950	Judean Hills	Immigrants Smallholders' Settlement	Tenuat Hamoshavim	Yemen	—
Oranim	1951	Jezreel Valley	Seminary		Various	245
Or Haner	1955	N. Negev	Agricultural Farm	—	—	—
Oron	1952	N. Negev	Workers' Camp	—	Israel	—
Orot	1952	S. Coastal Plain	Smallholders' Settlement	Tenuat Hamoshavim	English-speaking countries	134
Or Yehuda Aleph	1951	Judean Plain	Rural (Suburban) Settlement	—	Africa, Iraq	12,800 incl. one incl. ono
Or Yehuda Beit	1950	Judean Plain	Rural (Suburban) Settlement	—	Iraq	
Otzem	1955	S. Coastal Plain	Smallholders' Settlement	Tenuat Hamoshavim	Rumania	—
Paamei Tashaz	1953	N. Negev	Immigrants Smallholders' Settlement	Tenuat Hamoshavim	Iran	—
Palmahim	1949	Judean Plain	Kibbutz	Hakibbutz Hameuhad	Israel, various	—
Pardes Hannah	1929	N. Sharon	Local Council	—	Various	6,350

I	II	III	IV	V	VI	VII
Pardes Hannah	1952	N. Sharon	Work Village	—	—	1.004
Pardesiya	1940	S. Sharon	Rural Settlement	—	Various	650
Parod (Kibbutz Gardosh)	1949	C. Upper Galilee	Kibbutz	Hakibbutz Hameuhad	Hungary	229
Pattish	1950	N. Negev	Immigrants Smallholders' Settlement	Tenuat Hamoshavim	Asia	—
Pedaya	1951	Judean Foothills	Immigrants Smallholders' Settlement	Tenuat Hamoshavim	Iraq	348
Peduyim	1950	N. Negev	Immigrant Smallholders' Settlement	Tenuat Hamoshavim	Yemen	—-
Peki'in Hahadasha	1955	W. Upper Galilee	Work Village	—	—	—
Perazon	1953	Jezreel Valley	Immigrant Smallholders' Settlement	Tenuat Hamoshavim	Iran	—
Petah Tikva	1878	Judean Plain	Town	—	Various	46,000
Petahya	1951	Judean Foothills	Immigrant Smallholders' Settlement	Ha'oved Hatziyyoni	Tunisia	361
Philadelphia Youth Village	1954	W. Upper Galilee	Youth Training Farm	—	Various	90
Porat	1950	S. Sharon	Immigrant Smallholders' Settlement	Hapoel Hamizrahi	Tripolitania	—
Poriya	1949	E. Lower Galilee	Work Village	—	Yemen	1,350
Raanana	1921	S. Sharon	Municipality	—	Various	9,200
Ramat Gan	1912	Judean Plain	Town	—	Various	65,150
Ramat David	1926	Jezreel Valley	Kibbutz	Ihud Hakibbutzim	E. Europe	355
Ramat Hadar	1938	S. Sharon	Smallholders' Settlement	Hamo'etza Hahaklait	Germany	305
Ramat Hadassah	1951	W. Lower Galilee	Youth Training Farm	Youth Aliya	Various	463
Ramat Hakovesh	1932	S. Sharon	Kibbutz	Hakibbutz Hameuad	E. Europe, Israel	—
Ramat Hasharon	1923	S. Sharon	Rural Settlement	—	Various	8,200
Ramat Hashophet	1941	Samaritan Foothills	Kibbutz	Hashomer Hatzair	Poland, Bulgaria, Hungary, Iraq	—

I	II	III	IV	V	VI	VII
Ramat Pinkas	1952	Judean Plain	Smallholders' Settlement	Hapoel Hamizrahi	Central and Eastern Europe, Turkey	95
Ramat Rahel	1926	Judean Hills	Kibbutz	Ihud Hakibbutzim	Israel	—
Ramat Raziel	1948	Judean Hills	Smallholders' Settlement	Herut Movement	Various, Eastern Europe	—
Ramat Tzevi	1942	E. Lower Galilee	Smallholders' Settlement	Tenuat Hamoshavim	E. Europe, Israel	188
Ramat Yishai	1925	Jezreel Valley	Suburban Settlement	--	Various	608
Ramat Yohanan	1932	Zebulun Valley	Kibbutz	Ihud Hakibbutzim	E. Europe, Israel	—
Ramim	1943	E. Upper Galilee	Kibbutz	Hakibbutz Hameuhad	Various	—
Ramot Hashavim	1933	S. Sharon	Smallholders' Settlement	Hamo'etza Hahaklait	Germany	500
Ramot Meir	1949	Judean Plain	Cooperative Settlement	Tenuat Hamoshavim	Israel, Western Europe	—
Ramot Menashe	1948	Samaritan Foothills	Kibbutz	Hashomer Hatzair	Poland, Bulgaria, Israel, Central Europe	318
Ramot Naphtali	1945	E. Upper Galilee	Cooperative Settlement	Tenuat Hamoshavim	Israel, Western Europe	—
Ramla	1948	Judean Plain	Town	—	Various	20,650
Rannen	1950	N. Negev	Immigrant Smallholders' Settlement	Tenuat Hamoshavim	Egypt (Karaite sect)	—
Regavim	1948	Samaritan Foothills	Kibbutz	Hakibbutz Hameuhad	Tunisia, Italy	—
Regba	1946	W. Upper Galilee	Cooperative Settlement	Tenuat Hamoshavim	Israel, Western Europe	260
Rehov	1951	Beit She'an Valley	Immigrant Smallholders' Settlement	Hapoel Hamizrahi	Iraq	—
Rehovot	1890	Judean Plain	Town	—	Various	29,500
Rekhasim	1956	Jezreel Valley	Rural Settlement	--	--	—
Reshaphim	1948	Beit She'an Valley	Kibbutz	Hashomer Hatzair	Poland, Israel, Rumania	—
Revadim	1948	S. Coastal Plain	Kibbutz	Hashomer Hatzair	Israel, Eastern Europe	190
Revaha	1953	S. Coastal Plain	Smallholders' Settlement	Hapoel Hamizrahi	Morocco, Iraq	466
Revaya	1952	Beit She'an Valley	Immigrant Smallholders' Settlement	Hapoel Hamizrahi	Iraq	—

I	II	III	IV	V	VI	VII
Revivim	1943	N. Negev	Kibbutz	Hakibbutz Hameuhad	Israel, Western Europe	—
Rinnatyah	1954	Judean Foothills	Immigrant Smallholders' Settlement	Tenuat Hamoshavim	Morocco	420
Rishon Le Zion	1882	Judean Plain	Town	—	Various	22,300
Rishpon	1936	S. Sharon	Smallholders' Settlement	Tenuat Hamoshavim	Central and E. Europe, Israel Balkans	468
Rosh Ha'ayin	1950	Judean Plain	Suburban Settlement	—	Yemen, Israel, E.Europe, various	8,000
Rosh Pinna	1882	E. Upper Galilee	Rural Settlement	—	Rumania, various	938
Ruhama	1913/44	S. Coastal Plain	Kibbutz	Hashomer Hatzair	Eastern Europe, Israel	—
Saad	1947	N. Negev	Kibbutz	Hapoel Hamizrahi	Central Europe, Britain, various	—
Saar	1948	W. Upper Galilee	Kibbutz	Hashomer Hatzair	Israel, Eastern and Central Europe	—
Safed (Tzephat)	—	E. Upper Galilee	Town	—	Various	9,400
Sarid	1926	Jezreel Valley	Kibbutz	Hashomer Hatzair	Israel, Eastern and Central Europe	650
Sarig	1951	Judean Plain	Rural Settlement	—	Various	—
Sasa	1949	Central Upper Galilee	Kibbutz	Hashomer Hatzair	N. America	—
Savyon	1954	Judean Plain	Plantation Village	—	—	82
Sede Boker	1952	Central Negev	Cooperative Farm	—	Israel, various	—
Sede David	1955	S. Coastal Plain	Smallholders' Settlement	Ha'oved Hatziyyoni	—	—
Sede Eliezer	1951	Huleh Valley	Immigrant Smallholders' Settlement	Ha...o'etza Hahaklait	Rumania, E. Europe	—
Sede Eliyahu	1939	Beit She'an Valley	Kibbutz	Hapoel Hamizrahi	Germany, Israel, Yemen	
Sedei Hemed	1952	S. Sharon	Smallholders' Settlement	Tenuat Hamoshavim	Iran, Caucasus, Poland, Israel	—
Sede Ilan	1949	E. Lower Galilee	Smallholders' Settlement	Hapoel Hamizrahi	Israel, Central and Eastern Europe	229
Sede Moshe	1956	S. Coastal Plain	Smallholders' Settlement	Tenuat Hamoshavim	—	28
Sede Nahum	1937	Beit She'an Valley	Kibbutz	Hakibbutz Hameuhad	Poland, Austria, various, Israel	—

I	II	III	IV	V	VI	VII
Sede Nehemiya	1940	Huleh Valley	Kibbutz	Ihud Hakibbutzim	Holland, Czechoslovakia, Israel	—
Sederot	1951	N. Negev	Rural Settlement	—	—	2,693
Sede Tzevi	1953	W. Negev	Smallholders' Settlement	Hamo'etza Hahaklait	Tunisia, Morocco	—
Sede Terumot	1952	Beit She'an Valley	Immigrant Smallholders' Settlement	Hapoel Hamizrahi	Iraq	—
Sede Uzziya	1950	S. Coastal Plain	Immigrant Smallholders' Settlement	Ha'oved Hatziyyoni	Tripolitania	—
Sede Warburg	1938	S. Sharon	Smallholders' Settlement	Hamo'etza Hahaklait	Germany, Eastern Europe, Israel	238
Sede Yaakov	1927	Jezreel Valley	Smallholders' Settlement	Hapoel Hamizrahi	E. Europe, Israel	403
Sede Yitzhak	1952	N. Sharon	Immigrant Smallholders' Settlement	Tenuat Hamoshavim	Poland, Iran, Yemen, various	—
Sede Yoav	1956	S. Coastal Plain	Kibbutz	Hashomer Hatzair	—	—
Sedom	1939	Dead Sea Coast	Industrial Settlement	—	Various	—
Sedot Akiva	1953	N. Negev	Smallholders' Settlement	Tenuat Hamoshavim	Rumania	—
Sedot Mikha	1955	Judean Hills	Smallholders' Settlement	Tenuat Hamoshavim	—	—
Sedot Yam	1940	N. Sharon	Kibbutz	Hakibbutz Hameuhad	Israel, Central Europe, various	555
Segev	1956	W. Upper Galilee	Smallholders' Settlement	Tenuat Hamoshavim	—	—
Segulla	1953	S. Coastal Plain	Smallholders' Settlement	Tenuat Hamoshavim	Israel	242
Shaalvim	1951	Judean Foothills	Cooperative Settlement	Poalei Agudat Israel	Israel, Central Europe	—
Shaar Ephraim	1953	Plain of Hepher	Immigrant Smallholders' Settlement	Tenuat Hamoshavim	Yemen	—
Shaar Ha'aliya	1948	Haifa	Immigrant Reception Center	—	-	—
Shaar Ha'amakim	1935	Plain of Zebulun	Kibbutz	Hashomer Hatzair	Yugoslavia, Rumania, Israel	607
Shaar Hagolan	1937	Kinnarot Valley	Kibbutz	Hashomer Hatzair	Czechoslovakia, Eastern Europe, Israel	—
Shaar Hepher	1940	Plain of Hepher	Smallholders' Settlement	Hamo'etza Hahaklait	Israel, Central Europe	331

I	II	III	IV	V	VI	VII
Shaar Menashe	1949	Village for Elderly People	—		Various	1,300
Shadmot Devora	1939	E. Lower Galilee	Smallholders' Settlement	Tenuat Hamoshavim	Israel, Central Europe	255
Shahar	1955	S. Coastal Plain	Smallholders' Settlement	Tenuat Hamoshavim	—	—
Shahariya	1955	S. Coastal Plain	Training Farm	Hakibbutz Hameuhad	—	—
Shalva	1952	S. Coastal Plain	Immigrant Smallholders' Settlement	Hapoel Hamizrahi	Tripolitania	—
Shamir	1944	Huleh Valley	Kibbutz	Hashomer Hatzair	Rumania, Israel	—
Shaphir	1949	S. Coastal Plain	Smallholders' Settlement	Hapoel Hamizrahi	Czechoslovakia	308
Shaphrir	1949	Judean Plain	Rural Settlement	—	Russia	407
Sharona	1938	E. Lower Galilee	Smallholders' Settlement	Tenuat Hamoshavim	E. Europe, Israel	256
Sharsheret	1946	N. Negev	Immigrant Smallholders' Settlement	Hapoel Hamizrahi	Tunisia, Israel	—
Shavei Zion	1938	W. Upper Galilee	Cooperative Settlement	Hamo'etza Hahaklait	Germany	260
She'ar Yashuv	1940	Huleh Valley	Smallholders' Settlement	Ha'oved Hatziyyoni	Western Europe, Rumania	—
Shedeima	1954	Judean Plain	Smallholders' Settlement	Hamo'etza Hahaklait	—	—
Shekhunat Beilinson	1938	Judean Plain	Suburban Settlement	—	Various	279
Shelomi	1950	W. Upper Galilee	Work Village	—	Yemen, Eastern Europe, Balkans	200
Sheluhot	1948	Beit She'an Valley	Kibbutz	Hapoel Hamizrahi	Central Europe, Israel	—
Shepharam	—	W. Upper Galilee	Town (Arab)	—	Israel	5,900
Shephayim	1935	S. Sharon	Kibbutz	Hakibbutz Hameuhad	E. Europe, Israel	616
Shepher	1950	Central Upper Galilee	Work Village	—	Yemen	133
Shepheya	1923	Mt. Carmel	Youth Training Farm	—	Various	355
Shetulim	1950	S. Coastal Plain	Immigrant Smallholders' Settlement	Tenuat Hamoshavim	Yemen	558
Shevut Am	1950	N. Sharon	Suburban Settlement	—	Tripolitania, various	5,800

I	II	III	IV	V	VI	VII
Shezor	1953	Central Upper Galilee	Work Village	—	—	—
Shibbolim	1952	N. Negev	Immigrant Smallholders' Settlement	Hapoel Hamizrahi	Iran	—
Shimron	1951	Jezreel Valley	Ma'abara	—	—	530
Shipha	1954	Jezreel Valley	Farm	—	—	—
Sho'eva	1950	Judean Hills	Work Village	Hapoel Hamizrahi	Iran	—
Shokeda	1957	N. Negev	Smallholders' Settlement	Hapoel Hamizrahi	—	—
Shomera	1949	Central Upper Galilee	Work Village	—	—	—
Shomrat	1948	W. Upper Galilee	Kibbutz	Hashomer Hatzair	Hungary, Israel Czechoslovakia	—
Shoresh	1948	Judean Hills	Cooperative Settlement	Ha'oved Hatziyyoni	Rumania	—
Shoshanat Ha'amakim	1951	Sharon	Suburban Settlement	—	—	80
Shoval	1946	N. Negev	Kibbutz	Hashomer Hatzair	S. Africa, Israel	—
Shoval (Kelahim)	1954	N. Negev	Immigrant Smallholders' Settlement	Ha'oved Hatziyyoni	Tunisia, Morocco	—
Shuva	1950	N. Negev	Immigrant Smallholders' Settlement	Hapoel Hamizrahi	Tripolitania	—
Siphsupha	1949	Central Upper Galilee	Immigrant Smallholders' Settlement	Tenuat Hamoshavim	Yemen	—
Sitriya	1949	Judean Plain	Immigrant Smallholders' Settlement	Tenuat Hamoshavim	Poland, Rumania	—
Tal Shahar	1948	Judean Foothills	Immigrant Smallholders' Settlement	Tenuat Hamoshavim	Rumania, various	—
Talmei Bilu	1953	N. Negev	Immigrant Smallholders' Settlement	—	Rumania, Iran	—
Talmei Elazar	1952	N. Sharon	Smallholders' Settlement	Farmers' Association	Israel, E. Europe	211
Talmei Yaffe	1950	S. Coastal Plain	Kibbutz	Ha'oved Hatziyyoni	Russia, Poland	—
Talmei Yehiel	1949	S. Coastal Plain	Immigrant Smallholders' Settlement	Tenuat Hamoshavim	Bulgaria, Rumania	349

I	II	III	IV	V	VI	VII
Ta'oz	1950	Judean Foothills	Immigrant Smallholders' Settlement	Hapoel Hamizrahi	Yemen	—
Tarum	1950	Judean Foothills	Immigrant Smallholders' Settlement	Hapoel Hamizrahi	Yemen	—
Te'ashur	1953	N. Negev	Smallholders' Settlement	Tenuat Hamoshavim	Israel	—
Tekuma	1949	N. Negev	Smallholders' Settlement	Hapoel Hamizrahi	Israel, Rumania, Central Europe	—
Tel Adashim	1923	Jezreel Valley	Smallholders' Settlement	Tenuat Hamoshavim	E. Europe, Israel	408
Telamim	1950	S. Coastal Plain	Immigrant Smallholders' Settlement	Tenuat Hamoshavim	N. Africa	—
Tel Aviv—Yapho (Jaffa)	1909	Judean Plain	Town	—	Various	371,000
Tel Hashomer	1934	Judean Plain	Suburban Settlement	—	Various	470
Tel Mond	1929	S. Sharon	Rural Settlement	—	Various	2,350
Tel Yitzhak	1938	S. Sharon	Kibbutz	Ha'oved Hatziyyoni	Poland, Israel	230
Tel Yoseph	1921	Jezreel Valley	Kibbutz	Ihud Hakibbutzim	Israel, Eastern Europe	—
Tenuvot	1952	Plain of Hepher	Immigrant Smallholders' Settlement	Tenuat Hamoshavim	Yemen	—
Tiberias (Teverya)	—	E. Lower Galilee	Town	—	Various	17,100
Tidhar	1953	N. Negev	Immigrant Smallholders' Settlement	Tenuat Hamoshavim	Morocco	—
Tiphrah	1949	N. Negev	Immigrant Smallholders' Settlement	Poalei Agudat Yisrael	Hungary, Czechoslovakia, Rumania	—
Timmorim	1949/54	S. Coastal Plain	Cooperative Settlement	Ha'oved Hatziyyoni	S. Africa, Israel, Tripolitania	—
Timrat	1955	Jezreel Valley	Farm	—	—	33
Tirat Karmel	1949	Mount Carmel	Rural Settlement	—	Eastern and Central Europe, Balkans	12,750
Tirat Tzevi	1937	Beit She'an Valley	Kibbutz	Hapoel Hamizrahi	Central Europe, Israel	—
Tirat Yehuda	1949	Judean Foothills	Smallholders' Settlement	Hapoel Hamizrahi	E. Europe	—
Tirosh	1955	Judean Hills	Smallholders' Settlement	Hapoel Hamizrahi	—	—

I	II	III	IV	V	VI	VII
Tivon	1938	W. Lower Galilee	Suburban Settlement	—	Various	3,970
Tzahal	1949	W. Upper Galilee	Smallholders' Settlement	Tenuat Hamoshavim	Israel, Western Europe	—
Tzaphriya	1949	Judean Plain	Smallholders' Settlement	Hapoel Hamizrahi	Hungary, Czechoslovakia	325
Tze'elim	1947	W. Negev	Kibbutz	Ihud Hakibbutzim	Hungary, N. Africa, various	—
Tzelaphon	1950	Judean Foothills	Immigrant Smallholders' Settlement	Tenuat Hamoshavim	Yemen	—
Tzemah	1950	Kinnarot Valley	Maabara	—	—	—
Tzeriphin	1949	Judean Plain	Educational Institution	—	—	128
Tzerupha	1949	Carmel Coast	Immigrant Smallholders' Settlement	Tenuat Hamoshavim	Algeria	382
Tzippori (Sepphoris)	1949	W. Lower Galilee	Immigrant Smallholders' Settlement	Tenuat Hamoshavim	Bulgaria, Israel Rumania	—
Tziklag	1952	Judean Foothills	Kibbutz	Hashomer Hatzair	Israel, Hungary	—
Tzomeha	1957	N. Negev	Smallholders' Settlement	Hapoel Hamizrahi	—	—
Tzophit	1933	S. Sharon	Smallholders' Settlement	Tenuat Hamoshavim	E. Europe, Israel	378
Tzor'a	1948	Judean Foothills	Kibbutz	Ihud Hakibbutzim	Israel, S. Africa	—
Tzova	1948	Judean Hills	Kibbutz	Hakibbutz Hameuhad	Various	—
Tzur Moshe	1937	S. Sharon	Smallholders' Settlement	Tenuat Hamoshavim	Greece, Turkey, Bulgaria	436
Tzuriel	1950	Central Upper Galilee	Work Village	Poalei Agudat Yisrael	Yemen	—
Udim	1948	S. Sharon	Smallholders' Settlement	Hamo'etza Hahaklait	Israel, Rumania, Central Europe	269
Uriel	1951	Judean Plain	Village for Blind	—	Various	—
Urim	1946	N. Negev	Kibbutz	Ihud Hakibbutzim	U.S.A., Central Europe	—
Usha	1937	Plain of Zebulun	Kibbutz	Ihud Hakibbutzim	Poland, Israel	328
Uzza	1950	S. Coastal Plain	Immigrant Smallholders' Settlement	Hapoel Hamizrahi	Tripolitania	—
Weizmann Agricultural School	1952	N. Negev	Youth Training Farm	—	Various	—

I	II	III	IV	V	VI	VII
Yaara	1950	W. Upper Galilee	Work Village	Tenuat Hamoshavim	Yemen	—
Yad Hanna A	1950	Plain of Hepher	Kibbutz	Israel Communist Party	Hungary	—
Yad Hanna B	1954	Plain of Hepher	Kibbutz	Hakibbutz Hameuhad	Hungary	—
Yad Mordekhai	1943	S. Coastal Plain	Kibbutz	Hashomer Hatzair	Poland, various	—
Yad Natan (Otzem)	1953	S. Coastal Plain	Smallholders' Settlement	Ha'oved Hatziyyoni	Czechoslovakia, Yugoslavia, Rumania	—
Yagel	1950	Judean Plain	Immigrant Smallholders' Settlement	Tenuat Hamoshavim	Iraq	320
Yagur	1922	Plain of Zebulun	Kibbutz	Hakibbutz Hameuhad	Israel, Eastern Europe	1,374
Yahad	1954	S. Coastal Plain	Rural Settlement	—	—	160
Yakhini	1950	N. Negev	Immigrant Smallholders' Settlement	Tenuat Hamoshavim	Iran, Yemen	—
Yakum	1947	S. Sharon	Kibbutz	Hashomer Hatzair	Various	341
Yanuv	1950	Plain of Hepher	Immigrant Smallholders' Settlement	Tenuat Hamoshavim	Tunisia	—
Yardena	1952	Beit She'an Valley	Smallholders' Settlement	Tenuat Hamoshavim	Iraq	—
Yarhiv	1949	S. Sharon	Immigrant Smallholders' Settlement	Tenuat Hamoshavim	Yemen	—
Yarkona	1932	S. Sharon	Smallholders' Settlement	Tenuat Hamoshavim	Morocco	120
Yashresh	1950	Judean Foothills	Immigrant Smallholders' Settlement	Tenuat Hamoshavim	Morocco	—
Yas'ur	1949	W. Lower Galilee	Kibbutz	Hashomer Hatzair	Hungary, Britain, Israel	234
Yatsiv	1949	Sharon	Rural Village	—	—	1,950
Yatzitz	1950	Judean Plain	Immigrant Smallholders' Settlement	Tenuat Hamoshavim	Tripolitania	453
Yavne	1949	Judean Plain	Rural Settlement	—	Various	2,300
Yavne'el	1901	E. Lower Galilee	Rural Settlement	—	Israel, N. Africa	1,800

I	II	III	IV	V	VI	VII
Yavor	1950	W. Upper Galilee	Seed growing Farm	—	—	25
Yedidya	1953	Plain of Hepher	Smallholders' Settlement	Tenuat Hamoshavim	Germany, Israel	333
Yehiam	1946	Central Upper Galilee	Kibbutz	Hashomer Hatzair	Hungary, Israel, various	
Yehud	1948	Judean Plain	Rural Settlement	—	Various, Turkey	6,100
Yemin Orde	1953	Carmel Coast	Youth Training Farm	Hapoel Hamizrahi	Various	152
Yesha	1956	N. Negev	Smallholders' Settlement	Tenuat Hamoshavim	Egypt	—
Yesodot	1948	Judean Foothills	Cooperative Settlement	Poalei Agudat Yisrael	Rumania, Central Europe, Poland	198
Yesud Hamaala	1883	Huleh Valley	Smallholders' Settlement	Hamo'etza Hahaklait	Israel, Eastern and Central Europe	450
Yikkon	1951	Plain of Hepher	Maabara	—	Rumania	—
Yinnon	1952	S. Coastal Plain	Immigrant Smallholders' Settlement	Tenuat Hamoshavim	Yemen	453
Yiphtah	1948	E. Upper Galilee	Kibbutz	Ihud Hakibbutzim	Israel, various	—
Yiphat (Gevat B)	1926	Jezreel Valley	Kibbutz	Ihud Hakibbutzim	Israel	841
Yiron	1949	Central Upper Galilee	Kibbutz	Hakibbutz Hameuhad	Israel, various	
Yish'i	1950	Judean Foothills	Immigrant Smallholders' Settlement	Hapoel Hamizrahi	Yemen	—
Yizre'el	1948	Jezreel Valley	Kibbutz	Ihud Hakibbutzim	Israel, various	—
Yizre'am	1953	N. Negev	Seed growing Farm	—	—	15
Yohanan	1951	S. Coastal Plain	Ma'abara	—	—	312
Yokne'am	1935	Jezreel Valley	Smallholders' Settlement	Hamo'etza Hahaklait	Various, Iraq	2,750
Yoshivya	1950	W. Negev	Immigrant Smallholders' Settlement	Hapoel Hamizrahi	Algeria	—
Yotvata	1951	S. Arava	Kibbutz	Ihud Hakibbutzim	Israel	—
Zanoah	1950	Judean Foothills	Smallholders' Settlement	Poalei Agudat Yisrael	Yemen	480

I	II	III	IV	V	VI	VII
Zarnuka	1948	Judean Plain	Rural (Suburban) Settlement	—	Rumania, various	693
Zavdiel	1950	S. Coastal Plain	Immigrant Smallholders' Settlement	Poalei Agudat Yisrael	Yemen	480
Zeitan	1950	Judean Plain	Smallholders' Settlement	Tenuat Hamoshavim	Tripolitania	440
Zekher Dov	1950	S. Coastal Plain	Smallholders' Settlement	Herut Movement	Poland, Israel	190
Zemorot	1955	S. Coastal Plain	Plantation Settlement	—	—	8
Zerahya	1950	S. Coastal Plain	Immigrant Smallholders' Settlement	Hapoel Hamizrahi	Iran	—
Zerua	1953	N. Negev	Smallholders' Settlement	Hapoel Hamizrahi	—	150
Zikhron Yaakov	1882	N. Sharon	Town	—	Israel, various	3,950
Zikim	1949	S. Coastal Plain	Kibbutz	Hashomer Hatzair	Israel, Rumania	150
Zimrat (Shuva Beit)	1957	N. Negev	Smallholders' Settlement	Hapoel Hamizrahi	Jerba	—

UNITED STATES

JEWISH POPULATION: 5,300,000

The history of the Jews in America begins with the time of its discovery. Many historians maintain that Christopher Columbus was a Spanish Jew from the province of Galicia. It is an established fact that many of his closest friends were Jewish Marranos who assisted him in his undertaking. Three Marranos, Luis de Santangel, chancellor of the royal household, Gabriel Sanchez, chief treasurer of Aragon, and Juan Cabiero, the chamberlain of King Ferdinand, succeeded in persuading Ferdinand and Isabella to sponsor and finance the expedition of Columbus. Columbus' vessels weighed anchor on August 3, 1492, exactly one day after the expulsion of the Jews from Spain. On their way out, they passed one of the ships which was carrying the exiles to other countries. Among those who accompanied Columbus were the Jews Alonzo de la Calle, Inspector Rodrigo Sanchez, Luis de Torres, the interpreter who was the first man of the expedition to set foot on American soil, Bernal, the fleet's physician, and Marco, the surgeon.

The main reason for the early emigration of Jews to America was the desire of Marrano-Jews to escape the persecutions of the Inquisition. In 1631, the Dutch captured Recife in Brazil, and a new Jewish community was founded there which lasted until 1654. Marranos and Jews from Holland settled there. It was the first Jewish community in America and was called Kahal Kodesh. It numbered about 5,000 souls. Their first Rabbi was Isaak Aboab who in his "Zecher Rav," the first Hebrew book written in America, recounted the story of his Recife congregation. When the colony was retaken by the Portuguese, the Jews departed, and a small group — 23 of them—came to New Amsterdam, now New York. Arriving on the ship St. Charles after having suffered horribly from piracy and storms, they encountered the hostility of the Dutch governor, Pieter Stuyvesant, who suggested to the Dutch West India Company that the whole group be expelled. The Directors of the Company, however, answered with an order to permit the Jews to reside and trade there but forbidding them to "exercise their religion in a synagogue or a gathering." In 1664, when the ownership of the Colony changed from Holland to England and its name was changed to New York, the restrictions against worship were removed, but the right to erect a synagogue was granted only in 1686. In 1695, the congregation Shearith Israel was established. In 1728, the first synagogue on the continent was erected in Mill Street. Noteworthy among the first 23 settlers was Asser Levy who fought valiantly for equal rights for the Jews.

The Jewish community grew slowly to some 300 at the time of the War of Independence in 1776. There were scattered Jewish settlers in New England at the beginning of the 18th century. Juda Morris, a converted Jew, became teacher of Hebrew at Harvard University and in 1735, he published "A Grammar of the Hebrew Tongue" (Dikduk Leshon Ivrith).

The second Jewish settlement in North America was at Newport, R.I. in 1658. Their synagogue, built in 1763, is the oldest synagogue still standing in the United States. The third Jewish settlement was in Philadelphia (1726), the fourth, in Savannah, Ga. where a congregation was organized in 1734, and the fifth in Charleston S.C. in 1750. During the whole of the 18th century, an increasing number of Jewish immigrants came to the English colonies and settled in various coastal cities.

* * *

The *first* wave of Jewish immigration until 1815 is called the *Spanish,* since most immigrants were descendants of Jews from Spain and Portugal and only a few from England and Germany. The *second* period of immigration from 1815 to 1880 is known as the *German* wave, the majority coming from Germany and only a few from Eastern Europe. In this period, the Jewish population grew from 3,000, in a total population of the country of 4,000,000, to 250,000, and established new settlements in St. Louis (1816), Cincinnati (1817), Chicago (1837), Cleveland (1837), and San Francisco (1849). Within the second half of the 18th century, practically all Jewish communities in the United States had already been established. Some of the German Jewish immigrants soon advanced from peddling to ownership of

large business enterprises and factories. They founded the American Jewish Reform Movement.

The *third* wave of immigration began in 1881 and continued until the World War in 1914, and is called the *Russian* wave, although it also included Jews from all countries of Eastern Europe. It was the largest immigration, increasing the population of Jews in the U.S. to 3,500,000. This immigration was caused by the oppression of the Jews in Europe, namely by the pogroms in Russia in 1881, expulsions in 1891, and the October pogroms of 1905 and by persecution in most of the eastern European countries.

The Jewish immigrants at first tended to become manual laborers and factory workers rather than traders. They played a conspicuous part in the rising labor movement. In the course of time, their condition improved and they began to participate in the ever-expanding industry and trade of the country.

In the period 1654–1954, at least 3,250,000 Jews immigrated to the United States and the balance of about 2,000,000 has to be attributed to the natural increase.

The growth of the Jewish population in U.S.A. in the period 1818–1954 was as follows: 1818—3,000; 1824—6,000; 1840 —15,000; 1848—50,000; 1877—230,000; 1888—400,000; 1897—938,00; 1905— 1,508,000; 1907—1,777,000; 1910—2,044,- 000; 1917—3,389,000; 1927—4,228,000; 1937—4,771,000; 1954—3,250,000; 1957 —5,300,000.

* * *

The concentration of over 5,000,000 Jews in the United States, consisting of almost half of the whole Jewish people, reflects a memorable shift in the Jewish center of population in the world from Europe to America. The Jewish community in the U.S.A., possessing freedom and economic and cultural opportunities, developed the largest center of Jewish life outside Israel and began to take over the leadership of the Jews in the diaspora.

Jews enlisted voluntarily in the War of Independence and in the Civil War. It is estimated that 6,000 Jews served in the Union Army and 1,500 with the Confederate forces. In the Union Army, there were about 700 Jewish officers of whom 21 were colonels and 8, generals. More than 250,000 Jews served in the United States Army in the First World War of 1914. Of this number, 10,000 were officers and 1,100 received citations for valor. A total of 550,000 Jews served in the United States armed forces during the Second World War, 10,000 of them died in action, 19 were generals and 2 admirals. More than 36,000 received awards for valor and merit.

The Jews participated in every phase of American life, exhibiting remarkable talent and ability. They created the clothing industry, and from the sweat-shops many immigrants from Eastern Europe rose to positions of successful manufacturers. Samuel Gompers developed the union movement by founding the AF of L. Jews were the pioneers who expanded and perfected the motion picture industry, among them: Lublin, Fox, Balaban, Warner, Zukor, Loew, Laemmle, Mayer, Mark, and Goldwyn. David Sarnoff of R.C.A. and W. S. Paley of the C.B.S. played

a prominent part in the development of radio and television. Jews pioneered in the merchandising field, developing department stores and mail-order establishments such as Macy's, Gimbels, and Sachs in New York and many others in other cities.

The concert stage has been enriched by such artists as Heifetz, Elman, Menuhin, Zimbalist, Rubinstein, Horowitz, Millstein, Bruno Walter, Klemperer, Ormandy, Reiner, and Bernstein. As composers, the following distinguished themselves: Ernest Bloch, Aaron Copland, and Arnold Schoenberg; in popular music—the composers Gershwin, Berlin, Kern, Romberg, Rodgers, Hart, Loesser, Hammerstein. The founders of the most respected newspapers were the Jews Adolph Ochs of the New York Times, Joseph Pulitzer of the old New York World, etc. Contributing immeasurably in medical research were the Nobel prize winner Selman Waksman who developed streptomycin; Bela Shick, inventor of the test to fight diphtheria, Jonas Salk producer of the polio vaccine, Goldberg who brought pellagra to a standstill; and Dr. E. J. Cohn, extractor of blood plasma and Gamma Gobulin, which have saved tens of thousands of lives since the Second World War.

Einstein, Michelson, and Rabi won the Nobel Prize for their great contributions to physics. Jewish scientists have played an outstanding part in the development of atomic power. From among Jewish students of law came the justices of the U.S. Supreme Court Brandeis, Cardozo, and Frankfurter. Jews have served as members of the Cabinet (Morgenthau), ambassadors, senators, and governors in Maryland, Idaho, Utah, Louisiana, Illinois, Florida, Oregon, New Mexico, New York, Connecticut, Colorado, and Arizona. There are about 100,000 Jewish farmers in America.

HIGHER EDUCATION:

The United States became the greatest center of Jewish learning and Jewish higher education in the diaspora. American Jewry has established two universities, the Yeshiva University in New York and Brandeis University at Waltham, Mass. and the Dropsie College for Hebrew and Cognate Learning in Philadelphia. It also maintains 4 Rabbinical Seminaries; the Rabbi Isaac Elhanan Theological Seminary of the Yeshiva University (Orthodox), The Hebrew Theological College of Chicago, (Orthodox), The Jewish Theological Seminary (Conservative), and the Hebrew Union College—Jewish Institute of Religion (Reform). Besides, there are Yeshivot training orthodox rabbis as Tora Va-Daat, Rabbi Haim Berlin, and others.

RELIGION AND CULTURE:

According to estimates of the leadership of the three Jewish religious trends in the U.S.A., the approximately 4,000 Jewish congregations are divided as follows: about 3,000 Orthodox congregations and houses of worship serving approximately 3,000,000; 600 Conservative congregations serving 1,000,000; and 520 Reform congregations serving 1,000,000. The vague estimates of the membership include the head and all members of the family and, in addition, disregard the fact that a considerable number of the five million American Jews are not affiliated with any religious denomination. During 1950–1955, 200 new synagogues were erected at a cost of 400 million dollars.

Of the 12 Hebrew Teachers Seminaries the foremost are the Teachers Institute and Seminary College of Jewish Studies, the Teachers Institute of Yeshiva University, the Herzliah Hebrew Academy, the Hebrew Union School of Education, all in New York; Gratz College in Philadelphia, and the Teachers Seminaries in Boston, Chicago, Baltimore, Pittsburgh, and Cleveland.

Outstanding scholars in Hebrew letters such as L. Ginzburg, David Neumark, and Israel Davidson, served as professors at the Theological Seminary. In the field of rabbinics men like Haim Heller, J. B. Soloveitschik, and S. Lieberman have achieved eminence. The Jewish historian, S. Baron and the historian of Jewish philosophy Harry Wolfson and many others have made outstanding contributions in other fields. Hebrew and Yiddish scholars, poets and writers have developed a remarkable Hebrew and Yiddish literature in the United States, to name only a few of them: Imber, Dolitzky, Schneour, Efross, Ribalow, Leivik, Opotashu, Niger, etc. The Jewish press in Yiddish, Hebrew, and English, the numerous Jewish publishing houses and many other cultural institutions reflect the increasing spiritual role of American Jewry within the Jewish people.

WELFARE:

A glorious chapter in the achievements of the American Jewish community are its activities in the field of welfare and relief. The funds raised voluntarily each year for Israel and overseas needs, as well as for local religious and social requirements, amount to *over half a billion* dollars.

American Jewry played a historical role in the establishment of the State of Israel with its indispensable political cooperation. The United Jewish Appeal aided Israel enormously in the resettling there of hundreds of thousands of refugees from Europe, the Middle East, and Africa and made a vital contribution to the economic development of the Jewish State in general. Among the manifold welfare institutions the 65 Jewish hospitals in the United States, all of which are non-sectarian, with over half of their patients being non-Jewish are worthy of note.

With the destruction of the great Jewish communities in Europe, America has become the most important center of Jewish cultural, social, educational, and spiritual life, second only to Israel.

THE POPULATION OF JEWISH COMMUNITIES IN THE U.S.A.

(According to the "American Jewish Year Book 1956")

State and City	Jewish Population
ALABAMA	
Anniston	140
Bessemer	126
Birmingham	4,150
Dothan	140
Gadsden	196
Huntsville	100
Jasper	125
Mobile	1,750
Montgomery	1,500
Selma	210
Tri-Cities	132[1]
Tuscaloosa	240
ARIZONA	
Phoenix	6,000
Tucson	5,000
ARKANSAS	
Blytheville	100
Ft. Smith	259
Helena	204
Hot Springs	525
Little Rock	1,000
Pine Bluff	275
Wynne	152[1]
CALIFORNIA	
Alameda, Contra Costa County	16,000
Alhambra	660[1]
Bakersfield	1,085
Belvedere	660[1]
Berkeley	1,800[1]
El Monte	330[1]
Elsinore	450
Fontana	140
Fresno	1,400
Long Beach	7,000
Los Angeles	400,000
Martinez	250[1]
Modesto	267
Oakland	12,000
Ontario-Pomona	600
Palm Springs	500
Pasadena	1,800
Petaluma	600
Redondo Beach	132[1]
Richmond	600[1]
Riverside	224

[1] 1954

State and City	Jewish Population	State and City	Jewish Population
Sacramento	4,000	Newtown	192
Salinas	300	Norwalk	3,000
San Bernardino	1,146	Norwich	2,200
San Diego	6,000	Putnam	120
San Francisco	51,000	Rockville	415
San Jose	2,000	Stamford	5,500
San Leandro	1,500[1]	Torrington	360
San Pedro	600	Wallingford	300
Santa Ana	450	Waterbury	5,000
Santa Barbara	400	Westport	360
Santa Cruz	140	Willimantic	425
Santa Monica	8,000	Winsted	137
Santa Rosa	160	Woodmont	250
Stockton	1,300		
Sunnyvale	100[1]	**DELAWARE**	
Tulare	146	Wilmington	6,500
Vallejo	400		
Ventura County	400	**DISTRICT OF COLUMBIA**	
		Washington	60,000
COLORADO			
Colorado Springs	400	**FLORIDA**	
Denver	16,000	Clearwater	170
Greeley	113	Daytona Beach	700
Pueblo	500	Ft. Lauderdale	560
		Gainesville	148
		Hollywood	2,500
CONNECTICUT		Jacksonville	4,300
Ansonia	700	Key West	120
Bridgeport	14,000	Lakeland	300
Bristol	250	Miami	75,000
Colchester	600	Orlando	1,000
Danbury	1,500	Pensacola	800
Derby-Shelton	340	Sarasota	450
Greenwich	875	St. Augustine	205
Hartford	26,000	St. Petersburg	2,300
Lebanon	140	Tallahassee	140
Manchester	700	Tampa	2,600
Meriden	1,200	West Palm Beach	2,300
Middletown	1,000		
Milford	800	**GEORGIA**	
Moodus	262	Albany	400
New Britain	3,000	Atlanta	11,500
New Canaan	110	Augusta	800
New Haven	20,000	Brunswick	108
New London	3,000	Columbus	1,000
		Dalton	102
		Macon	800

[1] 1954

State and City	Jewish Population	State and City	Jewish Population
Savannah	3,150	Lafayette	425
Valdosta	240	Marion	156
		Michigan City	320
IDAHO		Muncie	225
Boise	120	Richmond	108
		Shelbyville	150
		South Bend	2,500
ILLINOIS		Terre Haute	875
Alton	148[1]	Vincennes	114
Aurora	400	Whiting	225
Belleville	165[1]		
Benton	150[1]	**IOWA**	
Bloomington	150	Cedar Rapids	420
Champaign	410	Council Bluffs	450
Chicago	282,000	Davenport	850
Chicago Heights	400	Des Moines	3,500
Danville	258	Dubuque	308
Decatur	343	Fort Dodge	116
East St. Louis		Iowa City	125
(included in So. Ill.)		Marshalltown	222
Elgin	480	Mason City	210
Galesburg	158	Muscatine	157
Harvey—Blue Island	155	Ottumwa	210
Joliet	604	Sioux City	2,284
Kankakee	270	Waterloo	450
Mattoon	125		
Park Forest	1,400	**KANSAS**	
Peoria	2,000	Leavenworth	115
Quincy	175	Topeka	200
Rockford	800	Wichita	1,000
Rock Island	2,000		
Southern Ill.	3,000	**KENTUCKY**	
Springfield	1,250	Ashland	175
Tri-Cities	132[1]	Lexington	1,000
Waukegan	1,000	Harlan Zone	195
		Henderson	140
INDIANA		Hopkinsville	122
Anderson	100	Louisville	8,250
East Chicago	400	Owensboro	125
Indiana Harbor	600	Paducah	150
Elkhart	150		
Evansville	1,450	**LOUISIANA**	
Ft. Wayne	1,200	Alexandria	390
Gary	3,000	Baton Rouge	750
Hammond	1,200	Lafayette	194
Indianapolis	8,000	Lake Charles	100
Kokomo	115[1]		

State and City	Jewish Population	State and City	Jewish Population
Monroe	900	Haverhill	2,500
Morgan City	115 [1]	Holyoke	1,600
New Iberia	104	Hyannis	250
New Orleans	9,200	Lawrence	2,540
Shreveport	2,300	Leominster	385
		Lowell	2,000
MAINE		Lynn	10,000
Aroostock City	120	Medway	150
Augusta	100	Milford	300
Bangor	1,200	Millis	123
Bath	100	New Bedford	4,000
Biddeford-Saco	262	Newburyport	437
Calais	137	North Adams	612
Lewiston-Auburn	1,400	North Attleboro	100
Pittsfield	120	Northampton	350
Portland	3,500	Peabody	1,200
Rockland	150	Pittsfield	2,250
Waterville	110	Plymouth	220
		Salem	1,600
MARYLAND		Southbridge	140
Annapolis	1,000	Springfield	10,000
Baltimore	78,000	Taunton	800
Cumberland	535	Ware	125
Easton Area	140	Webster	140
Frederick	150	Worcester	10,500
Hagerstown	316		
Havre de Grace	100	**MICHIGAN**	
Pocomoke City	100	Ann Arbor	210
St. Mary's County	109	Battle Creek	155
Salisbury	227	Bay City	800
		Benton Harbor	830
MASSACHUSETTS		Detroit	72,000
Athol	210	Flint	3,000
Attleboro	120	Grand Rapids	1,650
Ayer	125 [1]	Iron City	161
Beverly	700	Iron Mountain	104
Boston	140,000	Jackson	200
Brockton	3,200	Kalamazoo	534
Clinton	112	Lansing	700
Fall River	4,500	Marquette County	175
Fitchburg	607	Mt. Clemens	300
Framingham	875	Muskegon	400
Gardner	140	Pontiac	700
Gloucester	350	Port Huron	130
Great Barrington	132	Saginaw	440
Greenfield	250	South Haven	460

State and City	Jewish Population	State and City	Jewish Population
MINNESOTA		Dover	150
Austin	125	Keene	112
Duluth	3,100	Laconia	120
Hibbing	230	Manchester	1,870
Mankato	122	Nashua	418
Minneapolis	23,000	Portsmouth	480
Rochester	120		
St. Paul	10,400	**NEW JERSEY**	
Virginia	140	Alliance	400
		Arlington	372 [1]
MISSISSIPPI		Asbury Park	3,000
Biloxi-Gulfport	160	Atlantic City	9,000
Clarksdale	380	Bayonne	8,300
Cleveland	250	Belleville	676 [1]
Greenville	525	Belmar	800
Greenwood	175	Bergenfield-Dumont	1,750
Hattiesburg	232	Bloomfield	1,681 [1]
Jackson	350	Boonton	240
Meridian	235	Bound Brook	350
Natchez	153 [1]	Bradley Beach	1,000
Vicksburg	275	Bridgton	600
		Burlington	250
MISSOURI		Caldwell	730 [1]
Hannibal	100 [1]	Camden	10,000
Hayti	200	Carmel	140
Joplin	200	Carteret	600
Kansas City	22,000	Cliffside Park	200 [1]
Springfield	240	Cranford	600
St. Joseph	1,002	Cresskill	265
St. Louis	55,000	Dover	700
		Dunellen	126
MONTANA		Elizabeth	10,500
Billings	100	Englewood	3,500
Butte	206	Englewood Cliffs	350
		Englishtown	260
NEBRASKA		Essex County	86,500
Lincoln	950	Fair Lawn	4,550
Omaha	6,500	Farmingdale	800
		Flemington	750
NEVADA		Fort Lee	1,400
Las Vegas	2,500	Freehold	1,000
Reno	320	Gloucester County	900
		Hackensack	1,600
NEW HAMPSHIRE		Hasbrouck Heights	440
Claremont	200	Heightstown	1,100
Concord	160	Hillside	4,087 [1]

State and City	Jewish Population	State and City	Jewish Population
Hoboken	1,300	Roselle	1,200
Irvington	7,388 [1]	Rutherford	1,000
Jersey City	20,000	Salem	220
Kearney	302 [1]	Somerville	634
Keyport	400	South Amboy	145 [1]
Lake Hiawatha	400	South Orange	2,298 [1]
Lakewood	2,800	South River	400
Leonia	450 [1]	Stelton	180
Linden	2,625	Summit	600
Long Branch	2,000	Teaneck	4,000
Lyndhurst	200	Tenefly	875
Madison	100	Toms River	1,000
Maplewood	2,240 [1]	Trenton	8,800
Maywood	600	Union	1,750
Metuchen	840	Vineland	2,000
Millburn	579 [1]	Westfield	384
Millville	200	West Orange	1,295
Montclair	890 [1]	Westwood	400
Morristown	1,000	Wildwood	600
Mt. Freedom	160	Woodbine	300
Mt. Holly	204	Woodbridge	1,000
Newark	57,000	Woodbury	540
New Brunswick	7,500		
Newton	175	**NEW MEXICO**	
New Arlington	1,980 [1]	Albuquerque	1,000
North Hudson County	8,000	Los Alamos	120
Nutley	501 [1]	Santa Fe	125
Orange	1,403 [1]		
Palisades Park	1,750	**NEW YORK**	
Park Ridge	200	Albany	9,000
Passaic	12,000	Amenia	132
Paterson	18,000	Amsterdam	500
Paulsboro	135	Auburn	250
Perth Amboy	5,100	Baldwin	1,400
Plainfield	4,100	Batavia	300
Penns Grove	140	Bay Shore	1,850 [1]
Pine Brook	175	Beacon	550
Pt. Pleasant	100	Binghamton	
Pompton Lakes	450	(incl. all Broome County)	3,000
Princeton	300	Bronxville	4,550
Rahway	960	Buffalo	22,000
Red Bank	1,200	Canadaigua	228
Ridgefield	500 [1]	Catskill	227
Ridgefield Park	360	Cedarhurst	21,000
Ridgewood	350	Cohoes	105
Riverside	170	Corning	100 [1]

State and City	Jewish Population	State and City	Jewish Population
Cortland	200	Mt. Vernon	15,750
Dobbs Ferry	1,050	Newburgh	2,500
Dunkirk	168	New Hyde Park	4,550
Ellenville	1,100	New Rochelle	8,400
Elmira	1,525	New York	2,050,000
Elmont	7,000	Manhattan	320,000
Floral Park	1,140	Bronx	475,000
Freeport	2,450	Brooklyn	475,000
Geneva	120	Brooklyn	870,000
Glen Cove	1,575	Queens	375,000
Glens Falls	700	Richmond	10,000
Gloversville	1,400	Niagara Falls	1,100
Great Neck	15,050	Norwich	140
Harrison	1,500	Nyack	276
Haverstraw	480	Oceanside	2,100
Hempstead (incl. E.		Ogdensburg	135
and W. Hempstead)	7,500	Olean	335
Herkimer	180	Oneida	106
Hornell	100	Oneonta	100
Highland Falls	105	Oswego	140
Hudson	900	Parksville	140
Huntington	2,800	Patchogue	1,750
Ithaca	800	Pawling	120
Jamestown	260	Peekskill	1,400
Jeffersonville	150	Plattsburg	340
Kerhonkson	175	Port Chester	2,300
Kingston	2,400	Port Jervis	560
Lake Huntington	175	Poughkeepsie	3,100
Larchmont	2,450	Rensselaer	100[1]
Liberty	620	Rochester	20,000
Little Falls	105	Rockville Centre	7,350
Livingston Manor	150	Rome	400
Loch Sheldrake-Hurleyville	750	Roslyn	7,000
Lockport	100[1]	Rye	965
Long Beach	8,750	Saranac Lake	100
Lynbrook	3,500	Saratoga Springs	500
Malone	122	Scarsdale	1,500
Massena	140	Schenectady	3,500
Merrick		Sharon Springs	165
(incl. North Merrick)	8,400	South Fallsburg	1,100
Middletown	1,500	Spring Valley	2,250
Monroe	350	Suffern	544
Monticello	1,200	Syracuse	11,000
Mountaindale	280	Tarrytown	1,050
Mt. Kisco	525	Troy	2,300
		Utica	3,500

State and City	Jewish Population	State and City	Jewish Population
Valley Stream	10,500	Lorain	800
Walden	140	Mansfield	308
Warwick	126	Marion	165
Watertown	450	Massillon	130
White Lake	354	Middletown	310
White Plains	12,000	New Philadelphia	180
White Sulphur Springs	100	Piqua	275
Woodbourne	200	Portsmouth	120
Woodbridge	650	Sandusky	100
Yonkers	23,000	Springfield	488
		Steubenville	1,000
NORTH CAROLINA		Toledo	6,500
Asheville	600	Warren	800
Charlotte	1,500	Wooster	128
Durham	360	Youngstown	5,500
Fayetteville	228	Zanesville	300
Gastonia	158		
Goldsboro	135	**OKLAHOMA**	
Greensboro	1,141	Ardmore	120
Hendersonville	118	McAlester	132[1]
High Point	208	Muskogee	151[1]
Raleigh	375	Oklahoma City	1,750
Wilmington	300	Seminole	124
Winston-Salem	428	Tulsa	2,020
NORTH DAKOTA		**OREGON**	
Bismarck	168	Eugene	120
Fargo	500	Portland	6,600
Grand Forks	122	Salem	210
Minot	110[1]		
		PENNSYLVANIA	
OHIO		Aliquippa	400
Akron	6,500	Allentown	3,250
Alliance	122	Altoona	1,100
Ashtabula	315	Ambridge	300
Bellaire	240	Beaver Valley	830
Canton	2,700	Berwick	119
Cincinnati	25,000	Bethelehem	1,000
Cleveland	85,000	Bloomsburg	102
Columbus	7,200	Braddock	600
Dayton	6,000	Bradford	600
East Liverpool	365	Bristol	176
Elyria	360	Brownsville	260
Fremont	114	Butler	645
Hamilton	500	Canonsburg	120
Lima	418	Carbon County	300

State and City	Jewish Population	State and City	Jewish Population
Carbondale	335	Oil City	360
Carnegie	268	Oxford	132[1]
Chambersburg	210	Philadelphia	226,700
Charleroi	200	Philipsburg	136
Chester	2,100	Phoenixville	268
Clairton	110	Pittsburgh	47,000
Coatesville	510	Pottstown	680
Connellsville	160	Pottsville	870
Coraopolis	152	Punxsutawney	108
Donora	160	Reading	3,500
DuBois	160	Sayre	105
Duquesne	200	Scranton	5,526
Easton	1,600	Sharon-Greenville	1,000[1]
East Pittsburgh	660[1]	Shamokin	250
Ellwood City	140	Shenandoah	444
Erie	1,750	Stroudsburg	222
Farrell	500	Sunbury	160
Glassport	120	Tarentum	175
Greensburg	4,500	Titusville	120
Hanover	120	Uniontown	900
Harrisburg	4,500	Vandergrift-Leachburg	120
Hazleton	1,400	Warren	120
Homestead	600	Washington	500
Honesdale-Hawley	100[1]	West Chester	360
Indiana	130	Wilkes-Barre	5,062
Irwin	120	Williamsport	850
Jeannette	200	York	1,100
Johnstown	1,600		
Kennett Square	114[1]		
Kittanning	275	**RHODE ISLAND**	
Lancaster	1,750	Newport	1,000
Lansdale	200[1]	Pawtucket	1,300
Latrobe	150	Providence	0,000
Lebanon	656	Westerly	100
Levittown	2,100	Woonsocket	795
Lewistown	250		
Lock Haven	350		
Mahonoy City	150	**SOUTH CAROLINA**	
McKeesport	2,500	Beaufort	116
McKees Rocks	160	Bishopville	116
Monessen	250	Charleston	2,192
Mt. Carmel	272	Columbia	500
New Castle	800	Georgetown	111
New Kensington	640	Greenville	550
Norristown	1,000	Orangeburg	118
North Penn	200	Spartanburg	210
		Sumter	250

State and City	Jewish Population	State and City	Jewish Population
SOUTH DAKOTA		Rutland	350
Aberdeen	123[1]		
Sioux Falls	350	**VIRGINIA**	
		Alexandria	650[1]
TENNESSEE		Arlington	900[1]
Chattanooga	2,200	Charlottesville	120[1]
Jackson	110	Danville	200
Knoxville	800	Fredericksburg	120
Memphis	8,000	Hampton	210
Nashville	2,700	Hampton Roads	165[1]
Oak Ridge	700	Harrisonburg	112
		Lynchburg	280
TEXAS		Martinsville	170
Amarillo	270	Newport News	1,700
Austin	900	Norfolk	7,500
Beaumont	625	Petersburg	500
Breckenridge	111	Portsmouth	2,100
Corpus Christi	1,100	Richmond	7,750
Corsicana	188[1]	Roanoke	650
Dallas	14,000	Suffolk	180
El Paso	2,700	Winchester	131
Ft. Worth	2,500		
Galveston	1,400	**WASHINGTON**	
Houston	17,000	Bellingham	140[1]
Kilgore	108	Bremerton	182
Laredo	184	Everett	125[1]
Longview	125	Seattle	9,500
Lubbock	315	Spokane	625
McAllen	125	Tacoma	650
Odessa	100		
Port Arthur	230	**WEST VIRGINIA**	
Rio Grande Valley	300[1]	Beckley	228
Rosenbe.g	100	Bluefield	300
San Angelo	100	Charleston	2,200
San Antonio	6,500	Clarksburg	280
Texarkana	129	Fairmont	200
Tyler	450	Huntington	750
Waco	1,200	Morgantown	150
Wharton	215	Parkersburg	100
Wichita Falls	300	Weirton	350
		Welch	144
UTAH		Wheeling	800
Ogden	100	Williamson	180
Salt Lake City	1,500		
		WISCONSIN	
VERMONT		Appletown	575
Burlington	1,000	Beloit	150

State and City	Jewish Population
Eau Claire	150
Fond du Lac	160
Green Bay	500
Kenosha	590
La Crosse	150
Madison	2,150
Manitowoc	184
Marinette	120
Milwaukee	30,000
Oshkosh	130
Racine	1,000
Rice Lake	100
Sheboygan	600
Stevens Point	105
Superior	481
Waukesha	100
Wausau	250

WYOMING

Cheyenne	500

COMMUNITY AND POLITICAL ORGANIZATIONS

American Jewish Congress (1917; re-org. 1922, 1938). Stephen Wise Congress House, 15 East 84th Street, N.Y.C. 28. Pres. Israel Goldstein; Exec. Dir. Isaac Tobin. Seeks to protect the rights of Jews in all lands; to strengthen the bonds between American Jewry and Israel; to promote the democratic organization of Jewish communal life in the United States; to foster the affirmation of Jewish religious, cultural, and historic identity, and to contribute to the preservation and extension of the democratic way of life.

American Jewish Committee (1906), 386 Fourth Avenue N.Y.C. 16. Pres. Irving M. Engel; Exec. V. P. John Slawson. Seeks to prevent infraction of the civil and religious rights of Jews in any part of the world and to secure equality of economic, social, and educational opportunity through education and civic action. Seeks to broaden understanding of the basic nature of prejudice and to improve techniques for combating it.

American Council for Judaism, Inc. (1943) 201 E. 57 St. N.Y.C. Pres. Clarence L. Coleman Jr.; Exec. Dir. Elmer Berger. Seeks to advance the universal principles of a Judaism free of nationalism, and the national, civic, cultural, and social integration into American institutions of Americans of Jewish faith.

Anti-Defamation League of B'nai B'rith (1913) 515 Madison Ave., N.Y.C. 22. Nat. Chm. Henry E. Schultz; Nat. Dir. Benjamin R. Epstein. Seeks to eliminate defamation of Jews, counteract un-American and anti-democratic propaganda, and promote better group relations.

International Jewish Labor Bund (1897). 25 E. St. N.Y.C. 21. Sec. Emanuel Nowogrudsky, Emanuel Scherer. Strives to enhance and develop Jewish nationhood without Jewish statehood or assimilation; believes in furthering secular Yiddish culture and the Yiddish language.

Jewish Labor Committee (1933). Atran Center for Jewish Culture, 25 E. 78th St. N.Y.C. 21. Nat. Chmn. Adolph Held; Exec. Sec. Jacob Pat. Aids Jewish and non-Jewish labor institutions overseas; aids victims of oppression and persecution; seeks to combat anti-Semitism and racial and religious intolerance abroad and in the U.S. in cooperation with organized labor and other groups.

Jewish Socialist Verband of America (19211). 175 E. Broadway N.Y.C. 2. Chairman Exec. Com. Max Gaft; Nat. Sec. I. Levin-Shatzkes. Promotes and propagandizes the ideals of social democracy among the Jewish working people, organizing lectures, open forums, symposiums, etc. through its branches in New York and other cities in the U.S.

Jewish War Veterans of the United States of America, Inc. (1896) 1712 New Hampshire Ave. N.W., Washington 9, D.C. Nat. Comdr. Reubin Kaminsky; Nat. Exec. Dir. Ben Kaufman. Patriotic; public relations.

National Community Relations Advisory Council (1944), 9 E. 38th St. N.Y.C. 16. Chmn. Bernard H. Trager; Exec. Dir. Isaiah M. Minkoff. Aims: To study, analyze, and evaluate the policies and activities of the national and local agencies; to ascertain the problem areas from time to time; to ascertain the areas of activities of these organizations and to conduct a continuous inventory of their projects; to serve as a coordinating and clearance agency for projects and policies, to eliminate duplication and conflict of activities, and to recommend further projects to member agencies; to seek agreement on and formulate policies.

World Jewish Congress (1936; org. in U.S. 1939). Stephen Wise Congress House, 15 East 84th Street N.Y.C. 28. Pres. Nahum Goldmann. Seeks to secure and safeguard the rights, status and interests of Jews and Jewish communities throughout the world; represents its affiliated organizations before the United Nations, governmental, intergovernmental and other international authorities on matters which are of concern to the Jewish people as a whole; promotes Jewish cultural activity and represents Jewish cultural interests before UNESCO; organizes Jewish communal life in countries of recent settlement; prepares and publishes surveys on contemporary Jewish problems.

RELIEF ORGANIZATIONS:

American Committee of OSE, Inc. (1940). 24 W. 40th St. N.Y.C. 18. Chmn. Bd. of Direct. Israel S. Wechsler; Exec. Dir. Leon Wulman. Aims to improve the health of the Jewish people by means of health education and popularization of hygiene; and by implementation of medical and public health programs among Jews with particular emphasis on children, youth, and migrants.

American Friends of the Alliance Israélite Universelle, Inc. (1946). 61 Broadway N.Y.C. 6. Pres. Marcel Franco. Ex. Dir. Saadiah Cherniak. Serves as liaison between Jews in America and the Alliance Israélite Universelle.

American Jewish Joint Distribution Committee Inc.—JDC (1914). 270 Madison Ave. N.Y.C. 16. Chmn. Edw. M. M. Warburg. Exec.

Vice-Chmn. and Sec. Moses A. Leavitt. Organizes and administers welfare, medical, and rehabilitation programs and distributes funds for relief and reconstruction on behalf of Jews overseas.

Amerian ORT Federation Inc. — Organization for Rehabilitation Through Training. (1924). 212 Fifth Ave. N.Y.C. 10. Pres. William Haber; Exec. Sec. Paul Bernick. Trains Jewish men and women in the technical trades and agriculture; organizes and maintains vocational training schools throughout the world.

Conference on Jewish Material Claims Against Germany, Inc. (1951). 270 Madison Ave. N.Y.C. 16. Pres. Nahum Goldmann; Sec. Saul Kagan. Receives funds from the Government of the German Federal Republic under the terms of the agreement between the Conference and the Federal Republic and utilizes these funds for the relief, rehabilitation, and resettlement of needy victims of Nazi persecution residing outside of Israel on the basis of urgency of need.

Freeland League for Jewish Colonization (1937; in U.S. 1941). 310 W. 86th St. N.Y.C. 24. Gen. Sec. I. N. Steinberg. Plans large-scale colonization in some unoccupied territory for those who seek a home and cannot or will not go to Israel.

Jewish Restitution Successor Organization (1947). 270 Madison Avenue N.Y.C. 16. Pres. Israel Goldstein; Exec. Sec. Saul Kagan. Acts to discover, claim, receive, and assist in the recovery of Jewish heirless or unclaimed property; to utilize such assets or to provide for their utilization for the relief, rehabilization, and resettlement of surviving victims of Nazi persecution.

United Jewish Appeal, Inc. (1939). 165 West 46th St. N.Y.C. 36. Gen. Chmn. William Rosenwald; Pres. Edward M. M. Warburg; Exec. V. Chmn. Herbert A. Friedman. National fund-raising instrument for American Jewish Joint Distribution Committee, United Israel Appeal, and New York Association for New Americans.

ZIONIST, PRO-ISRAEL ORGANIZATIONS:

American Committee for Weizmann Institute of Science, Inc. (1944). 250 W. 57th St. N.Y.C. 19. Pres. Abraham Feinberg; Exec. V. Chmn. Meyer W. Weisgal. Supports the Weizmann Institute of Science for scientific research in Rehovot, Israel.

American Friends of the Hebrew University (1931). 9 E. 89 St. N.Y.C. 28. Pres. Daniel G. Ross; Exec. Dir. Frederick R. Lachman. Represents and publicizes Hebrew University in the U.S.; serves as fund-raising arm and purchasing agent; processes American students and arranges exchange professorships in the United States and Israel.

American Fund for Israel Institutions (1941). 267 W. 71 St. N.Y.C. 23. Chmn. Exec. Com. Samuel Rubin; Exec. V. P. Itzhak Norman. Federated fund-raising agency for leading educational, cultural, and traditional institutions in Israel; serves as a medium for cultural exchange between the United States and Israel.

American Red Magen David for Israel, Inc. (1941). 225 W. 57 St. N.Y.C. 19. Pres. Louis Rosenberg. Exec. Dir. Charles W. Feinberg. Functions as the national membership organization in support of Magen David Adom, Israel's first aid agency and official Israeli Red Cross service.

American Technion Society (1940). 1000 Fifth Avenue, N.Y.C. 28. Pres. David Rose. Exec. Dir. William H. Schwartz. Supports the Haifa Technion, Israel's Institute of Technology, and promotes the technical and industrial development of Israel.

American Zionist Committee for Public Affairs (1954). 1737 H St. N.W., Washington, D.C. Chmn. Philip S. Bernstein. Exec. Dir. I. L. Kenen. Conducts and directs public action on behalf of the Amerian Zionist movement bearing upon relations with governmental authorities with a view to maintaining and improving friendship and goodwill between the United States and Israel.

American Zionist Council. (1939; reorg. 1949). 342 Madison Av. N.Y.C. 17. Chmn. Irving Miller; Exec. Dir. Jerome Unger. Carries on an informational program on the American scene, stresses the fostering of Jewish culture and the Hebrew language in American-Jewish life and the intensification of Zionist youth work.

Ampal—American Israel Corporation (1942). 17 E. 71 St. N.Y.C. 21. Pres. Abraham Dickenstein; Chmn. Exec. Com. Benjamin R. Harris. Seeks to develop trade relations between the U.S. and Israel and assists in development of economic and agricultural resources of Israel.

Bachad Organization of North America (1950). 154 Nassau St. N.Y.C. 38. Exec. Dir. Issachar Ben-David. Fosters and promotes ideals of religious pioneering in Israel; maintains agricultural training farm and school, as well as professional department to guide and assist those interested in pioneering and professions in Israel.

Betar-Brit Trumpeldor of America, Inc. (1929). 276 W. 43 St. N.Y.C. 36.

Bnei Akiva of North America (1939). 154 Nassau St. N.Y.C. 38. Treas. Nachman Pessin; Dir. Meir Kahane. Seeks to awaken the interest of members in religious labor Zionism through self-realization in Israel; maintains training farms and leadership seminars.

Federated Council of Israel Institutions (1949). 38 Park Row N.Y.C. 38. Pres. David L. Meckler; Exec. V. P. Abraham Horowitz. Central fund-raising organization for independent religious, educational, and welfare institutions in Israel which are not maintained by the various fund-raising agencies of the Zionist Organization.

Habonim, Labor Zionist Youth (1920). 200 Fourth Ave. N.Y.C. 3. Mazkir Daniel Mann. Trains Jewish youth to become chalutzim in Israel; stimulates study of Jewish life, history, and culture; prepares youth for the defense of Jewish rights everywhere; prepares Jewish youth for active participation in American Jewish community life.

Hadassah, The Women's Zionist Organization of America, Inc. (1912). 65 E. 52nd St.

N.Y.C. 22. Pres. Mrs. Herman Shulman; Exec. Dir. Hannah L. Goldberg. Seeks to foster creative Jewish living in the U.S.; conducts health, medical, social service, child rehabilitation, vocational education, and land reclamation and afforestation activities in Israel.

Hagdud Haivri League Inc. (American Palestine Jewish Legion). (1929). 1009 President St. Brooklyn 25, N.Y. Nat. Commdr. Elias Gilner; Nat. Adj. Irving Lilienfeld. Seeks to uphold the ideals of the Jewish Legion which fought for the liberation of Palestine in World War I, to assist Legion veterans in settling in Israel, and to help establish in Israel a Legion House (Bet Hagdudim) for veterans.

Hashomer Hatzair Zionist Youth (1925). 38 W. 88th St. N.Y.C. 24. Exec. Sec. Ruth Reis; Educ. Dir. David White. Educates youth and provides agricultural training for pioneering and collective life in Israel.

Hechalutz Organization of America, Inc. (A functional arm of the Jewish Agency and the World Zionist Organization). (1935). 33 E. 67 St. N.Y.C. 21. Pres. Aron Spector; Sec. Asher Wallfish. Provides agricultural, industrial, and educational training for American Jewish youth in preparation for life in Israel; offers advice, guidance, and assistance to professionals who desire to settle in Israel; cooperates on work-and-study summer tours of Israel.

Jewish Agency for Palestine, American Section (1929). 16 E. 66 St. N.Y.C. 21. Chmn. Nahum Goldmann; Exec. Dir. Gottlieb Hammer. Recognized by the State of Israel as the authorized agency to work in the State of Israel for the development and colonization of that country, for the absorption and settlement of immigrants there, and for the coordination of the activities in Israel of Jewish institutions and associations operating in these fields; conducts a worldwide Hebrew cultural program; disperses information about Israel and assists in research projects concerning that country; promotes, publishes, and distributes books, periodicals

and pamphlets concerning developments in Israel and Zionist and Jewish history.

Jewish National Fund, Inc. Keren Kayemeth LeIsrael (1910). 42 E. 69 St. N.Y.C. 21. Pres. Harris J. Levine; Exec. Direc.-Sec. Mendel N. Fisher. Raises funds to purchase and develop the soil of Israel.

Junior Hadassah, Young Women's Zionist Organization of America (1920). 65 E. 52 St. N.Y.C. 22. Pres. Frayda Ingber. Exec. Sec. Aline Kaplan. In Israel maintains the Children's Village of Meier Shfeyah and the Junior Hadassah Library at the Hadassah Henrieta Szold School of Nursing; supports Jewish National Fund projects; conducts an educational program for membership to strengthen democracy and the American Jewish community.

Labor Zionist Organization of America Poale Zion (1905). 45 E. 17th St. N.Y.C. 3. Chmn. Central Com. Herman Seidel. Act. Sec. David Breslau. Supports labor and progressive forces in Israel, democratization of American Jewish community life, and American pro-labor legislation.

League for National Labor in Israel, Inc. (1935). 276 W. 43rd St. N.Y.C. 36. Chmn. Beinesh Epstein; Gen. Sec. Morris Giloni. Extends moral and financial help to the non-socialist National Labor Federation of Israel (Histadrut Ha-Ovdim Ha-Leumit), and acquaints the American public with its aims and activities.

League for Religious Labor in Eretz Israel, Inc. (1941). 154 Nassau St. N.Y.C. Exec. Dir. Isaac B. Rose. Promotes in the United States the ideals of the Torah Va-Avodah (religious labor) movement; assists the religious pioneers in Israel.

Mizrachi Hatzair-Mizrachi Youth of America (merger of Junior Mizrachi Women and Noar Mizrachi of America), (1952). 242 Fourth Ave. N.Y.C. 3. Nat. Pres. Rona Grossman; Exec. Dir. Benjamin Saxe. Aims to aid in the upbuilding of Israel in accordance with the Torah and traditions of Israel; spreads the religious Zionist ideal among the youth of America through varied cultural and educational programs.

Mizrachi–Hapoel Hamizrachi Organization of America, (1911). 80 Fifth Ave., N.Y.C. 11. Pres. Isaac Stollmen; Nat. Exec. Sec. Samuel Spar. Seeks to rebuild Israel as a Jewish commonwealth in the spirit of traditional Judaism and to strengthen Orthodox Judaism in the Diaspora.

National Committee for Labor Israel (Israel Histadrut Campaign), (1923). 33 E. 67 N.Y.C. 21. Nat. Chmn. Joseph Schlossberg; Nat. Sec. Isaac Hamlin. Provides funds for the various social welfare, vocational, health, cultural, and similar institutions and services of Histadrut for the benefit of workers and immigrants and to assist in the integration of newcomers as productive citizens in Israel.

National Young Judaea, (1909). 16 E. 50 St. N.Y.C. 22. Nat Chmn. Mrs. J. Leonard Weiss. Nat. Dir. Amram Prero. Seeks to develop in the U.S. a Jewish youth rooted in its heritage and dedicated to serving the Jewish people in America and Israel.

Palestine Economic Corporation, Inc. (1926)). 400 Madison Av. N.Y.C. 17. Pres. and Chmn. of the Board of Direct. Robert Szold; Exec. V.P. Ernest Nathan. Fosters economic development of Israel on a business basis through investments.

Palestine Foundation Fund (Keren Ha-Yesod), Inc. (1922). 16 E. 66th St. N.Y.C. 21. Pres. Benjamin G. Browdy. Sec. Irving S. Galt. Fiscal arm of the Jewish Agency for Palestine.

Pioneer Women. The Women's Labor Zionist Organization of America, Inc. (1925). 29 E. 22 St. N.Y.C. 10. Pres. Chaya Surchin; Exec. Sec. Rose Kriegel. Seeks to build Israel along cooperative lines and achieve social improvements in the U.S.; sponsors social welfare, agricultural, and vocational training and rehabilitation projects in Israel.

Poale Agudath Israel of America, Inc. (1948). 147 W. 42 St. N.Y.C. 36, Pres. Leo Jung, Samuel Schonfeld, Samuel Walkin, Noah Chodes; Exec. Dir. Shimshon Heller. Aims

to educate and prepare youth throughout the world to become Orthodox chalutzim in Israel; to support Orthodox communities in Israel.

Progressive Zionist League—Hashomer Hatzair, (1947). 38 W.68 St. N.Y.C. 24. Pres. Avraham Schenker; Treas. Yitzchak Frankel. Seeks to encourage American community support for Israel *kibbutz* movement; engages in fund raising for Israel, particularly on behalf of *chalutz* (pioneering) movement; seeks to fight for rights of Jews everywhere.

United Labor Zionist Party (Achdut Ha-Avodah—Poale Zion), (1920; re-org. 1947). 305 Broadway, N.Y.C. 7. Nat. Sec. Paul L. Goldman; seeks to establish a democratic socialist order in Israel and strengthen the Jewish labor movement in the U.S.

United Zionist—Revisionists of America, Inc. (1925). 276 W. 43 St. N.Y.C. 36. Pres. Leo Wolfson; Exec. Dir. Seymour Rosenberg. Aims to mobilize support for the establishment of a free Jewish commonwealth within the historic boundaries of the land of Israel.

Women's League for Israel, Inc. (1920). 1860 Broadway, N.Y.C. 23. Pres. Mrs. William Prince; First V. Pres. Mrs. David L. Isaacs. Provides shelter, vocational training and social adjustment services for young women newcomers to Israel.

World Confederation of General Zionists, (1946). 501 Fifth Ave. N.Y.C. 17. Pres. Israel Goldstein; Gen. Sec. Kalman Sultanik. In Israel encourages private and collective industry and agriculture; advocates the system of free and universal education in Israel, under government control. Issues monthly bulletins, pamphlets, booklets, and reports in English, Yiddish, and Spanish.

Zionist Archives and Library of the Palestine Foundation Fund, (1939). 250 W. 57 St. N.Y.C. 19. Dir. and Librarian Sylvia Landress. Serves as an archive and information service for material on Israel, Palestine, the Middle East, and Zionism.

Zionist Organization of America, (1897). 145 E. 32 St. N.Y.C. 16. Pres. Mortimer May; Sec. and Exec. Dir. Sidney Marks. Seeks to safeguard the integrity and independence of Israel as a free and democratic commonwealth by means consistent with the laws of the U.S.; to assist in the economic development of Israel; and to strengthen Jewish sentiment and consciousness as a people and promote its cultural creativity.

COUNCIL OF JEWISH FEDERATIONS AND WELFARE FUNDS

729 Seventh Ave., New York City

President: HERBERT R. ABELES, Newark
Secretary: MILTON KAHN, Boston
Treasurer: SYLVAN GOTSHAL, New York
Exec. Dir.: PHILIP BERNSTEIN

REGIONAL OFFICES

New England Region—Office address: 72 Franklin St., Boston 10, Mass.; Martin Greenberg, Regional Director.

New York Region—Office address: 165 W. 46th St., New York 36.

Central Atlantic Region—Office address: Fox Building, Room 1011, 16th & Market Sts. Philadelphia 3, Pennsylvania; Simon Krakow, Regional Director.

East Central Region—Office address: 1001 Huron Rd., Room 218, Cleveland, Ohio; Benjamin Schneider, Regional Director.

West Central Region—Office address: 59 E. Van Buren St., Chicago 5111. Frank W. Newman, Regional Director.

Southeastern Region—Office address: 41 Exchange Pl. S.E., Room 1001, Atlanta, Ga. David Zeff, Regional Director.

Western States Region—Office address: 353 Kearny St., Room 501, San Francisco 8, Calif. Louis Weinstein, Regional Director.

The following communities comprise at least 95 *per cent* of the Jewish population of the United States. Listed for each community is the local central agency — federation, welfare fund, or community council—with its address and the names of the president and executive director.

The names "federation," "welfare fund," and "Jewish Community Council" are not definitive and their structures and functions vary from city to city. What is called a federation in one city, for example, may be called a community council in another. In the main these central agencies have responsibility for some or all of the following functions: (a) raising of funds for local, national, and overseas services; (b) allocation and distribution of funds for these purposes; (c) coordination and central planning of local services, such as family welfare, child care, health, recreation, community relations within the Jewish community and with the general community, Jewish education, care of the aged and vocational guidance, to strengthen these services, eliminate duplication and fill gaps; (d) in small and some intermediate cities, direct administration of local social services.

In the Directory, the following symbols are used:

(1) Member agency of the Council of Jewish Federations and Welfare Funds.

(2) Receives support from Community Chest.

ALABAMA
Bessemer

Jewish Welfare Fund[1], P.O.Box 9. Pres. Hyman Weinstein. Exec. Sec. Rabbi J. S. Gallinger

Birmingham

United Jewish Fund[1] (incl. Ensley, Fairfield, Tarrant City). Organized 1937. 700 N. 18 St. (3). Pres. Fred W. Nichols. Exec. Sec. Mrs. Benjamin A. Roth

Mobile

Jewish Welfare Federation[1,2]. Pres. Maurice E. Olen. Sec.-Treas. Sidney Simon, 459 Conti St.

Montgomery

Jewish Federation.[1] Organized 1930. Pres. James Loeb. Sec. Hannah J. Simon, P.O. Box 1150

Tri-Cities

Jewish Federated Charities[1] (incl. Florence, Sheffield, Tuscumbia). Organized 1933. Co-Chmn. Philip Olim and Louis Rosenbaum Sec. William Gottlieb, Florence

ARIZONA
Phoenix

Jewish Community Council[1] (incl. surrounding communities). Organized 1940.1510 E. Camelback Rd. Pres. Nat G. Silverman. Exec. Dir. Hirsh Kaplan

Tucson

Jewish Community Council[1,2]. Organized 1942. Pres. David Kramer, 2221 E. Broadway. Exec. Dir. Benjamin N. Brook.

ARKANSAS
Little Rock

Jewish Welfare Agency[1,2] (incl. England, Levy, North Little Rock). Organized 1912. 732 Pyramid Life Building. Pres. Arnold L. Mayersohn, 304 Rock St. Exec. Dir. Miss Adele I. Sanders

CALIFORNIA
Bakersfield

Jewish Community Council of Greater Bakersfield[1] (incl. Arvin, Delano, Shafter; Taft, Wasco). Organized 1937. Pres. Oscar Katz, 2000 Chester Ave., Sec. Ethel Ferber

Fresno

United Jewish Welfare Fund[1] (incl. Fresno, Madera Counties). Sponsored by Jewish

Welfare Federation. Organized 1931. P.O. Box 1328 (15). Pres. Dr. H. M. Ginsburg. Exec. Dir. Rabbi David L. Greenberg.

Long Beach

United Jewish Welfare Fund.[1] Sponsored by Jewish Community Council. Organized 1934 2026 Pacific Ave. (6). Pres. Sam E. Leddell, 35 Pine St. Exec. Dir. Joshua Marcus

Los Angeles

Federation of Jewish Welfare Organizations[1,2] Organized 1911. 590 N. Vermont Ave. (4). Pres. Steve Broidy. Exec. Dir. Martin Ruderman

Los Angeles Jewish Community Council.[1] Sponsors United Jewish Welfare Fund (incl. Los Angeles and vicinity). Organized 1934. 590 N. Vermont Ave. (4). Pres. Judge Stanley Mosk. Exec. Sec. Julius Bisno

Oakland

Jewish Welfare Federation[1,2] (incl. Alameda, Berkeley, Emeryville, Hayward, Martinez, Piedmont, Pittsburg, Richmond, San Leandro, Central Contra Costa County). Organized 1945. 724—14 St. (12). Pres. Sam Clar, 131 Harrison (9). Exec. Dir. Harry J. Sapper

Petaluma

Petaluma Jewish Community Council. Organized 1939. 740 Western Ave. Pres. M. Chertok. Sec. Mrs. Al Kaufman

Sacramento

Jewish Community Council of Sacramento and Superior California. Organized 1935. 505 California Fruit Bldg. (14). Pres. Frank Goldstein, 725 K St. Exec. Dir. Charles T. Shafrock

Salinas

Monterey County Jewish Community Council. Organized 1948. 326 Park St. Pres. Leon Aidelberg. Sec. Mrs. A. Hasolkorn

San Bernardino

Jewish Community Council[1] (incl. Colton, Redlands). Organized 1936. 3512 E. St. Pres. Irving Moss. Sec. Rabbi Norman Feldheym

San Diego

United Jewish Fund[1] (incl. San Diego County). Organized 1935. 333 Plaza, Room 301 (1). Pres. Morris W. Douglas. Exec. Dir. Albert A. Hutler

Federation of Jewish Agencies. Organized 1950. 333 Plaza, Room 301 (1). Pres. Dr. A. P. Nasatir. Exec. Dir. Albert A. Hutler

San Francisco

Jewish Welfare Federation of San Francisco[1,2] Marin County and the Peninsula. Organized 1910; reorganized 1955. Pres. Lloyd W. Dinkelspiel. Exec. Directors: Hyman Kaplan; Sanford Treguboff, 230 California St. (4)

San Jose

Jewish Community Council[1,2] (incl. Santa Clara County). Organized 1936; reorganized 1950. Pres. Mrs. Lee Kaufman. Exec. Sec. Mrs. Herbert Schwalbe, 1269 Magnolia St. (26).

Stockton

Jewish Community Council[1,2] (incl. Lodi, Tracy, Sonora). Organized 1948. 134⁵ N. Madison St. (3). Pres. Max Sweet

Vallejo

Jewish Welfare Fund, Inc. Organized 1938 P.O.Box 536. Pres. Dr. Morris Zlot. Sec. Nicholas B. Cherney

Ventura

Ventura County Jewish Council[1] (incl. Camarillo, Fillmore, Ojai, Oxnard, Port Hueneme, Santa Paula, Ventura). Organized 1938. P.O.Box 908. Pres. Paul Poling, 626 South Seaward Ave. Exec. Sec. Mrs. Lee L. Lizer. Exec. Dir. Rabbi Joseph Glaser

COLORADO

Colorado Springs

Colorado Springs Allied Jewish Fund. Organized 1953. Chmn. Dr. Phineas Bernstein, 1351 Hillcrest Avenue.

Denver

Allied Jewish Community Council.[1] Sponsors Allied Jewish Campaign. Organized 1936. 201 Mining Exchange Bldg. (2). Pres. M. M. Katz, 1125 7th St. Exec. Dir. Nathan Rosenberg

CONNECTICUT

Bridgeport

Bridgeport Jewish Community Council[1] (incl. Fairfield, Stratford). Sponsors United Jewish Campaign. Organized 1936. 360 State St. Pres. Irving Rubinstein, 9 Greenfield Knolls. Exec. Dir. Mrs. Clara M. Stern

Danbury

Jewish Federation.[1] Organized 1945. 141 Deer Hill Ave. Pres. Frederick L. Adler. Treas. Sidney Sussman

Hartford

Jewish Federation.[1] Organized 1945. 74 Niles St. (5). Pres. A. I. Savin, 869 Farmington Ave. Exec. Dir. Bernard L. Gottlieb

Meriden

Jewish Welfare Fund, Inc.[1] Organized 1944. 127 E. Main St. Pres. Paul Baron. Sec. Rabbi Albert N. Troy

New Britain

New Britain Jewish Federation.[1] Organized 1936. 33 Court St. Pres. Martin H. Horwitz

New Haven

Jewish Community Council[1] (incl. Hamden, W. Haven). Sponsors Jewish Welfare Fund (1939). Organized 1928. 152 Temple St. (10). Pres. Samuel Goodwin, P.O.Box 358. Acting Exec. Dir. Benjamin N. Levy

New London

Jewish Community Council of New London. Organized 1951. Pres. Moses Savin. Sec. Hyman Wilensky, 325 State St.

Stamford

United Jewish Appeal.[1] 132 Prospect St. Chmn. Samuel Zales, Rockrimmon Rd. Exec. Sec. Mrs. Leon Kahn

Waterbury

Jewish Federation of Waterbury.[1,2] Organized 1938. 24 Grand St. (2). Pres. Howard R. Matzkin. Exec. Dir. Ralph Segalman

DELAWARE
Wilmington

Jewish Federation of Delaware[1] (Statewide) Organized 1935. 900 Washington St. Pres. Honorable Daniel L. Herrmann. Exec. Dir. Simon Krakow

DISTRICT OF COLUMBIA
Washington

Jewish Community Council of Greater Washington. Organized 1939. 1420 New York Ave., N.W.(5). Pres. Albert E. Arent. Exec. Dir. Isaac Franck

United Jewish Appeal of Greater Washington, Inc. Organized 1935. 1529—16 St., N.W.(6). Pres. Leopold V. Freudberg. Exec. Dir. Louis E. Spiegler

FLORIDA
Jacksonville

Jewish Community Council[1] (incl. Jacksonville Beach). Organized 1935. 425 Newnan St. (2). Pres. Harry Gendzier, P.O.B. 2666. Exec. Dir. Ben Stark

Miami

Greater Miami Jewish Federation[1] (incl. Dade County). Organized 1938. 420 Lincoln Road, Miami Beach (39). Pres. Aron Kanner, 242 Shoreland Bldg. Exec. Dir. Benjamin B. Rosenberg

Pensacola

Pensacola Federated Jewish Charities.[1] Organized 1942. Pres. Abe Goldstein. Sec. Mrs. C.M. Frenkel, 108 W. Brainard St.

Sarasota

United Jewish Appeal. Pres. Harry N. Waldman.

St. Petersburg

Jewish Community Council. Pres. Dr. D. L. Mendelblatt, Medical Square

Tampa

Jewish Welfare Federation of Tampa.[1] Organized 1941. 325 Hyde Park Ave. (6). Act. Pres. Edward I. Cutler. Exec. Dir. Nathan Rothberg

West Palm Beach

Federated Jewish Charities of Palm Beach County.[1] Organized 1938. 506 Malverne Road. Pres. Dr. Arthur I. Shain. Sec. Samuel A. Schutzer

GEORGIA
Atlanta

Jewish Social Service Federation of Atlanta,[1,2] Organized 1905. 41 Exchange Pl. S.E. Pres. Abe Schwartz, 710 Peachtree St., N.E. Exec. Dir. Edward M. Kahn

Jewish Welfare Fund[1] (incl. DeKalb and Fulton Counties). Organized 1936. 41 Exchange Pl. S.E. Pres. Ben J. Massell. Exec. Sec. Edward M. Kahn

Jewish Community Council, 41 Exchange Pl. S.E. Pres. Abe Goldstein, 458 Peachtree St., N.E. Exec. Dir. Edward M. Kahn

Augusta

Federation of Jewish Charities.[1] Organized 1943. Richmond County Courthouse. Chmn. Sam Silverstein, 2235 McDowell St.

Columbus

Jewish Welfare Federation.[1] Organized 1941. Pres. Sam Weil. Sec. Maurice Kravtin, c/o Novelty Shop, 1027 Broadway

Macon

Federation of Jewish Charities. Organized 1942. P.O.Box 237.

Savannah

Savannah Jewish Council,[1] Sponsors United Jewish Appeal and Federation Campaign. Organized 1943. 511 Abercorn St. Pres. Raymond Rosen, 1 Barnard St. Exec. Dir. Paul Kulick

Valdosta

Jewish Joint Communities Charity Fund of the Florida Border Region[1] (incl. Adel,

Homerville, Nashville, Quitman). Chmn. Al H. Siskind, 117 W. Hill. Send mail to: Rabbi Louis Gorod, Magnolia St.

IDAHO
Boise
Southern Idaho Jewish Welfare Fund.[1] Organized 1947. Pres. Kal Sarlat, 929 Main St. Treas. Martin Heuman

ILLINOIS
Aurora
Jewish Welfare Fund.[1] Organized 1935. 20 N. Lincoln Ave. Pres. Carl Kaufman, 115 Central Ave. Sec. Zalmon Goldsmith

Chicago
Jewish Federation[1,2] Organized 1900. 231 S. Wells St. (4). Pres. Dr. Samuel S. Hollender. Exec. Dir. Samuel A. Goldsmith

Jewish Welfare Fund.[1] Organized 1936. 231 S. Wells St. (4). Pres. Frederick W. Straus. Sec. Samuel A. Goldsmith

Decatur
Jewish Federation.[1] Pres. Irving Melnik. Sec. Mrs. Sam Loeb, 22 Edgewood Court

East St. Louis
Jewish Federation of Southern Illinois. 417 Missouri Ave.

Elgin
Jewish Welfare Chest[1] (incl. St. Charles.) Organized 1938. Pres. Warren Rubnitz, 202 S. Grove St. Treas. Irvin Berman

Joliet
Joliet Jewish Welfare Chest[1] (incl. Coal City, Dwight, Lockport, Morris, Wilmington). Organized 1938. 226 E. Clinton St. Pres. Harris Lewis. Sec. Rabbi Morris M. Hershman

Peoria
Jewish Community Council[1] (incl. Canton, E. Peoria, Morton, Pekin, Washington). Organized 1933. 245 N. Perry Ave. (3). Pres. Ben J. Weinstein. Exec. Dir. Abraham F. Citron

Rock Island—Moline
United Jewish Federation of Rock Island and Moline.[1] Organized 1938. 1804—7 Ave. Pres. Albert K. Livingston. Sec. Mrs. E. Brody

Rockford
Jewish Community Board.[1] Organized 1937. 1502 Parkview. Pres. Dr. Alfred C. Meyer. Exec. Dir. Allan Bloom

Southern Illinois
Jewish Federation of Southern Illinois[1] (incl. all of Illinois south of Carlinville). Organized 1942. 435 Missouri Ave., East St. Louis. Pres. Jacob J. Altman. Exec. Dir. Hyman H. Ruffman

Springfield
Jewish Federation[1,2] (incl. Ashland, Athens, Atlanta, Jacksonville, Lincoln, Pana, Petersburg, Pittsfield, Shelbyville, Taylorville, Winchester). Organized 1941. 730 East Vine St. Pres. Dr. J. M. Salzman. Exec. Dir. Miss Dorothy Wolfson

INDIANA
East Chicago
East Chicago Council of Jewish Welfare Funds.[1] Pres. Simon Miller, 3721 Main St., Fin. Sec. Mrs. Louise Singer, 4008 Parrish Ave.

Evansville
Jewish Community Council.[1] Organized 1936 100 Washington Ave. (13). Pres. Louis Mack, 6610 Washington Ave. Exec. Sec. Rabbi Martin B. Ryback

Fort Wayne
Fort Wayne Jewish Federation[1,2] (incl. surrounding communities). Organized 1922. 204 Strauss Bldg. (2). Pres. Sidney Hutner, 1701 N. Harrison St. Exec. Dir. Joseph Levine

Gary
Jewish Welfare Federation[1] (incl. Crown Point). Organized 1940. 568 Washington St. Pres. Harry W. Nelson, 653 Taft. Exec. Dir. Harold B. Nappan

Hammond

United Jewish Appeal of Hammond, Inc.[1] Organized 1939. Pres. Hyman Shneider. Exec. Sec. Mrs. Ulrick B. Steuer, 246 Belden Pl., Munster

Indianapolis

Jewish Welfare Federation.[1,2] Organized 1905. 615 N. Alabama St.(4). Pres. Samuel Kroot. Exec. Dir. Oscar A. Mintzer

Lafayette

Federated Jewish Charities[1] (incl. Attica, Crawfordsville). Organized 1924. Fowler Hotel. Pres. Prof. Itzak Walerstein, 1334 Sunset Lane, West Lafayette. Sec. Mrs. Sara Belman

Marion

Marion Federation of Jewish Charities (incl. Grant County). Organized 1935. Pres. Sam Fleck. Sec. Mrs. Barbara Resneck

South Bend

Jewish Community Council of St. Joseph County.[1] Organized 1946. 308 Platt Bldg.(1). Pres. Fred Baer, 218 Odd Fellows Bldg. Exec. Dir. Bernard Natkow

Jewish Welfare Fund. Organized 1937. 308 P' tt Bldg.(1) Pres. Louis Spiser. Exec. Dir. Norman Edell

Muncie

Muncie Jewish Welfare Fund.[1] Beth El Temple, 525 W. Jackson St. Pres. Ben Hertz. Sec. Rabbi Maurice Feuer

Terre Haute

Jewish Federation of Terre Haute[1] (incl. Marshall, Paris). Organized 1922. Pres. Arthur Justin, 526 Wabash Ave. Sec. Mrs. Leon L. Blum, 3200 Ohio Blvd.

IOWA

Cedar Rapids

Jewish Welfare Fund.[1] Organized 1941. Pres. Leo Smulekoff. Sec. Mrs. A. L. Smulekoff, 1826—2nd Ave. S.E.

Davenport

Jewish Charities.[1] Organized 1921. 12th & Mississippi Ave. Pres. Ben Comenitz

Des Moines

Jewish Welfare Federation.[1] Organized 1914. 507 Empire Bldg. (9). Chmn. Ellis Levitt. Exec. Dir. Sidney Speiglman

Sioux City

Jewish Federation.[1,2] Organized 1943. P.O. Box 1468. Pres. A. M. Grueskin. Exec. Dir. Oscar Littlefield

Waterloo

Waterloo Jewish Federation.[1] Organized 1941. Chmn. Robert Vidis, 221 E. 4th St.

KANSAS

Topeka

Topeka-Lawrence Jewish Federation[1] (incl. Emporia, Lawrence, St. Marys). Organized 1939. Pres. Stanley Leeser. Sec. Louis Pozez, 626 Kansas Ave.

Wichita

Mid-Kansas Jewish Welfare Federation[1] (incl. August, El Dorado, Eureka, Dodge City, Great Bend, Hosington, Hutchinson, McPherson). Organized 1935. Pres. Sheldon Beren; Exec. Dir. Edward Weil, Union National Bank Bldg.

KENTUCKY

Louisville

Conference of Jewish Organizations[1] (incl. Jeffersonville, New Albany, Ind.). Sponsors United Jewish Campaign. Organized 1934. 622 Marion E. Taylor Bldg.(2). Chmn. Norbert Friedman, 213 S. Third St. Exec. Dir. Clarence F. Judah

LOUISIANA

Alexandria

Jewish Community Council.[1] Organized 1938. P.O. Box 612. Pres. Si Sherman.

Monroe

United Jewish Charities of Northeast Louisiana.[1] Organized 1938. P.O. Box 2503. Pres. I. S. Marx. Sec.-Treas. Alan F. Sugar, Jr.

New Orleans

Jewish Federation of New Orleans.[1,2] Organized 1913. 211 Camp St.(12). Pres. Nat Friedler, 2032 Audubon St. Exec. Dir. Harry I. Barron

New Orleans Jewish Welfare Fund.[1] Organized 1933. 211 Camp St.(12). Pres. Label A. Katz. Exec. Sec. Harry I. Barron

Shreveport

Jewish Federation.[1] Organized 1941. 802 Cotton St.(6). Pres. Dr. G. J. Woolhandler. Exec. Dir. Maurice Klinger

MAINE
Bangor

Jewish Community Council[2] (incl. Old Town, Orono, and outlying towns). 28 Somerset St. Pres. Morris D. Rubin, 8 Harlow St. Exec. Dir. Milton Lincoln

Portland

Jewish Federation.[1] Sponsors United Jewish Appeal. Organized 1942. 341 Cumberland Ave. Pres. Harold J. Potter. Exec. Dir. Jules Krems

MARYLAND
Baltimore

Associated Jewish Charities.[1] Organized 1920. 319 W. Monument St.(1). Pres. Abraham Krieger, 1211 S. Conkling St. Exec. Dir. Harry Greenstein

Jewish Welfare Fund.[1] Organized 1941. 319 W. Monument St. (1). Pres. Louis J. Fox. Exec. Dir. Harry Greenstein

Cumberland

Jewish Welfare Fund of Western Maryland[1] (incl. Frostburg and Oakland, Md., Keyser and Romney, W. Va.). Organized 1939. Pres. Adolph Hirsch. Sec. Robert Kaplan, P.O.Box 327

MASSACHUSETTS
Boston

Associated Jewish Philanthropies, Inc. (central planning, coordinating and budgeting agency for 22 local health, welfare, educational and group work agencies). Organized 1895. 72 Franklin St.(10). Pres. Benjamin A. Trustman, 200 Devonshire St. (10). Exec. Dir. Sidney S. Cohen

Combined Jewish Appeal of Greater Boston, Inc.[1] (central fund raising agency for support of local, national, overseas and Israeli agencies for Boston and surrounding communities). Organized 1940. 72 Franklin St.(10). Pres. Louis P. Smith, 80 Boylston St. Exec. Dir. Sidney S. Cohen

Jewish Community Council of Metropolitan Boston. Organized 1944. 44 School St.(8). Pres. Morris Michelson, 18 Tremont St. Exec. Dir. Robert E. Segal

Brockton

United Jewish Appeal Conference[1] (incl. Rockland, Stoughton, Whitman). Organized 1939. 66 Green St. Chmn. Hyman Wexler, 76 Morse Ave. Exec. Dir. Harry Minkoff

Fall River

Jewish Community Council.[1] Sponsors Fall River United Jewish Appeal, Inc. Organized 1938. 56 No. Main St. Pres. Abraham Tulchin, 56 N. Main St. Chmn. UJA. Benjamin Green

Fitchburg

Jewish Federation of Fitchburg.[1] Organized 1939. 66 Day St. Pres. Philip Salny

Holyoke

Combined Jewish Appeal of Holyoke[1] (incl. Easthampton). Organized 1939. 378 Maple St. Pres. Isadore M. Ziff. Exec. Dir. Samuel Soifer

Lawrence

Jewish Community Council of Greater Lawrence.[1] Sponsors United Jewish Appeal. Organized 1939. 580 Haverhill St. Pres. Abe Rappaport, 117 Broadway. Exec. Dir. Mark Hazel

Leominster

Jewish Community Council.[1] Organized 1939. Pres. Seymour Tharler. Sec. Robert Breitbarth, 92 Blosson St.

Lowell

United Jewish Appeal of Lowell.[1] Organized 1940. 105 Princeton St. Co-Chmn. Jacob Sherman and Edward Ziskind. Exec. Dir. Rabbi Joseph Warren

Lynn

Jewish Community Federation of Greater Lynn[1] (incl. Lynnfield, Marblehead, Nahant, Saugus, Swampscott). Organized 1938. 45 Market St. Pres. Charles Shulman, 12 Dale St., Swampscott. Exec. Dir. Albert M. Stein

New Bedford

Jewish Welfare Federation of Greater New Bedford. Organized 1949. 388 County St. Pres. Arthur Goldys. Exec. Dir. Saul Richman

Pittsfield

Jewish Community Council[1] (incl. Dalton, Lee, Lenox, Otis, Stockbridge). Organized 1940. 235 East St. Pres. Dr. Morris Geller, 255 North St. Exec. Dir. Herman Shukovsky.

Springfield

Jewish Community Council[1] Sponsors United Jewish Welfare Fund. Organized 1938. 1160 Dickinson. Pres. Arthur Paroshinsky, 1214 Main St. Exec. Dir. Benjamin Wolf

Worcester

Jewish Federation.[1] Sponsors Jewish Welfare Fund. Organized 1946. 274 Main St. (8). Pres. Jacob Hiatt. Exec. Dir. Melvin S. Cohen

MICHIGAN

Bay City

Northeastern Michigan Jewish Welfare Federation (incl. East Tawas, Midland, West Branch). Organized 1940. Pres. Erwin I. Sherman. Sec. Mrs. Dorothy B. Sternberg, 201 Cunningham Bldg.

Benton Harbor

Jewish Community Fund of Berrien County, Inc. Organized 1942. Pres. Harold Friedman. Treas. Ivan B. Goode, RR 2, Coloma

Detroit

Jewish Welfare Federation.[1,2] Sponsors Allied Jewish Campaign. Organized 1926. Fred M. Butzel Memorial Bldg. 163 Madison (26). Pres. Judge Theodore Levin. Exec. Vice-Pres. Isidore Sobeloff

Flint

Jewish Community Council.[1] Organized 1936. 810 Sill Building (2). Pres. Louis E. Rudner, 117 W. Kearsley. Exec. Dir. Irving Antell

Grand Rapids

Jewish Community Fund of Grand Rapids.[1] Organized 1940. Pres. Samuel Kravitz. Sec. Mrs. Sam Horowitz, 910 Calvin S.E. (6)

Kalamazoo

Kalamazoo Jewish Welfare Council, Inc. Organized 1949. Pythian Building. Sec. Ben Graham

Lansing

Jewish Welfare Federation of Lansing.[1] Organized 1939. Pres. Samuel Fox. Sec. Mrs. Herbert S. Hahn, 825 N. Francis

Pontiac

Jewish Welfare Federation Council of Pontiac.[1] Organized 1936. 44 Mohawke Rd. Pres. Dr. Harry Arnkoff. Sec. Mrs. Ann Newhouse

Saginaw

Jewish Welfare Federation[1] (incl. surrounding communities). Organized 1939. Pres. Ben Goldman. Sec. Isadore Lenick, 300 Atwater St.

MINNESOTA

Duluth

Jewish Federation and Community Council.[1] Organized 1937. 416 Fidelity Bldg. (2). Pres. Dr. Samuel N. Litman. Exec. Dir. Ben Z. Lazarus

Minneapolis

Minneapolis Federation for Jewish Service.[1] Organized 1931. 512 Nicollet Bldg.—Room 718. Pres. Dr. Samuel G. Balkin. Exec. Sec. Norman B. Dockman

St. Paul

United Jewish Fund and Council.[1] Organized 1935. 311 Hamm Bldg.(2). Pres. Mack Wolf. Exec. Dir. Dan S. Rosenberg

MISSISSIPPI
Greenville

Jewish Welfare Fund of the Greenville Area[1] Organized 1952. 512 Main St. Pres. Irving Sachs. Sec. Harry Stein

Jackson

Jewish Welfare Fund, Pres. Albert Mitchell

Vicksburg

Jewish Welfare Federation.[1] Organized 1936. 1209 Cherry St. Pres. Louis L. Switzer. Sec.-Treas. Sam L. Kleisdorf

MISSOURI
Joplin

Jewish Welfare Federation, Inc.[1] (incl. surrounding communities). Organized 1938. P. O. Box 284. Pres. Samuel Rosenberg. Sec. Dexter Brown

Kansas City

Jewish Federation and Council of Greater Kansas City[1,2] (incl. Independence, Mo. & Kansas City, Kan.). Organized 1933. 20 W. 9th St. Bldg. (5). Pres. Daniel L. Brenner. Exec. Dir. Abe L. Sudran

St. Joseph

Federated Jewish Charities.[1] Organized 1916. 2208 Francis St. Pres. Morris L. Rosenthal. Exec. Sec. Mrs. S. L. Goldman

St. Louis

Jewish Federation of St. Louis[1,2] (incl. St. Louis County). Organized 1901. 1007 Washington Ave.(1). Pres. Earl Susman. Exec. Dir. Herman L. Kaplow

NEBRASKA
Lincoln

Jewish Welfare Federation[1,2] (incl. Beatrice) Organized 1931. 1209 Federal Securities Bldg.(8). Pres. Max Rosenblum. Dir. Louis B. Finkelstein

Omaha

Federation for Jewish Service.[1,2] Sponsors Jewish Welfare Fund (1930). Organized 1903. 101 N. 20 St.(2). Pres. Jack W. Marer. Exec. Dir. Paul Veret

NEW HAMPSHIRE
Manchester

Jewish Community Center.[1,2] Sponsors United Jewish Appeal. 698 Beech St. Pres. William S. Green, 291 Ray St. Exec. Dir. Ben Rothstein

NEW JERSEY
Atlantic City

Federation of Jewish Charities of Atlantic City.[1] Sponsors United Jewish Appeal of Atlantic County. Organized 1924. Medical Science Building, 101 S. Indiana Ave. Pres. Benjamin Kramer, 110 N. Virginia Ave. Exec. Dir. Irving T. Spivack

Bayonne

Jewish Community Council.[1] Sponsors United Jewish Campaign. Organized 1938. 1050 Boulevard. Pres. Jerome J. Rose. Exec. Dir. Barry Shandler

Camden

Jewish Federation of Camden County[1,2] (incl. all of Camden Community). Sponsors Allied Jewish Appeal. Organized 1922.. Marlton Pike, Delaware Township, Camden 10. Pres. Norman Heine, 126 No. Broadway (2). Exec. Dir. Bernard Dubin

Elizabeth

Eastern Union County Jewish Council[1] (incl. Roselle, Rahway, Union, Cranford, Linden). Sponsors Elizabeth United Jewish Appeal. Organized 1940. 1034 E. Jersey St. Pres. Israel Cardonsky. Exec. Dir. Louis Kousin

Hackensack

United Jewish Appeal of Hackensack, Inc.[1] Organized 1940. 211 Essex St. Pres. Sidney Goldberg. Sec. Irving Warshawsky

Jersey City

United Jewish Appeal.[1] Organized 1939. 604 Bergen Ave.(4). Chmn. George R. Milstein. Act. Exec. Sec. Harry Weinberg, 50 Glenwood Ave.

New Brunswick

Jewish Federation of New Brunswick, Highland Park & Vicinity.[1] Organized 1948. Raritan and So. Adelaide Aves., Highland Park. Pres. Abraham Halpern. Exec. Dir. Josef Perlberg

Newark

Jewish Community Council of Essex County[1] Sponsors United Jewish Appeal of Essex County (1937). Organized 1922. 32 Central Ave. Pres. Ralph Wechsler. Exec. Dir. Herman M. Pekarsky

Passaic

Jewish Community Council of Passaic — Clifton and Vicinity[1] (incl. Garfield, Lodi, Wallington). Sponsors United Jewish Campaign. Organized 1933. 184 Washington Pl. Pres. Aaron D. Endler, E-34 Barry Gardens. Exec. Dir. Max Grossman

Paterson

Jewish Community Council.[1] Sponsors United Jewish Appeal Drive. Organized 1933. 390 Broadway (1). Pres. Jack Stern. Exec. Dir. Max Stern

Perth Amboy

Jewish Community Council[1] (incl. South Amboy). Sponsors United Jewish Appeal. Organized 1938. 316 Madison Ave. Pres. Harold Levy. Exec. Dir. Martin E. Danzig

Plainfield

Jewish Community Council of the Plainfields.[1] Sponsors United Jewish Appeal. Organized 1937. 403 W. 7 St. Pres. Dr. Arthur Saitz. Exec. Dir. Aaron Allen

Trenton

Jewish Federation of Trenton.[1] Organized 1929. 18 S. Stockton St. (10). Pres. Arthur Teich. Exec. Dir. Milton A. Feinberg

NEW MEXICO
Albuquerque

Jewish Welfare Fund[1] (Albuquerque and vicinity). Organized 1938. Pres. Irwin S. Moise, Simms Bldg. Exec. Sec. Mrs. Rana Adler, 2416 Pennsylvania St., N.E.

NEW YORK
Albany

Jewish Community Council, Inc.[1] Organized 1938. 78 State St. (7). Pres. Maurice Freedman. Exec. Dir. Max Gettinger

Jewish Welfare Fund (incl. Rensselaer). 78 State St. (7). Chmn. William B. Barnet. Exec. Dir. Max Gettinger

Binghamton

United Jewish Fund of Broome County,[1] 155 Front St. Chmn. Maurice D. Sall, 19 Edgecomb Rd. Exec. Dir. Joseph M. Moseson

United Federation. Organized 1937. 155 Front St. Exec. Dir. Joseph M. Moseson

Buffalo

United Jewish Federation of Buffalo, Inc.[1,2] Organized 1903. Sidway Bldg., 775 Main St.(3). Victor Wagner, 115 Ash St. Exec. Dir. Sydney S. Abzug.

Elmira

Council of Jewish Communal Leadership.[1] Organized 1942. Federation Bldg. Pres. Lester M. Jacobs. Exec. Dir. Mortimer Greenberg

Glens Falls

Glens Falls Jewish Welfare Fund. Organized 1939. Chmn. Charles Garlen. Fin. Sec. Joseph Saidel, 206 Glen St.

Gloversville

Jewish Community Center of Fulton County[2] (incl. Johnstown). 28 E. Fulton St. Pres. Joseph Lazarus. Exec. Dir. Rubin Lefkowitz

Hudson

Jewish Welfare Fund.[1] Organized 1947. 414 Warren St. Pres. Samuel Siegel. Sec. Joel Epstein

Kingston

Jewish Community Council, Inc.[1] 265 Wall St. Pres. Herman J. Eaton. Exec. Dir. Sol J. Silverman

Middletown

United Jewish Appeal.[1] Organized 1939. c/o Middletown Hebrew Association, 13 Linden Ave. Chmn. Otto Heimbach. Exec. Sec. Mrs. Paul Cooper

Newburgh

United Jewish Charities.[1] Organized 1925. 360 Powell Avenue. Pres. Seymour Greenblatt, 1 Water St. Exec. Dir. Murray Gunner

New York City

Federation of Jewish Philanthropies of New York[1,2] (incl. Greater New York, Westchester, Queens and Nassau Counties). Organized 1917. 130 E. 59 St. (22). Pres. Salim L. Lewis. Exec. Vice-Pres. Dr. Maurice B. Hexter, Joseph Willen

United Jewish Appeal of Greater New York[1] (incl. New York City and metropolitan areas and Westchester, Queens, Suffolk and Nassau Counties). Organized 1939. 220 W. 58 St. (19). Pres. Monroe Goldwater. Exec. Vice-Pres. Henry C. Bernstein, Samuel Blitz

Brooklyn Jewish Community Council. Organized 1939. 16 Court St., Brooklyn (1). Pres. Judge Maximilian Moss. Exec. Dir. Dr. Chaim I. Essrog

Niagara Falls

Jewish Federation, Inc.[1] Organized 1935. 685 Chilton Ave. Pres. Dr. Boris A. Goldden. Exec. Dir. Mrs. May Chinkers

Port Chester

Jewish Community Council.[1] Sponsors United Jewish Campaign. Organized 1941. 258 Willett Ave. Pres. George Gruber. Exec. Dir. David Shuer

Poughkeepsie

Jewish Welfare Fund. Organized 1941. 54 N. Hamilton St. Chmn. Dr. Marc Eckstein. Exec. Dir. Julius Dorfman

Rochester

United Jewish Welfare Fund.[1] Organized 1937. 129 East Ave. (4). Pres. David J. Rosenthal. Exec. Dir. Elmer Louis

Jewish Community Council. 129 East Ave. (4). Pres. Arthur M. Lowenthal. Exec. Dir. Elmer Louis

Saranac Lake

Jewish Community Center, 13 Church St. Pres. Morris Dworski. Sec. Joseph Goldstein

Schenectady

Jewish Community Council[1] (incl. surrounding communities). Sponsors Schenectady UJA and Federated Welfare Fund. Organized 1938. 300 Germania Ave. (7). Pres. Paul Dworsky. Exec. Dir. Samuel Weingarten

Syracuse

Jewish Welfare Federation, Inc.[1] Sponsors Jewish Welfare Fund (1933). Organized 1918. 201 E. Jefferson St. (2). Pres. Lewis R. Goldner, 101 Green St. Exec. Dir. Norman Edell

Troy

Troy Jewish Community Council, Inc.[1] (incl. Green Island, Mechanicville, Waterford, Watervliet). Organized 1936. 87 First St. Pres. Samuel A. Mintz.

Utica

Jewish Community Council.[1] Sponsors United Jewish Appeal of Utica. Organized 1933. 211 Foster Bldg., 131 Genesee St. (2). Pres. Mrs. Florence Sitrin, 23 Pleasant St. Exec. Dir. James M. Senor

NORTH CAROLINA

Charlotte

Federation of Jewish Charities.[1] Organized 1940. P.O.Box 2612. Pres. Sol Levine. Sec. Ben Jaffa, Jr.

Gastonia

Jewish Welfare Fund.[1] Organized 1944. c/o Temple Emanuel, 320 South St. Pres.

Marshal Rauch, 1111 Belvedere Ave. Sec. Rabbi J. B. Cohen

Greensboro

Greensboro Jewish United Charities, Inc.[1] Pres. Milton Weinstein. Sec. Albert Jacobson, 601 N. Elm St.

Hendersonville

Jewish Welfare Fund. Organized 1946. Pres. Morris Kaplan. Sec. George D. Heyman, 312 Eighth Ave. W.

High Point

Jewish Federated Charities. Sec. Rabbi W. B. Gold

Winston-Salem

Jewish Community Council of Winston-Salem, Inc.[1] Organized 1937. 201 Oakwood Dr.(5). Pres. Robert Sosnik. Sec. Rabbi Ernst J. Conrad

NORTH DAKOTA

Fargo

Fargo Jewish Federation, (incl. Jamestown, Moorhead, Valley City, Wahpeton & Detroit Lakes, Minn.) Organized 1939. Pres. Julius Sgutt. Sec. Paul P. Feder, P.O.B. 1947

OHIO

Akron

Jewish Social Service Federation.[2] Organized 1914. Strand Theatre Bldg., 129 S. Main St.(8). Pres. Dr. Samuel E. Rosenfeld. Exec. Dir. Nathan Pinsky

Jewish Welfare Fund of Akron, Inc.[1] (incl. Barberton, Cuyahoga Falls). Organized 1935 Strand Theatre Bldg., 129 S. Main St.(8). Pres. Abe I. Ostrov. Exec. Dir. Nathan Pinsky

Canton

Canton Jewish Community Federation.[1] Organized 1935; reorganized 1955. 1528 Market Ave. N.(4). Pres. Ben M. Dreyer. Exec. Dir. Leonard Sebrans

Cincinnati

Jewish Welfare Fund.[1] Organized 1930. 1430 Central Parkway (10). Pres. Charles M. Messer. Exec. Dir. Martin M. Cohn

United Jewish Social Agencies.[1,2] Organized 1896. 1430 Central Parkway (10). Pres. Frederick Rauh. Exec. Dir. Martin M. Cohn

Federation of Jewish Agencies. Organized 1946. 1430 Central Parkway (10). Pres. Alfred J. Friedlander. Exec. Dir. Martin M. Cohn

Cleveland

Jewish Community Federation of Cleveland[1,2] Organized 1903. 1001 Huron Rd. (15). Pres. Max Simon. Exec. Dir. Henry L. Zucker

Columbus

United Jewish Fund.[1] Organized 1952. 55 E. State St. (15). Pres. Troy A. Feibel. Exec. Dir. Benjamin M. Mandelkorn

Jewish Community Council. Organized 1940 55 E. State St. (15). Pres. Joseph Zox. Exec. Dir. Benjamin M. Mandelkorn

Dayton

Jewish Community Council of Dayton[1,2] Organized 1943. Community Services Bldg., 184 Salem Ave.—Room 240(6). Pres. Louis Broock. Exec. Dir. Robert Fitterman

Lima

Federated Jewish Charities of Lima District[1] Organized 1935. P.O.Box 152. Pres. Nathan Levy, 2155 W. Market Sec. Joseph E. Berk

Steubenville

Jewish Community Council[1] (incl. Mingo Junction, Toronto). Organized 1938. 314 National Exchange Bank Bldg. Pres. Myer Pearlman. Treas. Mrs. Marcus L. Ginsburg

Toledo

Jewish Community Council[1] Organized 1936. 206 Michigan, Room 308. Pres. George S. Davidson. Exec. Dir. Marvin G. Lerner

United Jewish Fund.[1] Organized 1948.
308 Frumkin Bldg. (2). Pres. Joseph Co-
han. Exec. Dir. Alvin Bronstein

Warren

Jewish Federation[1] (incl. Niles). Organized 1938. Pres. Abe Knofsky. Sec. Maurice
I. Brown, 600 Roselawn Ave., N.E.

Youngstown

Jewish Federation of Youngstown, Inc.[1,2]
(incl. Boradman, Campbell, Girard, Lowell-
ville, Struthers). Organized 1935. 505 Gyp-
sy Lane (4). Pres. Joseph Ungar. Exec. Dir.
Stanley Engel

OKLAHOMA
Ardmore

Jewish Federation.[1] Organized 1934. Co-
Chmn. Sidney Yaffe, 23 B St., S.W. and
Max Roberson, 412 I St., S.W.

Oklahoma City

Jewish Community Council.[1] Organized
1941. 312 Commerce Exchange Bldg.(1).
Pres. Sam Singer. Exec. Dir. Julius A.
Graber

Tulsa

Tulsa Jewish Community Council.[1] Sponsors United Jewish Campaign. Organized
1938. Castle Bldg., 114 W.3 St.(1). Pres.
Ohren Smulian, 316 So. Main St.(3).
Exec. Dir. Emil Salomon

OREGON
Portland

Jewish Welfare Federation of Portland[1,2]
(incl. State of Oregon & adjacent Washington communities). Organized 1920. 1643
S.W. 12 Ave. Pres. Arthur Senders. Exec.
Sec. Milton D. Goldsmith

Oregon Jewish Welfare Fund.[1] Organized
1936. 1643 S.W. 12 Ave.(1). Pres. Jack
W. Olds. Sec. Milton D. Goldsmith

PENNSYLVANIA
Allentown

Jewish Federation of Allentown.[1] Organized

1948. 245 N. 6 St. Pres. Morris Sendero-
witz, Jr. Exec. Dir. George Feldman

Altoona

Federation of Jewish Philanthropies.[1,2]
Organized 1920. 1308—17 St. Pres. Abraham Colbus. Exec. Dir. Irving Linn

Butler

Butler Jewish Welfare Fund[1] (incl. Butler
County, Chicora, Evans City, Mars). Organized 1938. 225 E. Cunningham St.
Chmn. Saul Bernstein. Sec. Maurice Horwitz

Coatesville

Coatesville Jewish Federation. Organized
1941. Pres. Benjamin Krasnick. Sec. Benjamin Rabinowitz, 1104 Sterling St.

Easton

*Jewish Community Council of Easton and
Vicinity.*[1] Sponsors Allied Welfare Appeal
Organized 1939. 660 Ferry St. Pres. Her-
bert Toff. Exec. Sec. Jack Sher

Erie

Jewish Community Welfare Council.[1,2]
Organized 1946. 133 W. 7 St. Pres. Max A.
Wolff. Exec. Dir. Herman Roth

Harrisburg

United Jewish Community[1] (incl. Carlisle,
Lykens, Middletown, Steelton). Organized
1933. 1110 N. 3rd St. Pres. Daron S.
Feinerman. Exec. Dir. Albert Hursh

Hazleton

Jewish Community Council. Sponsors Fede-
rated Jewish Charities Drive. Laurel and
Hemlock Sts. Pres. Arnold Sukenik. Exec.
Dir. Bernard Natkow

Johnstown

Jewish Community Council.[1] Pres. Seymour
S. Silverstone, 602 U.S. Bank Bldg. Vice-
Pres. Samuel H. Cohen, 801 Viewmont
Ave.

Lancaster

United Jewish Community Council[1] (incl.
Lancaster County excepting Ephrata).

Organized 1928.   219 E. King St. Pres. Lewis Siegel. Exec. Dir. Irving Ribner

Norristown

Jewish Community Center.[1,2]   Organized 1936. Brown and Powell Sts. Pres. Paul H. Rudberg, 1502 Plymouth Blvd. Exec. Dir. Rabbi Harold M. Kamsler

Philadelphia

Federation of Jewish Agencies of Greater Philadelphia.[1,2] (Consolidation of *Allied Jewish Appeal* and *Federation of Jewish Charities).* Pres. Abraham L. Freedman, Packard Bldg.

Pittsburgh

United Jewish Federation of Pittsburgh[1,2] Organized 1912; reorganized 1955. 200 Ross St.(19). Pres. Louis Caplan. Acting Exec. Dir. James D. Bronner

Pottsville

United Jewish Charities[1] (incl. Minersville, Pine Grove, St. Clair, Schuylkill Haven). Organized 1935. 508 Mahantongo St. Sec. Rabbi Samuel Mendelowitz

Reading

Jewish Community Council.[1] Sponsors United Jewish Campaign. Organized 1935. 134 N. 5 St. Pres. Max Fisher. Exec. Sec. Harry S. Sack

Scranton

Scranton-Lackawannna Jewish Council[1] (incl. Lackawanna County). Organized 1936. 601 Jefferson Ave. Pres. M. L. Hodin. Exec. Sec. George Joel

Sharon

Shenango Valley Jewish Federation[1] (incl. Greenville, Grove City, Sharon, Sharpsville, Pa.) Organized 1940. 8 W. State St. Sec. Bernard Goldstone

Uniontown

United Jewish Federation[1] (incl. Masontown). Organized 1939. Pres. Morris Frank. Sec. Irving N. Linn, 195 Derrick

Washington

Federated Jewish Charities, 733 Washington Trust Bldg. Pres. Ben. H. Richman. Sec. A. L. Stormwind

Wilkes-Barre

Wyoming Valley Jewish Committee.[1] Sponsors United Jewish Appeal. Organized 1935. 60 South River St. Pres. Arthur Silverblatt. Sec. Louis Smith

York

United Jewish Appeal,[1] 120 E. Market St. Sec. Joseph Sperling

Jewish Organized Charities. Organized 1928. 120 E. Market St. Pres. Mose Leibowitz. Exec. Sec. Joseph Sperling

RHODE ISLAND
Providence

General Jewish Committee of Providence, Inc.[1] (incl. East Greenwich, East Providence, West Warwick, Bristol). Organized 1945. 203 Strand Bldg.(3). Pres. Henry J. Hassenfeld. Exec. Dir. Joseph Galkin

Woonsocket

Woonsocket United Jewish Appeal, Inc. Organized 1949. P.O.Box 52. Chmn. Samuel J. Medoff. Sec. Mrs. Paul Bernon

SOUTH CAROLINA
Charleston

Jewish Welfare Fund,[1] 58 St. Philip Street (10). Pres. Aaron Solomon. Exec. Sec. Nathan Shulman

SOUTH DAKOTA
Sioux Falls

Jewish Welfare Fund[1] (incl. Flandreau, S.D.; Jasper, Luverne, Pipestone, Minn.). Organized 1938.   255 Boyce Greeley Bldg. Pres. Isadore Pitts, 1805 W. 22nd St. Treas. Louis R. Hurwitz

TENNESSEE
Chattanooga

Jewish Welfare Federation.[1] Organized 1931. 511 E. 4 St. (3). Co-Chmn. I. Rosen-

blatt and Sam A. Rosen. Exec. Dir. William
L. Grossman

Knoxville

Jewish Welfare Fund.[1] Organized 1939.
Chmn. Sam A. Rosen. Fin. Sec. Milton Collins, 621. W. Vine Ave.

Memphis

Federation of Jewish Welfare Agencies[1,2]
(incl. Shelby County). Organized 1906. Ten
North Main Bldg.(3). Pres. Julius Frank.
Exec. Sec. Jack Lieberman

Jewish Welfare Fund[1] (incl. Shelby County)
Organized 1934. Ten North Main Bldg.(3).
Pres. Aaron Brenner. Exec. Dir. Jack
Lieberman

Nashville

Jewish Community Council[1] (incl. 19 communities in Middle Tennessee). Sponsors
Jewish Welfare Fund. Organized 1936.
3500 West End Ave.(5). Pres. Julian Zan-
der. Exec. Dir. Sam A. Hatow

TEXAS

Austin

Jewish Community Council of Austin.[1] Organized 1939. P.O.Box 9307. Pres. Dr. Morris Polsky. Sec. Bernard Goldberg, 2808½
Hemphiss Pk.

Corpus Christi

Corpus Christi Jewish Community Council.
Organized 1953. 750 Everhart Rd. Pres.
Edgar Hurst, 601 Wilson Tower. Exec. Dir.
Harold H. Benowitz

Dallas

Jewish Welfare Federation.[1,2] Organized
1911. 403 Southland Bldg., 209 Browder
St. Pres. Henri L. Bromberg, Jr., Mercan-
tile Bank Bldg. Exec. Dir. Jacob H. Kravitz

El Paso

Jewish Community Council[1] (incl. surround-
ing communities). Organized 1939. 401
Mills Bldg. P.O.Box 1485. Pres. Robert H.
Given. Exec. Dir. Victor Grant

Fort Worth

J wish Federation of Fort Worth.[1] Organized 1936. 308 Burk Burnett Bldg.(2). Pres.
Abe M. Herman. Exec. Dir. Eli Fahn

Galveston

*Galveston County United Jewish Welfare
Association.*[1] Organized 1936. P.O.Box 146.
Pres. Ben Levy. Sec. Mrs. Ray Freed

Houston

*Jewish Community Council of Metropolitan
Houston*[1] (incl. neighboring communities).
Sponsors United Jewish Campaign. Organ-
ized 1937. 2020 Herman Drive (4). Pres.
Gerald Rauch, P.O.Box 243. Exec. Dir.
Albert Goldstein

Port Arthur

*Federated Jewish Charities and Welfare
Funds.*[1] Organized 1936. P.O.Box 442.
Pres. Dr. Harvey H. Goldblum. Treas. Sam
Wyde

San Antonio

Jewish Social Service Federation[1,2] (incl.
Bexar County). Organized 1924. 307 Aztec
Bldg.(5). Pres. William Alter. Exec. Dir.
Louis Lieblich

Tyler

Federated Jewish Welfare Fund.[1] Organized
1938. Pres. Bernard Wolf. Sec.-Treas. Isador
Frenkle, People's National Bank Bldg.

Waco

*Jewish Welfare Council of Waco & Central
Texas.*[1] Organized 1929. P. O. Box 2214.
Pres. Dr. Walter P. Kochman. Exec. Dir.
E. Edwin Swirsley

UTAH

Salt Lake City

*United Jewish Council & Salt Lake Jewish
Welfare Fund.*[1] Organized 1936. Pres. Alvin
I. Smith. Exec. Dir. Philip M. Stillman,
72 W. 2nd South

VERMONT

Vermont Jewish Council. Pres. Rabbi Jacob
Handler, 134 Crescent St., Rutland. Sec.
Jacob Kaplan

VIRGINIA

Hampton

Jewish Community Council[1] (incl. Phoebus) Organized 1944. 18 Armistead Ave., Phoebus. Pres. Milton Familant. Sec. Rabbi Allan Mirvis

Newport News

Jewish Community Council.[1] Organized 1942 98—26th Street. Pres. Theodore H. Beskin. Exec. Dir. Charles Olshansky

Norfolk

Norfolk Jewish Community Council, Inc.[1] Organized 1937. 700 Spotswood Ave. (7). P.O. Box 6012. Pres. Bertram S. Nussbaum. Exec. Dir. Morton J. Gaba

Petersburg

United Jewish Community Fund.[1] Organized 1938. Co.-Chmn. Louis Hersh & Morton Sollod. Sec. Alex Sadle, 1651 Fairfax Ave.

Portsmouth

Jewish Community Council. 314 Court St. Exec. Sec. Mrs. Ruth Silverman Scher

Richmond

Jewish Community Council.[1] Organized 1935. 2110 Grove Ave.(20). Pres. David Arenstein. Exec. Dir. Julius Mintzer

WASHINGTON

Seattle

Federated Jewish Fund & Council[1] (incl. surrounding communities). Organized 1937. 725 Seaboard Bldg.(1). Pres. Archie S. Katz. Exec. Dir. Samuel G. Holcenberg

Spokane

Jewish Community Council[1] (incl. Spokane County). Sponsors United Jewish Fund (1936). Organized 1927. 725-726 Paulsen Bldg.(1). Pres. Rabbi William Sanderson. Sec. Robert N. Arick

Tacoma

Tacoma Federated Jewish Fund.[1] Organized 1936. Co.-Chmn. Kenneth Farber and Bailey Nieder. Sec.-Treas. Bernard Simon, 3914 N. 15th.

WEST VIRGINIA

Charleston

Federated Jewish Charities of Charleston, Inc.[1] (incl. Dunbar. Montgomery). Organized 1937. 804 Quarrier St., Rms. 407-8. Pres. Lester J. Mann. Exec. Sec. Charles Cohen

Huntington

Federated Jewish Charities.[1] Organized 1939. P.O. Box 947. Pres. M. D. Friedman. Sec.-Treas. E. Henry Broh

Wheeling

Jewish Community Council[1] (incl. Moundsville). Organized 1933. Pres. John Wiseman. Treas. Isadore Rubinstein, 30 Poplar Ave.

WISCONSIN

Green Bay

Green Bay Jewish Welfare Fund.[1] Pres. Louis J. Levitas. (P.O.B.53)

Kenosha

Jewish Welfare Fund.[1] Organized 1938. 306 Kenosha National Bank Bldg. Pres. Harry L. Marcus. Treas. Burton Lepp

Madison

Madison Jewish Welfare Fund, Inc.[1] Organized 1940. 905 University Ave. Pres. Laurence Weinstein. Exec. Dir. Kenneth Wasser

Milwaukee

Jewish Welfare Fund.[1] Organized 1938. 135 W. Wells St.(3). Pres. Harry Bloch, Jr. Exec. Dir. Melvin S. Zaret

Racine

Jewish Welfare Council.[1,2] Organized 1946. Pres. Dr. Maurice Kadim. Sec. David Hulbert, 423 Main St.

Sheboygan

Jewish Welfare of Sheboygan.[1] Organized 1927. Pres. Robert Mullen. Fin. Sec. Mrs. Abe Alpert, 2119 N. 19th St.

EDUCATION

According to a survey by the Commission for the Study of Jewish Education in the U.S.A. about 400,000 children attended Jewish schools in 1954. Of them, 52% enrolled in Sunday schools and 48% in weekday schools and Yeshivoth, i.e. 38% in the Talmud Torah and Hebrew Schools 8% in the Yeshivoth, 2% in Yiddish schools. Since 1945, the enrollment has been increasing annually; in 1952–1954 the increase was 19%, while in the period 1948–1954, the number of pupils grew from 240,000 to 400,000, an increase of 67% within seven years.

The bright picture of the remarkable growth of the attendance in the Jewish schools in recent years is, however, marred by the fact that the majority are enrolled in the Sunday schools where the classes are limited to only 1–2 hours a week, making adequate Hebrew instruction impossible.

According to an estimate of the Jewish Education Committee, no less than 75% of Jewish children in the U.S.A. received some Jewish education in 1954–55, including those who have attended Sunday schools or other schools for a very short time. The percentage of children enrolled at *one* time in all types of Jewish schools is about 50%.

A gratifying fact is the increasing number of pupils in the all-day Jewish schools, the so-called Yeshivoth, where, in addition to the curriculum of a public school, they receive an intensive Hebrew instruction of 3–4 hours daily. The enrollment of the 174 Yeshivot and elementary Yeshivoth (Yeshivoth Ketanoth) reached in 1955 the number of 35,000, while only 3,000 attended Yeshivoth in 1933. In the period 1951–1954 alone, the increase in the Yeshivoth enrollment was 50%.

Enrollment in Jewish Day-Schools in New York reached 28,000 in 1956—2,000 more than in the preceding year, i.e. an increase of 10%. Enrollment in Jewish Day-Schools in the *U.S.A.* is 47,000.

Day-Schools of all types amount to 220.

American Jews are spending 35 million dollars annually for Jewish education. The average tuition for a pupil is in the Reform Sunday schools $35 a year, in the Talmud Torahs, attended mostly by orthodox children, $75–$110, and in the Yeshivoth Ketanoth, $360–$450.

An unsolved problem is the shortage of Hebrew teachers. In the 12 seminaries with their 1,200 students, only about 120 graduate yearly, while 500 are required. The total number of Jewish teachers is about 4,200, namely 2,000 in Hebrew schools, 500 in Yeshivoth, 200 in Yiddish schools, and 1,500 in Sunday schools and as private instructors.

Of the 700 Jewish schools in New York and its suburbs approximately 60% are Orthodox, 20% Conservative, 10% Reform, and 10% Yiddish schools. Of the 407,000 Jewish children of school age in New York only 110,000 or about 27% are enrolled in a Jewish school at one time. The total number of children in New York City who received any Jewish instruction amounts to about 60%. The percentage in the suburbs of New York is about 80%. In Chicago, over 22,500 children are enrolled in the Jewish schools;

in Philadelphia and Los Angeles, 18,000 each, in Washington 7,000.

The situation of Jewish education in the U.S.A. has been considerably improved recently as far as enrollment is concerned. The curriculum, however, of Hebrew instruction and the time devoted to it in a great many of the schools, with the exception of the Yeshivoth, are being restri ~d to such an extent as to thwart the main objectives of a real Jewish education.

SCHOOLS OF HIGHER JEWISH LEARNING

Baltimore Hebrew College and Teachers School, 1201 Eutaw Place, Baltimore, Md.
Sponsored by Board of Jewish Education, 1201 Eutaw Place, Baltimore, Md. Organized 1919. Departments: High School, College and Teachers Training, Adult Education classes. A college of higher Hebrew learning to train and qualify teachers for Jewish religious schools and provide opportunities for Jewish study to adults. Pres.: Samuel J. Keiser. Dean: Dr. Louis L. Kaplan.

Brandeis University, Waltham, Mass.
The only Jewish sponsored non-sectarian university in the United States. Established 1948. Liberal arts and sciences. Graduate school. School of Arts. Pres.: Abraham S. Sacher.

College of Jewish Studies, 72 East 11 Street, Chicago, Ill.
An institute of higher Jewish learning for the training of teachers in youth and adult education. Organized by Board of Jewish Education in 1924. The College maintains the Leaf Library of some 30,000 volumes of Judaica and Hebraica. Pres.: Dr. Samuel M. Blumenfield.

Dropsie College for Hebrew and Cognate Learning, Inc. Broad and York Streets, Philadelphia, Penn.

Organized 1905. Offers post-graduate education in Hebrew learning and other branches of Semitic culture; confers degree of Doctor of Philosophy. Maintains library. Publishes *Jewish Quarterly Review.* Pres.: Dr. Abraham A. Neuman.

Gratz College, Broad and York Streets, Philadelphia, Penn.
Organized 1895. Departments: School of Observation and Practice (for children), College Course. Trains teachers and provides training for advanced Jewish studies. Authorized to grant B.A., M.A., and Ph.D. degrees. Pres.: Dr. Solomon Grayzel.

Hebrew Teachers College, 43 Hawes Street, Brookline, Mass.
Sponsored by Associated Jewish Philanthropies of Boston. Organized 1921. Departments: High School, Hebrew Teachers College. Graduate. Maintains a library. Dean: Dr. Eisig Silberschlag.

Hebrew Teachers Training School for Girls, 311 East Broadway, New York, N.Y.
Sponsored by Union of Orthodox Congregations. Organized 1924. Departments: Junior High and High School, Seminary, Post-Graduate. Deans: M. Elias, P. Churgin.

Hebrew Theological College, 3448 Douglas Blvd., Chicago, Ill.
Organized 1922. Departments: Rabbinics, Pre-Rabbinical, Teachers Institute, Graduate. Prepares young man for the Orthodox rabbinate; trains teachers and *shochtim.* Pres.: Rabbi Oscar Z. Fasman.

Hebrew Union College — Jewish Institute of Religion, Clifton Ave., Cincinnati, Ohio and 40 West 68 Street, New York, N.Y.
Sponsored by Union of American Hebrew Congregations. Organized: (1) Cincinnati School, 1875; (2) New York School, 1922. Departments: Rabbinical; Ph.D. Degree, Doctor of Hebrew Letters Degree, School of Education. Educates men for the Reform Rabbinate and for Jewish scholarship and research; trains teachers and educational directors for Jewish religious schools. Publications: *HUC-JIR Bulletin; Hebrew Union College Annual.* Pres.: Dr. Nelson Glueck.

Hebrew Union School of Education and Sacred Music (Reform), 40 West 68 Street, New York, N.Y. Trains teachers, cantors, and music directors.

Herzliah Hebrew Teachers Institute, Inc., 314 West 91 Street, New York, N.Y. Organized 1921. Departments: Hebrew Teachers Institute; Hebrew Junior High and High Schools. All courses instructed in Hebrew. Dean: Moses Feinstein.

Jewish Teachers Seminary and People's University, 154 East 70 Street, New York, N.Y. Sponsored by Labor Zionist Organization, Workmen's Circle, Sholem Aleichem Institute, Pioneer Women, and other cultural organizations. Organized 1918. Dir.: Dr. Ph. Friedman.

Jewish Theological Seminary of America, 3080 Broadway, New York, N.Y. Organized 1886; reorganized 1902. The primary purpose of the Seminary is the training of Conservative rabbis and teachers. The courses at the Teachers Institute lead to graduate degrees of Master of Hebrew Literature, Master of Religious Education, and Doctor of Religious Education. The Seminary College of Jewish Studies is a school of advanced Jewish studies, leading to a Bachelor's Degree. The Seminary School of Jewish Studies is an extension department which offers evening courses in Judaism and problems of modern Jewish living. "Eternal Light" presents weekly radio broadcasts of programs of Jewish and general religious interest. Pres.: Dr. Louis Finkelstein. Publications: *Seminary Progress. Seminary Register. You and Judaism.*

Rabbinical College of Telshe, 706-18 East 105 Street, Cleveland, Ohio. Organized 1875 in Telshe, Lithuania; since 1941 in U.S.A. Ordination for the Orthodox Rabbinate. Preparatory academy, graduate school, pedagogical institute. Pres.: Rabbi Elijah M. Bloch.

University of Judaism, 612 South Ardmore Avenue, Los Angeles, Calif. Sponsored by West Coast Branch of the Jewish Theological Seminary of America, 3080 Broadway, New York, N.Y. Organized 1947. Departments: Graduate, Teachers, Institute, Extension. Trains Jewish community leaders for religious, educational, recreational, and philanthropic institutions. Dir: Simon Greenberg.

Yeshivath Torah Vadaath and Mesivta Rabbinical Seminary, 141 South 3 Street, Brooklyn, N.Y. Organized 1918. Offers Jewish education leading to Orthodox rabbinical ordination and maintains a Hebrew Teachers Institute. Pres.: Menashe Stein.

Yeshiva University, Amsterdam Avenue and 186th Street, New York, N.Y. Foremost Orthodox institution of Jewish higher learning. Departments: (1) Rabbi Isaac Elchanan Theological Seminary. Leads to ordination. Organized 1897. (2) College of Liberal Arts and Sciences. Leads to B.A. and B.S. degrees. Organized 1928. (3) Teachers Institute. Organized 1921. (4) Bernard Revel Graduate School. Leads to degree of Doctor of Hebrew Literature. Organized 1937. (5) Harry Fischel School for Higher Jewish Studies. Leads to degree of Master of Hebr Literature. Organized 1945. (6) Insitute of Mathematics. Leads to M.S. (7) School of Education and Community Administration. Leads to degree of M.B. and Ph.D. Organized 1948. (8) Talmudical Academy (4 branches). Leads to High School diploma. Organized 1915. (9) Institute for Advanced Research in Rabbinics. Trains for leadership in education and research. Organized 1948. (10) Albert Einstein College of Medicine opened in 1955. Pres.: Dr. Samuel Belkin.

Yeshiva Beth Midrash Elion, Lakewood, N.J. Institution of higher Talmudical studies. Pres.: Rabbi Aaron Kotler.

RABBINICAL AND RELIGIOUS ORGANIZATIONS

Agudath Israel of America, Inc. (1912). 5 Beekman Street, N.Y.C. 38. Admin. Pres. Michael G. Tress; Exec. V. P. Morris Sherer.

Seeks to organize religious Jewry in the Orthodox spirit, and in that spirit to solve all problems facing Jewry in Israel and the world over. *Jewish Opinion—Dos Yiddishe Vort.*

American Conference of Certified Cantors (1953). 40 West 68 Street, N.Y.C. 23. Pres. Benjamin Grobani; Exec. Sec. Wolf Hecker. Devotes itself to the highest ideals of the cantorate, enhancing status and security of individual cantors. American Conference of Certified Cantors Bulletin.

Association of Jewish Chaplains of the Armed Forces (1946). 145 East 32 Street, N.Y.C.16. Pres.: David Max Eichorn; Sec.: Samson M. Goldstein. Seeks to promote fellowship among and advance the common interests of all chaplains in and out of the service.

Central Conference of American Rabbis(1889). 40 West 68 St., N.Y.C.23. Pres.: Barnett R. Brickner; Exec. V.P.: Sidney L. Regner. Seeks to conserve and promote Judaism and to disseminate its teachings in a liberal spirit. *CCAR Journal; Yearbook.*

Jewish Reconstructionist Foundation, Inc. (1940). 15 West 86 Street, N.Y.C. 24. Pres.: Maurice Linder; Exec.Dir.: Herbert Parzen. Dedicated to the advancement of Judaism as a religious civilization, to the upbuilding of Eretz Yisrael, and to the reconstruction of Jewish life everywhere. *The Reconstructionist.*

National Council of Young Israel (1912). 3 West 16 Street, N.Y.C. 11. Nat. Pres.: N. Honig. Seeks to educate Orthodox youth and adults through youth work and adult Jewish studies; to prove that Judaism and Americanism are compatible; to help in the development of Israel in the spirit of Torah. *Armed Forces Bulletin; Institute Bulletin; Young Israel Viewpoint; Youth Activities Program Service.*

Synagogue Council of America (1926). 110 West 42 St., N.Y.C. 36. Pres.: Abraham J. Feldman; Exec.Dir.: Marc H. Tanenbaum. Provides over-all Jewish religious representation in the United States, acting in the interest of Orthodox, Conservative, and Reform Judaism.

Union of Amerian Hebrew Congregations (1873). 838 Fifth Ave., N.Y.C. 21. Pres.: Maurice N. Eisendrath; Admin. Sec.: Louis I. Egelson. Serves and develops American Liberal Synagogues; helps to establish new congregations; promotes Jewish education; maintains the Hebrew Union College—Jewish Institute of Religion. *American Judaism; Jewish Messenger; Jewish Teacher; Synagogues Service Bulletin.*

Rabbinical Alliance of America (1944). 141 So. 3rd Street, Brooklyn 11, N.Y. Pres.: Mendel Feldman; Exec. Dir.: Chaim U. Lipshitz. Seeks to further traditional Judaism; helps support the Mesivta Rabbinical Seminary and other institutions of higher learning; seeks to maintain professional competency among members; helps to establish Jewish modern Orthodox communities throughout the United States and supply all Jewish communities with all religious functionaries. *Igud Newsletter.*

Rabbinical Assembly of America (1900). 3080 Broadway, N.Y.C. 27. Pres.: Harry Halpern; Exec. Sec.: Wolfe Kelman. Serves as the professional organization of Conservative rabbis. *Proceedings.*

Rabbinical Council of America, Inc. (1923; reorg. 1935). 331 Madison Avenue, N.Y.C. 17. Pres.: J. Sharfman; Exec. Sec.: Israel Klavan. Promotes Orthodox Judaism in the community; supports institutions for study of Torah; stimulates creation of new traditional agencies. *Marriage and Home; RCA Quarterly; Rabbinic Registry; Sermon Manual.*

Union of Ethiopian Hebrew Congregations and Rabbis (1954). 550 Fifth Ave., N.Y.C. 17. Pres.: C. M. Cragg Jr.; Sec. Treas.: James H. Geyer. Aims to be the voice of Falasha Jewry on the national level in all matters affecting the American community, to make known the many positive contributions of Falasha Jewry to Judaism, and to combat anti-Semitism among large sections of the Negro Americans. *African Israelite.*

Union of Orthodox Jewish Congregations of America (1898). 305 Broadway, N.Y.C. 7.

Pres.: Moses I. Feuerstein; Sec.: Saul Bernstein. Services the Orthodox Synagogues; serves as authoritative spokesman for Orthodox congregations in the U.S. and Canada. *Jewish Action; Jewish Life; Kashruth Directory; Hachayil; P'rakim.*

Union of Orthodox Rabbis of the United States and Canada, Inc. (1902). 132 Nassau St., N.Y.C. 38. Chmn.: Eliezer Silver; Exec. Dir. Meyer Cohen. Seeks to foster traditional Judaism, promote higher Torah learning; strengthen authority of Orthodox Rabbinate, and disseminate knowledge of traditional Jewish rites and practices among the Jewish masses.

Union of Sephardic Congregations, Inc. (1929) 99 Central Park West, N.Y.C. 23. Pres.: David de Sola Pool; Sec.: Simon S. Nessim. Promotes the religious interests of Sephardic Jews.

United Synagogue of Ameria (1913). 3080 Broadway, N.Y.C. 27. Pres.: Charles Rosengarten; Exec. Dir.: Bernard Segal. Services affiliated Conservative congregations and their auxiliaries in all their religious, educational, cultural, and administrative needs. *Adult Education Newsletter; Synagogue School; United Synagogue Review.*

World Union for Progressive Judaism, U.S. Office (1926). 5017 Washington Blvd., St. Louis 8, Mo. Am. Dir.: Ferdinand M. Isserman. Promotes and coordinates world-wide efforts on behalf of Liberal Judaism. *Bulletin.*

NATIONAL JEWISH EDUCATIONAL AGENCIES

American Association for Jewish Education, 1776 Broadway, New York, N.Y.
Organized 1939. Affiliated: 40 Bureaus. It strives to promote Jewish education in the United States and Canada. It offers services in the fields of educational research and community organization for Jewish education. Sponsors the National Board of License and the National Council on Jewish Audio-Visual Materials.

PUBLICATIONS: *Jewish Education Newsletter* (bi-monthly), *Pedagogic Reporter* (bi-monthly), *Trends and Developments* (annually), *Research and service bulletins* (occasionally), *Jewish Education Register and Directory* (biennially). Pres.: Harry Starr. Exec. Dir.: Judah Pilch.

B'nai B'rith Hillel Foundations Inc., 165 West 46th Street, New York, N.Y.
Sponsored by B'nai B'rith. Organized 1923. Maintains 71 foundations and 147 counselorships at colleges and universities in the U.S.A. and Canada. Conducts religious and cultural activities.

PUBLICATIONS: *Hillel Notes. Hillel Newsletter. Hillel Little Book Series.* National Dir.: Rabbi Arthur J. Lelyveld. Program Dir.: Rabbi Alfred Jospe.

Commission on Jewish Education of the Union of American Hebrew Congregations (Reform), 34 West 6th Street, Cincinnati 2, Ohio.
Sponsored by Union of American Hebrew Congregations and the Central Conference of American Rabbis. Organized 1923. Affiliated: 475 schools (mostly Sunday schools), with approximately 100,000 pupils. Formulates objectives of Jewish religious education in Liberal schools; prepares curricula; publishes textbooks.

PUBLICATIONS: *The Jewish Teacher* (quarterly) *The Youth Leader* (quarterly), *American Judaism* (monthly). Chairman of Commission: Dr. Solomon B. Freehof. Dir. of Educ.: Dr. Emanuel Gamoran.

Hebrew Teachers Federation of America (Histadruth Ha-Morim), 165 West 46 Street, New York, N.Y.
Reorganized 1944. Affiliated: 30 groups and associations. Program: To intensify the study of the Hebrew language and literature in the Jewish schools in America. To improve the professional status of Hebrew teachers. Chairman: Shemeon Pollack. Exec. Dir.: Zevi Glatstein.

Jewish Folk Schools of the Labor Zionist Movement, 45 East 17th Street, New York, N.Y. Organized 1910. Organizes and supervises Jewish schools where both Hebrew and Yiddish are taught. Strives to educate Jewish youth in the spirit of Jewish tradition, love of Israel, and identification with labor. Maintains over 50 afternoon elementary schools, of which 10 have secondary developments, as well as 3 all-day elementary schools. Publishes textbooks for its schools.

PUBLICATIONS: *Yiddish Dertziung. Yomtov Bletter.* Dir.: L. Rubinstein.

Mizrachi National Education Committee, 1133 Broadway, New York, N.Y. Organized 1939. Affiliated: 79 schools. Program: Organizes and supervises Yeshivot and Talmud Torahs; prepares and trains teachers. Publishes textbooks and educational literature.

PUBLICATIONS: *Gilyonenu* (monthly). *Vaad Bulletin* (monthly). Pres.: Charles Gold; Exec. Dir.: Isidor Margolis.

National Council of Beth Jacob Schools, Inc., 150 Nassau Street, New York, N.Y. Organized 1942. Affiliated: 17 all-day schools, 1 evening high school, with 4,622 pupils. Program: Jewish education for girls in the spirit of the Torah.

PUBLICATIONS: *Beth Jacob Journal* (quarterly). Pres.: I. Rosenweig. Dir.: D. Ullmann.

National Council for Jewish Education, 1776 Broadway, New York, N.Y. Founded 1926. Represents the Jewish education profession. Serves as a clearing house and exchange with Israel for cultural and religious materials and for the promotion of Hebrew education (IGUD) and the Jerusalem Examination. Sponsors the National Board of License.

PUBLICATIONS: *Jewish Education. Shevilei Hahinuch* (quarterly). Pres.: David Rudawsky.

Sholem Aleichem Folks Institute, Inc., 22 East 17th Street, New York, N.Y.

Organized 1918. Affiliated: 17 schools, 1,020 pupils. Maintains afternoon schools (5 days per week), one all-day school, kindergartens, a high school, and adult courses. The school program includes mainly the study of Yiddish language and literature and also Hebrew and the Bible and Jewish history and tradition.

PUBLICATIONS: *Kinder Journal* (in Yiddish, monthly). *Sholem Aleichem Bulletin* (in Yiddish and English, monthly). *Jubilee Book.* Pres.: Dr. Solomon Simon. Exec. Dir.: Saul Goodman.

Torah Umesorah (National Society of Hebrew Day Schools), 132 Nassau Street, New York, N.Y. Organized 1944. Affiliated: 54 schools, with 6,000 pupils. Program: Founding and promoting of Yeshivoth.

PUBLICATIONS: *Olomeinu—Our World* (children's monthly). *The Jewish Parent. News Notes* (bi-monthly). Pres.: Samuel C. Feurstein. Exec. Dir.: Dr. Joseph Kaminetsky.

United Synagogue Commission on Jewish Education, 3080 Broadway, New York, N.Y. Affiliated: about 400 Conservative Congregational schools. Program: Promotes higher educational standards in the schools conducted by the Conservative congregations in America.

PUBLICATIONS: *The Synagogue School* (quarterly). Chairman: Rabbi Elias Charry. Exec. Dir.: Dr. Abraham E. Millgram.

The Workmen's Circle—Educational Department, 175 East Broadway, New York, N.Y. Organized 1918. Affiliated: 92 schools, 5,000 pupils. Spreads Jewish culture and education, mainly in Yiddish, among Workmen's Circle membership.

PUBLICATIONS: *Culture and Education* (Yiddish monthly). *Kinder Zeitung* (Yiddish, children's monthly). Educ. Dir.: Zalman Yefroykin.

JEWISH PERIODICALS

ALABAMA

Jewish Monitor (1948). P.O.B. 9, Bessemer. Rabbi Joseph S. Gallinger.

ARIZONA

Arizona Post. 121 East 29 St., Tucson. Fortnightly.

Phoenix Jewish News (1947). 528 W. Granada Rd., Phoenix. Joseph Stocker. Bi-monthly.

CALIFORNIA

B'nai B'rith Messenger (1897). 739 S. Hope St., Los Angeles 17. Davis Weissman. Weekly.

California Jewish Voice (1922). 406 S. Main St., Los Angeles, 13. B. Gach. Weekly.

Heritage–Jewish Family Weekly. 5322 Wilshire Blvd., Los Angeles, 36. Weekly.

Jewish Community Bulletin and Emanu-El (1946). 40 First St., San Francisco 5. Eugene B. Block. Weekly.

Jewish Star (1949). 1119 Mission St., San Francisco 3. Alfred Berger. Monthly.

Literarishe Heftn (1946). 10143 Mountair Ave., Tujunga. Boris Dimondstein. Quarterly; Yiddish.

Southwestern Jewish Press (1915). 333 Plaza Bldg., San Diego 1. Maxwell Kaufman. Fortnightly.

Valley Jewish News (1942). 5730 Lankershim Blvd., North Hollywood. Jess Nathan. Weekly.

COLORADO

Intermountain Jewish News (1912). Mining Exchange Bldg., Denver 2. Robert S. Gamzey. Weekly.

CONNECTICUT

Connecticut Jewish Ledger Publications, Inc. (1929). 179 Allyn St. Abraham J. Feldman. Weekly.

Jewish Argus (1935). 62 Cannon St., Bridgeport 3. Isidore Goldman. Monthly.

DELAWARE

Jewish Voice (1931). 604 W. 38 St., Wilmington 2. Simon R. Krinsky. Monthly.

DISTRICT OF COLUMBIA

American Jewish Journal (1944). 996 National Press Bldg., Washington 4. David Mondzac. Quarterly.

Jewish Veteran (1940). 1712 New Hampshire Ave., N.W. Washington 1. Warren Adler. Monthly.

National Jewish Ledger (1930). 836 Tower Building, 14 & K Sts., N.W. Washington 5. K.C. Gerber. Weekly.

National Jewish Monthly (1886). 1003 K St., N.W. Washington 1. Edward E. Grusd. Monthly.

FLORIDA

American Jewish Press. P.O.B. 2973, Miami.

Florida Jewish Journal. P.O.B. 190 St. Petersburg 2. Monthly.

Jewish Floridian (1927). 120 N.E. Sixth St., Miami 18. Fred K. Shochet. Weekly.

Our Voice (1932). 506 Malverne Rd., West Palm Beach. Samuel A. Schutzer. Fortnightly.

Southern Jewish Weekly (1924). P.O. Box 5588. Jacksonville 7. Isadore Moscovitz. Weekly.

GEORGIA

Southern Israelite Newspaper and Magazine (1925). 390 Courtland St., N.E. Atlanta 3. Adolph Rosenberg. Weekly and bi monthly.

ILLINOIS

Chicago Israelite (1884). 116 S. Michigan Ave., Chicago 3.

Chicago Jewish Forum (1942). 82 W. Washington St., Chicago 2. Benjamin Weintroub. Quarterly.

Hapardes. 1220 Independence Blvd. Chicago 23. Hebrew.

Jewish Way-Undzer Weg (1946). 3159 W. Roosevelt Rd., Chicago 12. Nathan Kravitz, Louis Shoicher. Monthly. English-Yiddish.

National Jewish Post. 130 N. Wells St., Chicago 6.

Sentinel (1911). 1702 S. Halsted St., Chicago 8. J. I. Fishbein. Weekly.

INDIANA

Indiana Jewish Chronicle (1921). 152 N. Alabama St., Indianapolis 4. Morris Strauss. Weekly.

Jewish Bulletin (1944). 2947 Ruckle St., Indianapolis 5. Samuel Deutsch. Bi-weekly.

National Jewish Post—Indiana Edn. (1935). Box 1633, Indianapolis 6. Gabriel M. Cohen, George Voss. Weekly.

IOWA

National Jewish Post (1952). 525 14 St., Sioux City. Weekly.

KENTUCKY

National Jewish Post—Kentucky Edn. (1931) 423 Citizens Bldg., Louisville 2. Gabriel M. Cohen. Weekly.

LOUISIANA

Jewish Ledger (1893). 608 Dryades St., New Orleans 12. Abraham Slabot. Weekly.

MARYLAND

Jewish Times (1919). 111 N. Charles St., Baltimore 1. Bert F. Kline. Weekly.

MASSACHUSETTS

Jewish Advocate (1902). 251 Causeway St., Boston 14. Alexander Brin, Joseph G. Weisberg. Weekly.

Jewish Civic Leader (1923). 11 Norwich St., Worcester 8. Irving I. Coven. Weekly.

Jewish Times (1915). 318 Harvard St., Brookline 46. Michael Shulman.

Jewish Weekly News (1945). 38 Hampden St., Springfield 3. Leslie B. Kahn. Weekly.

North Shore Jewish Press (1951). 31 Exchange St., Lynn.

MICHIGAN

Detroit Jewish News (incoporating *Detroit Jewish Chronicle*) (1941). 17100 West Seven Mile Rd., Detroit 35. Philip Slomovitz. Weekly.

Hebrew Observer. 416 Transportation Bldg., Grand Rapids 2.

MINNESOTA

American Jewish World — Minneapolis-St. Paul (1912). 735 Palace Bldg., 40 S. 4 St., Minneapolis 1; 709 Pioneer Bldg., St. Paul 1. L. H. Frisch. Weekly.

St. Paul Jewish News (1953). 2055 Jefferson Ave., St. Paul 5. Harry L. Kraines, Freida Kraines.

MISSOURI

Kansas City Jewish Chronicle (1920). 306 Ridge Bldg., 913 Main St., Kansas City 5. Victor Slone. Weekly.

National Jewish Post—Missouri Edn. (1948). 722 Chestnut St., St. Louis 1. Gabriel M. Cohen. Weekly.

St. Louis Jewish Tribune (1943). 722 Chestnut St., St. Louis 1. Herman Schachter. Monthly.

NEBRASKA

Jewish Press (1921). 101 No. 20 St., Omaha 2. Harry Halpert. Weekly.

NEW JERSEY

Jewish Bulletin. 90 Ivy Lane, Englewood. Bi-weekly.

Jewish News (1947). 24 Commerce St., Newark 2. Harry Weingast. Weekly.

Jewish Record (1939). 200 Central Bldg., Atlantic City. Sara W. Singer. Weekly.

Jewish Standard (1931). 924 Bergen Ave., Jersey City 6. Morris J. Janoff. Weekly.

Jewish Times. 1005 "C" St., Belmar. Weekly.

NEW YORK

Buffalo Jewish Review (1912). 35 Pearl St., Buffalo 2. Elias R. Jacobs. Weekly.

Jewish Chronicle (1941). 639 S. State St., Syracuse 3.

Jewish Ledger (1924). 32 South Ave., Rochester 4. Donald Wolin. Weekly.

Long Island Jewish Press. 149 N. Franklin St., Hempstead. Monthly.

Westchester Jewish Tribune (1950). 113 So. 3 Ave., Mount Vernon. Eugene J. Lang. Monthly.

NEW YORK CITY

Adult Jewish Leadership. 1776 Broadway, 19. Monthly.

Alliance Voice—Farband Shtimme. See *Farband Newsletter.*

American Academy for Jewish Research, Inc., Proceedings of (1930). 3080 Broadway 27. A. S. Halkin. Annual: English-Hebrew.

American Hebrew (1879). 48 W. 48 St. 19. Leo Glassman. Weekly.

American Jewish Home. 3920 Laurel Ave., Brooklyn 24. Monthly.

American Jewish Press. 96 Warren St., New York 7.

American Jewish Review. 251 W. 42 St., 17. Monthly.

American Jewish Year Book (1899). 386 Fourth Ave. 16. Morris Fine. Annual.

American Judaism (formerly *Liberal Judaism, Jewish Layman, Topics and Trends*) (1951). 838 Fifth Ave. 21. Samuel Silver. Quarterly.

American Zionist (formerly *New Palestine*) (1921). 145 E. 32 St., 16, Ernest E. Barbarash. Monthly.

Anti-Defamation League Bulletin. 212 Fifth Ave., 16. Bernard Simon. Monthly.

Assembly Bulletin. 1776 Broadway, 19. Monthly.

Aufbau — Reconstruction (1934). 2700 Broadway, 25. Manfred George. Weekly; German-English.

Bitzaron (1939). 1141 Broadway 1. Maurice E. Chernowitz. Monthly; Hebrew.

Bronx Jewish Review. 244 W. 65 St., 23. Weekly.

Brooklyn Jewish Center Review (1933). 667 Eastern Parkway, Brooklyn 13. Joseph Kaye. 32 South Ave., Monthly.

Bulletin fun Freien Yiddishen Club (1949). 19 W. 27. St.. Quarterly.

Central Conference of American Rabbis Yearbook. 40 W. 68 St., 23. Annual.

Central Conference of American Rabbis Journal. 40 W. 68 St., 23. Quarterly.

Commentary (1945). 34 W. 33 St., 1. Eliot E. Cohen. Monthly.

Congress Record. 15 E. 84 St., 28. Monthly.

Congress Weekly (1935). 15 E. 84 St., 28. Samuel Caplan, Herbert Poster. Weekly.

Current Events in Jewish Life. 15 E. 84 St., 28. Quarterly; English-Yiddish.

The Day—Jewish Journal (1914). 183 E. Broadway, 2. Solomon Dingol, David L. Meckler. Daily; Yiddish.

Der Yid (1953). 157 E. Broadway, 2. A. Rosmarin. Weekly.

Economic Horizons (1949). 16 E. 66 St., 21. Ernest Aschner. Monthly; English-Spanish.

Egyeii Elet — Society Life (1921). 1265 Walton Ave., Bronx 52. Charles Brown. Weekly. English-Hungarian.

Facts and Opinions (1941). 25 E. 78 St., 21. Joseph Kissman. Monthly; Yiddish.

Farband Newsletter (1912). 45 E. 17 St., 3. Louis Segal. Quarterly; Yiddish-English.

Farband Stimme. 45 E. 17 St., 3. Mayer L. Brown. Yiddish.

Folk un Velt (1952). 15 E. 84 St., 28. J. Glattstein. Monthly; Yiddish.

Freeland (1946). 310 W. 86 St., 24. J. N. Steinberg. Monthly.

Freie Arbeiter Stimme (1890). 33 Union Sq. 3. Solo Linder. Fortnightly; Yiddish.

Furrows (1942). 45 E. 17 St. 3. Steve Jay. Monthly.

Gerechtikeit (1918). 1710 Broadway. S. A. Farber. Monthly; Yiddish.

Growing Up. 201 E. 57 St., 22.

Haboneh (1935). 45 E. 17 St. 3. Maier Deshell. Monthly.

Hadar (1938). 276 W. 43 St. 36. Pinchas Aryeh Stopler. Bi-monthly; English-Yiddish.

Hadassah Headlines. 1819 Broadway, 23. Monthly.

Hadassah Newsletter (1920). 65 E. 52 St., 22. Jesse Zel Lurie. Monthly.

Hadoar Hebrew Weekly (1921). 120 W. 16 St. 11. M. Maisels. Weekly; Hebrew.

Hadoar Lanoar (1926). 120 W. 16 11. Simchah Rubinstein. Fortnightly; Hebrew.

Harofe Haivri—Hebrew Medical Journal (1927). 983 Park Ave., 28. Moses Einhorn. Semi-annual; Hebrew-English.

Headline Parade (1945). 1776 Broadway 19. Samuel J. Citron. Quarterly.

Hechalutz. 80 E. 11 St., 3. English-Hebrew.

Histadrut Foto-News (1948). 33 E. 67 St. 21. Nahum Guttman. Monthly.

Historia Judaica (1938). 40 W. 68 St. 23. Guido Kisch. Semi-annual.

Horeb (1933). Yeshiva University, 186 St. and Amsterdam Ave., 33. Abraham Weiss. Annual; Hebrew.

In Jewish Bookland (1945). 145 E. 32 St. 16. Solomon Grayzel. Monthly.

In the Common Cause. 9 E. 38 St., 16. Quarterly.

Israel Digest (1949). 11 E. 70 St., 21. Joshua H. Justman. Weekly; English-Yiddish.

Israel Economic Horizons. See *Economic Horizon.*

Israel Horizons. 38 W. 88 St., 24. Monthly.

Israel—Life and Letters (1945). 267 W. 71 St., 23. Itzhak Norman. Monthly.

Israel Speaks (1947; re-org. 1948). 34 Park Row 38. Paul Orentlicher. Fortnightly.

Israel y America Latina. 16 E. 66 St., 21. Monthly; Spanish.

JEC Bulletin (1943). 1776 Broadway 19. Louis L. Ruffman and Morris Epstein. Bi-monthly.

Jewish Action. 305 Broadway, 7. Monthly.

Jewish American. 183 E. Broadway, 2. Weekly; Yiddish.

Jewish Audio-Visual Review (1951). 1776 Broadway, 19. Samuel D. Freeman. Annual.

Jewish Book Annual (1942). 145 E. 32 St., 16. S. I. Liptzin.Annual; English-Hebrew-Yiddish.

Jewish Braille Review (1931). 101 W. 55 St., 19. Jacob Freid. Monthly; English Braille.

Jewish Center Program Aids (1945). 145 E. 32 St., 16. Miriam R. Ephraim. Quarterly.

Jewish Center Worker (1939). 145 E. 32 St., 16.

Jewish Community (1947). 165 W. 46 St. 11 Louis Stein. Quarterly.

Jewish Daily Forward (1897). 175 E. Broadway, 2. Harry Rogoff. Daily; Yiddish. (Eastern edn., Baltimore; Western edn., Chicago).

Jewish Daily News Bulletin (1917). 231 W. 58 St. 19. Boris Smolar. Daily.

Jewish Daily Yiddish Bulletin (1922). 660 First Ave., 16. Aleph Katz. Daily; Yiddish.

Jewish Education Committee Bulletin (1940) 1776 Broadway, 19. Louis L. Ruffman. Quarterly.

Jewish Education Newsletter. 1776 Broadway, 19.

Jewish Education Register and Directory (1951). 1776 Broadway 19. Judah Pilch.

Jewish Examiner (1929). 427 Flatbush Ave., Ext., Brooklyn 1. Louis D. Gross. Weekly.

Jewish Farmer (1908). 386 Fourth Ave. 16. Benjamin Miller. Monthly; English-Yiddish.

Jewish Forum (1917). 305 Broadway 7. Isaac Rosengarten. Monthly.

Jewish Frontier (1934). 45 E. 17 St. 3. Marie Syrkin. Monthly.

Jewish Horizon (1938). 80 Fifth Ave., 11. William Herskowitz. Monthly.

Jewish Labor Bund Bulletin. 25 E. 78 St., 21. Monthly.

Jewish Life (1946). 22 E. 17 St. 3. Louis Harap. Monthly.

Jewish Life [Orthodox] (1946). 305 Broadway 7. Saul Bernstein. Bi-monthly.

Jewish Mail (1950). 43 Canal St. 2.

Jewish Newsletter (1948). P. O. Box 117. Washington Bridge Station 33. William Zuckerman. Fortnightly.

Jewish Parent (1948). 5 Beekman St. 38. Joseph Kaminetsky. Bi-monthly.

Jewish Social Service Quarterly (1924). 1841 Broadway, 23. Herbert H. Aptekar. Quarterly.

Jewish Social Studies (1939). 1841 Broadway 23. Salo W. Baron, Koppel S. Pinson, Abraham G. Duker. Quarterly.

Jewish Spectator (1935). 110 W. 40 St., 18. Trude Weiss-Rosmarin. Monthly.

Jewish Teacher (1932). 838 Fifth Ave. 21. Emanuel Gamoran. Quarterly.

Jewish Telegraph Agency, Inc. (1917). 660 First Ave., 16. Boris Smolar. Daily.

Jewish Veteran (1930). 50 W. 77 St. 24. Martin Freyer. Monthly.

Jewish Way (1939). 870 Riverside Dr., 32. Alice Oppenheimer. Monthly; German-English.

Jewish Weekly News Digest (1935). 231 W. 58 St. 19. Boris Smolar. Weekly.

Judaism (1952). 15 E. 84 St., 28. Robert Gordis, Theodore Friedman. Quarterly.

Jewish World (1954). 276 W. 43 St., 36. S. Rosenberg. Monthly.

Kinder Journal (1920). 22 E. 17 St. 3. Lipa Lehrer. Bi-monthly. Yiddish.

Kinder Zeitung (1935). 175 E. Broadway, 2. Z. Yefroikin. 5 times a year; Yiddish.

Kosher Butchers Voice (1932). 935 Eastern Parkway, Brooklyn 13. Arnold Posy. Weekly; Yiddish-English.

Kosher Food Guide (1935). 105 Hudson St. 13. George Goldstein. Quarterly.

Kultur Un Dertziung—Culture and Education (1930). 175 E. Broadway, 2. N. Chanin, Z. Yefroikin. 7 times a year; Yiddish.

Labor in Israel Newsletter. 33 E. 67 St.,, 9. Monthly.

Labor Zionist. 45 E. 17 St., 3. Monthly.

Menorah Journal (1915). 20 E. 69 St. 21. Henry Hurwitz. Quarterly.

Midstream (1955). 250 W. 57 St., 19. Shlomo Katz. Quarterly.

Der Mizrachi Weg (1935). 80 Fifth Ave. 11. Aaron Pechenick. Bi-monthly. Yiddish.

Morgen Freiheit (1922). P.O. Box 42. 35 E. 12 St. 3. Paul Novick. Daily; Yiddish.

Musaf Lakore Hatzair (1945). 120 W. 16 St. Chaim Leaf. Fortnightly; Hebrew.

National Jewish Post — Nat. Edn. (1946). 110 W. 40 St. Gabriel M. Cohen. Weekly.

News from World Jewish Congress. 15 E. 84 St., 28.

Newsletter—International Council of Jewish Women. 130 E. 59 St., 22.

New Yorker Wochenblat (1935). 41 Union Sq. 3. Isaac Liebman. Weekly; Yiddish.

Oholim (1942). 175 E. Broadway, 2. Samuel H. Setzer. Bi-monthly; Hebrew.

Oifn Shvel (1941). 310 W. 86 St., 24. N. Steinberg. Monthly; Yiddish.

Olomeinu—Our World (1945). 5 Beekman St., 38. Bernhard Merling. Monthly; English-Hebrew.

Opinion (1931). 17 E. 42 St. 17. Earle D. Marks. Bi-monthly.

Or Hamizrach (1954). 1133 Broadway, 10. Aaron Pechenik. Quarterly.

Palestine and Zionism (1946). 250 W. 57 St., 19. Sylvia W. Landress. Bi-monthly.

Pedagogic Reporter. 1776 Broadway, 19. Zalmen Slesinger. Bi-monthly.

Pedagogisher Bulletin (1941). 1776 Broadway 19. Yidel Mark. Bi-monthly; Yiddish.

Pioneer Woman (1926). 29 E. 22 St. 10. Helen Atkin. Monthly; English-Yiddish.

Proceedings of the American Academy for Jewish Research. 3080 Broadway, 27. Annual; English-Hebrew.

Proceedings of the Rabbinical Assembly of America. 3080 Broadway, 27. Annual.

Program in Action (1950). 1776 Broadway 19. Judah Pilch. Bi-monthly.

Publication of the American Jewish Historical Society (1893). 3083 Broadway, 27. Isidore S. Meyer. Quarterly.

Queens Jewish News (1949). 129 W. 52 St. 19. Eugene J. Lang. Monthly.

Rabbinical Council Record. 331 Madison Ave., 17. Quarterly.

Reconstructionist (1936). 15 W. 86 St., 24. Eugene Kohn. Fortnightly.

Sefer Hashana. 165 W. 46 St., 19. Hebrew.

Sephardic Home News (1946). 2265 Cropsey Ave., Brooklyn, 14. Jack Baker.

Seminary Progress. N.E. Corner, Broadway and 122 St., 27. Monthly.

Seven Arts Feature Syndicate (1922). 660 First Ave., New York 16. Nathan Ziprin.

Sheviley Hahinuch (1939). 1776 Broadway 19. Zvi Scharfstein. Quarterly; Hebrew.

Student Zionist. 342 Madison Ave., 17. Quarterly.

Synagogue Light (1933). 12 Dutch St., 30. Joseph Hager. Monthly.

Synagogue School (1942). 3080 Broadway 27. Abraham E. Millgram. Quarterly.

Talpioth (1943). 186 St. and Amsterdam Ave. 33. Samuel K. Mirsky. Quarterly; Hebrew.

Technion Monthly (1940; re-org. 1949). 1000 Fifth Ave. 28. Sydney Gross. Monthly.

Technion Year Book. 1000 Fifth Ave., 28.

Tel Hai. 675 Eighth Ave., 18. Fortnightly.

Undzer Veg (1927). 305 Broadway, 7. Charles Freilich. Paul L. Goldman. Fortnightly; Yiddish.

United Israel Bulletin (1944). 507 Fifth Ave. 17. David Horowitz. Bi-monthly.

Unzer Stimme—Our Voice (1937). 175 Fifth Ave., 10. William Katz. Semi-annual; Yiddish-English.

Unzer Tsait (1940). 25 E. 78 St., 21. Emanuel Scherer. Monthly; Yiddish.

Der Wecker (1921). 175 E. Broadway 2. I. Levin-Shatzkes. Fortnightly; Yiddish.

Di Velt. 255 W. 34 St., 1. Monthly; Yiddish.

Veiter (1952). 65 University Place. Moshe Steingart. Bi-monthly.

Workmen's Circle Call (1937). 175 E. Broadway, 2. Nathan Chanin. Bi-monthly.

World Over (1940). 1776 Broadway, 19. Ezekiel Schloss, Morris Epstein. Fortnightly.

Dos Wort Library (1934). 175 E. Broadway 2. Samuel H. Setzer. Monthly; Yiddish.

Yedies Fun Yivo—News of the Yivo (1943). 1048 Fifth Ave., 28. Shlomo Noble. Quarterly; Yiddish-English.

Dos Yiddishe Folk (1909). 145 E. 32 St. 16. Simon Bernstein. Monthly; Yiddish.

Yiddisher Folklor (1954). 1048 Fifth Ave., 28. Chaneh Gordon-Mlotek. Yiddish.

Yiddisher Kemfer (1905). 45 E. 17 St. 3. Jacob Gladstone, Baruch Zuckerman, B. Sherman. Weekly; Yiddish.

Yiddishe Kultur (1938). 189 Second Ave. 3. Nachman Mayzel. Monthly; Yiddish.

Yiddishe Kultur Inyonim. 15 E. 84 St., 28. Quarterly; English-Yiddish.

Yiddishe Shprakh (1941). 1048 Fifth Ave., Yudl Mark. Quarterly; Yiddish.

Dos Yiddishe Vort. 5 Beekman St., 38. Monthly; Yiddish.

Yivo Annual of Jewish Social Science (1946). 1048 Fifth Ave., 28. Mordecai Kosover. Annual.

Yivo Bleter (1931). 1048 Fifth Ave., 28. M. Kosover, L. Lehrer, S. Noble. Annual; Yiddish.

Young Guard (formerly *Youth and Nation*) (1934). 38 W. 88 St. 24. Ruth Reis. Bi-Monthly. English-Hebrew.

Young Israel Viewpoint (1912). 3 W. 16 St. 11. Norman Cohen. Bi-monthly.

Young Judaean (1910). 16 E. 50 St., 22. Millicent Rubenstein. Monthly.

Zionist Information Service (1948). 145 E. Millicent Rubenstein. Monthly.

Zukunft (1892). 25 E. 78 St. Mng. Ed. N.B. Minkoff. Monthly; Yiddish.

NORTH CAROLINA

American Jewish Times-Outlook (1934); reorg. 1950). 603 Southeastern Bldg., Greensboro. Chester A. Brown. Monthly.

Carolina Israelite (1940). P.O. Box 2505, 223 Builders Bldg., Charlotte 1. Harry L. Golden. Monthly.

OHIO

American Israelite (1854). 626 Broadway, Cincinnati 2. Henry C. Segal. Weekly.

American Jewish Archives (1948). 3101 Clifton Ave., Cincinnati 20. Jacob R. Marcus. Semi-annual.

Every Friday (1927). 1313 American Bldg., Cincinnati 2. Samuel M. Schmidt. Weekly.

Hebrew Union College Annual (1924). Hebrew Union College, 3101 Clifton Ave., Cincinnati 29. Abraham Cronbach, Sec. Edit. Bd. English-French-German-Hebrew.

Jewish Independent (1906). 216 Film Exchange Bldg., 2108 Payne Ave., Cleveland 14. Leo Weidenthal. Weekly.

Jewish Review and Observer (1887). 1104 Prospect Ave., Cleveland 15. Howard M. Wertheimer. Weekly.

Jewish Voice-Pictorial (1938). P.O.Box 6116, Cleveland 18. Leon Wiesenfeld. Quarterly.

Jewish World. 10526 Superior Ave., Cleveland 6. Weekly; Yiddish.

Ohio Jewish Chronicle (1921). 35 E. Livingston Ave., Columbus 15. Ben Z. Neustadt. Weekly.

Stark County Jewish News. 1409 22 St., N.E. Canton 4. Fortnightly.

Studies in Bibliography and Booklore. 3101 Clifton Ave., Cincinnati 20. Semi-annual.

Youngstown Jewish Times (1936). P.O. Box 1195. Youngstown. Harry Alter. Weekly.

OKLAHOMA

Southwest Jewish Chronicle (1929). 919 Braniff Bldg., Oklahoma City 2. E. F. Friedman. Quarterly.

Tulsa Jewish Review (1930). P.O.Box 396, Tulsa 1. Emil Salomon. Monthly.

PENNSYLVANIA

American Jewish Outlook (1934). 1037 Forbes St., Pittsburgh 6. Shirley Levine. Weekly.

Jewish Criterion (1892). 422 First Ave., Pittsburgh 19. Milton Susman. Weekly.

Jewish Exponent (1887). 1608 Spruce St., Philadelphia 3. Arthur Weyne. Weekly.

Jewish Herald (1937). 422 Hamilton St., Allentown.

Jewish Pictorial Leader 1929 Murray Ave., Pittsburgh 17. Louis Yale Borkon. Monthly.

Jewish Quarterly Review (1910). Broad and York Sts., Philadelphia 32. Abraham A. Neuman, Solomon Zeitlin. Quarterly.

Philadelphia Jewish Times (1925). 1928 Spruce St., Philadelphia 24. Jeff Keen. Weekly.

RHODE ISLAND

Jewish Herald. 121 Dyer St., Providence 3. Weekly.

TENNESSEE

Hebrew Watchman (1925). 116 Union Ave., Memphis 3. Milton W. Goldberger. Weekly.

Observer (1934). 730 Commerce St., Nashville 3. Jacques Back. Weekly.

TEXAS

Jewish Beacon (1947). P.O.Box 630, 1209 Caroline St., Houston 1. Maurice Krinsky. Weekly.

Jewish Digest (1955). 1719 Caroline St., Houston 1, Bernard Postal. Monthly.

Jewish Herald-Voice (1906). P.O.Box 153, 1719 Caroline St., Houston 1. D. H. White. Weekly.

Texas Jewish Post (1947). P.O. Box 742. Jessard A. Wisch. Fort Worth 1. Weekly.

Texas Jewish Press. 312 N. Alamo St., San Antonio 2. Quarterly.

VERMONT

Vermont Jewish Voice (1942). 34 Henderson Terrace, Burlington.

WASHINGTON

Transcript (1942). 727 Seaboard Bldg., Seattle 2. Mrs. Marion Q. Rose. Monthly.

WISCONSIN

Jewish Press—Milwauker Wochenblat(1918). 1721 N. 12 St., Milwaukee 5. Isador S. Horwitz Weekly; Yiddish-English.

Wisconsi. Jewish Chronicle (1921). 120 E. Detroit St., Milwaukee 2. Edwarde F. Perlson. Weekly.

PRINCIPAL JEWISH HOSPITALS AND HEALTH AGENCIES

NEW YORK

New York City

American Committee of OSE, 24 W. 40th St. (world-wide organization for child care, health, and hygiene).

Beth David Hospital, 612 Allerton Ave., Bronx (Institution for Chronically ill).

Beth-El Hospital, Rockaway Parkway and Linden Blvd., Brooklyn.

Beth Israel Hospital, Stuyvesant Park East.

Bronx Hospital, Fulton Ave. & E. 169th St., Bronx.

Brooklyn Women's Hospital, 1395 Eastern Parkway, Brooklyn (Special hospital for Obstetrics and Gynecology).

Hillside Hospital, 75–59 26rd St., Glen Oaks, Queens (Special hospital for mental and nervous diseases).

Jewish Board of Guardians, 228 East 19th Street (Child guidance and treatment).

Jewish Child Care Association, 1646 York Ave. (Child care institution, foster homes).

Jewish Family Service, 113 West 57th Street.

Jewish Memorial Hospital, Broadway and 196th St.

Jewish Sanitarium and Hospital for Chronic Diseases, 86 West 49th Street, Brooklyn (Hospital for Chronically Ill).

Lebanon Hospital, Grand Concourse and 173rd Street, Bronx.

Long Island Jewish Hospital, 270–05 76th Ave., New Hyde Park, L.I.

Louise Wise Child Adoption Center, 48 West 68th St. (Child care, foster homes, adoptions).

Maimonides Hospital of Brooklyn, 4802 Tenth Ave., Brooklyn.

Montefiore Hospital, Gun Hill Rd. & Bainbridge Ave., Bronx.

Mount Sinai Hospital, 100th Street & Fifth Ave.

New York Guild for the Jewish Blind, 1880 Broadway.

Liberty

The Workmen's Circle Sanatorium, Box 111 (hospital for tuberculosis).

ARKANSAS

Hot Springs

Leo N. Levi Memorial Hospital, Prospect Ave.

CALIFORNIA

Los Angeles

Cedars of Lebanon Hospital, 4833 Fountain Ave.

City of Hope, National Medical Center 208 W. 8th St. (hospital for tuberculosis, other chest diseases, cancer, leukemia, and heart surgery).

SAN FRANCISCO

Maimonides Hospital & Hebrew Nursing Home, 2356 Sutter Street (Hospital for chronically ill).

COLORADO

Denver

Jewish National Home for Asthmatic Children at Denver, 3447 W. 19th Ave. (Institution for asthmatic and allergic children).

Ex-Patients' Sanatorium for Tuberculosis & Chronic Disease, 8000 East Montview Blvd.

Jewish Consumptives' Relief Society Hospital, P.O.Box 537 (Hospital for tuberculosis and other chest diseases).

National Jewish Hospital, 3800 E. Colfax Ave. (Hospital for tuberculosis and chest diseases).

FLORIDA
Miami Beach

Mount Sinai Hospital of Greater Miami, 4300 Alton Road.

ILLINOIS
Chicago

Michael Reese Hospital, Ellis Ave. & 29th St.

Mount Sinai Hospital, 2750 West 15th P' :e.

Winfield Hospital, Winfield. (Hospital for tuberculosis).

MARYLAND
Baltimore

Mount Pleasant, Greenspring & Belvedere Ave. (Hospital for tuberculosis).

MASSACHUSETTS
Boston

Beth Israel Hospital, 330 Brookline Ave., Brookline.

Jewish Memorial Hospital, 45 Townsend St., Roxbury (Hospital for chronically ill).

Jewish Tuberculosis Sanatorium of New England, Rutland.

MISSOURI
St. Louis

Jewish Sanatorium Division, The Jewish Hospital of St. Louis, Route 1, Box 610, Robertson (Hospital for chronically ill).

Miriam Hospital for Convalescence and Rehabilitation, 501 Bacon Ave.

NEW JERSEY
Brown Mills

Deborah Sanatorium, Trenton Road. (Hospital for tuberculosis).

PENNSYLVANIA
Philadelphia

Philadelphia Psychiatric Hospital, Ford Road & Monument Ave.

ASIA

ADEN

BRITISH CROWN COLONY

JEWISH POPULATION: 800

At the time of the British occupation of the harbor of Aden in 1839, there were only about 250 Jews in the area. In succeeding decades, as British rule became more firmly entrenched, the community expanded to 5,000 in the city and about an additional 2,000 in the protectorate, in the main as a result of immigration from Yemen, although a number of Egyptian and Iraqi Jews also settled there. The first synagogue was established in Aden in 1858. Not until eighty years later, however, was the local Jewish community council formed (1938), under the presidency of Bentob Messa. The wealthy Messa family erected a synagogue and a new school building in the town of Aden, while another school was maintained in Sheikh 'Othman.

The Jews permanently residing in the colony of Aden and the surrounding protectorates on the eve of the birth of Israel did not exceed 4,500, or about 0.8 per cent of the estimated total population. By and large, they were concentrated in the city of Aden and in Sheikh 'Othman, where they lived in their own separate quarters and engaged principally in shopkeeping.

The position of the Jews of Aden began to deteriorate in the late 1930's as a result of the spreading interest in the Palestine Arab cause throughout the countries of the Arab Middle East, an interest fostered at that time by German and Italian propaganda. An anti-Jewish outbreak occurred in December, 1938, in Aden Colony. More serious riots took place in the community nine years later (1947), immediately after the UN General Assembly's adoption of the partition resolution, at which time 80 Jews were killed, as many wounded, and most of the Jewish shops, many of the homes, and the few public buildings were burned and their contents looted.

The Jews of Aden, who had previously trickled into Palestine, soon began to think of organized emigration to Israel. The fact that the Port of Aden served as the assembly center for Israel-bound emigration from Yemen and the point of origin for "Operation Magic Carpet" enabled the Jews in the colony and the protectorates to take advantage of the same facilities. As late as March, 1950, there were still as many as 4,000 Jews in the colony; by the end of June 1951, their number had been reduced to less than 2,000, and now, only 800 remain.

JEWISH COMMUNITY COUNCIL
OF ADEN

Pres.: M. Bentob Messa. Chairman: Selim Menahem Banin. Sec.: B. J. Yaish.

Beth Din, Rabbi: Yehia Abraham, dayan, and Rabbi Isaac Salem Jacob.

World Jewish Congress, Aden Committee. Pres.: M. Bentob Messa. Sec.: B. J. Yaish, Section A, Street No. 2, Camp.

Tomchei Aniyim Society, Pres.: Samuel Menahem Shelimay.

Jewish Temporary School, Menahem Messa's house. All 150 Jewish children attend the school. Education Committee's Chairman: B. J. Yaish.

Hatikvah Club, Section A, Street No. 2, Camp. Founded 1944. Pres.: Myer Samuel.

Brit Ivrit Olamit Organization, Chairman: Miss Mary Judah.

3 SYNAGOGUES:

Magen Abraham, Section A, Street No. 3. Founded 1901 by Menahem Messa. Attached to this synagogue is a Bet Midrash. Rabbi: Isaac Salem Jacob.

Magen David, Section A, Street No. 3. Rabbi: Mori Salch Yenia.

Succath Shalom (1924), Section A, Street No.1. Attached to the synagogue is a Bet Midrash. Three funds: Refuah we 'Hayeem (for sick), Aniye Ha'eer (for poor), and Hathan we'Khalla (for help for marrying couples). Cantor: Solomon Cohen.

Selim School for Boys and Girls, Principal: Dr. D. Griffin Warwick.

AFGHANISTAN

JEWISH POPULATION: 4,000

A tradition is current among Afghans that they are descendants of the lost ten tribes of Israel, and the native chronicles refer to them as "Beni Israel." However, this belief has not prevented the Afghans from oppressing the Jews residing in the country.

It is difficult to find reliable information about the present population of the Afghan Jewish community. Our estimation of 4,000 Jews is based on recent reports, but there are other estimations which place the number at anywhere from 2,000 to 10,000.

The Jews are subject to all forms of discrimination. Until recently, they were

forced to pay the heavy taxes imposed on "infidels." They must report for military service but are not permitted to carry arms and are employed in the lowest menial work of the army.

They were not persecuted a hundred years ago, although they lived in separate quarters. They were said then to have numbered 40,000 in 60 communities. However, in 1878–80, thousands of Jews from Herat fled to Persia after they were ordered to pay a heavy war tax. As late as 1927, the number of Jewish communities was still 60. Following the assassination of Nadir Shah in 1933, anti-Jewish measures were intensified. Jews were expelled from various parts of the country and concentrated mainly in Herat and in the capital, Kabul. They were forbidden to travel about the country and not allowed to trade in any commodity other than piece goods. The country's only newspaper, which is government-owned, is full of anti-Jewish diatribes. In 1946, when Afghanistan applied for membership in the United Nations, the American ambassador in Kabul was assured that there was no persecution of Jews.

The community is organized on a patriarchal system. The heads of families select the community head *(Kalantur)* who represents the Jews before the authorities. He also is responsible for the collection of the head-tax, which every male over 15 years of age must pay. The internal affairs of the community are administered by a council called *"Hevra"* (society), composed of the heads of the important families. The *Hevra* takes care of the poor, adjudicates civil disputes, and imposes penalties for Sabbath violations or other religious laws, and even inflicts corporal punishment and fines for criminal offenses under threat of excommunication. A religious court, "Beth-Din," composed of learned men *(mulla)* deals with religious cases such as divorces.

Boys start their education at schools maintained in synagogues at the age of three and continue until 15. They attend the synagogual religious school called "Midrash" where they are taught to read and translate the Bible and prayers. Later on they learn Mishna. They also receive instruction in writing and arithmetic. Girls are excluded from school.

The Jews of Afghanistan who live in the north among a Persian-speaking population speak a dialect of Persian; the majority of Afghans, however, speak "Pushtu." The Afghan Jews have a number of peculiar religious customs. For example, shoes are removed at the door of the synagogue and the worshipers sit on the floor. Also, at Rosh Hashana, every family slaughters a sheep in memory of the sacrifice of Isaac.

The overwhelming majority of Jews live in a state of utter poverty and destitution. During the great famine of 1944, about 1,000 emigrated to India and from there to Palestine. The news of the emergence of the State of Israel roused Messianic hopes among them and strengthened their determination to emigrate to Israel. Jewish organizations have made repeated representations to the Afghanistan government to permit emigration to Israel. It can be assumed that if permission were granted, the majority of Jews would leave for Israel without hesitation. In 1950, the Afghan Jews appealed to the Government of Israel for assistance since they were being systematically deprived of every possibility of earning a living and forced to sell their possessions. Moreover, they were being jailed. Due to the intervention of the World Jewish Congress, some of them were released. Emigration to Israel has been going on for years. By 1941, about 2,000 Afghan Jews had settled in Palestine. From 1942 to 1949, about 1,000 more arrived in Israel. The ban against emigration to Israel was lifted in 1951. At this time, over 5,000 Afghan Jews are citizens of the State of Israel.

KABUL (500 Jews)

Jewish Community. The Jews in this capital city are dispersed throughout the area and rent their apartments from Moslems. There is no central synagogue in Kabul — only private prayer rooms. There is, however, a Jewish religious school (Midrash) where almost all Jewish children receive religious instruction in Hebrew prayers and Torah.

HERAT (2,500 Jews)

Jewish Community. Maintains 8 synagogues and rabbis. Each synagogue has a religious school. It is the largest Jewish settlement in the country.

BALKH (200 Jews)

Jewish Community. 3 synagogues and religious schools. Rabbinate. Some of the Jews are farmers.

BAHREIN ISLANDS

(BRITISH PROTECTORATE)

JEWISH POPULATION: 400

Jews settled on the Bahrein Islands in the late 19th century. Originating from Iraq, Iran, and India, the Bahrein Jews are engaged in commerce and handicrafts.

Until recently, the Jews led a peaceful life. However, recent events in Palestine have caused a deterioration in their situation. Demonstrations against the Jews took place in 1947 and were accompanied by widespread looting; the synagogue was completely gutted and many Jews injured and one killed. Since the establishment of the State of Israel, relations have deteriorated even further so that now the Jews consider their emigration to Israel as the only solution to their problem.

Jewish Community of Bahrein. There is one synagogue but no Jewish school. Most of the Jews appear to be in a position to earn their livelihood. Ten families are said to be wealthy and 13 poor.

BURMA

JEWISH POPULATION: 210

All Jews in Burma are immigrants from other countries; the majority are British, the remainder Indian citizens. The economic situation is rather sound but not stable. Relations with non-Jews and the attitude of the press and the Government toward the Jews have always been cordial. Relations with the State of Israel are also very friendly resulting recently in the establishment of an Israel consulate in Rangoon and in the recent visit of Burma's Prime Minister U Nu in Israel.

In 1944, the Jewish population was 700. Since then, 400 have emigrated to Israel, England, America, or Australia. 155 members of this small Sephardic community live in the capital, Rangoon, while about 55 Beni-Israels have their homes in *Mandalay*, Upper Burma. There is no Jewish school so that the children attend English schools and receive no religious instruction For this reason, some Jews are leaving for Israel to insure their children a Jewish education.

Jewish Community of Burma, Address: 26 St. 85, Rangoon. The Jewish Community is led by a 5-man Board of Trustees which forms the committee of the Mashmea Yeshua Synagogue, built about 1896.
Pres.: E. S. Meyer (Mogul St. P.O.B.1170).
Sec.: S. Jacob.

The Israeli Club, 22, Sandwith Road, Rangoon. Jewish Sunday School, 25 pupils.
Jewish Youth Club for social and cultural activities.

CHINA

JEWISH POPULATION: 400

Ancient Chinese Jewish communities had a tradition that Jews came to China in the days of King Solomon. Other theories are that they arrived either from Persia sometimes between 58 and 75 C.E. or from India between 960–1126. By the 8th century C.E., Jews were sufficiently numerous for the emperor to have appointed a special officer to supervise them. Marco Polo, at the end of the 13th century, testified to the important role of the Jews in Cathay.

During those early years, the Jews of China avoided intermarriage, were faithful to Judaism, enjoyed complete equality, and reached high office.

There is evidence that the Chinese Jews once had a flourishing religious and communal life and maintained numerous synagogues. But of all the ancient communities, we know only the history of the one in Kai-fung-foo, or Kaifeng, the capital of Honan. In the Anglican Church of that city a stone tablet engraved in 1489 in Chinese characters contains the following legend: "Our religion came to China during the reign of the Han Dynasty, between 200 B.C. and 200 A.D." The first Kai-fung-foo synagogue was built in 1163. The community, however, slowly deteriorated through the centuries and gradually lost its Hebrew traditions. By 1866, the synagogue had vanished. In 1940, nevertheless, a few hundred fully assimilated Jews still lived in Kai-fung-foo.

The modern Jewish settlement in China dates from the 1840's when a number of British Jews came to Shanghai. Later, the Sassoons and Kadoories opened branches of their firms in Shanghai and here built the first synagogue. Until 1905, Shanghai Jewry was overwhelmingly Sephardic.

Larger numbers of Russian Jews settled in Harbin from where they spread over many cities of China.

Thus most of the Chinese Jewish communities came into being, among them the larger community of *Tientsin,* and existing communities, like that of *Peiping,* increased in size. The Jewish communities were well developed, and, in addition to Shanghai, Harbin, and Tientsin also existed in Mukden, Dairen, and a few other places as well. In 1936, there were 13 Jewish papers in China: 9 in Russian, 3 in English, and 1 in German-English.

Before the great influx of German and Austrian Jews to Shanghai began, the number of Jews in China was estimated as between 12,000 and 15,000: Harbin 7,000, Shanghai 4,000, Tientsin 2,000, and the rest of China about 1,500. About 90 to 95 percent of this total were from Russia and about 1,000 from Europe, America, and India.

The total Jewish population at the outbreak of the war amounted to about 26,000 souls. It began to decrease rapidly at the end of the war due to repatriation and the changed political and economic situation. Between 1946 and 1953, 16,000 Jews emigrated. As a result, fewer than 1,200 Jews remained in the whole of China in the latter half of 1952.

The attitude of the "Nationalist" Chinese authorities toward the Jews was always described as friendly. Anti-Semitism was unknown either among the people or in government circles. With the advent of the Communist regime, Jewish schools, hospitals, and clubs were taken over by the Association of Friends of the Soviet Union (except the club in Shanghai), but the religious institutions and synagogues were not molested.

At the end of June, 1957, 400 Jews were residing in China and registered as follows with the Shanghai Jewish Council: Shanghai 109, Harbin 229, Tientsin 55, and 4 Jews in Dairen, and Mukden.

The Jewish Community in China is in rapid decline and its end is near. With the anticipated departure of most of the Jews, the Council of the Jewish Community in Shanghai envisages in its printed report of June 1957 the probability of terminating its existence in the not too distant future. Almost all the Jewish families with children left Shanghai before July 1954. In 1952, 364 Jews left China, 99 of whom migrated to Israel and 265, to other countries. In 1953, 201 emigrated to Israel and 100, to other places; of these, 161 were from Shanghai, 72 from Tientsin, 63 from Harbin, and 4 from Dairen. During the first six months of 1954, 85 Jews emigrated. Of the remaining Jews, 285 are either in possession of or awaiting emigration visas and 100 are registered as sick and awaiting placement abroad by Jewish organizations. Thus, only a small fraction of China's present Jewish residents is expected to remain.

The economic situation of the Jews residing in China deteriorated since the establishment of the Communist regime. The Jews live mostly as petty merchants, office workers, and shop keepers. The steadily progressing nationalization by the

Communist government has undermined their economic positions and forced them to emigrate.

SHANGHAI (109 Jews)

The largest and most important Jewish community in China was that of Shanghai. The community was founded by Sephardic Jews from Hongkong and India. They brought with them Jewish clerks for whom the first synagogue in Shanghai was built. Shortly thereafter, a Jewish school was established. After the Russo-Japanese war, a number of Russian and Polish Jews founded the first Ashkenazic congregation (Ohel Moshe) in 1907. Considerable numbers of Russian Jews settled in Shanghai after the Russian Revolution of 1917. By 1932, the community had grown considerably and the congregation Ohel Moshe built its own synagogue. An official Ashkenazi Community was founded under the name of Kehillah Ivrit Ashkenazit. By 1937, it numbered about 4,500 souls; it had its own premises, Talmud Torah, and a weekly paper in Russian and Yiddish.

The influx of German Jews started in 1937, and in September of that year, a German Jewish congregation was founded. It built its own synagogue served by two rabbis and seven cantors and a Hebrew school.

In 1938, large numbers of Central European Jews began to flock to the International Settlement and the Chinese Section of Shanghai which until August, 1939 required no visas and had no admission restrictions. Within a single year—from August, 1938 to August, 1939, about 20,000 Jews from Germany, Austria, and Czechoslovakia found refuge there. The Jewish Spiritual Body was then established with a membership of 18,000. It's executive was Rabbi Joseph Zeitlin. In August, 1939, restrictions on the admission of refugees were instituted.

Although the Chinese Section of Shanghai was occupied by the Japanese, they did not at first interfere in any way with the arrival and settlement of Jews.

The situation changed radically with the outbreak of the war in the Pacific and the occupation of all Shanghai by the Japanese. In 1943, the Japanese ordered all "stateless persons" (meaning Jewish refugees) to move to the district of Hongkew, which, in effect, became a Jewish ghetto. It was administered by the Japanese military authorities. The Jewish homes, stores, and workshops outside Hongkew were taken over by the Japanese against nominal compensation.

The total Jewish population of the ghetto, according to the census of 1943, comprised 15,342 souls: 13,511 German and Austrian Jews and 1,234 Polish Jews and others. Over 12,000 were dependent on relief. Despite the difficult political and economic situation, social and cultural activities flourished. There was a multitude of social organizations and some of the former European Yeshivoth of Mir, Lubavitch, Klotzk, and Telshe were reorganized in Shanghai with an enrollment of about 400 students. All Orthodox schools had a total enrollment of about 800 pupils, and two secular schools—1,200 pupils. The ORT conducted technical courses which were attended over a period of years by thousands of students. There was a theatre in the ghetto performing in German and Yiddish. Many important rabbinical works were published together with new works by Jewish writers and translations of Hebrew and Yiddish classics. There were many periodicals, mostly weeklies and monthlies.

When the war with Japan ended, there were 14,874 Jewish refugees in Shanghai. Soon the exodus commenced. In 1946, 2,175 Jews left Shanghai; in 1947, 5,555, and in the first half of 1948, another 2,000. When in November 1948, the Chinese Communist armies drew near to Shanghai, there were in the city over 10,000 Jews. The wealthier among them began fleeing to Hongkong and Canton, the others appealed to Jewish organizations for help for emigration. The Israel Government delegated a consul to Shanghai, and a mass migration to Israel began by sea and by air. As a result, about 10,000 Jews from Shanghai and other Chinese cities came to Israel by the second part of 1952.

Council of the Jewish Community of Shanghai. Established in 1949. Originally, its purpose was to coordinate the activities of the Jewish Communities in Shanghai and to handle the migration of Jews to Israel. The Joint provides financial assistance to the Council. Due to the steady decrease in the number of Jewish residents in Shanghai because of emigration, the two Jewish communal bodies, the Ashkenazi Jewish Communal Association and the Sephardic Jewish Communal Association, agreed to centralize all Jewish activities under the leadership of the Council. The leaders of the Council have had numerous personal interviews with government officials who have always been helpful. The Government released the Council's blocked funds, allotted flour for matzot, reduced taxes on several communal properties in Shanghai and Harbin, and protected one of the Jewish cemeteries from trespassers. The Government, however, in line with a general decree, requisitioned four houses belonging to AJDC and being held by the Council for the Joint depriving the Council of the needed income from these buildings. Chairman: P. I. Yudalevich. Treasurer: K. I. Kusher.

Ashkenazi Jewish Communal Association, Originated in 1901. Membership: 120. Chairman: P. I. Yudalevich.

Sephardi Jewish Communal Association, Organized about 1875. Membership: 46. Chairman: R. D. Abraham.

Shanghai Jewish Club, Conducts cultural activities. Chairman: P. I. Yudalevich.

Shanghai Hebrew Relief Society and Shelter Houses, Pres.: P. I. Yudalevich.

New Synagogue, Route Tenant de La Tour. In 1953, both the Ashkenazic and Sephardic houses of worship agreed to abandon their separate premises and hold religious services only at this synagogue. Mr. Ezekiel Abraham acts as shochet in an honorary capacity.

HARBIN (229 Jews)

The Jewish community of Harbin was established in 1902. It grew after the Russo-Japanese war and became the center through which thousands of Jews came to China after the Russian Revolution. The majority emigrated to America, Australia, etc., but thousands stayed on. In 1920, the community counted 12,000 souls and had a democratically elected community council of 40 persons. The Harbin Jewish community was one of the most active in China; it had several Jewish political organizations and a considerable number of fine Jewish communal buildings and institutions, including branches of the Hebrew Association, Wizo, a library, a dramatic society, and a Jewish high school whose language of instruction was Hebrew for Jewish studies and Russian for general subjects. Harbin even had two Jewish newspapers, one in Russian and the other in Yiddish.

The position of the Harbin Jews began to deteriorate as the "White" Russians started to exercise considerable influence there. They conducted an anti-Jewish campaign in their press. Following the occupation of Manchuria by Japan in 1931, murder and arrests of the wealthier Jews took place, frequently with a view to extort large amounts of money from them.

The end of the war brought to Harbin first the Soviet Army, then the Nationalist Chinese Government, and soon thereafter, the Chinese Communists, and the emigration of Jews to Israel increased.

By now, few Jews remain in this once prosperous Jewish community. All that is left of it are the buildings of the former Jewish schools, kitchens, old-age home, and other institutions.

Harbin Jewish Community. The community has been able to maintain itself without outside assistance mainly because the Government has waived the taxes formerly imposed on its real estate.

TIENTSIN (55 Jews)

The third largest Jewish community in China was in Tientsin, amounting to about 2,000–2,500 Jews. Only about 50 to 100 of them were from Europe or America; the rest stemmed from Russia. They established a flourishing fur industry and developed a considerable community activity with their own school and religious institutions. Since 1934, the community had its own publication: a weekly supplement on Jewish affairs added to the Russian newspaper. The situation worsened considerably with the occupation of the city by the Japanese who in 1938 and 1939 arrested many Jewish leaders.

After the end of the war, the Tientsin Jewish community began to decline through emigration. In August, 1950, there were still several hundred Jews there, but the number has since decreased.

Tsientsin Hebrew Society. Maintains the Tsientsin Hebrew Shelter House and Society.

FIJI ISLANDS

JEWISH POPULATION: 70

The Jewish communal life is unorganized. The largest Jewish community of 30 is in the capital Suva, followed by Kokas 10, Jongo 10. Most are Sephardim.

HADHRAMAUT

(BRITISH PROTECTORATE)

JEWISH POPULATION: ESTIMATED AT 500

A large proportion of the people of Hadhramaut is nomadic. A number of tribes have groups of Jews under their protection who are useful to the natives as craftsmen and artisans. The Jews are, nevertheless, treated as inferiors by the Muslims, although if a Jew of one tribe were to be harmed by a member of another tribe, his own tribe would defend him with arms. The Jewish silversmiths are particularly prized. No information on the number of Jews there is available and the figure of 500 is merely a vague estimate.

HABBAN

Jewish Community. Habban is a small town lying about 225 miles northeast of Aden and about 150 miles west of Mukalla. According to the local legend, the Habbani Jews settled in the area before the destruction of the second Temple. Nonetheless, religious traditions and the knowledge of Hebrew are kept alive. They have copies of the Talmud and even of the Shulhan Arukh. They are strict observers of Judaism in accordance with the practices and customs of the Jews of Arabia. A few have succeeded in making their way to Israel, and the others are looking for an opportunity to follow. Their position appears to have deteriorated considerably. The present ruler of the Habban tribe, in order to force the Jews to accept Islam, has imposed heavy taxes and financial exortions upon them. It is assumed that the persecution of Jews has also spread to other parts of the country.

HONG KONG

JEWISH POPULATION: 230

Congregation "Ohel Leah." Synagogue "Ohel Leah," 70 Robinson Rd. Built by Sir Jacob Sasson in 1901. Pres.: L. Kadoorie (St. George Buildings, room 39). Sec.: J. Moses.

There are 30 children who have no regular Jewish education.
Jewish Recreation Club. Founder: Sir Elly Kadoorie in 1909. Pres.: H. Kadoorie.
Benevolent Society. Pres.: A. Raymond.

INDIA

JEWISH POPULATION: 25,000

Indian Jewry is composed of three main sections, the largest being the *Bene-Israel* whose origins in India are said to be traceable to the period subsequent to the destruction of the First Temple in Jerusalem. They closely resemble the native Indians in dress and general appearance and number about 17,000, mostly in Bombay State. (See the *History of the Bene-Israel in India* by Haeem Samuel Kehimakar). The next section are those of *Iraqi origin* known as Yehudim the majority of whom live in Bombay and Calcutta where they immigrated in the wake of David Sassoon, known as the Prince of the Captivity in Baghdad and founder of the famous House of Sassoon in India in 1832.

The smallest section consists of the so-called Cochin Jews on the east coast of Malabar, in the southeastern part of India. This Jewish group numbers about 2,000 residing in four communities of which Cochin is the largest followed by Ernakulam and by two fishing and agricultural villages, Parur and Malla. The majority are colored Jews with Biblical names, but there are also a few thousand white Jews in this region with Spanish or German surnames. They maintain excellent relations with the Indians and, as farmers and artisans, are economically rather well off.

According to ancient legends, the Jews came to Malabar during the period of the

First Temple. There is, however, evidence that the community dates from the time of the destruction of the Second Temple. There exist two large copper plates in the synagogue of Cochin on which are engraved charters dated 379 A.D. granted by the Maharaja Chaskara Ravi Varma conferring on the Jewish leader Joseph Rabban the title of Raja of the Principality of Anjuvannan, whose capital Cranganore, near Cochin, was the port of the region. The charter included privileges for the Prince Rabban as riding elephants, wearing red garments, and being preceded and followed by slaves sounding trumpets and carrying gold-tasselled parasols over the Prince. The Jewish Prince received the right to collect taxes and tolls from ships and was exempted from paying any taxes to the Maharaja of Cochin.

The Jewish autonomy of Anjuvannan prospered for nearly twelve centuries. Mario Solo, Vasco da Gama and the Jewish travellers Benjamin of Tudela and Rabbi Nissim of Barcelona visited the capital, Cranganore. The latter wrote: "I always longed to see a Jewish ruling prince and there I saw one with my own eyes." Greedy neighbors and internal uprisings weakened the state and Cranganore was finally destroyed and never rebuilt. The Jewish population settled in the neighboring towns and dwindled rapidly in numbers.

Their language is Malayalam, akin to the dialects of their neighbors, and they wear native dress. Only a few know Hebrew, but Hebrew prayers are known by all. They are now emigrating to Israel out of love for Zion, and it is expected that the entire community will be transplanted there soon.

In *Bombay,* where the great majority of India's Jews reside, the two largest schools are the Sir Jacob Sassoon High School and the Sir Elly Kadoorie School. In the former, the bulk of the students are drawn from the Iraqi section of the Indian Jewish community, and the latter has a majority of Bene-Israel children. The two schools have eleven classes in their primary and secondary educational system. The matriculation examination is conducted by the Bombay University, which is the only university in India, and perhaps in the entire Orient, to grant a graduate degree in Hebrew. The schools are financed by trust funds, donations, and subscription fees. Government grants are given on condition that the schools remain open to members of other communities (as all other schools are). The E.E. Sassoon and the Sir S. J. David are smaller Jewish schools. All these institutions include in their curricula Jewish history and Hebrew as well as Hindi, the national language, and a regional language. Instruction is in English.

In *Calcutta,* the Elias Meyer Talmud Torah and the Jewish Girls' School teach up to the matriculation standard of Calcutta University. Since the majority of the community in Bombay and Calcutta are poor, all the above-mentioned institutions are frequented by the poorer classes, while the more well-to-do are sent to schools abroad.

The two Jewish youth movements which provide some form of "Sunday school" Jewish education or environment are Habonim and Maccabi. Jewish education is closely linked with Jewish religious observance so that the synagogues promote Jewish training in the orthodox fashion. There are ten synagogues in Bombay State, three in Calcutta, and eight in Cochin. The Zionist movement in India, well over thirty years old, has served to foster interest in Israel, Hebrew, and Aliyah.

BOMBAY
JEWISH POPULATION: 16,000

Central Jewish Board, P.O.Box 47. The Central Jewish Board, founded in 1946, is recognized by the Central and State Governments as the Jewish representation in Bombay State, and embraces all the Jewish institutions in Bombay and the Bombay State, which are represented on the Board by the two delegates each, It gives expression to the views and aspirations of the Jews, provides for their political representation, and promotes their general interest and welfare. The Executive Committee of the Board is elected by the delegates of its constituents at general assemblies. President: Dr. E. Moses. Secretary: P. S. Gourgey.

SYNAGOGUES:

Etz Haeem, Umerkhadi (90 members). Pres.: Moses Solomon Massil. Sec.: Moses Benjamin. Hazan: Nehemia ben Nehemia.
Gate of Mercy, (Erected 1776). 254 Samuel Streeet, Mandvi. Pres.: S. M. Sogavker. Sec.: R. Ben Samuel. Hazan: Joseph Isaac.
Magen Chasidim, 8 Moreland Road (200 members). Pres.: Solomon Samson. Sec.: Enoch Samuel. Hazan: Isaac Elijah.
Tifereth Israel, 92 Clerk Road, Jacob Circle. Pres.: Samson Raymond. Sec.: Enoch R. Moses. Hazan: Abraham Joseph.
Agudath Israel, Pres.: D. Goldsmith.
The Jewish Religious Union. Pres.: S. S. Aptekar. Sec.: A. M. Chinchokkar.

All India Zionist Federation, Pres.: J. S. Ezra. Sec.: P. S. Gourgey.
Sir Elly Kadoorie School, Mazagaon (for Bene Israel children). Founded 1875. 315 boys and 200 girls, 24 teachers. Principal: Miss Rebeca Reuben. Pres.: A. M. Chinchokkar. Sec.: Samson Rahamin.
Sir Jacob Sassoon School (For Iraqi Jews), Pres.: Solomon Judah. Founded 1885. 158 boys and 110 girls. Principal: Mrs. A. Joseph. Sec.: Joseph Judah.
Jewish Relief Association. Pres.: David Sommer. Sec.: S. W. Cohn.
The Bene Israel Stree Mandal, Pres.: Mrs. Rachel I. J. Daniel. Sec.: Miss Sybil R. Benjamin.
World Ort Union, P.O.Box 47.
Bombay Zionist Association, Meadows Street, Fort Bombay. Pres.: M. D. Japheth. Sec.: P. S. Gourgey.
Wizo, Pres.: Miss Mozelle Nathan. Sec.: Miss Sarah Moses.
Jewish Club, Pres. Sir Alwyn Ezra. Sec.: M. D. Sopher.
Jewish Co-operative Banking Society Ltd. Pres.: S. Benjamin. Sec.: Hanokh Benjamin.
Bnei Akiva Movement, 100 members.
Habonim, Pres.: Albert Manasseh. Sec.: Victor Moses.
Maccabi Association, Pres.: R. Mathalone. Sec.: Nissim D. Marshall.

AHMEDABAD
(Gujarat, Bombay Province)
(Jewish population: 150)

Synagogue "Magen Abraham," Pres.: Dr. A. S. Erulker; Sec.: John I. Benjamin. Hazan: Elija Isaac.
Zionist Association. Pres.: Elijah Hyams. Sec.: Abraham Samuel.

ALIBAG
(Kolaba District, Bombay Province)
(Jewish population: 550)

Synagogue "Magen Aboth" (90 members), Pres.: David Jacob. Sec.: Nahashone Jacob. Hazan: Eliyahu Moses Dandekar.

MHASVA
(Janjira State, Bombay Province)
(Jewish population: 100)
Synagogue "Shaar Hathefilah," (30 members)
Pres.: Benjamin Aaron. Sec.: Hanokh David. Hazan: Manasseh Benjamin.

POONA
(Bombay Province)
Synagogue "Succath Shelomo," 93 Rasta Peth (180 members). Pres.: G. R. Solomon. Sec.: D. M. Joseph. Hazan: S. Elias.

REVDANDA
(Kolaba District, Bombay Province)
Synagogue "Beth El" (Founded 1842, rebuilt 1877). Pres.: Samuel Solomon. Sec.: B. Shalome. Hazan: Ahmaim Simon.

ROHA ASHTAMI
(Kolaba District, Bombay Province)
Synagogue. Sec.: Joseph Aaron.

SURAT
(Bombay Province)
Jewish Cemetery Fund, Chairman: E. O. Sampson. Sec.: S. Joseph.

THANA
(Bombay Province)
Synagogue "Shaar Hashamaim." Pres.: Samuel Shalome. Sec.: Jacob Joseph. Hazan: Samson Benjamin.

CALCUTTA
(West Bengal Province)
(Jewish population: 2,200)
Jewish Association of Calcutta, Norton Bldgs. 1 & 2. The Association is recognized by the Central and State Governments as the official spokesman of the Jews in West Bengal. All Jewish organizations and communal bodies are united in the Association which promotes the general welfare and safeguards the interests of its constituents. The Association's Governing Body of 15 members is elected for two years at a general meeting of the delegates of its 10 constituents which consist of synagogues, social work groups, charitable societies, and clubs.

In this mainly Sephardic community, the welfare work is carried on by the Jewish Women's League, Oseh Hesed Board and "Baby Welcome." Only about 30 families of the Jews in Calcutta are prosperous, while the overwhelming majority are destitute and dependent upon charitable aid. The younger generation is organized in the Maccabi, Calcutta Jewish Youth Council, and Young People's Congregation. Aside from religious instruction given by the synagogues there are two Jewish schools: Jewish Girls' and Jeshurun Free School and the Elias Meyer Free School and Talmud Torah for boys. The budget of these day schools is covered by the Jewish Community and the Corporation of Calcutta with governmental subsidies. The Jewish Association's official organ is "Shema." The Jewish population of Calcutta has decreased from 4,000 in 1945 to 2,200, or nearly 45%, in 1955. For the first time, the Calcutta Community has engaged a Rabbi. He is Rabbi Mazliach, born in Calcutta and a recent graduate of the Jewish Theological Seminary of New York. Pres.: J. R. Jacob. Sec.: E. S. Gubbay.

SYNAGOGUES:

Beth Din, Members: D. H. J. Cohen (Hazan); S. Rasabee and E. J. Samuel.

Beth-El Synagogue, 26/1 Pollock Street. Pres.: M. E. Gubbay. Sec.: D. J. Cohen. Rabbi: A. Twena.

Maghen David Synagogue, 109–110 Canning Street. Pres.: A. Curlender. Sec.: J. M. David. Rabbi: David Jacob Cohen.

Neveh Shalom Synagogue, 9 Jackson's Lane. Pres.: Elias Ezra. Sec.: J. Jacob. Rabbi: Abraham Ezekiel.

Jeshurun Free School, 8b Pollock Street. Pres.: M. E. Gubbay. Sec.: D. J. Cohen.

Jewish Girls' School, 8a Pollock Street. Pres.: M. E. Gubbay. Sec.: D. J. Cohen.

Elias Meyer Free School and Talmud Torah for Boys (150 pupils), Pres.: Mrs. Flora Meyer. Sec.: Ben Arakie.

Mussa Board, Sec.: S. K. Sadka.

Oseh-Hesed Board, Pres.: E. J. Samuel. Sec.: I. Musleah.

Jewish Refugees Relief Association, 3 Theatre Road. Pres.: D. J. Cohen. Sec.: B. V. Jacob.

Wizo Federation, Pres.: Mrs. J. R. Jacobs. Sec.: Mrs. Rembaum.

Zionist Organization, Chairman: Major L. Tajkef. Sec.: Miss R. Abraham.

Judean Club, Chairman: Miss R. M. Luddy. Sec.: Charles Ezra.

Jewish Youth Council, Pres.: S. Ezra. Sec.: B. V. Jacob.

Maccabi Club, Pres.: A. Arakie. Sec.: E. Sopher.

COCHIN
(Jewish population: approximately 3,000)

South Indian Jews Association, Jew Town, Cohin.

The Association embraces the Jewish institutions in the Cochin and Travancore States and particularly the synagogues and societies in Ernakulam, Cochin, Chenamangalam, Parur, and Malla, and is recognized as the Jewish representative body by the Central and State Governments.

The synagogues provide religious instruction. Hebrew is taught by private teachers. Worthy of note among the youth organizations are the Habonim Club in Cochin and the Shomrim in Parur. The Cochin Jews have asked for transfer to Israel.

Pres.: S. S. Koder. Sec.: R. A. Salem.

ERNAKULAM
(Travancore-Cochin State)
(Jewish population: 2,000)

South Indian Jews' Association, Pres.: S. S. Koder. Sec.: R. A. Salem.

The Kumbhagam Synagogue, Jews Street (Built 1600; rebuilt 1940). Hazan: Abraham Abraham. Treasurer: Abraham Eliavoe.

Kudaknambhagarn Synagogue, Jews Street (Built 1300; rebuilt 1919).

Young Israel Society, Basin Road. Sec.: E. Elias.

Zionist Association, Pres.: S. S. Koder.

JEW TOWN
(Travancore-Cochin State)
(Jewish population: 400)

South Indian Jews' Association, Pres.: Shabdai S. Koder. Sec.: R. A. Salem.

Synagogue Parathesi (Built 1568; rebuilt 1664). (White Jews). Hazan: E. M. Roby.

Synagogue Kadvoom Bhagam (Built 1544), Treasurer: Issacai Judah.

Synagogue, Theckoom Bhagam (Built 1667), (Black Jews).

Cochin Zionist Association, Pres.: S. S. Koder.

Habonim, Sec.: E. O. Roby.

PARUR
(Travancore-Cochin State)
(Jewish population: 300)

Hebrew Congregation, Jews Street (Synagogue built 1616). Hazan: M. E. Meyer.

Jewish Welfare Society, Jews Street (Founded 1947).

Hebrew Educational Society, (Founded 1918). *Talmud Torah School.*

CHENAMAGALAM
(Travancore-Cochin State)

Hebrew Congregation (Synagogue built 1614). *Hebrew School.*

MALLA
(Travancore-Cochin State)

Hebrew Congregation (Synagogue built 1597). *Hebrew School.*

BANGALORE
(Mysore Province).

There is a small Jewish community.

DELHI

Jewish Welfare Association.

MADRAS
(Madras Province)

There is a small Jewish community.

Jewish Relief Association, Madras Sub-Committee. Sec.: Mrs. L. Wolff, Dunduan 4b, Nungambakam High Road, Madras, 6.

Publications: "Jewish Advocate," monthly, English, 63/67 Meadows St., Fort Bombay. "Shema," monthly, English, Norton Building 1/2, Old Court House Corner, Calcutta.

PERIODICALS:

Fortnightly

News from Israel, 50, Pedder Rd., Cumballa Hill, Bombay, 26.

Monthlies

Maccabi, Plot No. 50, Ai Mai Merwanji Rd., Parel, Bombay, 12.

Shema, Norton Bldgs., 1/2 Old Court House Corner, Calcutta.

INDONESIA

JEWISH POPULATION: 450

The Jewish population is concentrated mainly in the three cities of Jakarta, Surabaya and Bandung. All three communities formed a central body named The Board of Jewish Communities in West Indonesia whose seat is in Jakarta. There is no Jewish teacher in spite of appeals of the Community to Jewish organizations abroad to secure one for them. Consequently, there are no opportunities for Jewish education. The community in Surbaya consists mainly of Sephardim, while the majority of the Jews in Jakarta are Ashkenazim.

Their economic situation is rather satisfactory. Their number, however, is declining. Some families emigrated due to lack of Jewish education for their children.

JAKARTA — 200 Jews

Jewish Community, Tanah Abang 11/25, Jakarta. 75 registered members. Pres.: Dr. H. de Vries. Sec.: I. Khazam. There is a Community room where regular religious services and other communal activities are held.

Zionist Organization of Indonesia, Same address as the Community. Pres.: F. Dias Santilhano. Sec.: I. Khazam.

Jewish Information Owce, Same address as the Community.

SURABAYA — 200 Jews

Jewish Community, Djl. H. Widodren 5, Surabaya. Pres.: I. E. Ehrenpreis. Sec.: Mrs. L. Juda Mussry.

Synagogue, Address: Kajoon 4, Surabaya.

BANDUNG — 50 Jews.

Jewish Community.

IRAN

JEWISH POPULATION: 75,000

In the Biblical period Persia was known as a friend of Israel. The Persian king Cyrus in 537 B.C.E. permitted the Jews living in captivity in Babylon to return to Palestine and rebuild the Temple of Jerusalem. Also, Darius I and Artaxerxes I sent Zerubabel and Nehemiah to continue the erection of the Temple. The traveler Benjamin of Tudela found in the 12th century large Jewish communities in Isfahan, Shiraz, Holwan, and Hamadan, which was a spiritual center because of the tombs of Mordecai and Esther. Under the rule of the Mongols in the 13th century, the condition of the Persian Jews was good, and the Jew Saad ad-Daula became vizier of the Mongol Empire of Arghun (1289–1291).

Under the rule of the Shia-Islamic dynasty of the Safavids the situation of the Jews became very precarious. In 1838, the Jews of Meshed were forced to convert to Islam and were called "New Moslems," but secretly, under the most dangerous circumstances, they continued observing Judaism until recently when many of them were able to emigrate to Israel.

Under the Kadjar dynasty (1795–1925), Jews were subjected to discrimination and to humiliating treatment leading to disintegration in Jewish life in Iran. With the rise of Riza Shah Pehlevi (1925–41), the Jews were granted civil rights, but the economic and social situation of the Iranian Jews remained most grievous. Antisemitism is widespread. The majority of the destitute masses are inadequately supported by international Jewish charitable organizations. Several thousands of them emigrated to Israel in recent years, and many more are awaiting the opportunity to emigrate.

The Jews in Iran have not formed centrally organized communities. They have the right to elect their deputy to Parliament (Majlis) like other minorities. The Jewish member of the Majlis is the president of a committee which represents Jewry before the Government. This central body, however, exerts little influence in the Jewish local communities of the country. There is no central community council of the 40,000 Jews in Teheran. Various committees are formed to take care of special needs. In the constitution of 1934, jurisdiction was granted to the Rabbinical Courts in all matters of the personal status of Jews.

In the provinces, each community has its own committee which supervises the school and cooperates with Jewish organizations such as the Jewish Agency, Alliance, JDC, and ORT.

It is estimated that 40,000 Jews live in Teheran, 15,000 in Shiraz, 8,000 in Isfahan, 4,000 in Hamadan, Kermanshah 3,500; Meshed 2,500 and smaller groups in Semandej, Yezd and in other towns and villages.

The majority speak a Persian-Jewish dialect, a mixture of Persian and Hebrew. Jews living in western Azerbaijan speak Turkoman and those of Kurdistan an Aramaic similar to the language of the Talmud.

The Jews enjoy legally all civil rights, but according to the existing practice, no Jew can become a judge or enter any civil service. The main occupation of the Jewish poor class is peddling, a certain number of Jews are engaged as craftsmen in weaving carpets, as coppersmiths, shopkeepers, or peasants. Most of them live in ghettos called Mahall-i Yahud.

The best and most frequented schools are those of the Alliance Israélite Universelle which were established in Persia in the latter decades of the 19th century. At present there are 23 Alliance schools with an enrollment of about 7,500. There is also a school of the Anglo-Jewish association. The local organization Ozar Hatorah maintains some 38 schools with a combined enrollment of some 4,000. A number of other pupils attend government schools, but education is hindered by the lack of funds to maintain the Jewish schools, as well as the lack of clothing and shoes for children to enable them to attend school. About 2,000 Jewish children receive no Jewish education. The Joint Distribution Committee is giving 2,500 of them a regular meal daily, clothing, and medical care. Education is also hampered by the necessity of sending the healthier children to work so that they may contribute to the maintenance of the family. Illiteracy among the Jews has gradually decreased to about 75 per cent. The ORT maintains vocational schools in Teheran, Isfahan, and Shiraz with an enrollment of 2,000. Only about 100 Jewish students are attending the Teheran University.

According to Israel statistics, a total of 30,769 Persian Jews immigrated into Israel from the establishment of the Jewish State in 1948 until the end of 1953.

TEHERAN — 40,000 Jews
Consistoire Israelite, Pres.: Dr. Bral.
Jewish Community Council—Pres.: Dr. Morad Arieh. Chief Rabbi: Yedidia Chofett.

Jewish Agency for Palestine—P. O. B. 121, Teheran.
Zionist Organization—Pres.: Moussa Taub.
Alliance Israelite — Pres.: Morteza Senehy.
World Jewish Congress Committee — Chairman: Moussa Kermanian (35 Churchill Av.)
Dames Israelites Iraniennes — Pres.: Miss Hekmat.
ORT — Pres.: Nematollah Mossanen.

SHIRAZ — 15,000 Jews
Jewish Community — Synagogue — Jewish school.

ISFAHAN — 6,000 Jews
Jewish Community, Pres.: Youna Saadia — *Synagogue — Jewish school.*

H.'MADAN — 4,000 Jews
Jewish Community. Pres.: Dr. Morad Simahy. *Synagogue — Jewish school.*

KERMANSHAH — 3,500 Jews
Jewish Community, Pres.: Jacob Khalidi.

MESHED — 2,500 Jews
SEMANDEJ
Jewish Community. Pres.: Hadji Jacob Igha-Dijani.

YEZD
Jewish Community. Pres.: Hadji Matatia Rioni.

PERIODICALS:
Alame Yahood, Zionist weekly, Persian, 35, Churchill Ave., Teheran.

IRAQ

JEWISH POPULATION: 6,000

The Jewish community in Iraq is the oldest in the world, outside that of Palestine, with a history of more than 2,500 years. Iraq was known in ancient times as the region of Babylonia and Mesopotamia to which the center of the Jewish people was transplanted in the two crucial periods after the destruction of the first and second temples.

The number of Iraqi Jews after the second world war was estimated at 140,000, 90,000 of them living in Baghdad and constituting 25% of the city's total population. The rest were distributed in Basra, Mosul, and the rural areas, especially in Iraqi Kurdistan. The Kurdish Jews speak Syriac, an Aramaic dialect, while the rest of the Iraqi Jews speak Arabic. Baghdad had over 50 Jewish schools and 26 synagogues. The Jews played an important part in public life during the British mandate, being among the best educated people. Heshoil Sasson was the first Minister of Finance in independent Iraq.

With the establishment of Iraq's independence, the situation deteriorated rapidly. In 1935, the teaching of Hebrew was prohibited and restrictions against Jews in public employment were established. In 1941, there were programs in Baghdad, Basra and Mosul during which 150 Jews were killed and stores and homes looted and destroyed. After the establishment of the State of Israel, a period characterized by growing hostility,

discrimination, persecution and confiscation of property began. Of all the Arab states, Iraq now is the most hostile toward Israel, and it is assumed that the small remnant of Jewry will not be able to remain in the country and will be compelled to emigrate.

Most of the Jews today live in Baghdad, and there are small groups in Basra and Mosul; the other provincial communities have been completely dismembered by the exodus of the Jews to Israel. The small number of Jews has been greatly affected by the wave of general hatred and suspicion toward them which became especially rampant after the defeat of Iraq during the Israel War of Independence.

The Jews were once represented in Parliament by six deputies and one senator in accordance with the law on minority representation. Following the Jewish emigration — with its corresponding decrease in Jewish population — all Jewish representation was abolished since the small number of the remaining Jews does not allow, constitutionally, for any representation.

In 1950, the Iraqi airlift to Israel began and by 1951 the exodus of 120,000 Iraqi Jews was completed. At the time of the exodus, the government froze the property of all Jews leaving the country estimated at $200,000,000, which was tantamount to expropriation.

Life for the Jews in Iraq has always

been unsure and they have constantly sought to emigrate whenever possible. In the first half of the 19th century, thousands of Iraqi Jews emigrated, and they are to be found in every principle city in the Orient.

BAGHDAD (5,000 Jews)

Jewish Community, President and Rabbi of the Community: Hakham Sasson Cadouri.

Former president and now member of the Community Council: Yehezkel Shem-Tov.

Frank Any School. This is the only Jewish school now in operation.

All the synagogues in Baghdad but one are closed. Some were taken over by the Moslems; the remaining ones were sold by the Jewish Community. Of the three Jewish hospitals in Baghdad, only one is functioning.

Jewish Community in Basra.

Jewish Community in Mosul.

JAPAN

JEWISH POPULATION: 900

The first Jewish congregation dates from 1889. After the Sino-Japanese war of 1890, Jewish immigrants from Russia built a synagogue in Nagasaki which existed until 1905. This group turned over their Sefer Torah to the Sephardic community in Kobe. Yokohama also had a small community until the earthquake of 1923. The Kobe community today owns its own synagogue. Antisemitism was unknown in Japan before the pact with Nazi Germany. In 1930, an anti-semitic organization was formed and in 1941 anti-semitic demonstrations were staged.

In the beginning, Japan welcomed German Jewish scientists, but after signing the German-Japanese cultural pact, Jewish refugees were dismissed by Japanese firms. Many Jews who had escaped from the Soviet-German war in 1941 were stranded in Kobe; Japanese authorities began to deport many of them to Shanghai and barred further immigration of transients. Some of the Jewish im-

migrants obtained visas for other countries. Only two small communities in Tokyo and Kobe are now in existence in Japan.

Some Japanese writers and intellectual circles hold the belief that the Japanese are descendants of the ten tribes of ancient Israel. In 1935, the Japanese-Israel Association was founded to spread Judaism among the Japanese people. They publish a periodical and claim to have a membership of a few thousand converts professing Judaism. American chaplains serving in Japan conduct classes in Jewish history, religion, and Hebrew for this Association. Some prominent Japanese scholars and social leaders participate regularly in their Sabbath services and cultural activities.

TOKYO (600 Jews)

The Jewish Community of Japan, 102 Hanezawa-Cho, Shibuya-Ku, Tokyo; P.O.B.257. Cable Address: Jewcom Tokyo. Telephone 40-2559. The Jewish Community in Tokyo has a membership of 100 and is registered with the Japanese Government. Its Executive Committee is elected annually at general meetings by the delegates of the Jewish Communities in the Tokyo-Yokohama and Kobe-Osaka areas. The Community maintains a branch of its office in the Kobe-Osaka area. They are affiliated with the World Jewish Congress. 75% of the Jews reside in the Tokyo-Yokohama region. The Japanese Jewish Community has received much help from the Jewish chaplains of the U.S. Army. Pres.: Anatole Ponve. Sec.: D. Stoliar.

Sunday School, Attendance: 60. Jewish soldiers of the U.S. Army have been volunteering as teachers.

Synagogue, Services conducted on Sabbaths and holidays.

Club, For social and cultural activities.

Jewish Women's Council, An auxiliary of the Club.

Jewish Welfare Board, Conducted by the Community.

KOBE (300 Jews)

Jewish Community, 40 members. Pres.: Rahmu Sasson. Sec.: Menri Amram.

Synagogue; Sunday School: 10 pupils, teacher: Mr. Gottlieb.

Jewish Center, At the Community.

LEBANON

JEWISH POPULATION: 10,000

The majority of the Jews are Lebanese citizens and reside in the capital Beirut (8,500) and in Saida (500). According to the Lebanese Government census of May, 1952, there were 5,920 Lebanese and 1,041 foreign Jews in the country, among them French, Greek, Persian, and Algerian nationals, as well as twelve "Palestinians." With approximately 3,000 Syrian Jews, who described themselves as "tourists," the number of Jews in Lebanon totals about 10,000.

The Jewish Community is recognized by the state and has extensive legal jurisdiction. The Community Council consists of 12 members who are elected every two years by the members of the Community. There are also various social institutions for the sick and needy and for the poor children including vacation camps, etc. Cultural activities are negligible.

In Beirut the Community maintains one Jewish school. The Alliance Israelite maintains elementary schools with an enrollment of 1,500; its budget is met by the Alliance and the Community jointly. While there is a lack of Jewish teachers, most of the Jewish children receive a satisfactory Hebrew education.

The number of Jews in Lebanon has not decreased considerably in recent years. Voids created by emigration have been filled by Syrian Jewish immigrants from Damascus and Aleppo. The co-existence of many Christian and Moslem minorities in the country has resulted in a situation more favorable for the Jews than in other Arab states. The relations between the Jews and the leaders of the Christian Maronites, who are afraid of Moslem domination of Lebanon, are friendly. They even repeatedly issued declarations in favor of a Jewish state in Palestine, but were, however, silenced later by nationalistic propaganda.

The situation deteriorated in 1952 due to the activities of Emile Bustani, of Haifa, who demanded in Parliament to discriminate against the Jews. Under this pressure, controls were imposed on the movement of Jews. There had been sporadic riots in 1948, accompanied by bombing of Jewish houses and institutions. During the fighting in Israel, a number of Jews "under suspicion" were arrested and sent to a concentration camp in Baal Bek. Moreover, emigration to Israel has been banned, and at the end of 1953, two Jewish youth organizations, the "Macabbi" and the Boy Scouts, were dissolved on the pretext of supplying military training which endangered the security of the State.

BEIRUT (8,500 Jews)

Jewish Community Pres.: Dr. Joseph Attie..

Sec.: Zaki Elia. Community's Educational Committee. Pres.: Toufic Attie.

Rabbinate: Chief rabbi ad interim: Bension Lechman, P.O.B. 1007; Eliahu Zeitouni, rabbi of the Sephardic section. There is one main synagogue and several smaller houses of prayer.

Besides the community school, there are the following schools of the Alliance Israélite: Kindergarten with 208 children; elementary school for girls with 300 pupils; elementary school for boys, 282 pupils; secondary school, 165 pupils. Director of the Alliance schools: M. E. Silvert. There is also a Bnai Brith Lodge.

SAIDA (500 Jews)

Jewish Community, Maintains a rabbi and a synagogue.

Jewish School of the Alliance: 4 classes with 56 pupils and 4 teachers. Dir.: Moise Kamine.

During the Israel War of Independence in 1948, the Jews in Saida were expelled from their homes which were then occupied by Arab refugees from Palestine. In 1950, 50 Jewish families returned to Saida and the Alliance school was reopened.

PAKISTAN

JEWISH POPULATION: 600

Before the establishment of Pakistan as an independent state, the country was a part of India, and the history of Indian Jewry includes also that of the Jews in Pakistan. The Jews are concentrated in the capital Karachi.

KARACHI

Congregation and Synagogue Magen Shalome, 90 Members. President: Simon A. Reuben. Vice Pres.: S. R. Samuel. Secretary: M. Solomon. Hazzan: David Hai Moses Madai.

Karachi Bene Israel Relief Fund Society, Address: Magen Shalome Synagogue. Pres.: D. S. Isaac. Sec.: B. D. Solomon.

Jewish Sports Club, Nathan Abraham Hall, Barnes St. and Lawrence Road. Pres.: D. S. Isaac. Secretary: J. Ezekiel.

PESHAWAR (N.W. Frontier Province).

There is a small Jewish community with 2 Synagogues.

Mr. Suliman Fatinalihoff Irani (near the clock tower) is in charge.

REPUBLIC OF THE PHILIPPINES

JEWISH POPULATION: 300

Jewish Community of the Philippines, 2029 Taft Avenue, Manila. 264 members. The Jewish Community of the Philippines is recognized by the Philippine Government. Its Board of Directors is elected annually by the membership at large. The Community, which has lost more than half of its members through emigration since 1947, has a Jewish Youth Group. The Bachrach Memorial Hall there is the center of social and cultural activities. President: Karl Nathan. Secretary: Ernest E. Simke.

Sunday School, 30 students. Director: Simeon Lowy.

Women's Auxiliary 80 members. President: Margot Nathan. Vice-President and Secretary: Ruth Geoffey.

PUBLICATION:

Information Bulletin (English). 1963 Taft Avenue, Malate, Manila. Publisher: Jewish Community of the Philippines. Editor: Simeon Lowy.

SINGAPORE

JEWISH POPULATION: 650

The Jewish Community of Singapore dates from about 1840. The street which contains a house in which Jewish divine service was first held is now known as Synagogue Street. The first building to be erected as a synagogue was the Maghain Aboth, opened in 1878. A second synagogue, Chesed-El, was built by Sir Menasseh Meyer in 1904. The Jewish Community of Singapore consists of both Sephardim and Ashkenazim. The former originated for the most part in Baghdad and India, the latter, in Central Europe.

The respected position of the Jews there is reflected in the fact that Mr. David Saul Marshall, a former President of the Jewish Community there and a devoted Jew, became in 1955 the first Chief Minister of Singapore.

Jewish Welfare Board, (Jewish community), P.O.Box 474. Membership: 200. Pres.: Mrs. Sally Meyer, 3 Oxley Rise, 9. Sec. Elie S. Shababo. Rabbi: Jacob Shababo, 2 Oxley Rise, Singapore 9. Orthodox.

Synagogue Maghain Aboth, Waterloo Street. Treasurers: I. A. Elias. S. E. Sherida, J. N. Shohet, D. S. Solomon, M. Lewin, D. S. Marshall.

Synagogue Chesed-El, Oxley Rise.

Talmud Torah, 22b Bencoolen Street. Built by the late Sir Menasseh Meyer.

Habonim, c/o 2, Amber Mansions, Singapore 9. Membership 60. Pres.: M. E. Elias. Sec.: Miss K. Elias.

Kadima. Quarterly 22b. Bencoolen St.—Singapore.

SYRIA

JEWISH POPULATION: 4,500

Syria is one of the most anti-Jewish countries in the Near East. As a result, the Jewish population there has steadily been declining. Persecution of Jews assumed brutal dimensions in 1947 with the Jewish community being forced to proclaim its opposition to Zionism and Jews being arrested and tortured by police. The death penalty was imposed for attempted illegal emigration to Palestine. The outrages culminated in pogroms in Aleppo resulting in 8 deaths, several hundred wounded, 12 synagogues burnt down, 150 houses and a number of other buildings destroyed. The damage was estimated at $2.5 million. There were also bomb-attacks in Damascus. All this was accompanied by governmental restrictions on the movement of Jews, exclusion from Government service and schools, and prohibitions against engaging in any trade and the sale of property. This situation led to a considerable emigration of Jews from Syria to Palestine, Lebanon, and overseas.

It is estimated that about 15,000 left Syria between 1943 and 1947 and about 5,000–6,000, since 1948. The number of Jews in Syria in 1947 was estimated at 13,000 (17,000 less than in 1931.) Upon reestablishment of freedom of movement for Jews, a constant stream of Jews began moving to Lebanon and Israel.

According to reliable reports, the Jews are at present undergoing persecution and live in constant fear. After sunset they do not dare leave their houses. The stoning of synagogues and Jewish homes is not a rare occurrence. The economic situation is deteriorating. Syrian policy has been directed towards ousting the Jews from the country's economic life.

Especially precarious is the situation of Jewish youth, the majority of whom had received no education or very little of it (not more than four years) in a Talmud Torah where the children are taught mainly prayers. A very small percentage of them attend the American College or the French Secondary School.

Legally, it is impossible for a Jew to leave except for Lebanon, and even for that country it is very difficult to obtain an exit permit. When given, the permit is issued against five-hundred Syrian pounds bail. If a man overstays the two weeks granted by the permit, his family is liable to prolonged interrogation and ill-treatment.

DAMASCUS — 2,000 Jews.

Jewish Community, President: Elie Mizrahi. Religious head: Rabbi Nissim Nedebo.

After his accession to power in 1954, President Attassi proclaimed that all the restrictions set up by the Shishakli regime were abolished. This declaration allowed the Jews to leave Syria for Lebanon.

A mass movement for departure started among the Jews of Damascus. Almost a thousand persons began liquidating their small business in order to leave Syria. The police, however, informed the community that restrictions on movement were still in force. In 1943, there were 11,000 Jews in Damascus which figure decreased to 2,500 in 1947 and to 2,000 in 1954.

ALEPPO — 1,600 Jews.

Jewish Community, President and Chief Rabbi: Hakham Moshe Mizrahi.

There are at present 1,600 Jews in Aleppo. In November 1953, they numbered 2,100, and in December 1952—almost 3,000, in 1947—11,000, in 1940—17,000, 1910—35,000.

The Jews are divided into two classes: the rich, living in the El-Jemeliyeh residential quarter and the working and lower middle-class, around the Fortress in the Old City called El-Qala'a, in "Hart El Yahood" (Jewish Quarter).

If even one member of a family leaves Aleppo for Israel, the entire family is questioned, often thrown into prison, or compelled to leave the city with but a small suitcase of personal belongings.

In the summer of 1953, the police informed all Jews living in Jewish owned houses administered by the Trustees of Jewish Absentees' Property that they had to leave their flats within 90 days and turn over the keys to the police. These orders, however, were later cancelled.

Theoretically, Jews can move freely inside Syria, but, in reality, they can only travel by the Damascus Railway for fear of being robbed on other routes.

The Damascus newspaper "Esh-Sham," of February 23, 1954, wrote that the Jewish cemetery of Aleppo would shortly be disposed of at an auction sale and added that the sale would bring the city of Aleppo 7 million Syrian Pounds.

QAMISHLIYEH — 900 Jews.

Jewish Community, President: Hakham Moshe Nahum.

Qamishliyeh is a Syrian frontier town in the North, bordering on Turkey. It is situated in the area called Kurdistan where the important minority of Kurds live. The Jews of Qamishliyeh speak Kurdish and Arabic. Contrary to the Jews of other communities in Syria, most of them are farmers.

The situation of the Qamishliyeh Jews is rather stable, and they are generally protected by the Kurds against Damascus influences.

There is one Jewish school in Qamishliyeh where the official language is Arabic. Children are taught the Bible and prayers.

THAILAND

JEWISH POPULATION: 120

BANGKOK

Jewish Community, President: Dr. F. Jacobson.. Address: 295, Suriwongse Road, Bangkok. Sec.: Mrs. A. Lyman. The only Jewish settlement is in the capital Bangkok. Dr. Jacobson is also the Honorary Consul of Israel. The number of Jews in Thailand is decreasing due to emigration. Religious services are held only on the High Holidays at the home of Dr. Jacobson. There are no facilities for Jewish education.

TURKEY

JEWISH POPULATION: 60,000

Historically, the Jewry of Turkey formed three groups: Jews who had lived in the Byzantine Empire and came under Turkish rule after the fall of the Byzantines; The Sephardim from Spain and Portugal; and Ashkenazim from Eastern and Western Europe.

Small Jewish communities were founded in Turkey in the Roman period. When the Turks conquered the regions which now comprise Turkey in the 14th century and ended Byzantine rule, they granted the Jews of the country religious liberty. Until the 19th century, Jews under the Ottoman regime were unrestricted by any special laws and enjoyed the favor of the sultans. Many individual Jews rose to high positions and glory, although the masses lived in ignorance and poverty. The Sephardim emigrated to the country after 1492 and soon played a prominent role in Jewish life, founding great communities in Smyrna and Salonika.

The reign of Selim the II (1566-74) initiated the decline of the Ottoman Empire which, accompanied by the decadence of Turkish Jewry, continued into the 19th century. The later sultans made the life of the Jews difficult by means of continuous chicanery and special laws. However, in the 19th century equal legal rights were granted to Turkish Jewry. In 1923, minority rights were stipulated for the Jews in the Treaty of Lausanne. The government adopted a hostile attitude toward the Jews and, particularly, toward Zionism. However, this attitude gradually became more liberal so that Turkey became a haven for Jewish refugees from Hitler.

In the beginning of the 20th century, there were about 375,000 Jews in Turkey. This number gradually dropped to 78,730 by 1927.

The new General Assembly of the Jewish community in Istanbul, consisting of 60 members, met for the first time in 14 years in 1949 and elected the so-called Secular Council of nine members. The Council was entrusted with the direction of community affairs as well as the election of a Rabbinical Council of 20 members. The president of the Secular Council, who is regarded as the president of the community, is Marko Nassi.

The Secular Council prepared new statutes for the community which were approved by Parliament.

Recent political events in Turkey strengthened a tendency to put an end to discrimination against racial and religious minorities.

Emigration to Israel has reduced the Jewish population of Turkey by more than 40 per cent, and it is responsible for the disappearance of many small communities. At the beginning of the emigration movement, the Jewish population totaled 75,000.

Since the passing of Hayim Bejarano,

the last Hakham Bashi (Chief Rabbi) of Turkey, about 20 years ago, Turkish Jewry has had no spiritual head. The attitude of the then Turkish government, among other reasons, prevented the election of a new Hakham Bashi. Only now has it been possible to proceed with these elections. In 1953, 66 delegates, representing the various Jewish communities in the country, assembled in Istanbul and elected Rabbi Raphael Saban to the highest post in the Jewish religious hierarchy in Turkey.

A very impressive inauguration ceremony took place in the Synagogue Neve-Shalom in Istanbul in the presence of many thousands of worshippers assembled inside and outside the synagogue. Leading representatives of the Turkish authorities as well as the consuls of foreign states, including Israel, were present at the ceremony. The Chief Rabbinate established a seminary to meet the shortage of spiritual leaders and teachers for the Jewish communities. The Seminary is located at Hasköy, a suburb of Istanbul.

Turkish Jewry is predominantly Sephardic. The Ashkenazim, numbering approximately 10,000, live mainly in Istanbul. There is one Jewish member of Parliament, Mr. Henry Soriano, elected May 1954. Since the establishment of the State of Israel, 30,000 Turkish Jews have emigrated there. Turkey is the only Moslem country maintaining friendly relations with the State of Israel.

ISTANBUL: 40,000 Jews

Hahambasilik, Yemenici sokak 23, Beyoglu, Grand Rabbinate of Turkey. Pres. of Rabbinical Council: Grand Rabbi R. Saban. Pres. of Lay Council: Marko Nassi. Secretary of Lay Council: Y. Salman. This is the central body of all Jewish organizations. It is composed of two councils: The Rabbinical Council, which is in charge of purely religious matters, and the Lay Council, in charge of administrative and budgetary matters. The Lay Council is also a contact of the World Jewish Congress. Both Councils are elected. The Grand Rabbinate is constituted on the basis of an ordinance dating from 1866. It is in permanent contact with the authorities and discharges itself of its representative duties of the community in all instances where it is necessitated. According to the official census of 1953, the percentage of literacy among Jews is 72.4%, more than double the non-Jewish population (34.6%). Turkish and French are increasingly replacing Ladino as their mother tongue.

Coordination, Yemenici sokak 23, Beyoglu. A special commission of the Grand Rabbinate of Turkey which coordinates all social and cultural activities of Jewish associations of Istanbul and their local section in Turkey. Pres.: Isaac Saban. Under this body comes:

Fakirleri Koruma Cemiyeti, Minare sokak 11-16, Beyoglu. B'nai B'rith. Pres.: I. Altabev.

Halat Musevi Hastanesi, Balat, Musevo Hastanesi Hospital Or Hahayim. Dir.: Dr. Akchiotti. Pres.: Cemil Avigdor.

Yetimleri Koruma Vebarindirma Cemineti, Yeminici sokak 23, Beyoglu. Orphanage. Pres.: M. Paul Heilpern.

Ihtiyarlar Yurdu, Yemenici sokak 2, Beyoglu. Home for the aged. Pres.: Mrs. Sophie Leites.

EDUCATION:

Kult Isleri Komisyonu, Yemenici sokak 23, Beyoglu. Mahazike Torah. Pres.: Haim Varon. The main cultural association. Provides for religious instruction of children from 7–16 years of age and maintains a seminary for the training of rabbis.

Mekteplere Yardim Komisyonu, Yemenici sokak 23, Beyoglu. Education commission. Pres.: Hugo Arditti. In charge of two primary schools — those of Hasköy — and one High School with a total of 631 pupils. The government makes an annual budgetary allocation toward the Jewish schools of the country with a view to covering the expenses involved in the teaching of the Turkish language and of Turkish culture. The main language of instruction is Turkish. Hebrew and French are taught as secondary languages. In the high schools, English is also taught as a secondary language. The study of Jewish subjects is limited to Hebrew; however, in the fourth and fifth grades of the primary schools 2 hours are assigned to religious instruction. An estimated 50% of the Jewish children in Turkey do not receive any Jewish education.

Yardim Ve Bakim Hayir Cemiyeti, Yemenici sokak 23, Beyoglu. Sedaka Umarpe. Pres.: Bedri Bension Pensoy.

Fakir Ve Mektep Cocuklarina Yardim Cemiyeti, Sisane Karakol. Mektep sokak 47, Yardim Han 1, Beyoglu. Mischne Torah. Pres.: Daniel Behar.

Hasta Ve Fakir Cocuklara Yardim Komisyonu, Yemenici sokak 23. Beyoglu. Commission for aid to the tubercular. Pres.: Alfred Nahum.

Goutte de Lait, Yemenici sokak 2, Beyoglu. Commission to aid infants. Pres.: Mrs. Anna Moskovitz.

IZMIR — 4,500 Jews

Jewish Community, Rabbinical Court. Pres.: Rabbi Boton. 2 Jewish schools: Talmud Torah, 300 pupils and Bne Brith School, 200 pupils.

ANKARA — 3,000 Jews

Jewish Community.

EDIRNE — 1,300 Jews

Jewish Community.

OTHER CITIES — 3,200 Jews

PUBLICATIONS:

L'Etoile du Levant — weekly — Independent — French. Editor: Isak Kohen. Beyoglu, Galipdede Cad 59, Istanbul.

Salom — weekly — Turkish and Ladino. Independent. Editor: Avram Leyon. Sair Ziya Pasa Caddesi, Bereket Han 24/5, Galata.

La Luz de Türkiya (Ladino, Turkish); weekly; Mumhane Caddesi No. 102, Galata, Istanbul.

La Vera Luz; weekly. Ladino and Turkish. Tahtakale, Prevuayans Han 12, Istanbul.

YEMEN

JEWISH POPULATION: 600

According to the tradition of the Yemenite Jews, they first settled in Yemen immediately after the destruction of the First Temple.

During the first centuries of the common Era, there were political and cultural relations between Yemen and Ethiopia, and in both countries the Jews played an important part until Christianity became the official religion in Ethiopia and Islam was established in Arabia.

In the 6th century, the South Arabian dynasty of the Himyarites were converted to Judaism, but their rule weakened because the majority of the population, and especially the noble families, continued to practice paganism. The Himyarite kings waged war several times against Aksum (Ethiopia). Dhu Nuwas, the last Jewish king of Yemen, retaliated for the persecutions of the Jews in the Byzantine Empire by executing Byzantine Christian merchants who crossed Arabia on their way to India. Subsequently, Dhu Nuwas, defeated by the Ethiopians, committed suicide, and many Yemenite Jews were slain by the Ethiopian invaders. However, a great number of Jews continued to resist in the mountains. The efforts of Ethiopian Christian missionaries to convert the Jews in the cities proved a failure. After the country of Yemen became subject to Persian rule, Judaism was tolerated by the Persian government, and the situation of the Jews improved. During the Moslem period, the position of the Yemenite Jews deteriorated. However, they contributed money to the Babylonian Jewish academies in the 11th century.

In the 12th century, the Jews of Yemen were subjected to severe persecution. Maimonides thereupon sent an epistle from Egypt to the Chief Rabbi of the Yemenite Jews, Rabbi Jacob Ben Nathanel, encouraging the Yemenite Jews to remain faithful to Judaism in spite of all persecutions. This had a great and lasting effect since the Yemenites recognized Maimonides as their religious leader.

During the following centuries, the constant wars resulted mostly in persecution of the Jews. In the middle of the 17th century, the Jews of Yemen became vic-

tims of the movement founded by Sabbetai Zevi. Many prepared to emigrate to Palestine, but were taken captive, and the Chief Rabbi of San'a, the greatest Jewish community of Yemen, was horribly tortured. In spite of persecution, some Jews held high offices, and the Jew Oraki (Salem Ben Aaron Aragi Hacohen) was the favorite of two successive imams and protected his correligionists. Jews served as royal ministers during recent centuries.

The elected leaders were the Nasi, generally a wealthy and mostly also a learned man, who represented the Jews of his community before the government of the imam, and the Mori, the rabbi. There were neither communal schools nor public welfare organizations or buildings. Nevertheless, the religious education of the Jews of Yemen was on a high level. In daily life, the Jews spoke Arabic, but they knew Hebrew and Aramaic, and almost all of them were well acquainted with the Bible and its commentaries, written by native authors. Numerous Midrashim were created in Yemen. The prayer book received special attention, and many native poets composed Piyutim. Cabala was popular among the Jews of Yemen. Mori Salem Shabezi (b. 1619) was considered the greatest poet of the Yemenite Jews.

Although the Jewish community enjoyed a wide degree of autonomy in the running of its internal affairs, a Jew was never equal to a Moslem. They were forbidden to ride a horse or to wear brightly colored clothes in public. Jews could not testify against a Moslem in court.

Most of the Yemenite Jews were either traders, craftsmen or laborers, and the great majority were desperately poor. Jewish gold and silversmiths had a deservedly high reputation for fine filigree work. There were also Jewish agricultural villages which have been described in a very favorable light by the Christian Arab writer, Amin ar-Rihani.

The largest community was that of San'a, the capital. Until the recent exodus, it is said to have numbered about 8,000 Jews. There were smaller communities in various towns, such as Sa'da Shamar and Kaukaban.

Until Portuguese Jews settled in Aden in the 16th century, the Jews of Yemen were almost unknown to Jews of other countries. In 1859, Jacob Saphir, of Jerusalem, visited Yemen and brought back reports of the plight of the Yemenite Jews. He was followed by the orientalists, Joseph Halevy, Eduard Glaser, Yomtob Zemach, and Hermann Burchard, who was murdered in Yemen in 1909. The reports written by these authors resulted in efforts to improve the situation of the Yemenite Jews. Despite the law prohibiting their emigration, the first group Aliyah of Yemenite Jews took place in 1882. From 1909 onwards, a larger number of Yemenite Jews succeeded in emigrating to Palestine after tremendous hardships.

On May 14, 1948, the Jewish population of Yemen numbered about 50,000. By September 19, 1950, when the last plane left Aden for Israel under "Operation Magic Carpet," there remained some 3,000 Jews. The precise number transported to Israel by air between December 1948 and September 1950 was 47,140. By February 1951, the Jewish Agency estimated that there were approximately 1,300 Jews in Yemen. In 1954, about 500 more went to Israel. There are an estimated 600 Jews in Yemen now.

LATIN AMERICA

ARGENTINA

JEWISH POPULATION: 400,000

The presence of Jews in Argentina goes back to the earliest Spanish colonization in the 16th century when Marranos settled there. In 1868, a Jew, Louis H. Brie, founded the first Jewish community of English, French, and German Jews. In 1889, a group of 135 Russian Jewish families arrived to devote themselves to agriculture. Jewish immigration increased through the establishment of the 14 ICA Colonies by Baron Hirsch. In 1898, the first of these agricultural colonies, Moisesville, was founded. There was an average annual immigration of 6–7,000 Jews, mainly from Eastern Europe and the Middle East, from 1920 to 1938, after which year immigration was increasingly curtailed; since 1946 immigration of non-farmers has been almost completely barred.

Around the year 1900, the Jews began a vigorous campaign against the white slave traders (Tmeiyim) and succeeded in banning them from the community until their disappearance. Since then the Jews developed a dynamic and diversified Jewish cultural life which is exemplified by their devotion to Jewish survival, Jewish education, and a keen interest in the welfare of the State of Israel. They play an important role in the general life of Argentina and contribute much to the progress of the country. Until recently, the Chevra Kadisha Ashkenazit, founded in 1894, also fulfilled the functions of a community Council. In 1949, it was converted into the Ashkenazic Community of Buenos Aires.

According to a Jewish survey by Dr. Kurbinsky (in "Problems of Education: 1953"), Argentina has 121 Jewish elementary schools and 4 day schools with a total enrollment of 13,790 pupils. Of these, 3,000 are in kindergartens and 9,880 in the other schools. About 1,000 students attend secondary schools in Buenos Aires. A negative feature in education is that the attendance in the last three grades of secondary schools is only 7% of the total number of pupils who began on the lower levels instead of the normal 40%. The enrollment in the Jewish schools is below the 20% of the total number of children of school age. However, a considerable number of children receive private instruction.

The majority of Argentina's Jews live in the capital; ranking next to Buenos Aires in the size of Jewish population are the communities of Rosario, Cordoba,

Eva Peron and Bahia Blanca. Small Jewish settlements are scattered in more than 800 towns and villages. The ICA colonies, concentrated mainly in the provinces of Santa Fe and Entre Rios, have an rural population of 8,300, of whom 2,289 are farmers (Magazine "Colonist Cooperator," 1954).

The Jews are active in the economic life of Argentina. They have been pioneers in establishing new enterprises such as housing, textiles, leather, furniture, and chemicals. 2,450 Jews are registered as manufacturers. According to a census in 1949, there are 1,400 Jewish physicians, 510 lawyers, 120 engineers, and 500 industrial experts.

BUENOS AIRES (280,000 Jews)

DAIA (Delegacion de Asociaciones Israelitas Argentina) Buenos Aires. Pasteur 633. Central body of Argentine Jewry, including Ashkenazim (82%) and Sephardim (18%), affiliated with the World Jewish Congress. Founded 1934, it has 60 branches in the Jewish communities outside Buenos Aires. The Executive of the DAIA is elected by a general assembly of delegates of its 82 constituent bodies in the capital and of its provincial branches. Hon. Pres.: Dr. Moises Goldman. Presidents: Dr. Jose Ventura, Dr. Abraham Mibashan, Dr. Isaac Goldenberg. Sec.: Hirsch Triwaks.

Congreso Judio Mundial, Corrientes 1979. Argentine office of the World Jewish Congress. Representative: Mark Turkow.

Union of Jewish Communities—Vaad Hakehiloth, Pasteur 633. Represents the vast majority of Argentine Ashkenazic Jews. The Sephardic community, numbering 55,000 persons, is the largest in Latin America and has its own organizations. President of the Union of Jewish Communities: Samuel Rabinowitz. Sec.: S. M. Cohen.

Central Zionist Council, Larrea 744. Pres.: Dr. Isaac Goldenberg. Comprises representatives of the following Zionist groups: Federacion Sionista Argentina (General Zionists), Cangallo 2194; Poale Zion, Ayacucho 532; Mapam; Mizrachi, Ecuador 454; Poel Mizrachi; Revisionists, Diaz Velez 3960–64; Wizo, Esparaza 27.

Vaad Hachinuch Harashi (Central Committee for Education), Ayacucho 868. The Vaad Hachinuch Harashi, called in Spanish "Cursas religiosas Israelitas," concentrates its activities on 61 schools and 22 kindergartens outside Buenos Aires and also supervises 6 schools in the capital. It supports the following two institutions:

The Institute of Jewish Studies (Machon Lelimudei Hayahaduz) which trains Hebrew teachers and prepares students for leading communal positions. It is directed by Dr. M. Emanueli, and

Teachers' Seminary for Girls with 60 students.

Jewish Community of Buenos Aires, Pasteur 633. The Community of the Ashkenazim in Buenos Aires has a membership of over 40,000. It maintains the rabbinate and the Vaad Hachinuch, contributing 40% to the budgets of the Jewish schools, and aids in the construction of school buildings. It also sponsored the Teachers Seminary. Pres.: Dr. Abraham Mibashan.

Rabbinate, Rabbis: Samuel I. Glicksberg, N. Zigman. There are in Buenos Aires and its suburbs 70 synagogues and houses of prayer.

Vaad Hachinuch: (Education Committee for Buenos Aires). Supervises 56 Hebrew and Yiddish schools with 356 teachers and 9,150 pupils. Most of them belong to the Bialik schools (Hebrew), Sholem Aleichem schools (Yiddish-Hebrew), or to the Tel Aviv schools and have their own magnificent buildings. Teachers' Seminary (Hebrew-Yiddish). Director: J. Mendelson. 24 classes with 25 teachers and 583 students.

Congregation Sefardi "Yesod Hadath": Lavalle 2449. Synagogue and Hebrew schools for the Sephardic section of the Jewish community.

Congregation Israelita Latina: Piedras 1164, Sephardic Synagogue and Hebrew School.

Sociedad Hebraica Argentina: Ayacucho 860. 2,500 members. Library and publication of works in Spanish on Judaism.

Jewish Colonization Association—ICA: Pasteur 644. Supervises 16 colonies founded by Baron Hirsch.

YIVO: Pasteur 633.

Writers' and Journalists' Association "Nomberg": Pres.: Jacob Botoshansky.

Publishing House of Polish Jews: Director Abr. Mitelberg. Published 100 volumes in Yiddish. There are also Yiddish publications: "Yidbuch," "Besaraber Yidn," "Cultur Congress," "Undzer Wort."

Histadruth Ivrith: (Organization for Hebrew Culture). Publishes Hebrew monthly "Darom" and maintains Hebrew courses. Pres.: Rab. A. Blum.

Maccabi (Sport organization): Tucuman 3135. 6,000 members.

Ezra Jewish Hospital: Terrada 1164.

Banko Israelita de Rio de la Plata: Organized 1939, merging 7 smaller Jewish banks. Pres.: Borris Knobel.

Banko Israelita de Buenos Aires: Founded 1940.

COMMUNITIES OUTSIDE BUENOS AIRES

Colony AVIGDOR (Prov. Entre Rios) (420 Jews).

Comunidad Israelita Avigdor, Pres.: H. Freudenstein. 100 members. Own building and synagogue. *Jewish school:* 1 teacher, 45 pupils. *Jewish library. WIZO; K.K.L.; Youth Association.*

AVELLANEDA (4,000 Jews)

Jewish Community, membership 500. Pres.: Z. Berdichevsky. Own building and synagogue. *Jewish School;* 320 pupils, 16 teachers. *Zionist Organization; Poale Zion; WIZO; Zion Youth; Dror; Gordonia.*

BAHIA BLANCA (3,000 Jews)

Asociacion Israelita, Espana 42 (Jewish community). 700 members. Own building and synagogue. Pres.: Jose Jaimovitz.

Jewish School: 180 pupils. 6 teachers. Supervised by "Asociacion hebres Dr. Herzl."

Circulo Cultural Sionista, Las Heras 37. Maintains Youth Club Macabi.

BASAVILBASO (Prov. ENTRE RIOS).
(2600 Jews)

Asociacion Mutual Israelita Argentina (Jewish community), Calle Dr. Bernardo. Uchitel 345. 480 members. Pres.: Simon Volkov. Own building. 2 Synagogues: "Tefila Lamashe" and "Beth Abraham."

Jewish School and Kindergarten: 120 pupils. 2 teachers.

Jewish Library; WIZO; Zionist Groups; Jewish Hospital. Branch of DAIA.

BERNASCONI (Prov. EVA PERON)
(800 Jews)

Asociacion Communidad Israelita Religiosa, Jewish community: 123 members. Own building. Synagogue. Pres.: Juda Marias.

Jewish School: 20 pupils, 1 teacher.

Jewish Library; Zionist Group; Women's Charitable Association.

GENERAL ROCA (RIO NEGRO)
(1,000 Jews)

Asociacion Colectividad Israelita de Rio Negro y Neuquen (Jewish Community of Rio Negro and Neuquen), Pres.: Leon N. Kaspin.

Comunidad Israelita de General Roca (Jewish community of General Roca), 66 members. Pres.: Hanina Teblum.

Jewish School: 43 pupils; 1 teacher.

Jewish Library.

Colony General Roca-Centro Cultural Israelita, 100 members. Own building. Synagogue. Library.

WIZO; Library; Zionist Youth Groups; Betar.

VILLA MARIA (Prov. CORDOBA).
(120 Jews)

Sociedad Israelita de Beneficencia, Entre Rios 654. Pres.: Feiwel Michalenvitz.

Jewish School: 16 pupils. 1 teacher. Library.

WIZO: Hebraica.

TUCUMAN (4,000 Jews)

Sociedad Union Israelita. Las Piedras 976/80. 600 members. Pres.: Selig Gorban.

Jewish School: 230 pupils. 5 teachers. Library.

Asociacion Israelita Sefardı (Sephardic Jewish community).

Dorshei Zion; Unidad Sionista; WIZO; Poalei Zion; Zionist Youth.

TRES ARROYOS (Prov. BUENOS AIRES) (100 Jews)

Sociedad Union Israelita (Jewish community).

Jewish School: 14 pupils. 1 teacher.

LAS PALMERAS (Prov. SANTA FE) (250 Jews)

Asociacion Israelita (Jewish Community), 60 members. Pres.: L. Tenenbaum.

Jewish School: 30 pupils. 1 teacher.

Synagogue. Library.

MOISESVILLE (Prov. SANTA FE). (1,500 Jews)

Asociacion Israelita (Jewish community), 515 members. Pres.: Akiva Gelbert. 4 Synagogues.

Jewish Teachers' Seminary: 45 students. 1 teacher.

Jewish School: 125 pupils. 6 teachers. 2 libraries.

WIZO; Zionist Groups; "Baron Hirsch" Hospital.

COLONY MONTEFIORE (Prov. SANTA FE). (400 Jews)

Asociacion Israelita de Beneficencia, Casilla 45. 55 members. Pres.: S. Galanter. Synagogue.

Jewish School: 125 pupils. 2 teachers. 2 libraries.

WIZO; 2 Cultural Centers; Women's Charitable Society.

MEDANOS (Prov. BUENOS AIRES) (600 Jews)

Asociacion Israelita "Ezra," 150 members. Pres.: Ezekiel M. Goldin.

Jewish School: 22 pupils. 1 teacher. Library.

Cultural Center for Youth. WIZO; Macabi.

NECOCHEA (170 Jews)

Centro Union Israelita (Jewish community), Moseno 157/59. 75 members. Pres.: Benjamin Berezovski.

SALTA (400 Jews)

Asociacion Alianza Israelita (Jewish community), Eva Peron 1045. 105 members. Pres.: Bernardo Vinograd.

Synagogue; Library; Zionist Groups.

Jewish School: 35 pupils. 1 teacher.

SANTE FE (4,000 Jews)

Sociedad Union Israelita Sionista (Jewish community) le de Mayo 2236/44. Pres.: David Goldin. Maintains all Jewish institutions. Own building. Synagogue.

Jewish School: 160 pupils, 6 teachers. Library.

WIZO; Mizrachi; Poale Zion.

Chevrah Kedischa Ashkenazi, 800 members. Maintains Shochet and subsidizes the Jewish School.

SAN JUAN (500 Jews)

Sociedad Israelita de Beneficencia, Cordoba 969. 190 members. Pres.: Louis L. Goldstein.

Synagogue; Library; WIZO.

Jewish School: 40 pupils. 1 teacher.

ZARATE (Prov. BUENOS AIRES) (150 Jews)

Sociedad Zrubovel.

Jewish School: 14 pupils. 1 teacher.

POSADAS (MISIONES) (400 Jews)

Union Israelita (Ashkenazim), 60 members. Pres.: Abish Fried.

Jewish School: 36 pupils. 2 teachers. Library.

Sephardic Jewish Congregation, Synagogue. Own building.

PARANA (2,500 Jews)

Asociacion Israelita de Cultura, M. Cascros 186 616 members. Pres.: Dr. A. Shapira. Own building. Library.

Jewish School and Kindergarten: 106 pupils 3 teachers.

Asociacion Israelita Argentina Sefardi.
Zionist Groups; WIZO; Women's Charitable Society.

PUNTA ALTA (Prov. BUENOS AIRES)
(150 Jews)

Circulo Cultural Israelita, Humberto 551.
Jewish School: 18 pupils. 1 teacher.

CATAMARCA (200 Jews)

Asociacion Israelita Argentina (Jewish community), Presidente Peron 656. 110 members. Pres.: Pedro Sayentz.
Jewish School: 50 pupils. 1 teacher. Library.
Sephardic Jewish Congregation.

CAMPANA (Prov. BUENOS AIRES)
(144 Jews)

Sociedad Cultural Israelita "Scholem Aleijem," Gral. Uriburn 811. Pres.: B. Sturm.

CONCEPCION DEL URUGUAY
(Prov. ENTRE RIOS) (230 Jews)

Centro Social Israelita Argentino, Ameghino 132. Synagogue. Library. Youth Center. Wizo.
Jewish School: 35 pupils. 1 teacher. Pres.: Dr. Abraham Salzman.

CONCORDIA (Prov. ENTRE DIOS)
(1,200 Jews)

Asociacion Agudas Israel Sephardi. Central Cultural Chalutz Youth. Synagogue.
Jewish School: 75 pupils. 2 teachers. Pres.: Adolpho Handlin.

CORONEL SUAREZ (Prov. BUENOS AIRES)
(1,200 Jews)

Asociacion Israelita (Jewish community), Calle Garibaldi 163. Synagogue. Library. Wizo. Youth center. Pres.: Abr. Brodski.

CORDOBA (8,000 Jews)

Centro Union Israelita (Jewish community), Alvear 254. 1,100 members. Synagogue. Zionist groups. Jewish hospital. Pres.: Salomon Belans.
Jewish School: Kindergarten and elementary school. 300 pupils. Hebrew-Yiddish department: Director and 4 teachers. Spanish Departments: Director and 10 teachers.

ROSARIO (Prov. DE SANTA FE)
(10,000 Jews) (Jewish Community)

Asociacion Israelita de Beneficencia, Paraguay 1152. 2,450 members. Synagogue. Sephardic Center. Zionist groups. House for Jewish Culture. Chalutz groups. Wizo. DAIA Branch.
4 Jewish Schools under Asociacion Israelita. 15 courses. 480 pupils. 9 teachers.

RIVERA (Prov. BUENOS AIRES)
(2,000 Jews)

Asociacion Israelita (Jewish community), 570 members. Synagogue. Library. Cultural Center. Zionist groups.
Jewish School: 170 pupils. 2 teachers.

RESISTENCIA (900 Jews)

Asociacion Israelita de Beneficencia, Ameghino 353. 350 members. Synagogue. Zionist groups. Library. Religious Commission. Cultural Center. Pres.: Manuel Las.
Jewish School: 128 pupils. 5 teachers.

PERIODICALS:

DAILIES:
Di Yidische Zaytung. Corrientes 2314, Buenos Aires, Yiddish.
Di Presse. Castelli 360, Buenos Aires, Yiddish.

TWICE WEEKLY:
Juedische Wochenschau. Hip. Irigoyen 2481, Buenos Aires, German-Spanish.

WEEKLIES:
Argentiner Lebn (Yiddish), Corrientes 2670, Buenos Aires.
Di Naie Zait. Ayacucho 352, Buenos Aires, Yiddish.
Hatikva. Colombres 74, Buenos Aires, Hungarian.
Mundo Israelita. Sarmiento 2396, Buenos Aires, Spanish.

Religiese Stimme (Yiddish), Ecuador 637, Buenos Aires.

Rosarier Lebn. Mitre 1546, Rosario. Spanish-Yiddish.

Tribuna. Cangallo 2122. Buenos Aires, Yiddish.

FORNIGHTLIES:

Di Yiddishe Welt (Yiddish), Cangallo 2194, Buenos Aires.

Dos Naie Wort. Pueyrredon 667, Buenos Aires, Yiddish.

Landsmanschaften (Yiddish), Velasco 1165, Buenos Aires.

Nueva Sion. Viamonte 2296, Buenos Aires, Spanish.

Renacimiento de Israel, Callao 257, Buenos Aires.

Undzer Welt. Corrientes 2791, Buenos Aires, Yiddish.

Undzer Wort (Yiddish), Corrientes 4136, Buenos Aires.

MONTHLIES:

Argentiner Beimelej, Serrano 436, Buenos Aires, Yiddish.

Argentiner Magazin. Jujuy 37, Buenos Aires, Yiddish.

Campana Unida pro Israel, Cangallo 1873, Buenos Aires.

D.A.I.A. "Informa", Pasteur 633, Buenos Aires.

Darom. Paraguay 2519, Buenos Aires, Hebrew.

Der Shpigl. Sarmiento 2221, Buenos Aires, Yiddish.

D.E.S.A., Pasteur 341, Buenos Aires.

Dos Freie Wort (Yiddish), Camargo 340, Buenos Aires.

El Colono Cooperador (Yiddish-Spanish). Corrientes 2387, Buenos Aires.

Eretz Israel. Pasteur 341, Buenos Aires.

Farn Folks Guezunt, Corrientes 2854, Buenos Aires, Yiddish.

Hador. Ayacucho 352, Buenos Aires, Spanish.

Illustrirte Literarishe Bleter (Yiddish-Spanish), Remedios Escalada de San Martin 2670, Dep. C., Buenos Aires.

Jazaq Veematz, Tucuman 3135, Buenos Aires.

Jedies (Yiddish), Libertad 773, Buenos Aires.

Jerusalem. Larrea 744, Buenos Aires, Spanish.

Kol Hanoar, Larrea 746, Buenos Aires.

La Luz. Pasteur 359, Piso 2ºA, Buenos Aires, Spanish.

O.S.F.A., Esparza 27, Buenos Aires.

Principios. Sta.Fe 174, Parana.

Revista de la Camara de Comercia Argentino-Israeli, Pasteur 341, Piso 6º, Buenos Aires.

S.H.A., Sarmiento 2223, Buenos Aires.

Shriften. Viamonte 2534, Buenos Aires, Yiddish.

Undzer Guedank (Yiddish), Viamonte 2296, Buenos Aires.

Vida de Israel, Corrientes 2241, Buenos Aires.

Yikuf (Yiddish), Valentin Gomez 3245, Buenos Aires.

BI--MONTHLY:

Davar, Sarmiento 2233, Buenos Aires.

PERIODICALS:

Aporte, Paso 481, Buenos Aires.

Argentiner Yivo Yedies (Yiddish), Pasteur 633, Buenos Aires.

Argentiner Yivo Schriften (Yiddish), Pasteur 633, Buenos Aires.

Congregacion. Libertad 785, Buenos Aires.

Di Yiddishe Froj (Yiddish-Spanish), Valentin Gomez 3245, Buenos Aires.

Grodner Opklangen (Yiddish), Valentin Gomez 3243, Buenos Aires.

Israel. Sarmiento 2153, Buenos Aires.

Juventud Libre. Serrano 341, Buenos Aires.

Mizrachi Stimme (Yiddish), Sarmiento 2888, Buenos Aires.

Nai Teater (Yiddish), Boulogne sur Mer 547/49, Buenos Aires.

Nuestra Palabra. Corrientes 4136, Buenos Aires

Shul Bleter (Yiddish), Sarrano 341, Buenos Aires.

Shul Schriften (Yiddish), Boulogne sur Mer 671, Buenos Aires.

QUARTERLIES:

Comentario, Tucuman 2137, Buenos Aires.

Davke. Montes de Oca 1275, Buenos Aires, Yiddish.

ANNUAL:

Holz-Industrial (Yiddish), Corrientes 2783, Buenos Aires.

ARUBA

JEWISH POPULATION: 130

Jews first settled in Aruba in 1929-30, coming from Colombia and Curacao. Of the island's 46 Jewish families, all but the 7 Dutch families are of East European origin. They live in two cities, Oranjestad (73) and San Nicolas (57).

The economic situation is satisfactory. Immigration is restricted. There is no anti-Semitism. Almost all the Jews are naturalized citizens.

There are 40 Jewish children in Aruba of whom only 5 are of school age attend-ing the public school without Jewish instruction. Most of the grownup youth are educated in the United States.

Lately, a Jewish Community has been formed. The Aruba Country Club also serves as a gathering place for the Jews on the Island. The address of the representatives of the Jewish Community (Israelietische Gemeente) is:

Pres.: Morris Serphos, P. O. B. 200, San Nicolas, *Aruba* Netherl. Ant. Sec.: David Schlachter.

BARBADOS

(BRITISH WEST INDIES)

JEWISH POPULATION: 104

The Jewish settlement, composed of East European immigrants, was established in 1933. There is no Jewish school. Eight children attend Christian schools. About 40 children are of school age.

Jewish Community Center: 256 Bridgetown, Barbados. Membership: 35. Pres.: Dr. Oscar Pillersdorf. Sec.: Ernest Sanders.

Religious Community: Maintains a synagogue. Pres.: Simon Altman.

WIZO, 35 members. Pres.: Mrs. Rose Altman.

BOLIVIA

JEWISH POPULATION: 4,200

During Spanish domination (1531–1825), a large number of Marranos came to Bolivia and established themselves in Potosi as silver miners. With the introduction of the Inquisition into Peru (1570), of which Bolivia was then a part, the Marranos were persecuted, imprisoned, and some burned. The rest were assimilated into the Catholic population.

The establishment of the republic in

1825 brought religious tolerance, and a few Jews subsequently settled in Bolivia. In 1905, the first immigrants, composed of Eastern European Jews and of Sephardim from the Near East, arrived in Bolivia, but until 1933, no more than 200 had settled in the country. Since 1933, about 6,000 German Jews were admitted, particularly after the governmental resolution of 1938 offering free land for farmers. On a single farm colony, at Villa Sacaba, 200 refugees were established, and other similar settlements were planned but, later abandoned. 7000 Jews immigrated to Bolivia in 1933-1942, but many of them left the country because of the climatic conditions. In 1940, a decree prohibited the admittance of Jews and even the issuance of transit visas to them. These restrictions were later somewhat modified, and the government admitted a number of Jewish war orphans in 1947, but since then, Jewish immigration is practically barred.

During the second world war there were antisemitic manifestations, mainly from the Germans living in Bolivia who were Nazi sympathizers.

Most of the Jews in Bolivia now are of German and East European origin. Only 10% of the Jewish population are Sephardim. During the last three years, the number of immigrants was about 200 (17 families from Israel). There are 300 to 350 Jewish industrial enterprises in the country and 400 Jewish stores. Three university professors are Jews. The Jewish economic situation is deteriorating. A very large part of the Jews deals with imports, which the government has stringently restricted. The majority of the Jewish population · Bolivia lives in La Paz; the rest are in Cochabamba, Oruro, Santa Cruz, Tarija, Sucre, and between 50 and 80 in other places.

LA PAZ (2,576 Jews)

Comite Central Judio de Bolivia Casilla 189, La Paz. This is the representative body of all Jews in Bolivia and co-ordinates the work of the other Jewish organizations. Pres.: Francisco Susz Guggenheim. Sec.: Eugenio Riegler. The Comite Central is recognized de facto by the government and has a sub-committee in Cochabamba and representatives in other towns.

Comunidad Israelita de Bolivia (Jewish community), Calle Canada, Casilla 2198. Membership: 380. German-speaking Jews. Pres.: Arturo Weil. Sec.: Manfred Cohen.

Circulo Israelita Landeata 84, Casilla 189. Membership: 300. East European Jews. Pres.: Abraham Valevici. Sec.: Abraham Weisman. Possesses its own building where all organizations have their headquarters.

Federacion Sionista Unida de Bolivia Casilla 1341. Founded 1943. 250 members. Pres.: Jose Winkler. Sec.: Eric F. Nebel.

Federacion Wizo Casilla 1341. Pres.: Baila Spiro. Sec.: Brana Burdman. 350 members.

B'nai B'rith Casilla 995. Pres.: Benno Siegelwachs. 50 members.

Sopro Diaz Romero 507, Casilla 975. Pres.: Izak Duizbek. Sec.: Willi Siemenhauer. Sopro is a welfare organization and maintains an Old Age home in Cochabamba and supports 12 orphans. 350 members.

Cid Macabi, Federico Ouaco Esq. Colorado. Pres.: Alfredo Weinheber. 200 members.

Juventud del Circulo Israelita Casilla 189. Pres.: Abraham Zanger. 75 members.

Liga de Damas, Casilla 416. Under the Comunidad. Pres.: Eva Krakauer. 200 members.

Colegio, Calle Canada, Casilla 2198. Under the Comunidad. Consists of a kindergarten (50 pupils), 6 grades of elementary school

(154 pupils), and two classes of high school (35 children). The Colegio has a total of 190 Jewish and 50 Gentile pupils. There are 11 teachers. Dir.: Rabbi Guenter Friedlander. About 200 Jewish children in La Paz attend Gentile schools.

Youth Organization Under the Circulo Israelita. Head: Abraham Zanger. 75 members.

COCHABAMBA
(900 Jews, mostly of German origin)

Comunidad Israelita Casilla 349. Pres.: Jacobo Kantorowitz.

Jewish School Maintained by the Comunidad.

Circulo Israelita Calle Baptista 134, Casilla 373. Pres.: Wolf Horowitz. Sec.: Ernst Hershtal.

Federacion Sionista Unida Casilla 74. Pres.: Abraham Mansbach.

ORURO (100 Jews)
Union Israelita Casilla 270. Pres.: Jacobo Geliebter.

SANTA CRUZ (65 Jews)
Comunidad Israelita.

SUCRE (25 Jews)
Colectividad Israelita Casilla 116. Pres.: Leo Peiser.

TARIJA (62 Jews)
Comunidad Israelita Casilla 4. Pres.: Sally Steyn.

PUBLICATIONS:

Die Zeit. Published by Comunidad Israelita of Cochabamba, German, Fortnightly.

Das Echo. Cochabamba. Pub.: Dr. Ludwig K. Stargardt, German, Fortnightly.

BRAZIL
JEWISH POPULATION: 120,000

From the day of the discovery of Brazil (1500), Jews have taken part in the life of the country. In 1503, a Marrano, Fernando de Naronha, came from Lisbon to Brazil with 6 vessels manned by Marranos. He discovered the island of St. John. Later, other Jews came from Portugal and introduced the sugar and tobacco industries and developed rice and cotton plantations. But in 1567 Portugal banned further immigration of Marranos. Marranos were among the leading citizens in Bahia.

In 1621, the Inquisition was established in Brazil, and many Marranos emigrated to neighboring countries. When Bahia was taken by Holland (1624), the Mar-

ranos there declared themselves as Jews and another 1,000 Jews arrived from Holland and settled in Bahia. In the following year, the Portuguese recaptured the city and reinstated the Inquisition. The Jews were compelled to go underground as Marranos. When the Dutch conquered the Pernambuco area, the Marranos returned openly to Judaism and became the nucleus of the *first great* Jewish community in America. *Recife* was often called "Port of the Jews" because of the importance of its Jewish trade. In Recife, there existed two large synagogues, and other congregations were established in Rio de Janeiro, Itamaraty and in Parahyba where Jacob Lagarto was chief rabbi of all Jewish communities. In 1638, however, the synagogues in Recife were closed through the intervention of the Calvanist clergy. In 1642, the Amsterdam Jews protested to the Dutch West India Company against the persecution of the Brazilian Jews and the Company directed the stadholder to abolish all restrictions. Manasseh Ben Israel persuaded the Amsterdam Jews to send two rabbis, Moses Raphael and Isaac Aboab, with 600 Jewish colonists to Brazil. Aboab wrote the poem "Zecher Rab," thus becoming the first known Hebrew writer in America.

When the Portuguese recaptured North Brazil from the Dutch (1654), the 5,000 Jews of Recife had to leave the city, and their synagogues and cemeteries were destroyed. Aboab led the majority back to Holland. A few went to Dutch Guiana and others to New York. Thus, Jewish communal life in Brazil was liquidated.

When in 1824 the independence of Brazil was proclaimed, Marranos in Belem returned to Judaism and established the *first modern congregation* in Latin America named Shaar Shamayim. Jewish communities were re-established also in Rio de Janeiro, Recife, Bahia, and Manaos. During the 19th century, Ashkenazim started to arrive from Germany, Alsace, and Holland. From the beginning of the 20th century, Jews started to filter into the interior. In 1903, the ICA founded the Philippson farmer colony near Santa Maria and in 1910, another colony, Quatro Irmaos consisting of two settlements "Baron Hirsch" and "Baronesse Clara" comprising 70 families was established. The largest wave of Jewish im-

migration to Brazil was in the years 1917–1924. The German and Central European Jews came as refugees in the decade 1923–1942—many of them bringing capital or specific skills. In the years following World War II, although there was no longer mass immigration, nonetheless many individuals came to the country. Today, the overwhelming majority of Jews, namely 105,000, in Brazil are Ashkenazim, of which 15,000 are German-speaking. There are also 15,000 Sephardim. The Jews of Brazil are essentially merchants, producers, factory and house owners, and professionals with a few artisans.

The Zionist Organisation "Unificada," embracing all the Zionist parties, sells about 14,000 Shekalim so that while the Zionist movement is numerically not strong, it is a decisive factor in Jewish life. It conducts the Israeli Campaign with good results.

The population of Brazil is composed of many races and racial mixtures, but all have equal rights. In the dictatorial epoch, many difficulties for Jewish immigrants were set up by secret decrees. There is a daily newspaper with antisemitic tendencies. Some Nazi immigrants are slipping into the country. One can hear or see antisemitic slogans and sometimes there is clearcut antisemitism. The present government revoked restrictive orders against Jewish immigrants; moreover, a Jew was appointed minister in the present government. Brazil voted for the Jewish State, maintaining diplomatic relations with it, and always had a positive attitude regarding Jewish questions despite a sizeable and influential Arabic minority in the country. Two Jews, Dr. Horacio Lafer and Moises Steinbuch, are members of the Brazilian Parliament.

Brazil has 19 Jewish all-day primary schools (all but 2 of them in Rio de Janeiro and in Sao Paulo), 4 secondary, and 2 high schools with a total of 3,500 pupils (out of a total of 20,000). They are licensed and controlled by the Government. The language of instruction is Portuguese and some of the subjects — mainly Jewish literature, history and language—are taught in Yiddish or Hebrew. Most of them also teach Hebrew as a subject. The education committee of all the schools in Sao Paulo is organized as part of the Federation; in Rio, it belongs to the Zionist Organization. About 20% of the schools belong to the "Progessives," 25%, to the religious sector, and the others are mainly under Zionist influence. Rio and Sao Paulo have 7 Jewish libraries. There are 3 orthodox, 2 liberal, and 2 Sepharadic synagogues.

The greatest part of relief is given to poor newcomers and disabled persons. Brazil has 3 financial institutions on a cooperative basis with banking functions, 2 Jewish hospitals, 4 old age homes, and 4 children's homes.

Confederacao Das Entidades Representativas Da Coletividade Israelita Do Basil, Av. Pres. Vargas 446, Rio de Janeiro. The Confederation is the representative body of Brazilian Jews and is recognized by the Government. It was established in September 1951. The Executive of the Confederation is elected by a national conference of delegates from the 8 Federations in Rio de Janeiro, Sao Paulo, Porto Alegre, Recife, Salvador, Bello Hori-

zonte, Curitiba, and Para. Pres.: Prof. Fritz Feigl. Sec.: Dr. S. Steinberg.

RIO DE JANEIRO (Distrito Federal)
(40,000 Jews in the city; 4,000 in the State of Rio de Janeiro)

Federacao Das Sociedades Israelitas do Rio De Janeiro, (Federation of Jewish Societies of Rio de Janeiro), Av. Pres. Vargas, 446 gr. 1501. Composed of representatives of 50 societies. Pres.: Prof. Fritz Feigl. Sec.: Dr. Moyses Palatnik, Dr. M. Gotthilf, Dr. A. Berezowsky.

Associacao Religiosa Israelita, (Jewish Religious Association), Rua Martins Ferreira, 52. 1,400 members. Pres.: Jose Israel. Sec.: Samuel Friedman.

Comunidade Israel, Rua Tenente Possolo, 8. 350 members. Maintains a temple at same address. Pres.: Jacob Schneider. Sec.: Jacob Palatnik.

EDUCATIONAL INSTITUTIONS:

Machlakah Lechinuch Uletarbut, Av. Pres. Vargas, 446/807. Under this is an Universidad Popular (82 students) and Moadon Ivri (150 members). 10 teachers. Dir.: A. Avissar.

Cadeira Extracurricular de Ciencias Hebraicas Na Faculdade de Filosofia, Chair for Hebrew, affiliated with the Faculty of Philosophy of the University. 2 teachers. 30 pupils.

Colegio Hebrea—Brasileiro Ginasial e Primario, Rua Desemb. Isidro, 68. Jewish elementary and high school. Dir.: Prof. Julio Dulberg. 39 teachers. 284 pupils.

Escola Hebr. Bras. Bialik Primario e Ginasial, Rua Jose Verissimo, 36. Hebrew elementary school and Bialik High School. Dir.: Dr. Moyses Fridman. Sec.: Edith Bastos. 19 teachers. 136 pupils.

Escola Hebr. Bras. Max Nordau, Rua Francisco Otaviano, 59. Dir.: Leao Schmelzinger. 11 teachers. 159 pupils.

Escola Hebr. Bras. Herzlia Primaria, Rua Ibituruna, 126. Dir.: Dr. Moyses Fridman. 12 teachers. 200 pupils.

Escola Hebr. Bras. A. Liessin, Rua das Laranjeiras. Dir.: Gina Fuks. 16 teachers. 235 pupils.

Escola Hebr. Bras. J. L. Perez, Rua Carvalho de Souza. Dir.: M. Jaschpan. 7 teachers. 133 pupils.

Escola Hebr. M. M. Sforim, Rua Filomena Nunes, 1160. Dir.: Dora Schechtman. 6 teachers. 74 pupils.

Ginasio Talmud Torah Primario, Rua Ibituruna, 37. Jewish religious school. Dir.: Prof. Moses Eshriqui. 39 teachers. 278 pupils.

Escola Professional ORT, Rua Maxwell, 454. Dir.: Tibirca de Oliveira. 16 teachers. 92 pupils.

Escola Isr. Bras. Scholem Aleichem, Rua Ribeiro Guimaraes, 454. Dir.: Moyses Genys. 10 teachers. 232 pupils.

Ginasio Isr. Bras. Scholem Aleichem, Rua Ribeiro Guimaraes, 454. Dir.: Dr. Marcos Cornet. 12 teachers. 88 pupils.

RELIGIOUS, CULTURAL, AND WELFARE ORGANIZATIONS:

Sociedade Cemiterio Israel (Chevra Kadisha), Rua Santana, 225. 2,500 members. Pres.: Rav M. Zingherevitch. Sec.: Jyme Reisenblit.

Synagoga Beth Israel, Rua Santana, 22. 100 members. Pres.: Salomao Oighenstein. Sec.: Moyses Goldberg.

Kahal Adass Jeshurun, Rua Barao Iguatemi, 442. 50 members. Pres.: Hersz Klajmic.

Library Ch. N. Bialik, Rua do Rosario, 171-3e. 400 members. Pres.: Moyses Roisenblit.

Library M. Klepfisz, Praça Floriano, 55a/206. 130 members. Pres.: Maxime Sztern.

Library Scholem Aleichem, Pr. 11 de Junho 212 sobr.

Circulo D. Amigos da Iwo, Pr. Floriano, 55 sola 206. Pres.: Israel Saubel. Sec.: Boruch Schulman.

Club "Hebraica," Rua das Laranjeiras, 346. 800 members. Pres.: Israel Saubel.

Socied. Israel. De Educacao. Pres.: Mancel Coslovsky.

Uniao Cultural Isr. Bras. (IKUF), Rua Ribeiro Guimaraes, 454.

Comite D. Amigos da Alliance Israelite Universelle, Av. Pres. Vargas, 446-1501. 300 members. Pres.: Dr. Fritz Feigl. Sec.: Dr. Alfred Gartenberg.

Associacao Fem. Isr. Bras., Rua Visc. Inhauma, 123/501. Pres.: Tcharna Lachtermacher.

Lar da Crianca Israelita, Rua Jose Higino, 240. 4,000 members. Pres.: Rosa Waissman.

Sociedade Benef. Israelita, Rua Lucidio Mendonca, 58. 2,500 members. Pres.: Jacob Gleizer.

Socied. Damas Bras. Israelitas, Rua Barata Ribeiro, 489. 300 members. Pres.: Esther Esquennazi.

Socied. Damas Isr. "Froien-Farein", Rua Barão de Itapagipe, 234. 3,000 members. Pres.: Cecilia Adler.

"União" Assoc. Benef. Israel, Trav. 11 de Agosto, 6-70. 1,285 members. Pres.: Kurt Delmonte.

União Benef. Maghen David, Rua Conde de Bonfim, 512. 200 members. Pres.: Tofic Nigri.

ZIONIST ORGANIZATIONS:

Organis. Sionista Unificada, Av. Rio Branco, 114-110. 600 members. Central Zionist organization. Pres.: Dr. Sal. Steinberg.

Keren Hayesod-Magbit, Av. Rio Branco, 114-110. Pres.: Jacob Schneider.

Keren Keayemeth Leisrael, Av. Pres. Vargas, 462-120. 400 members. Pres.: Salomon Deutscher.

Poale Sion Hitachduth, Rua do Rosario, 171-30. 400 members. Pres.: Israel Dines.

Sionistas Gerais, Av. Pres. Vargas, 446-1502 A. 180 members. Pres.: José Adler.

Poale Sion Linke, 80 members. Pres.: José Mauer-Wind.

Hashomer Hatzair, Rua Machado de Assis, 6. 500 members. Pres.: Aron Berezowsky.

Mizrahi, 50 members. Pres.: Mauricio Roisenblit.

Sionistas Revisionistas, Rua 7 de Setembro, 209-40. 250 members. Pres.: Norbert Schenker.

WIZO, Av. Pres. Vargas, 435-50. 3,500 members. Pres.: Heny Landau. Sec.: Raquel Gaiger.

Mulheres Pioneiras, Rua do Rosario, 171-30. 1,100 members. Pres.: Sara Lintezky.

RABBIS:

Dr. *I. S. Emmanuel,* Rua 5 de Julho, 376. Conservative.

Dr. *Jacob Fink,* Rua Marriz e Baros, 470/304. Orthodox.

Dr. *Henrique Lemle,* Rua Cel. Afonso Romano, 26/201. Liberal.

STATE OF PARANÁ
(approximately 1,600 Jews)

Centro Moisaico do Paraná (Jewish community of Paraná), Rua Cruz, Machado, 126, Curitiba, Parana. Pres.: Jose J. Knopfholz. Sec.: Pinkus Fabisiewicz. 300 members. *Synagogue.* Pres.: Esra Kulysz.

Centro Moisaico de Ponta Grossa (Jewish community of Ponta Grossa), Ponta Grossa, Paraná. 50 members. Pres.: Emilio Wagner.

Escola Israelita Brasileira Salomão Guelman, Alameda Lourenco Pinot, 299, Curitiba, Paraná. Jewish school. 6 teachers. 130 students. Dir.: Dr. Mancel Scliar.

Sociedade Beneficiente do Centro Moisaico do Paraná, Rua Cruz Machado, 216, Curitiba, Paraná. Welfare organization. 150 members. Pres.: Salomão Yashievicz.

Organizacão Sionista Unificada. 250 members. Pres.: Dr. Manoel Scliar.

WIZO. 50 members. Pres.: Ester Guelman. Sec.: Clara Guelman.

Other Organizations: WIZO Juvenil, Dror, Betar, Alguemeine, Poale Zion, Brit Cherut Hazoar.

SÂO PAULO (45,000 Jews)

Federacao das Sociedas Israelitas do Estado de Sao Paulo (Jewish Federation of the State of Sao Paulo), Pr. Ramos de Azevedo 302. Composed of representatives of 49 societies. Pres.: Abram Hocherman. Sec.: Boris Aronzon.

Congregacão Israelita Paulista. Jewish congregation. German-speaking Jews. 2,800 members. Pres.: Alberto Stahl.

Comunidade Hebraica de S. Paulo, R. Odovio Mendes 380. Sephardim. Pres.: Gabriel Kibrith.

Kehal Machzikei Hadaas, Rua Bela Cintra 2254.

EDUCATIONAL INSTITUTIONS:

Escola Israelito Bras. Luis Fleithich, Rua Bresser 783.

Escola Isr. de Pinheiros, R. Artur Azevedo 1781.

Ginasio Hebraico Brasileiro Renaseenca, Rua Protos 790.

Seminario Hebraico, Rua Prates 790.

Sociedade Bras. de Talmud Tora, Rua Tocoutins 296.

(There are 4 other small schools, making a total of 9 in São Paulo.)

RELIGIOUS, CULTURAL, WELFARE, AND MISC. ORGANIZATIONS:

Sinagoga Ahavath Reim, Rua Guarani 253.

Sinagoga Israelita Brailerira, Rua 25 de Marco 710.

Sinagoga Isr. de Pinheiros, Rua Arturole Azevedo 1781.

Asilo dos Velhos, Rua Dr. Pinto Ferrez 910. Old Age Home.

Associacão Cultural Religios. Isr. Bras. de Vila Mariana, Rua Dr. Pinto Ferrez 548.

Centro Recreativo Cultural, Rua dos Bandeirantes 369.

Circulo Israelita de S. Paulo, Praça Ramos de Azevedo 302. 800 members.

Policlinca Lineth Hatzedek, P. Ribeiro de Lima 400.

Sociedade Beneficiente Ezra, Rua Guarani 62.

Sociedade Beneficiente Isr. Brasileira, Rua Jose Paulino 70.

Sociedade Cooperativa de Credito Popular de B. Retiro, R. Ribeiro de Lima 573.

Sociedade Relig. Isr. de Ultimo Coridade, R. de Grace 105-10.

Sociedade Unico Isr. Paulista, R. Odorico Mendes 380.

União Israelita do Brasil, Rua Bresser 47.

Associacăo da Mocidade, Barno da Thepetininga 275.

Associacăo Relig. Isr. de Santo Andre, R. Ona Elija Flaguer 268, St. Andre.

Associacăo de Socorro dos Israelitas de Wolya, R. de Graca 83.

Centro Cultural Dr. E. Ringelbaum, R. Ribeeiro de Lima 571.

Centro Cultural e Progresso, R. Jose Saulino 64.

Centro Isr. de Cambuei, R. Texeira Mendes 115.

Instituto Culturale Isr. Brasileiro (Casa do Poso), Rua de Graca 83.

Unico Central dos Israelitas Polenses, R. de Graca 83.

ZIONIST ORGANIZATIONS:

Organizacăo Sionista Unificada do Est. de S. Paulo, Av. Ipiranga 652-10e. Pres.: Ad. Corinaldi.

WIZO, Rua F. de Abril 277-S. 12. Pres.: Mme. Feller.

Allegemeine, Poale Zicn, Linke Poale Zion, Hashomer Hatzair, Dror-Gordonia, Mizrachy, Revisionistos, Cheruth, Macabi, Ligo pro Palestina.

RABBIS:

David Volt, Rua Piates 611. Orthodox.

Prof. Dr. Frutz Pinkus, Al. F. Cordin 281. Liberal.

PÔRTO ALEGRE (12,000 Jews)

Federacăo das Associacoas Israelitas, Av. Osvaldo Aranha 1076. Composed of 12 societies. Pres.: Dr. N. Steinbruck. Sec.: Ing. Cantergi.

Circulo Social Israelita, Av. Osvaldo Aranha 1076. 1,650 members. Pres.: Dr. Valerio Malinsky.

Gremio Esportivo Israelita, Henrique Dias 73. 350 members. Pres.: Mauricio Shestasky.

Moadon Ivri, Av. Osvaldo Aranha 1076. 60 members. Pres.: Dr. Samuel Goldfeld.

Damas de Caridade. 320 members. Pres.: Guilhermina Maltz.

EDUCATIONAL INSTITUTIONS:

Escola Educacăo e Cultura, Av. Osvaldo Aranha 1076. 5 teachers, 350 pupils. Dir.: Dr. Mario Kaufman.

Talmud Tora. 4 teachers. 120 pupils. Dir.: Bernardo Fishman.

RELIGIOUS, CULTURAL AND CHARITABLE INSTITUTIONS:

Sociedade Cooperativa de Pequenos Creditos de Responsabilidade Limitada, Henrique Dias 73. 610 members. Pres.: Mario Citrin.

POLITICAL AND ZIONIST ORGANIZATIONS:

Organizacăo Sionista Unificada do Biasil, Av. Osv. Aranha 1076. 351 members. Pres.: Dr. Waldemar Cantergi.

Poalei Sion Hitachdut. 300 members.

Organizacăo Sionista Revisionista. 220 members.

Sionistas Gerais. 40 members.

WIZO. 1,000 members.

Moetzet Hapoalot. 450 members. members.

Ichud Hanoar Hachalutzi(Dror-Gordonia). 270 members.

Hashomer Hatzair. 70 members.

BELEM (STATE OF PARÁ)
(300 Jews)

Centro Israelita do Pará (Jewish community), Caixa postal 691. 200 members. Pres.: Abr. Athias. Sec.: D. J. Bentes.

BELLO HORIZONTE (STATE OF MINAS GERAIS)
(2,400 Jews)

Federacăo das Instituicoes Israelitas de Minas Gerais, Av. Paraná 81. Federation of Jewish Institutions of Minas Gerais. Consists of 9 societies. Pres.: Isaac Cohen.

Associacao Cultural Israelita, Caixa postal 630.

Unico Israelita, Av. Afonso Pena, 1568.

Organ. Sionista Unificada, Av. Afonso Pena 1120.

RECIFE (STATE OF PERNAMBUCO)
(3,200 Jews)

Federacão das Organizacoas Israelitas do Estado de Pernambuco, R. da Gloria 215. Consists of 9 societies. Pres.: Samuel Schorr.

Centro Israelito de Pernambuco, Recife, R. Gloria 215. Pres.: Samuel Guiverts.

Organization Sion Unificada, Recife, Rue da Gloria 215. Includes all parties.

SALVADOR (STATE OF BAHIA)
(856 Jews)

Sociedade Israelita da Bahai. 187 members. Pres.: Isaac Kin.

Federacão das Instituicoes Israelites do Estado de Bahia. Consists of 9 societies. Pres.: Isaac Uderman.

Cemiterio Israelita. 158 members. Pres.: Salomon Pasternak.

Escola Israelita-Brasileira "Jacob Dinezon." 1 teacher. 56 pupils. Dir.: Samuel Cohen.

Sinagoga Beith Israel. 140 members. Pres.: Rubem Miller.

Ezra da Bahia. 112 members. Pres.: Leao Schmukler.

Organizacão Sionista Unificada. 87 members. Pres.: Salomão Pasternak.

WIZO. 68 members. Pres.: Mirjam Chindler. Sec.: Mindel Kin.

PUBLICATIONS:

Imprensa Israelita, Av. Pres. Vargas, 435–15 o, Rio de Janciro. Yiddish. Weekly. Circulation: 7,600. Poale Sion Hitachduth. Ed.: David Markus.

Aonde Vamos, Av. 13 de Maio 23, sala 1538, Rio de Janeiro. Weekly. Portuguese. Circulation: 3,500. Owner: Aron Neumann.

Cronica Israelita, Caixa Postal 4091, São Paulo. Fortnightly. Portuguese-German. Zionist. Circulation: 2,000. Ed.: Dr. Hirchberg.

Diaro Israelita, Av. Pres. Vargas 435, Rio de Janeiro. Weekly. Yiddish. Circulation: 3,000. Ed.: S Gandelman.

Journal Israelita, Rua Buenos Aires, 90–60. Weekl,. Portuguese. Circulation: 4,000. Ed.: A. Sampaio.

Nossa Voz, Rua Ribeiro de Lima 592, São Paulo. Portuguese-Yiddish. Bi-weekly. Circulation: 4,000. Progressive.

O Novo Momento, Rua Jose Paulino 872, Sao Paulo. Weekly. Yiddish.

Boletim da A.R.I., Rua Martins Ferreira 52, Rio de Janeiro. Monthly. Portuguese-German.

Boletim de Centro Israelita Brasiliero, "Bene Herzl", Rua Barata Ribeiro 489, Rio de Janeiro. Monthly.

Boletim da Confederacao, Av. Pres. Vargas 446, grupo 1501, Rio de Janeiro. Monthly.

Brasil-Israel. Av. Ipiranga 536 andar, Sao Paulo. Monthly. Portuguese. Circulation: 5,000. Ed.: Bertha Kagan. Zionist.

Choshlim-Forjadores (Portuguese-Hebrew), Rua Real Grandeza 188, Rio de Janeiro.

Novo Noticiaro Israelita, Av. Rua Branca, 114–11, Rio de Janeiro. Monthly. German.

O Reflexo, Rua Ribeiro de Lima 592, São Paulo. Monthly. Portuguese.

Zionistishe Bleter, Av. Pres. Vargas 446, sala 1502, Rio de Janeiro. Quarterly. Portuguese-Yiddish.

BRITISH GUIANA
JEWISH POPULATION: 30

At first Marranos, later avowed Jews settled in the Guianas practically from the beginning of the Spanish occupation. The Marranos threw off their disguise, and other Jews joined them whenever the Dutch or the British obtained control of any part of the territory. In British Guiana, on the Pomeroon River, a relatively large Jewish settlement, "Neu-Middleburg." was formed in 1648, in the Dutch period. First under the Dutch, and later under the British, the settlers were given a measure of autonomy. The Jewish settlements—in course of time there were others—suffered severely in the local wars and also from attacks by runaway slaves and were in the end all abandoned. Most of the Jews emigrated to the British West Indies or were absorbed into the general population. At present, there is a Jewish group in the capital Georgetown.

CHILE

JEWISH POPULATION: 35,000

The largest group in the Jewish community consists of East Europeans (15,000), followed by the German-speaking group (14,000), and Sephardim (2,500) hailing from Greece, Turkey, and Gibraltar.

In 1914, the number of Jews did not exceed 200. In 1930, there were 6,000. In 1933, the influx of Jews from Germany started. Since 1939, immigration has been considerably restricted, and in the last few years, only 200–300 were admitted annually.

Jews play an important role in the development of industry, especially in textiles plastics, fur, clothing, chemistry, and import and export. They are also represented in the professional sector with 100 Jewish physicians, 50 lawyers, 50 engineers, 10 university professors, etc. 50 Jewish families are engaged in agriculture.

The first attempts to organize a Jewish community were made after World War I by the formation of the Circulo Israelita which had erected its own building. In 1948, the Hevra Kadisha was converted into the "Jewish Religious Kehila." At present, there are in the community seven congregations bearing the name Hevra Kadisha but functioning as full-fledged congregations. There are 4 synagogues—3 in Santiago and 1 in Temuco, but there are a few more groups for worship in private homes, so-called "Minyanim." The prevailing language of the Jews is Spanish, but the Yiddish and German-speaking groups conduct clubs in their respective languages.

The Jewish schools are day-schools with the Spanish curriculum of a public school and with additional instruction in Hebrew and Yiddish. The schools have their own buildings and are supervised by the joint education committee "Vaad Hachinuch." It comprises 4 schools in Santiago and 3 in other cities with a total enrollment of 1,100 Jewish children.

About 3,300 Jewish children are attending the public schools, thus only 25% of the Jewish children of Chile are getting a Jewish education.

The community is Zionist minded. The Zionist groups have a membership of about 5,000 and the Zionist youth 1,500. There are also two Chalutz training farms. The Jews are also active in the political life of the country: one is a congressman and one a senator, both of the Radical Party; they were elected mainly by non-Jewish voters.

SANTIAGO (25,000 Jews)

Comite Representativo de la Colectividad Israelita de Chile Serrano No. 20-IV Piso, Dep. "H," Santiago.

The above representative body of Jewry is recognized de facto by the Government. The Executive of 15 members of the Comite Representativo is elected by an assembly of 71 delegates representing 31 affiliated organizations.

Pres.: Gil Sinay. Sec.: Robert Levy. Rabbi: Dr. Nathan B. Blum, Providencia 365–dep. 22, Santiago (Conservative).

Soc. Cult. Isr. "B'ne Jisroel" (German-speaking). Pres.: Sigfried Landau. Rabbis: Egon Loewenstein, Casilla 4571, Santiago (Liberal). Manfred Lubliner, Casilla 9571, Santiago. Sec.: Alejandro Lande. Membership: 1500.

Sociedad Israelita Jevra Kedischa (Religious Congregation). Pres.: Marcos Dubinovsky. Rabbi: Dr. David Gruenwald, Copiapo 476, Santiago. (Orthod). Sec.: Guillermo Stern. Membership: 700.

Circulo Israelita (East-European). Pres.: Juan Faivovich. Sec.: Adolfo Chechilnitzky. Membership: 700.

Comunidad Israelita Sefaradi Santiago. Pres.: Leon Couriel. Sec.: Leon Alaluf. Membership: 400.

Congregation Majzike Hadath.

Union Israelita Polaca de Chile. Pres.: Dr. Jonas Allerhand. Sec.: Salomon Bajraj. Membership: 250.

Soc. Cult. "M.A.Z.E," (Hungarian Jews). Pres.: Fernando Flesch. Sec.: Dr. Basilio Unger. Membership: 250.

Centro Cult. "Haguibor." (Hungarian Jews).

Pres. Louis Schlesinger. Sec.: Ernesto Yung. Membership: 150.

Comite Judio "Concordia" (Hungarian Jews). Pres.: Emerico Grosz. Sec.: Nicolas Grunfeldt. Membership: 150.

Vaad Hajinuj. Director: Guillermo Rosenberg. Sec.: Miguel Maldavsky. 60 teachers. 1,100 pupils. Supervising 4 schools in Santiago, including the day-schools:

Colegio Bialik, Santiago, founded in 1946.

Instituto Hebreo with Kindergarten, Santiago and one Jewish school in each: Valparaiso, Temuco and Concepcion.

Federacion Sionista de Chile. Pres.: Miguel Maldarsky. Sec.: Mario Francos, Casilla 5007, Santiago. It comprises the following groups:

Partido Sion. Gen. Pres.: Rosa de Steinsapir. Sec.: Miguel Maldavsky. Membership: 1,000.

Partido Poale Sion (Mapai). Pres.: Leon Fliman. Membership: 1,000.

Partido "Mapam". Membership: 500.

Partido Revisionista. Pres.: Isidoro Arensburg. Membership: 120.

Misraji. Pres.: Jaime D. Berant. Membership: 80.

"WIZO". Pres.: Adela de Flatau. Sec.: Sara de Beloj. Membership: 1,500.

Pioneras de Chile (Mapai). Pres.: Rosa de Oxman. Sec.: Juana de Gleiser. Membership: 400.

ZIONIST YOUTH GROUPS:

Hanoar Hatzioni, Akiba, Hapoel Hamizrachi, Hashomer Hatzair, Gordonia (Mapai), *Betar* (Revisionist).

VALPARAISO (1,200 Jews)

Sociedad Union "Israelita" (Jewish community).

Communidad Israelita "Habonim".

Soc. Israel Benef. "Max Nordau" (Sefaradi).

Jewish School. 65 children. Recently erected own building.

RANCAGUA (60 Jews)

Soc. Isr. Benef. Baron "Hirsch" (Jewish community).

CONCEPCION (120 Jews)

Centrosion "Dr. Epstein" (Jewish community). Jewish School.

TEMUCO (100 Jews)

Comunidad Israel (Jewish Community). Jewish School.

VALDIVIA (60 Jews)

Centro Israel "Dr. Herzl".

JEWISH PUBLICATIONS:

"Mundo Judio" (weekly). Editor: Jacobo Gomberoff, Zionist, Spanish. Circulation: 2,000. Serrano 202, 3⁰, Pico, Santiago.

"Boletin B'ne Jisroel" (monthly). Editor: B. Kopfstein, Zionist. Avenida Portugal 810, Santiago. Circulation: 2,000.

"Dos Idishe Wort" (twice-weekly). Yiddish-Spanish, Zionist. Circulation: 2,000. Serrano 871, Santiago.

COLOMBIA

JEWISH POPULATION: 9,000

The first Jewish settlements, consisting of Sephardim from Curacao, were established in Barranquilla and Cali in the beginning of the 16th century but were destroyed by the Inquisition in Cartagena. Eastern European Jews began to come to Colombia after 1920. In 1927, about 100 families immigrated from Palestine. The main influx of German Jews took place in the Nazi period (1933-1942). In 1938, the government promulgated the first restrictions against Jewish immigration and in 1939, barred it completely. Today, the Jewish population of Colombia is composed of Ashkenazim—East European and German-speaking—and of Sephardim. The majority live in the three principal cities, Bogota, Barranquilla, and Cali; the rest in Medellin and other smaller places. Jews are engaged in industry and trade. The economic situation is good. Only one-third of the Jewish children in Colombia attend Jewish schools; the rest attend Christian or American schools. All communities are affiliated with the World Jewish Congress.

BOGOTA

(5,800 Jews: 4,000 East Europeans, 1,200 German-speaking, 600 Sephardim)

Comite Central de Bogotá. Pres.: Jose Baum. Sec.: Dr. Migual Gruetzenhendler. Carrera 10, 18–61. The Central Committee is composed of three representatives each of the following:

Centro Israelita de Bogotá, Calle 23, 12–39. Pres.: David M. Rubinstein. V. Pres.: Dr. Manuel Goldstein. Sec.: Jacobo Master. Pres.: Jacobo Master. 476 members. Has its own building. East European Jews.

Asociacion Israelita Montefiore, Carrera Calle 20, 37–54. Founded 1938. Pres.: Jose Baum. Sec.: Fritz Kamm. 420 members. German-speaking Jews. Own building.

Comunidad Hebrea Sefaradi, Calle 77, 11–63. Pres.: Cesare Saravalle. Sec.: José Haim. 60 members. Sephardim. Founded 1912.

Federacion Sionista, Calle 52, 14–49. Pres.: Abraham Feldman.

WIZO, Calle 52, 14–49. Pres.: Mrs. I. Reinis 580 members.

KKL Committee. Dir.: Mr. Karakushansky.

Asociacion de Damas Israelitas. Welfare society. 150 members.

Bnei Brith, Calle 20, 4-81. 22 members. Pres.: Dr. I. Grutzhendler.

Caja de Socorros (Assistance Fund). 100 members.

Macabi Sport Club. 30 members. Head: Ernest Nathan.

Colegio Colombo Hebreo. Jewish school. 25 teachers (19 gentiles, 4 Jews). 250 pupils. Consists of a kindergarten (40 pupils), elementary school (165 pupils), and 2 high school classes (24 pupils). Dir.: David Cahane. Of the estimated 800 Jewish children of school age in Bogota, only 250 attend the Jewish school; the others attend Christian schools.

CALI
(1,300 Jews: 550 East Europeans, 500 German-speaking, 250 Sephardim)

Union Federal Hebrea Cali, Calle 12, 7-39. Central Jewish body in Cali and province of Cali. Pres.: L. Pessel. Sec.: Elias Castel.

Sociedad Hebrea de Socorros, Avenida 9a, 10-15. Membership: 165 East European Jews (men only). Pres.: Samuel Kirjner. Sec.: Itko Balagura.

Centro Israelita de Beneficencia Ezrath Israel, Avenida 3, 8-58. Membership: 52 Sephardim. Pres.: Clemente Halfon. Sec.: Abraham Milhem.

Sociedad Cultural Israelita, Avenida 7, 15-61. Membership: 170 German-speaking Jews. Pres.: Moritz Dorfzaun.

Organization Sionista, Avenida 9a, 10-15. Pres.: Moises Arbetman.

WIZO, Avenida 9a, 10-15. Pres.: Fany Braiman. 150 members.

Asociacion Deportiva Hebrea, Avenida 9a, 10-15. Sport group. 185 members. Pres.: Samuel Kirjner.

Colegio Hebreo Jorge Isaacs, Carrera 15 Sur, 15-81. Jewish school. 160 pupils. 11 teachers (3 Jewish). The school consists of a kindergarten, 5 grades elementary school,

and 1 grade of high school. Pres.: Jaime Edery. Dir.: Israel Nedwesky.

Rabbi: Feiwel Brecher, Calle 16, 6-31. Orthodox.

PROVINCE OF CALI:
MANIZALES (75 Jews)

Sociedad Hebrea de Socorros. Pres.: Carlos Wagenberg.

PEREIRA (100 Jews)

Centro Israelita. Pres.: Abraham Rosenbaum, Almacen La Sirena.

PALMIRA (100 Jews)

Centro Israelita. Pres.: Efraim Behar.

POPAYÁN (50 Jews)

Centro Israelita. Pres.: Isaac Sason..

Unaffiliated Jews also live in the following cities: Armenia (35), Tuluá (20), Buga (60), Buenaventura (30).

BARRANQUILLA
(920 Jews: 420 East Europeans, 150 German-speaking, 350 Sephardim)

Federacion Hebrea, Apartado Aereo 249. Central Jewish body. Pres.: Salomon Cohen. Sec.: Moises Pancer.

Centro Israelita Filantropico, Apartado Nacional 525. Founded 1929. The oldest community. Membership: 160 East European Jews. Has its own building. Pres.: H. Pogerselsky. Sec.: E. Graubart.

Comunidad Hebrea Sefaradi, Apartado Aereo 986. Membership: 65 Sephardim. Has its own building. Pres.: S. Mizrahi. Sec.: M. Koudari.

Sociedad Bnei Brith, Apartado Aereo 521. Members: 80 German-speaking Jews. Has its own synagogue. Pres.: Herbert Pogozelski. Sec.: Manfred Gotthilf.

WIZO, c/o Centro Filantropico. Membership: 75. Pres.: Mrs. Margarita Wertheim.

Club "Union." Social club.

Colegio. Jewish school. Maintained by the Centro Israelita since 1946. Consists of a kinder-

garten and 5 grades. 75 pupils. 6 teachers
(2 Jews). There are about 150 Jewish children of school age in Barranquilla half of
whom attend Catholic schools.

MEDELLIN
(420 Jews: 350 East Europeans, 60
German-speaking, 10 Sephardim)

Sociedad Union Israelita de Beneficiencia (Jewish community), Calle 56, 52-73. Founded
1928. Membership: 97. Located in its own
building. Pres.: Bernardo Rabinowich. Sec.:
Leo Resnik, Apartado Nacional 374.

Sociedad Hebrea pro Ayuda Mutual. Founded
1930. Membership: 20. Pres.: Ernesto Lub-
insky. Apartado Aereo 1164.

Theodor Herzl Elementary School. Maintained
by the Union Israelita. 67 pupils. 7 teachers
(1 Jew).
About 30 Jewish children attend Christian
schools.

WIZO. 120 members. Pres.: Mrs. Estella
Farberoff.

Maccabi. Sport club. 15 members.

CARTAGENA (45 Jews)
Jewish Club Union (Jewish community). Pres.:
Mordecai Kalisher, Almacen Electra, Calle
Larga, Edificio Ganem.

SANTA MARTA (35 Jews)
Jewish Community. Pres.: Arturo Sarazanski,
Calle de las Carretas.

PERIODICALS:
Fortnightly:

Das Blatt, Calle 22b, 22-07, Bogotá. Owned
and edited by Ernst Elsner. Published
in German. Circulation: 800.

Monthlies:

El Amanecer, Apartado Aereo 20-90, Cali.

Kojavim, Apartado Aero 5778, Bogota D.E.

Menorah, Carrera 9, 13-87, Bogotá. Owned
and edited by Isaac Celnik. Pub. in Spanish
every 3-4 weeks. Circulation: 800.

Technion, Apartado Aereo 7542, Bogota D.E.

Irregulars:

Artza, Avenida 4 No.4-66, Cali.

El Macabeo, Apartado Aero 1691, Medellin.

COSTA RICA

JEWISH POPULATION: 1,200

The first Jews came to Costa Rica from
Curacao. After World War I, Jews from
Turkey and, later, also from Poland started to immigrate to the country. About
1,000 German Jews came to Costa Rica
between 1933 and 1949. They are mainly
occupied in trade and the shoe and clothing industries. Some are employed in agriculture, and a few possess farms in Puerto
Lima. The vast majority of Jews lives in
the capital, San José, only 20 families are
in Cartago (Centro Israelita in Cartago.

Pres.: José Rosenstein), and a few more
are scattered in Alajuelo and elsewhere.
The Zionist Center is also the focal point
of the Jewish Community. In 1940 and
1941, antisemitic attempts were made to
nationalize trade and industry, thus elim-
inating Jews from their economic positions, but due to a great deal of effort,
these discriminatory practices were abandoned. In 1948, there were anti-Jewish
riots as a result of German propaganda,
but the new president, José Figueres, re-

assured the Jews and promised to safe-guard their rights fully. New immigration of Jews is barred.

Centro Israelita Zionista, Apartado No. 1473, San José. 276 members. Recognized by the government as the representative body of the Jews. President: Salomon Shifter. Vice-President: Judko Steinberg. Treasurer: Max Teitelbaum. Secretary: Rabbi Hirsz Zelko-wicz.

Synagogue: "Centro Israelita," Apartado 1473, San José.

ORGANIZATIONS AND INSTITUTIONS:

Jewish School, Apartado 1473, San José. Teacher: H. Klepfish. 120 pupils. Evening Hebrew courses for adults, attended by 40 students.

WIZO, Apartado 1473, San José. Director: Mrs. Esther Gudes. Secretary: Mrs. Amalia Steinberg.

Club Zionista, Apartado 1473, San José. Director: José Zonzinski. Secretary: Abraham Waltman.

Hapoel Hamizrachi, Apartado 1473, San José. Director: Rabbi H. Zelkowicz. Secretary: A. Aisenmann.

Histadrut, Apartado 1473, San José. Director: A. Doremblum. Secretary: A. Waltman.

Keren Kayemet and *Keren Hayesod,* Apartado 1473, San José. President: Judko Steinberg. Secretary: José Zonzinski.

Defenza Contra Anti-Semitismo, Apartado 1473, San José. President: Leon Giberstein.

CUBA

JEWISH POPULATION: 10,000

The Jewish population consists of two groups: 5,200 Ashkenazim and 2,300 Se-phardim.

The history of the Jews in Cuba can be traced to the 16th century when Mar-ranos from Spain immigrated there. How-ever, the influx of Jews did not begin in earnest until the end of the 19th century when Rumanian Jews, naturalized in the United States, established themselves in Cuba. Jews befriended the Cuban libera-tor José Martin and helped him in his fight for the freedom of the country. In 1906, the first Jewish community, the United Hebrew Congregation, was organ-ized. Sephardic Jews from Turkey and Syria, and later from Mexico, began to come to the country and formed their congregation, "Sheveth Ahim," in 1914. In 1920–25, there was a considerable im-migration of East European Jews, and in 1939–41, of German Jews. Almost all the newcomers had intended to proceed from Cuba to the United States; some succeed-ed in their plans, but many encountered difficulties and settled in Cuba perma-nently. From 1933 to 1943, more than 6,000 Jews immigrated.

Further Jewish immigration met with increasing obstacles and was finally almost completely barred after 1947.

About 70% of the Jewish community are naturalized citizens of Cuba. Since 1948, 250 Jews, of whom 150 were re-fugees and about 100, Cuban citizens have emigrated to Israel.

In 1924, the Centro Israelita was founded. In 1925, the European Jews organized their own "Centro Israelita de Cuba" which later became the representative body of most of the Jewish organizations. Simultaneously, the religious society "Adas Israel" was founded in 1925 and, later, Ahduth Israel whose aim was to organize a religious Kehilla in Cuba.

At present, the Jewish population in Cuba consists mainly of two groups, the Sephardim and the East Europeans. The majority, 5,100, of which 4,500 are Ashkenazim and 1,100 Sepharadim, live in Havana.

The Jewish Chamber of Commerce estimates that at present about 600 persons or about 10-15% of the merchants are Jews. There is a noticeable participation of Jews in industry where they engage mainly in the manufacture of clothing, leather goods, furniture, and shoes.

The naturalized citizens receive equal treatment by the government. There is no organized anti-Semitism in the country. There are Zionist, welfare, women's organizations, and Zionist youth groups of all shades. In the 3 elementary Jewish schools, there are only 450 children out of a total of 1,350; thus only 33% receive Jewish instruction.

HAVANA (5,600 Jews)

Centro Israelita de Cuba

Repeated efforts have been made to establish a representative body of Cuban Jewry. The Centro Israelita of East European Jews has for many years served as the real center of commercial life. In 1939, a separate Central Committee was founded and existed until 1945, when it was converted into a Consejo Central (Central Council). The Consejo Central was dissolved at the end of 1947. Since then, several endeavors have been made to renew the Central Committee.

In 1950, the *"Patronato"* Society was formed with 600 members for the purpose of building a Community House. This was recently erected. The *"Patronato"* has recently established the Centro Israelita de Cuba, representing all parts of the Jewish population. Pres.: Kalman Vodonas. Sec.: Julio Steinberg and Asher Stuchinsky.

Centro Israelita de Mariano, Real 100, Mariano-Havana. Regional center in Havana suburb. 80 members. Pres.: Abram Kosolchik.

United Hebrew Congregation, Av. de los Presidentes 502. Founded in 1904 by American Jews. 120 members.

Synagogue Beth Israel. Reform. Rabbi: Mordechai Turman.

Sephardi Shevet Achim, Prado 557. Formed in 1914. 450 members. Maintains a synagogue and the Theodore Herzl school.

Centro Israelita, Egido 504. Founded in 1925. Maintains the largest school in Havana, the Colegio Autonomo, and a library. 500 members. Pres.: Kalman Wodonos.

Comunidad Israelita. Pres.: Chil Holc. 300 members. Maintains the Instituto Hebreo Tajkemony school.

Adas Israel Synagogue. Pres.: Kalman Wodonos. 50 members.

Kneset Israel, Jesus Maria 103. Pres.: Mordechai Brikman. 75 members. Maintains a synagogue.

Zionist Organization, Prado 260. 375 members. It is the most influential group, concerned mainly with the Israel campaign and Zionist affairs. Pres.: Isaac Berezdivin. Vice-Pres.: Sender Kaplan.

Hanoar Hazioni. 80 members.

Hapoel Hamizrachi. 70 members.

Hashomer Hatzair. 120 members.

WIZO, Prado 260. The largest organization in Havana. 1,350 members, divided into a Yiddish-speaking section of 600, 450 Sephardim, a Vedado group of 100, Young Wizo of 200, and *Hana Senesh* group—75 members.

Camara de Comerciantes e Industriales Hebreos (Jewish Chamber of Commerce), Muralla 474. 250 members. Activities: Legal aid and arbitration. Pres.: L. Zomerszajn.

Asociacion Feminina Hebrea de Cuba, Bernaza 216. Social welfare society. 780 members. Pres.: Mrs. B. Pincus

Logia B'nai B'rith Maimonides, Av. de los Presidentes 502. Pres.: Marco Pichon. 400 members.

Club Israel, Carmen 421, esquina a D'strampes in Vibora, Havana. A regional club in Havana suburb.

Union Hebrea "Shevet Ahim," Prado 557, Altos, Habana. Pres.: Maurice Egozi. Sec.: Solomon Carazi.

SCHOOLS:

Colegio Autonomo del Centro Israelita, Santa Suarez, Havana. The largest school in Havana. Has its own building. Offers 7 grades. 320 pupils; 14 teachers (6 of these are Jewish). (Spanish-Yiddish-Hebrew).

Instituto Hebreo Tajkemony, Calle 10, No.51, Vedado, Havana. Maintained by the Comunidad Hebrea with 60 pupils (Hebrew-Yiddish)—6 grades.

Colegio Hebreo Sepharadita Teodor Hertzel.

Maintained by Shevet Achim with 70 pupils, 6 grades (Spanish-Hebrew).

Library. Maitained by the Centro Israelita. Contains 3,000 books.

PERIODICALS:

Havaner Lebn. Bi-weekly newspaper. Yiddish-Spanish. Ed.: Sol 153, Havana.

Almanaque Hebres Vida Habanera, Annual. Yiddish-Spanih, Sol 153, Havana.

MATANZAS (130 Jews)

Centro Israelita de Matanzas (Jewish community), Rio 130. 40 members. Pres.: Jacobo Segal.

SANTA CLARA (90 Jews)

Centro Israelita de Santa Clara (Jewish community). Independencia 65, 20 members.

CAMAGUEY (100 Jews)

Centro Israelita de Camaguey (Jewish community). Oscar Primelles 314. Pres.: J. Lipsztajn.

SANTIAGO DE CUBA (75 Jews)

Union Israelita de Oriente (Jewish community). Mariano Corona 273. 70 members, almost all Sephardim.

MANZANILLO (15 Jews)

Union Israelita Shevet Achim (Jewish community), Enrique Villuendas 73.

CURACAO

JEWISH POPULATION: 700

Curacao is the second oldest Jewish community in the Western Hemisphere (Surinam being the oldest).

The earliest Jewish settlement was established in 1650 with the arrival of a group of 12 Jewish families. The Dutch authorities had sent the Jews to develop the agriculture of the island. Some of these first families remained permanently prominent there. Special privileges were granted to the Jewish colonists giving them land they selected, exemption from taxes for ten years, and the right to rest on the Sabbath. This was the first published charter of religious liberty granted to Jews in the New World.

In 1654, when Portugal conquered Brazil from the Dutch, a number of Jews fled to Curaçao and previous restrictions on the freedom of movement of Jews were removed. In 1656, Congregation "Mikveh Israel" was founded. About 90 Jews left Curaçao for America in 1693, and some of them, including the Touro family, went to Newport. In 1740, a group of Jews organized a new congregation "Neveh-Shalom" in Otrabanda and founded their own synagogue (1743).

A Jewish school (Midrash) was established in 1858. In 1863, a group broke away from the Mikveh Israel congregation and established a Reform Temple under the name of Emanuel. Some Jews became very prominent in the life of the island in the first part of the 20th century and were honored by the Queen of Holland; among them Mark S. L. Maduro, President of the Colonial Council, A. Jesurun, President of the Chamber of Commerce, and H. J. Cohen Henriques, Postmaster of the colony.

The present Jewish community is composed of 300 Jews of East European origin, the rest being Portuguese-Dutch and Sephardim. They are engaged in trade and banking. The general economic situation is good. There are 68 Jewish merchants, and 14 professionals. Immigration is restricted. More than 75% of the Jews are citizens. The attitude of the Government and the press is unbiased.

Congregation "Mikveh Israel" (Jewish community). Membership: 64 families (or about 300 persons). It is headed by a Board of Elders.

Synagogue. Rabbi: Is. Jessurun Cardozo. The Rabbi is a government official.

Congregation "Emanu-El." Reform. Membership: 25 families (40 persons) of Dutch-Portuguese origin.

Club "Union." Scharloveg 41. 89 members (about 300 persons) of East European origin. The Club was founded in 1932. Pres.: Jacob Groisman. Sec.: S. Gittman, Leon Seibeld. The Union maintains a synagogue and a supplementary Jewish school "Moriah," conducted by Rabbi Cardozo, with 35 pupils.

Jewish Aid Committee, conducting also the Israeli Fund. Head: William Cohen.

WIZO. 60 members.

OZE. Supervised by the Union.

Library. Maintained by the Union.

Macabi. 50 members. Under the supervision of the Union. It engages in sports and cultural work.

PUBLICATION:

Mikveh Israel—Monthly. Editor: Rabbi Cardozo. Circulation: 800.

DOMINICAN REPUBLIC

(SANTO DOMINGO)

JEWISH POPULATION: 600 JEWS

The first Jewish community in Santo Domingo, established in the 16th century, has disappeared completely. The present Jewish settlement dates from the second half of the 19th century. The first Sephardic immigrants have established themselves rather well, and a Jew, Generoso Marchena, became governor of the country in 1893. General Gregoria Luperon (1839–1897) outlined a project for a large settlement of Russian Jews, but it was never realized.

After the first World War, 55 Jews arrived from Eastern Europe. From 1933 to 1943, 1,100 more Jews arrived, including a group who intended to settle as farmers in the colony known as *Sosúa*. This Jewish colony was established as a result of the conference in Evian (1938) for the resettlement of European refugees. The Dominican Republic announced its readiness to admit 100,000 refugees as farmers. The Agro-Joint was formed for the resettlement of Jewish refugees in the country. The project to establish an autonomous Jewish area in the Dominican Republic stirred up a sharp controversy between its adherents and Zionist opponents. In the beginning, over a thousand Jews from Germany, Austria, and Czechoslovakia came to the country, but by 1946, only a third of these remained. The failure of the project was due mainly to adverse climatic and other local conditions and the remoteness of the area from a Jewish center. In 1940, 37 Jews arrived and founded the cooperative colony of Sosúa. In 1942, the colony had 472 people. However, due to the inadequate composition of this group, the colony begun to disintegrate, and by 1948, the population had fallen to 308 families only half of which were occupied in agriculture. Today, 200 Jews live in Sosúa and its vicinity; 100 of these are farmers.

CIUDAD TRUJILLO (130 Jews)

Centro Israelita de la Republica Dominicana. Apartado No. 5 — Ciudad Trujillo. This is the name of the Jewish congregation in the capital. It has its own building and maintains a synagogue, a Jewish school, and a library. The community is composed of Rumanian, German, and Polish Jews. It displays a keen interest in all Jewish affairs, particularly those of the State of Israel. Pres.: Rudolf Herzberg, M.P. Sec.: Fritz Khuenel.

Zionist Organization. Representative: S. Sanders, Arzobispo Merino 110, Apartado 753, Ciudad Trujillo.

SOSUA (200 Jews)

This Jewish colony is populated now by only 60 families, including 53 children. In spite of favorable economic conditions, many of its inhabitants have left for larger Jewish communities.

Administration of the Jewish Colony of Sosúa: The Administration maintains a *Jewish School,* 50 pupils, *Synagogue,* and a *Library.*

SANTIAGO

Located near Sosúa, Santiago has a small Jewish group—10 families— affiliated with the Jewish Community of Sosúa.

ECUADOR

JEWISH POPULATION: 3,000

The beginning of Jewish immigration to Ecuador dates back to 1904 when a few Ashkenazi families settled in the capital Quito, and some Sephardim arrived in Guayaquil. Immigration increased substantially during the Hitler regime in Germany, and it is estimated that in 1933–1943, about 3,000 Jews came to Ecuador. In 1950, the number of Jews was about 4,000. The German Jews were the first to found industrial establishments in the country. 80% of the German Jews settled in Quito, contributing much toward the development of the city. In 1948, there were 150 new industries, created by their initiative.

At the beginning, the press welcomed Jewish immigration, but later on, anti-Semitic propaganda aroused resentment against the Jews.

Since 1945, many Jews have left the country, reducing the Jewish population to less than half their previous number. The Jews are concentrated mainly in Quito and Guayaquil. Two thirds of Ecuador's Jews are German-speaking. The rest are East-Europeans and Sephardim. Their economic situation is rather unsatisfactory.

Until recently, there was no Jewish school in Ecuador. In March 1954, a Jewish kindergarten was established by two Israeli women. Quito has 80 Jewish children attending the Government or the American School. Guayaquil has 70 children of whom 30 attend a public school where Jewish religion is taught an hour per week.

QUITO

Asociacion de Beneficencia Israelita (Calle Venezuela 616), founded in 1938, 400 members. Pres.: D. Rapaport. Sec.: Dr. M. Weiser.

Federacion Sionista del Ecuador, Calle Guayaquil 926, Casilla 2405, Quito, 220 members. Pres.: Bela Fish.

WIZO (Calle Venezuela 616) 340 members. Pres.: Ida Windmueller-Polack.

Loge Bnei Brith, 70 members (Calle Venezuela, Almacen Vogue). Pres.: Kurt Lenk.

Sociedad Feminina Israelita, 225 members, headed by Kate Kaufman. Welfare work.

The small groups of Jews in Ambato (25), Cuenca (20), and Riobamba (15) are supervised by the Beneficencia.

GUAYAQUIL—300 Jews

Centro Israelita, 9 de Octubre No.106. Pres.: Gustav Gumpel. Membership: 75.

Kultusgemeinde, 9 de Octubre No.106, Casilla 3664 (Religious Congregation). Pres.: Ludwig Herz. Membership: 120.

Federacion Sionista, 9 de Octubre 106. Pres.: Ernst Gruanauer. Membership: 50.

Beneficienca Israelita, Casilla 4021, Luque 208. Pres.: Max Stern. Membership: 56.

WIZO, 9 de Octubre 106. Pres.: Martha Scharfstein. Membership: 85.

Juedischer Frauenverein, 9 de Octubre 106. Pres.: Magda Kantorowitz. Membership: 130.

Periodical: "Informaciones," Casilla 2552, Quito, fortnightly. German-Spanish. Editor: Dr. Miguel Schwind.

EL SALVADOR

JEWISH POPULATION: 275

The first Jewish settlers arrived in the 19th century. The peak of immigration was in the years 1920 30. Only 50 persons arrived during the Hitler period.

At present, there are 260 Jews, of whom 185 are German-speaking, 50 East-European, and 25 Sephardim. Almost all of the Jews, with the exception of 5 from *Santana*, are residents of San Salvador.

There are no restrictions on immigration, the admittance of immigrants depends on individual permission from the Government and is based on an occupational qualification (skilled workers). Almost all of the Jews are naturalized, with the exception of American and French citizens who prefer to maintain their citizenship.

Comunidad Israelita de El Salvador, 255 Jews. The Comunidad was founded in 1944. Pres.: Eugenio Liebes. Sec.: Ernesto Dreyfus.
Synagogue, built in 1951. Rabbi: Alex Freund. There is no Jewish school. The 40 Jewish children attend the American School where Rabbi Freund is the teacher of Jewish religion.
Organizacion Sionista, headed by Carlos Bernhard, 60 members.
WIZO, 50 members. Pres.: Mrs. Charlie Rich. Ernesto Liebes is Honorary Consul of Israel.

GUATEMALA

JEWISH POPULATION: 1,000

The first Jewish immigrants to Guatemala came in 1848 from Posen, Germany. Among these was Louis Schlesinger (1820-1900) who distinguished himself through his pioneering achievements in the industrialization of the country. Sephardic Jews began to immigrate in 1920 and organized the first Jewish society, "Maguen David," in 1923. Following them came the East European Jews who formed their own club called "Ezra." The number of German Jews immigrating to Guatemala increased considerably in 1930-1940, now constituting the majority of Guatemalan Jewry. The Jewish Community is at present composed of 500 German Jews, 200 Sephardim, and 150 East European Jews. Of them, 90% live in the capital, Guatemala City, and the remaining 10% in the towns of Quezaltenango and Antigua, and a few live on scattered farms. Further immigration of Jews has been barred. Relations between Jews and Christians are friendly, but occasionally, there have been anti-semitic manifestations such as the 1949 anti-Jewish demonstrations.

The sport club Maccabi, founded in

1928, is also the cultural center for the youth. There is one Hebrew teacher who is in charge of the Jewish education of about 75 youths and also officiates as cantor. Only the Sephardic synagogue has its own building; the German and East European Jews hold their Sabbath services in rented halls. The community displays keen interest in the State of Israel and since 1949, 20 Jews have emigrated there.

GUATEMALA CITY

Comunidad Israelita de Guatemala. Embraces the three congregations, the Sociedad Israelita de Guatemala (German Jews), the Sociedad Maguen David (Sephardim) and the Sociedad Centro Hebrea (East European Jews). The Comunidad Israelita as well as the three constituent congregations are recognized by the government. President: Enrique Engel.

Sociedad Israelita de Guatemala, 8a. Av.9-35, Guatemala City, C.A. Membership: 400. President: Engel. Secretary: Guillermo Griffel.

Centro Hebreo, 10 C.P. No.2 Altos, Guatemala City. Synagogue. Membership: 200. President: Gerardo Man. Secretary: David Wizel.

Sociedad Maguen David. Synagogue. 7a. A.N. No. 108, Guatemala City. Membership: 250. President: Jose Habie. Secretary: Alfredo Cohen.

Jewish School, 7a Calle P., No.8, Guatemala City. 75 pupils. Teacher: Professor Rosenstein.

Organization Sionista de Guatemala, Apartado No.105, Guatemala City. Membership: 140. President: E. W. Heineman. Secretary: Alfredo Cohen.

WIZO, 6a. Av. S, No.17, Guatemala City. Membership: 80. President: Mrs. Ilse Stein. Secretary: Mrs. Felly Tennenbaum.

Maccabi Sport Club. Membership: 70. A.N. No. 108.

HAITI

JEWISH POPULATION: 200

The first Jewish immigrants, composed of 9 families from Syria, arrived in Port-au-Prince, capital of Haiti, thirty years ago. During the second World War, 20 more Jewish families immigrated from Germany and Poland. There is neither a synagogue nor a Jewish school. Religious services are held only on the High Holidays in the home of one of the Syrian Jews. The Syrian Jewish families are the only ones resisting the growing disintegration of Jewish life being caused by intermarriage and the lack of Jewish education for the children.

Contact with the Jewish world is very weak, but the Jews of Haiti display a keen interest in the State of Israel. The annual campaign for Israel is a manifestation of their desire to keep alive their connection with the Jewish people.

The economic difficulties of the country have also had their impact upon the Jews who are for the most part merchants with a few tobacco manufacturers. Because of their precarious spiritual and economic position, many are anxious to emigrate.

The head of the Jewish settlement is: M. Grill, 43 Rue du Quai, P.O.B. 171.

HONDURAS

JEWISH POPULATION: 150

The first Jewish immigrants from Eastern Europe came in 1920. In 1947, a Jewish Relief Committee was formed which also serves as the administration of the Jewish Community which then numbered 129 persons. Due to emigration, this number has been reduced in recent years to 85, all of them Ashkenazim. Further immigration to the country is barred. There is no Jewish school for the 25 children. Honduras has recognized the State of Israel and Mr. Jacobo Weizenblut, of Tegucigalpa, acts as Honorary Consul of Israel.

TEGUCIGALPA (40 Jews)

Jewish Community. There is a private house of prayer (minyan) but no facilities for Jewish education. An Israel campaign is conducted annually. In the nearby town of *San Pedro Sula* live about 45 Jews who are affiliated with the community of Tegucigalpa. The head of the Community of Tegucigalpa is Mr. Herman Weizenblut.

JAMAICA

BRITISH WEST INDIES

JEWISH POPULATION: 1,500

The Jewish community, composed of Sephardic fugitives from the Spanish and Portuguese Inquisitions, goes back to the 17th century. Under the name of "Portugals," they concealed their true faith from Spanish persecutors. When the British occupied the Island in 1655, they came out into the open as Jews. Jewish communities existed in the early days at Port Royal, Kingston, Spanish Town, and Montego Bay, where there were synagogues. In the course of the 18th century, there was an Ashkenazi influx from England and Germany. Restrictions against Jews were abolished in 1831, mainly through the efforts of Moses Delgado. Since 1921, the only synagogue in the Island is in Kingston. Jews take an active interest in all civic affairs: Altaront E. Da Costa was mayor of Kingston, and Sir Alfred D'Costa is a member of the Jamaica Privy Council. The Jewish Community consists of some 1,400—the majority residing in Kingston and St. Andrew. There are approximately twenty Jews who are Justices of the Peace (magistrates).

KINGSTON

United Congregation of Israelites, located in The Jewish Home, 37 Duke Street. Dedicated 1889. President: S. C. Henriques. Secretary: D. Sampson. Membership: 300.

Synagogue Shaare Shalom. Same address as above. Rabbi: Henry P. Silverman (Conservative), 6 Haining Road, Cross Roads P.O. St. Andrew.

Religious School of the Synagogue, Duke Street. Director: Rabbi Henry P. Silverman. Secretary: E. De Souza. (Pupils: 90).

Sunshine Circle for Local Jewish Aid. Established 1942. President: Mrs. H. P. Silverman. Secretary: Mrs. Alan Delgado.

Jewish Ladies Organization (for the Jewish Home). President: Mrs. N. N. Ashenheim. Secretary: Mrs. Alan C. L. Delgado.

Jewish Literary Society. Established 1936. President: Mrs. Leslie Ashenheim. Secretary: Mrs. R. Brandon. Membership: 100.

Friends of the Hebrew University. President: Caryll De Pass. Secretary: Mrs. Aaron Matalon.

Keren Hayesod. Established 1941. President: Mrs. O. K. Henriques.

WIZO. President: Mrs. O. K. Henriques. Secretary: Mrs. A. Daube. Membership: about 90.

MEXICO

JEWISH POPULATION: 25,000

The overwhelming majority of the Jews in Mexico lives in Mexico City and only about 2,500 live in 17 provincial towns of whom the most important are Guadalajara (480 Jews), Monterrey (350), Tijuana, Vera Cruz, Puebla, and Cuernavaca. Of the 24,000 Jews, according to the estimate of the Central Jewish Committee, 14,500 are Ashkenazim and 9,500 are Sephardim. (This does not include the Indian Jews, approximately 1,500, who are listed separately below.) According to their origin, 16,000 are from Eastern Europe, 1,500 are German Jews, 3,000 Sephardic, 2,500 from Damascus and about 500 from Aleppo.

In the 17th century there was in Mexico a Jewish community which had come from Spain to escape persecution. This community, however, was destroyed by the Inquisition. In the 19th century, a few German and French Jews immigrated to Mexico. Immigration of East European Jews took place in 1921–24, and the Sephardim began to come to the country in larger numbers after 1928. Further Jewish immigration was barred entirely after 1937. Jews have made a remarkable contribution toward the industrial progress of the country. They were pioneers in the manufacture of textiles, metals, plastics, electrical appliances, and clothing. In Mexico, they are well organized and have developed intensive activities in various cultural and social welfare fields and display a keen interest in the State of Israel.

The first Jewish community was organized in 1909 by the Sephardi immigrants from Aleppo, but their synagogue was not built until 1931. In 1912, other Sephardim formed the Allianza Monte Sinai and opened their synagogue in 1940. In the same year, 1940, the Sephardic congregation "Kahal Kodesh Rabbi Jehuda Halevi" was founded; in 1950, the congregation's Hebrew school "Tarbuth Sephardi" was inaugurated in its own building. There are two other Sephardic societies:

Union y Progreso (1924) and "La Fraternidad" (1940).

The first club of Ashkenazim, Juventud Israelita, was founded in 1917. American Jews living in Mexico established a Young Men's Hebrew Association in 1918. In the wake of increasing Jewish immigration from Europe, Nidhei Israel was organized, together with a rabbinate and home for the aged, becaming the largest congregation and synagogue with a membership of about 1,000 families.

In 1932, the Federacion de Sociedades Judios, representing various Jewish groups, was created. In 1937, the Federacion was reorganized as the Jewish Central Committee of Mexico (Comite Central Israelita de Mexico) and is now the representative body of Mexican Jewry. The Central Committee is appointed by various organizations which send it their delegates. The Central Committee is recognized de facto by the government. The World Jewish Congress Committee is a sub-committee of the Central Committee.

There are branches of all Jewish and Zionist parties and Jewish youth organizations. The community also has eight Jewish schools, with about 2,000 pupils. 85% of the Jewish children attend Jewish schools. In 1925, there were 325 Jewish students in the University of Mexico. The diversity of Jewish organized life is reflected in the great number of Jewish organizations. Mexico City has 66 Jewish organizations, of which 10 are religious, 9 communal, 8 cultural, 10 charitable, 10 Zionist, 10 youth groups, and 9 miscellaneous. Religious life is concentrated in 7 synagogues, 2 temples and 2 *minyanim*.

MEXICO CITY
(Jewish population: 20,000—12,000 Ashkenazim, 8,000 Sephardim)

Comite Central Israelita de Mexico (Central Jewish Committee of Mexico), San Luis Potosi No.7. President: Dr. S. Bibring. Vice-Presidents: Mino Kovo, Gregory Shapiro, Paul Drucker. Sec.: Jacobo Frumin.

ORGANIZATIONS AND INSTITUTIONS:

Anti-Defamation Committee, Bolivar 36-505.
"Ars Medici" (Jewish Physicians' Association), Yucatan 67.
Banco Mercantil de Mexico (Jewish Bank), V. Carranza 47.
Bene Akiba, Avenida Mexico 11.
Beneficencia "La Buena Voluntad," Monterrey 359.
Beneficencia "Monte Sinai," Coahuila 30.
B'nai B'rith Lodge, Bolivar 36-505.
Casa de Salud "Ashl" (Jewish Recreation Center), Madero 41, Cuernavaca, Mor.
Centro Cultural, Cuba 81.
Centro Social Damasqueño, Coahuila 30.
Chug Ivri, Adolfo Prieto 133.
Committee of the World Jewish Congress, San Luis Potosi No.7.
Folks Ligue (People's League), Pino Suarez 27.
General Zionist Organization, Chapultepec 300.
Hapoel Hamizrachi, Avenida Mexico 11.
HIAS, Cuba 81.
"IWO," Mesones 40.
Jewish Chamber of Commerce, Cuba 81.
Jewish National Funds, Chapultepec 300.
Joint Distribution Committee, Cuba 81.
Juventud Sefaradit de Mexico, Monterrey 359.
"Kadima" Club, Avenida Mexico 103.
Keren Hayesod Campaign, Chapultepec 300.
Kultur Un Hilf (Association for Cultural and Aid), San Cosme 56.
Mapam Party and Hashomer Hazair, Mexicali y Juan Acatlan, Altos.
Association of Friends of the Hebrew University, Versalles 72-15.
Mizrachi Organization, Avenida Mexico 11.
Organizacion Poalei Zion, Insugentes 180.

Organizacion Sionista Sefaradit, Monterrey 359.

"ORT," Palma Norte 417-107.

OSE, Yucatan 67.

Pioneer Women's Organization, Insugentes 180.

Zionist Revisionists, Amsterdam 229.

Sedaka Umarpe, Cordoba 167.

Technion (Association of Jewish Engineers and Architects), Yucatan 67.

WIZO, Chapultepec 300.

Women's Mizrachi Organization, Versalles 72-15.

Zionist Youth (Hanoar Hazioni), Chapultepec 300.

SCHOOLS:

The Jewish School (1,100 pupils), San Lorenzo 290.

Javne Mizrachi School (625 pupils), Agrarismo 221.

Sephardic Tarbuth School (634 pupils), Adolfo Prieto 133.

Tarbuth Mount Sinai School (450 pupils), Zacatecas 120.

Hebrew Tarbuth School (294 pupils), Lago Nelu 55.

New Jewish School (298 pupils), Reforma 915.

Academy "Zedaka Umarpe" (200 pupils), Cordoba 167.

Yeshiva Etz Chaim (20 pupils), Amsterdam 234.

SYNAGOGUES:

Adat Israel, 5 de Febrero 633, Alamos.

Agudath Achim, Academia 19.

Nidjei Israel, Justo Sierra 71. Rabbi: D. S. Rafalin, Campeche 351—102. Pres.: Samson Feldman.

Rabi Yehuda Halevi, Monterrey 359.

Sedaka Umarpe, Cordoba 238.

Tefereth Israel, Belisario Dominguez 21.

Templo Hipodromo, Yucatan 15. Rabbi: Dr. Jacob Avigdor, Ometusco 52.

Templo Monte Sinai, Justo Sierra 83; Queretaro 102.

PUBLICATIONS:

Asi Es (monthly), Bolivar 36-107.

Centro Deportivo Israelita (monthly, Spanish-Yiddish), Juana Gutierrez de Mendoza 76, Col. Periodista.

Der Weg (3 times weekly). Publisher: Sonya Rosenberg; editor: Jaim Lazdeiski. Orizaba 149.

Di Shtime (bi-weekly), Pedro Moreno 129, Editor: M. Rubenstein.

Dos Wort (fortnightly), Insurgentes 180.

Prensa Israelita (weekly, Spanish), Anaxagoras 556 A, Depto 1.

Forois (fortnightly), Laplace 26-2.

Tribuna Israelita (monthly, Spanish), Bolivar 36-505.

Avanguard (irregular, Yiddish), Apartado Postal 25028.

Di Sionistiche Shtime (irregular, Yiddish), Chapultepec 300).

El Heraldo de Israel (irregular), Av. Amsterdam 229.

En Guardia, (irregular), Apartado Postal 25028.

Freeland (bi-monthly, Spanish). Apartado Postal 181.

Freiwelt (irregular), Saltillo 70.

Tribuna Sionista (irregular, Yiddish), Av. Amsterdam 229.

Zionistishe Bleter (Yiddish), Chapultepec 300.

Kultur Leben (annual), Cuba 81.

MONTERREY, N.L.

(Jewish population: 130 Jewish families)

Centro Israelita "Hatikva," Monterrey, N.L. (Own building containing Jewish center, synagogue and school.)

GUADALAJARA, JAL.

(Jewish population: 120 families)

Centro Israelita, Juarez 600.

Jewish Hebrew School (75 pupils), Guadalajara.

TIJUANA, B.C.

(Jewish population: 60 families)

Centro Israelita "Hatikva" de Tijuana, Calle 4a, No.431, Tijuana.

INDIAN JEWS

Apart from the above-mentioned 24,000 Jews, there is a Jewish group of Mexican natives, the so-called Indian Jews. Some of them maintain that they stem from the *Marranos* of Spain. Their number is estimated to be 1,500. They are organized in the following groups: *Synagogue "Kahal Kodesh,"* Calle Caruso 254, Col. Vallejo, Mexico, D.F. Under the leadership of the attorney, Benjamin Ramirez, this is their largest group. (Membership: 75 families).

Group in Iguala, Altamirano Str. 22, Guerara. Under the leadership of Baltazar E. Rodriguez. Membership: 15 families.

Group in Cocula, Domicilio Conocido, Cocula Edo., Guerara. Under leadership of Mrs. Zenovia E. Roman. Membership: 35 families.

Group in Venta Prieta, Hidalgo. Under leadership of Enrique Tellez. Membership: 18 families.

Congregation in Cananea, Sagara, Ave. Juarez 167. Under leadership of Aurelio L. Romero. Membership: 10 families.

NICARAGUA

JEWISH POPULATION: 200

This small Jewish community is composed of Jews who immigrated to the country after the first World War from Eastern Europe and Germany. Jewish immigration was negligible because of the country's climatic conditions and its isolation from larger Jewish centers. Since 1930, immigration of Jews has been barred. There are no facilities for Jewish education. The interest of the Jews in the State of Israel is rather keen and they contribute generously to the annual Israel campaign. There is also an honorary Israeli Consul, Dr. Laszlo Weiss, Apartado Postal 9, Managua. 90% of the Jews live in the capital, Managua.

MANAGUA (200 Jews)

Union Israelita, Apartado Postal 67. The Union maintains a synagogue and a library. Pres.: Abr Gorn. Sec.: M. Lauczyner.

PANAMA

JEWISH POPULATION: 2,000

The Jewish community in Panama is 100 years old. The first Sephardic immigrants came from the Carribean Islands. The Dutch-Portuguese Synagogue is the oldest in Panama. The immigrants developed trade, the sugar industry and ship and house building and achieved a prosperous economic position. Their congregation, Kol Kadosh Yaakov, is modeled after American reformed congregations, engaging a Reform rabbi and maintaining a Sunday school for the children.

The second Jewish group consists of Jews from the Middle Eastern countries such as Palestine, Syria, Egypt, Iran and Iraq. They established facilities for the religious and traditional education of their children, and their congregation, "Sheveth Ahim," has a Talmud Torah school and a youth club.

The third group is made up of East European Jews, mostly from Rumania, organized in the Beneficencia Israelita.

The Jews are concentrated mainly in Panama City and Colon. There is also a settlement of East European Jews in Balboa and smaller groups in Ciudad de Chitré, Santiago de Varagua and David.

The three congregations in Panama City are separated from each other, united only by their common interest in the welfare of the State of Israel through the Israel Appeal. Efforts are being made to revitalize the Comite Representativa de la Sociedad Israelita de Panama which previously had comprised representatives of all three congregations. The Jewish Welfare Board of the USA is active in Panama for the Jews in the American army units stationed in the Canal Zone area. The Board also supports the communal activities of the three Jewish communities, maintaining a Jewish chaplain Rabbi Nathan Witkin who also takes interest in the activities of the civil Jewish population.

The only Jewish school is that of the Sephardic congregation Sheveth Ahim conducted by Rabbi Levy of Israel. Due to his efforts, the congregation has now started to erect a Talmud Torah building. Among the other sections of Panamanian Jewry, Jewish education is neglected.

About 250 children are without any Jewish education.

The economic position of the Jews is rather unsatisfactory. Immigration to the country requires a special government permit which, however, is denied to those born in Asiatic countries including Israel. Antisemitic manifestations are rare. 90% of the Jews are Panamanian citizens. The Beneficencia Israelita in Panama City, the Centro Israelita, and Union Israelita in Colon are affiliated with the World Jewish Congress.

PANAMA CITY

(950 Jews—500 Sephardim, 250 Dutch-Portuguese, 200 East European)

Sociedad Israelita Sheveth Ahim. 120 Sephardic members. Pres.: David Angel, Apartado 1268. *Synagogue:* Rabbi: N. Levy. *Jewish School.* 40 children. Principal: Rabbi Levy.

Beneficencia Israelita, P. O. B. 1878. Founded 1944. 60 members of East European origin. Has its own building, library. Pres.: Dr. I. Glattstein. Sec.: Dr. Salem Kusnezky.

Congregation "Kol Shearith Israel." Membership: 120 Dutch-Portuguese Jews. Pres.: S. Fidanque, Avenue Tivoli 16. Reform temple. Rabbi: Harry Merfeld. *Jewish Sunday School.*

Zionist Oragnization of Panama.

WIZO. 80 members. Pres.: Helena Borenstein, Avenida Central 121.

COLON

(450 Jews—250 Sephardim, 100 Dutch-Portuguese, 100 East European)

Centro Israelita Cultural, Apartado 513. Membership: 30 East European Jews. Own building. Pres.: Harry Kris.

Union Israelita "Agudath Ahim." 60 Sephardic members. Own building. Pres.: Alberto Malca.

Congregation "Kol Kodesh Yaakov." 32 members of Dutch-Portuguese origin. Reform.

WIZO. 20 members. Pres.: Fanny Kaplan.

PARAGUAY

JEWISH POPULATION: 1,100

The immigration of Jews to Paraguay, mainly from Poland, started in 1912. By 1930, the Jewish population had increased to 1,200, 200 of them Sephardim. From 1933 to 1943, about 800 German Jews entered the country. 1947 brought 743 Jews. Simultaneously, emigration of Jews from Paraguay to Argentina exceeded immigration. The majority of the Jewish population, namely 70%, lives in the capital, Asunción; of these 90% are Ashkenazim and 10% Sephardim. About 15 families live in *Villarrica*. There is a Jewish agricultural settlement in Colonia Fancia. The economic situation of the Jews is rather satisfactory.

ASUNCION—700 Jews

Consejo Representativo Israelita, General Diaz 276, Asuncion. The central body representing Paraguayan Jewry. Pres.: Aaron Karlik. Sec.: Ruben Cegla.

Alianza Israelita del Paraguay, (The Jewish Community), General Diaz 276, Asuncion. President: Aaron Karlik. Vice-President: Dr. Martin Meyer. Secretary: Dr. Isaac Fridman.

Central Jewish Committee. Pres.: Dr. Pascual Nemirovsky.

Congregacion Israelita y Templo Latino, Iturbe 430. Sephardic synagogue..

JOINT, 25 de Mayo esquina Paragueri T. 7583. Representative: Max Brudner.

Hanoar Hechalutz, (Pioneer Youth for Israel).

WIZO, General Diaz 276.

Mutual Aid, Eligio Ayala 338.

Union Hebraica del Paraguay, General Diaz 276. Pres.: I. Goldenberg.

Synagogue of Union Hebraica, General Diaz 276. Ashkenazi synagogue.

Jewish School (70 pupils), General Diaz 276. Sponsored by Alianza Israelita del Paraguay.

Zionist Organization.

Periodical: *"Habima,"* monthly, Spanish, Zionist.

PERU

JEWISH POPULATION: 4,000

Many Marranos from Portugal settled in Peru early in the history of the country. At the beginning of the 16th century, they achieved a dominant position in the country's economy, especially in trade and commerce. So rapidly did their influence and numbers grow that in 1569 Spain introduced the Inquisition in Peru. The Inquisition lasted until 1806 during which time 131 Jews were condemned of whom

24 were burned at the stake. In 1639, the largest auto-da-fe took place: 63 Jews were condemned, ten to death by fire. Among these were Manuel Bantista Perez, considered the richest man in Peru, from whom the Inquisition confiscated a sum equivalent to one million dollars. Another person burned was the prominent poet Francisco Maldonado de Silva, of Chile, who was executed in Lima in 1639 after

12 years of imprisonment during which time he displayed unshakable loyalty to the Jewish faith and while in prison converted two Catholics to Judaism. After this wholesale slaughter, the Jews were given a respite following the payment of 200,000 ducats to the governor.

The Jewish population in the 17th century numbered about 6,000. Due, however, to governmental repressions, the Jews could not retain their religious identity. About 1870, many Alsatian Jews came to Peru and established a Jewish community, but after 50 years they were completely assimilated and only an old Jewish cemetery in Lima remains of them.

Anti-semitism in Peru is from time to time quite intensive. There are manifestations of it in the press. The immigration of Jews is practically closed. The government reserves the right to select immigrants and rejects any application by a Jew. The government is unwilling to grant naturalization to Jews so that only 30% are naturalized. The majority of Jews, 3,600, lives in Lima, 25 in Arequipa, 10 in Trujillo, 25 in Iquitos, 10 in Pinia, and 15 in Ica. Most of them are of East European origin, with the exception of about 150 families of German-speaking Jews and 150 families of Sephardim. The economic position of the Jews is satisfactory. They contributed considerably in the fields of trade, commerce, and manufacturing, but hold almost no governmental positions.

LIMA (3,600 Jews)

Asociacion de Sociedadas Israelita del Peru, Enrique Villar y Carlos Arrieta. Pres.: Jaime Zaidman. Rabbi: Abraham Shalem, Avenida 1605, Lima. The Association comprises the following communities:

1) *Sociedad Union Israelita del Peru,* Iquique 530–542, Apartado 183. Membership: 600 East European Jews. Rabbi: M. Brenner. Pres.: S. Portnay. Sec.: H. Zwilich.
2) *Sociedad de Beneficencia Israelita,* 1870, Jiron de la Union 554, Oficina No.7, Apartado 2082. Consists of 150 German-speaking Jews. Pres.: Dr. S. Holzer Sec.: Dr. Fritz Kaiser.
3) *Sociedad de Beneficencia Israelita Sefaradim,* Carlos Arrieta 1198. 150 Sephardic members. Pres.: S. Sarfaty. Sec.: A. Eskenazy.

WIZO. Pres.: Raquel Salem. 300 members.
Zionist Organization. Pres.: Jose Rosenbach. 200 members.
Pioneer Women. Pres.: Czarna Goldenberg.
Friends of the Hebrew University. Pres.: Dr. Holtzer.
Ayuda Local. Supervised by the Union. Pres.: Lusia Batiewski. 200 members.
Damas 1870. Supervised by Sociedad 1870. Pres.: Gertrude Hertzka. 70 members.
Bikur Cholim. Pres.: Morris Halfin. 460 members.
OZE. Pres.: Cyrla Sterental. 300 members.
Asociacion de Medicos. Pres.: Dr. Holtzer. 15 members.
Magen David. Pres.: Dr. Julius Karl.
Cooperativa Israelita. Pres.: Marcos Perelman. 300 members.
Colegio Leon Pinello. Maintained by the Association. Consists of a kindergarten, five grades of elementary school, and three classes of high school. 450 pupils. 24 teachers (5 Jews). (400 Jewish children attend Christian schools.) Dir.: Ernesto Erman. The work of the Colegio is conducted by a special committee headed by Dr. Marcos Roitman, Israel Consul.

YOUTH GROUPS:

Youth groups are under the supervision of the Zionist Organization conducted by a Youth Council: *Betar,* 140 members. *Hanoar Hazioni,*

140 members. *Brith Hatzohar*, 60 members. *Centro Juvenil T. Hertzel*, 40 members. *Hebraica*, 30 members. *Young WIZO*, 60 members.

PUBLICATIONS:

Nosotros, Spanish. Monthly. Calle Gallos 285-B, Lima. Ed.: Roberto Feldman.

PUERTO RICO

JEWISH POPULATION: 250

There is evidence that following the establishment of the Inquisition in Spain, a great many Jews migrated to Puerto Rico. They, however, left or became so assimilated as to have lost their identity. Of the estimated 200 Jewish families now living in Puerto Rico, only about three families are of Sephardic origin. The others either immigrated from Eastern Europe during the past thirty years or moved to the Island from the Continental United States after it became a territory of the United States in 1898, following the Spanish-American War.

Prior to the second World War, there was no organized Jewish society in Puerto Rico. The Jewish Community Center came into being at that time, spurred by a desire to serve the many servicemen of the Jewish faith who were stationed there. Following the war, the community, which comprised only 25 families in 1952, continued to grow. It aided in various Jewish national and international financial drives, organized a chapter of Hadassah and a Sunday School, and otherwise stimulated interest in Judaism. It is now well on its way to becoming a permanent cultural and religious institution.

The Jews also play an important role in the economic life of the Island. 90% of them live in the capital, San Juan, and in the neighboring town of Santurce. They are now building their first community center.

SAN JUAN—SANTURCE (350 Jews)

Jewish Community Center of Puerto Rico, 903 Ponce de Leon Ave. Santurce. Box 9232, Santurce. The membership is made up of 150 families living in San Juan and Santure. Pres.: Simon Benus; Sec.: Paul Venze and Mrs. Maurice Nagle.

Synagogue— The first permanent Synagogue, Shaara Zedek, was opened in 1955 in San Juan. The Rabbi is Isadore Goodman, graduate of New York Yeshiva University. Chairman: Aaron Levin.

Sunday School. 53 pupils; 4 volunteer teachers. Maintained by the Community Center. Director: Dr. G. Samuels.

SURINAM

JEWISH POPULATION: 410

Surinam (Dutch Guiana) is the oldest permanent Jewish settlement in the Western Hemisphere. According to the archives of the Portuguese Jewish community of Paramaribo, Jews had settled in that territory as early as 1639. It is believed that they came from Holland and Italy. In 1643, they appear to have been sufficiently numerous to warrant the services of a rabbi, for there exists a marriage certificate dated the 14th of Elul, 5403 (1643).

A second contingent of Jewish settlers came from England. They arrived in Surinam in 1652, and a third influx took place in 1666 when a number of Jews under the leadership of Joseph Nunez de Fonseca, known also as David Nassi, came from Cayenne and British Guiana, where they had moved after the French conquest of Cayenne. They settled at some distance from Thorarica, in the so-called Joden Savanne or Jewish Savannah. They soon attained a certain prosperity and formed a stable element in the Jewish community which has lasted till modern times.

The British governor well recognized the importance of encouraging these capable settlers, and it was decreed that all Jews coming to Surinam for colonization would be considered British-born subjects. This proved to be of particular significance after February 1667, when Surinam surrendered to the Dutch fleet, and British subjects were free to leave the colony.

However, the Dutch governor, who well realized the importance of the Jewish settlers, refused to let them go. Only two years later did the Dutch authorities give the Jews of Surinam a formal promise that they would be allowed the free exercise of their religion.

On the Joden Savanne the second Surinam synagogue was erected in 1685. In all, there were 570 Jewish persons in Surinam in 1695. In the next ten years, the number of German Jews increased rapidly, so that by the end of 1704 they were half as many as their Portuguese co-religionists.

Throughout the 18th century, anti-Semitism grew slowly but surely in the West Indies colony. In 1767, it was even proposed—although in vain—that a ghetto be instituted in Paramaribo.

After some differences between the Portuguese and "Hoogduitsche" or German Jews, the latter, in 1734, formed a separate community under the name of Congregation Neve Shalom.

In 1825, all special privileges granted to the Jews in former times were discarded; as Dutch citizens they enjoyed full equality.

A year previously the "Hoogduitsche" community had built another synagogue.

At the beginning of the 20th century, approximately 1,500 Jewish citizens were living in Surinam occupying honorable positions and controlling the principle property of the colony, but in 1923, there were only 818 Jews left there.

Committee for Jewish Affairs (Jewish Relief Fund/Armbestuur der Ned.Israel. Gemeents) President: Mr. J. S. Samuels. Keizerstraat 72, Paramaribo. Secretary: Mr. C. Emanuels, Keizerstraat 72A, Paramaribo.

SYNAGOGUES:

Portuguese Jewish Congregation, Mr. M.H.H. Hendriques Robles. Gravenstraat No. 186, Paramaribo.

Netherlands Jewish Congregation, Mr. B. Geleerd, Oude Charlesburgweg No. 9, Paramaribo.

Rabbi: J. A. Bueno de Mesquita (Orthodox), Gravenstraat No.7, Paramaribo, and Acting Rabbi Dr. J. Meyer.

Committee for Jewish Education, formed in 1954. Two classes, each twice weekly. Hebrew, Jewish history and customs. Enrollment 25.

Courses for adults in Bible and Jewish history.

Surinaamse Zionisten Bond. President: Mr. Ph. A. Samson, Herenstraat 7, Paramaribo.

PUBLICATION:

"Teroenga." Periodical. Editor: Ph. A. Samson, Herenstraat 7, Paramaribo.

TRINIDAD

(BRITISH WEST INDIES)

JEWISH POPULATION: 180

Trinidad, which was discovered in 1498, was included in the bishopric of Cuba in the early 16th century and was therefore ruled by the Inquisition. Consequently no Jew could live there until 1783 when the Inquisition terminated its rule in Cuba and its dependencies. Jewish settlements in Trinidad thus go back to the end of the 18th century, but organized Jewish life did not begin until 1938 when a number of refugees from Central Europe began to settle on the island. In 1900, there were 31 Jews living there. In 1893, Sir Nathaniel Nathan was appointed senior puisne judge of Trinidad. In 1898, he became attorney-general, and from 1901 to 1903, he acted as chief justice of Trinidad.

A number of American Jewish soldiers

and officials went to Trinidad following the granting of military bases to the United States in 1941. The economic effects of the American construction work were soon felt and led to some relaxing of the immigration restriction. Today, the Jewish community consists of 55 families, of whom 36 are of East European origin, 13 German-speaking, and 6 Sephardim. 230 Jews live in the capital, Port of Spain, and 35 Jews live in San Fernando.

Centro Israelita, 44 Frederick Street, Port of Spain. Pres.: Dr. B. Pulver.

Council of Jewish Organisations, P.O.Box 467. Pres.: E. Green.

Hebrew School, 65, Park Street, Port of Spain. 25 pupils. Dir.: Mrs. Fanny Lapscher.

Jewish Religious Society, 65, Park Street, Port of Spain. 50 members. Maintains a synagogue. Pres.: L. Elenberg. Sec.: Sudman Baruch.

URUGUAY

URUGUAY

JEWISH POPULATION: 40,000

The Jewish population in Uruguay at the end of the last century consisted of only a few people. The first groups of Jews came from Eastern Europe. There was also Jewish immigration from Turkey and other oriental countries, but to a lesser extent. From 1901–1925, the number of Jews in Uruguay rose to 1,800. In the period 1926–1930, 6,500 Jews immigrated from Eastern Europe and from 1933–1943, approximately 8,000 arrived. A few thousand more have come since the end of the second world war.

In 1916, the Hevra Kadisha with a membership of 300 was organized. In 1932 the Ashkenazic community was established and engaged the first rabbi in the country, Rafael Taigaroski. In the same year, the Sephardic congregation was also founded and had as its rabbi the late Isaac Algazi, an author of several Jewish works. The congregation of German-speaking Jews was organized in 1936. All these congregations, as well as the Society of Hungarian Jews, have their own synagogues.

In Uruguay, the most democratic country in Latin America, the Jews enjoy equal rights with other citizens, although a new political party, The National Revolutionary Movement, has an avowed anti-Semitic platform.

Ninety-five percent of the Jews live in the capital, Montevideo. They are divided into a majority of East Europeans (25,000) and a minority of German-speaking (7,000) and Sephardic Jews (8,000). Immigration to Uruguay is severely restricted and was balanced by emigration of the younger elements to Israel and the United States.

Friendly relations between Uruguay and the State of Israel have become traditional, and Professor Rodriguez Fabregat, Uruguay's delegate to the United Nations and a staunch advocate for Israel, is very popular among the Jews. Uruguay supported the Zionist cause in 1945 in San Francisco at the birth of the UN and in 1947, at the UN sessions in New York.

A large number of Jews participate in the economic and political life of the country. It is estimated that their occupational distribution is as follows: 60% merchants, 15% industrialists, 10% artisans, 10% salesmen, 3% laborers, 1.5 officials, and 0.5% professionals.

The Vaad Hachinuch supervises 13 daily supplementary schools in Montevideo with a total enrollment of 1,500 children, which means that only 25% receive a Jewish education. The Vaad also maintains evening courses for young people and a Hachshara farm for the Zionist Youth. The budget of the schools is met mainly by the Jewish Community. The curriculum includes Hebrew, Yiddish, and Jewish history and religion. Two Jewish schools function outside the capital, one in Paysandú and the other in Las Piedras.

The Community in Montevideo supports 5 synagogues, 14 houses of worship, 25 "minyanim," 2 Yeshivot, and 6 rabbis.

About 1,000 Jews live in small cities and villages outside Montevideo, such as Minas, Paysandú, Las Piedras, Rivera, Mercedes, Piriapolis, Rocha, Flores, and Salto.

Comite Central Israelita del Uruguay (Central Jewish Committee of Uruguay), Rio Negro 1308, Montevideo. All communities are united in the Comite Central, which is an affiliate of the World Jewish Congress. The Comite Central is elected by the delegates of the four principal Jewish communities. Each of these communities appoints four members to the Comite Central. It is recognized de facto by the Uruguayan Government. Pres.: Dr. P. Nemirovsky. Sec.: Dr. J. Bernstein and Dr. I. H. Nahmias.

MONTEVIDEO (36,000 Jews)

Comunidad Israelita de Montevideo, Durazno 1118. Jewish community composed of East European Jews. Membership: 3,500. Pres.: K. Strikovsky. Rabbis: Jehoshua Deutsch, Durazno 1159; Samuel Katz, José L. Terra 2578; Aron Lashover, Ybicuy 1096; J. Wiesel, Canelones 836.

Comunidad Israelita Sefaradi del Uruguay, Buenos Aires 329. Jewish community of Sephardic Jews. Membership: 1,400. Pres.:

Alegere Sasson. Sec.: Jacobo Duenas. Rabbinate vacant.

Nueva Congregacion Israelita, Rio Branco 1168. Jewish community of German-speaking Jews. Membership: 1,500. Pres.: Dr. Fedor Hirschlaff. Rabbi: Dr. Fritz Winter, J. Herrera y Obes 1205. Conservative.

Sociedad Israelita Hungara del Uruguay. Society of Hungarian Jews of Uruguay. Membership: 350. Pres.: Desiderio Berger. Sec.: Dr. Tiberio Kertesz.

JEWISH SCHOOLS:

Vaad Hajinuj, Durazno 1118. Membership: 600. Pres.: Jacobo Elechman. Sec.: S. Sajachevsky.

Escuela Scholem Aleijem, Constitucion 2484. Dir.: Jaime Warzaguer. 430 students. 10 teachers.

Escuela Bet Meir (Mizraji), Andes 1180. Dir.: Isaac Falk. 160 students. 6 teachers.

Escuela Doctor Herzl, Marcelino Berthelot 1861. 130 students. 4 teachers.

Escuela Beth Jacob, Constitucion 2317. Dir.: Schmul Geebart. 110 students.

Escuela de la Nueva Congregacion Israelita, Rio Branco 1168. Dir.: Rabbi Dr. Fritz Winter. 110 students. 2 teachers.

Escuela Adas Yreim, Ejido 912. Dir.: Abraham Filop. 80 students. 2 teachers.

Escuela Jaim N. Bialik, Lindoro Forteza 2580. 60 students. 1 teacher.

Escuela Tecnica ORT, Minas 1717. Dir.: Jorge Friedman. 60 students. 2 teachers.

Escuela Dr. Jaim Arlazaroff, Rio Branco 1119. Dir.: M. Hartztein. 30 students. 2 teachers.

Escuela Dr. B. Z. Mosensohn, Mariano Sagasta 92. Dir.: Israel Sandberg. 30 students. 1 teacher.

Escuela de la Ciudad de Salto, Brasil Calle 1630, Salto. Dir.: M. Moskowicz. 20 students. 1 teacher.

Escuela Ajad Haam, Grecia 3752. 15 students. 1 teacher.

Yeshiva Rabbi Kook, Andes 1180. Dirs.: Rabbi Samuel Burstein, Rabbi Chaim Abelson. 120 students. 2 teachers.

Talmud Torah Majzikey Hadath, Defensa 2356 y J. L. Terra 2484. 160 students. 3 teachers.

Talmud Torah Eliezer Ben Yehuda, Buenos Aires 329. Dir.: Meir Masliah. 50 students. 3 teachers.

Talmud Tora Chafetz Jaim, Marsella 2689. 20 students.

ZIONIST ORGANIZATIONS:

Consejo Central Sionista del Uruguay, Andes 1460. Central Zionist Council of Uruguay. Pres.: Pedro Grzywacz. Sec.: Abraham Liberman. Comprises 18 Zionist groups.

Federacion Sionista del Uruguay (General Zionists), Andes 1460. Zionist Federation of Uruguay. Pres.: Jacobo Lezcs.

Poale Sion-Hitajdut, Rio Branco 1119. 250 members. Sec.: Zwi Schapiro.

Sionistas Revisionistas, Durazno 1077. 250 members. Pres.: Isaac Erdman.

Mizraji, Andes 1180. 130 members. Pres.: Elias Wainrach.

Mujeras de Mizraji, Andes 1180. 400 members. Pres.: Clara de Bergstein.

Hapoel-Hamizraji, Andes 1180. 60 members. Pres.: José Miller.

WIZO, Andes 1168. 3,600 members. Pres.: Mrs. Sofia de Walfish. Sec.: Mrs. Eugenia de Kaplan.

Femenina Pioners, Rio Branco 1119. 800 members. Pres.: Clara Bergstein. Sec.: B. Kroszinski.

Organizacion Sionista Dr. Teodoro Herzl, Sarandi 316. Pres.: Aron Cheres. Sec.: Jacques Medina.

Union Sionista, Reconquista 227/2. Pres.: Jorge Neulander.

ZIONIST YOUTH GROUPS:

Federacion Juvenil Sionista (Zionist Youth Federation), Andes 1460. Pres.: Meir Halberthal.

Han.. r Hazioni, Soriano 937. Sec.: Josef Leibovich.

Haschomer Hatzair, Julio H. y Obes 1128. 150 members. Sec.: Arie Starovieschik.

Bney Akiva, Andes 1180. 150 members. Sec.: Lescz.

Ijud Hanoar Hajalutzi, Rio Branco 1119. Sec.: J. Silberstein.

Betar, Durazno 1077. 60 members. Sec.: Warner Leopold.

Kadimah, Canelones 935. Sec.: Nenyc Westzenfeld.

Comite de Colaboracion Economica con Israel, Convencion 1253. Pres.: Miguel Krell.

CULTURAL, SOCIAL, RELIGIOUS, WELFARE, AND MISCELLANEOUS ORGANIZATIONS:

Bene Berith Oriental, Canelones 1216. Pres.: Israel Nemirovsky.

Agudas Israel, Constitucion 2317. Pres.: Erwin Schnurmann.

Vaad Hair, Canelones 828. Orthodox society. Pres.: Wolf Katz. 600 members.

Federacion de Israelitas Polacos, San Jose 875. 200 members. Pres.: I. Lewy.

JOINT, Palacio Salvo.

ORT, Minas 1717. Pres.: Dr. Geza Sussman.

OSE, Florida 1418.

IWO, Durazno 1118. Pres.: Alter Szyman.

FINANCIAL AND COMMERCIAL INSTITUTIONS:

Banco Palestino Uruguayo, Treinta y Tres 1385. Founded 1950. Pres.: Jacobo Goluboff.

Corporacion Comercial Israelita, Rondeau 1437 Pres.: Salomon Piatigorsky.

PUBLICATIONS:

Folksblat, Canelones 870. Yiddish daily. Zionist. Ed.: Moises Orzuj. Dir.: Abraham Schwartz. Circulation: 2,500.

Unser Fraint, Jhy Obes 1171. Leftist Yiddish daily. Circulation: 1,500.

Der Moment, Andes 1146. Orthodox-Zionist Yiddish weekly. Circulation: 1,500. Ed.: Bernardo Margulies.

Gaceta Israelita, Cerrito 663. Zionist. Spanish weekly. Circulation: 7,000. Eds.: Moises Garber, José Wainstein. Dir.: Moises Gerber.

Amanecer, Buenos Aires 329. Fortnightly.

Revista Familiar Israelita. Bartolome Mitre 1578. Spanish fortnightly. Zionist. Ed. and Dir.: Abraham Halpern.

Boletin Informativo. German weekly. Rio

Branco 1168. 2,000 copies. Ed.: Nueva Congregacion Israelita. Dir.: Georg Freund. *Semanario Hebreo,* Canalones 870. Fortnightly,

Unobhenigke Yiddishe Tribune (Yiddish), Larranga 1782. Monthly. *Sintesis,* Florida 1418. Quarterly.

VENEZUELA

JEWISH POPULATION: 5,900

Jewish immigration to Venezuela started a hundred years ago. The first arrivals —in 1850—were Sephardim from North Africa. In 1873, 30 Jews from the Carribean Islands entered the country. In 1935, Venezuelan Jewry numbered about 1,500, mostly from Eastern Europe. After 1933, German Jews began coming in considerable numbers. Immigration, however, was barred at the end of World War II.

Jews have contributed greatly to Venezuela's trade and industry and to the modernization of her capital, Caracas. They display a keen interest in the State of Israel and in the Jewish education of the community.

Of the total Jewish population in Venezuela, approximately 3,700 are of East European origin, about 1,400 are Sephardim, and 800, German-speaking Jews. The majority lives in Caracas; the rest are distributed throughout the country. There are many Jewish industrial enterprises dealing with ready-made clothing, textiles, and furniture. In Caracas alone there are 250 Jewish industrial enterprises. 1,000 Jewish stores, and 100 Jewish professionals. Maracaibo has 20 Jewish industrial enterprises, 50 stores, and 5 professionals; Valencia, 5 industrial enterprises and 22

stores; Maracay 20 Jewish stores. The economic situation is, in general, good. Only 6 families are welfare cases in Caracas and 1 in Maracaibo.

Although the official immigration law does not make any distinction, nevertheless special instructions given to the consuls abroad make the immigration of Jews to Venezuela impossible. Naturalization is also very difficult. Only about 60% of the Jews are naturalized, including 3,000 native-born children. There is no anti-semitism or attacks on Jews by the press.

CARACAS

(about 5,000 Jews—600 German-speaking, 300 Sephardim, 500 Hungarian)

Union Israelita de Caracas, Avenida Codazzi, San Bernardo. 466 members, including 80 German-speaking Jews. Pres.: M. Rottenberg. Sec.: Dr. Max Knoll Scherf. An affiliate of the World Jewish Congress. Maintains 2 synagogues and a cemetery.

Congregation of East European Jews. Synagogue, Avenida Ustaric. Pres.: Welwel Zygelbaum. Rabbi: Meir Shapira.

Asociacion Israelita de Venezuela, Sur 17–25. Membership: 50 Sephardim. Pres.: Leon Taurel. Maintains a synagogue and a rabbi. Affiliated with the World Jewish Congress.

Association of Hungarian Jews, c/o Union Israelita de Caracas, Avenida Codazzi. Pres.: Mr. Kewesz.

WIZO, Avenida Codazzi. Members: 500. Pres.: Mrs. Estereicher.

Organizacion Sionista Unida, Avenida Urdaneta (Veroes a Ibarras), Edeficio. Caracas local No. 5. Pres.: Dr. Max Knoll Scherf.

OZE, Under the supervision of the Union Israelita. 150 members. Pres.: Mrs. Capler.

Asociacion de Medicos "Israel," 50 members. Pres.: Dr. Calabres.

Asociacion de Los Judios Bucovinos, 125 members. Pres.: Dr. Max Knoll Scherf.

Colegio Moral y Luces "Herzl-Bialik." Maintained by the Union Israelita de Caracas. It consists of a kindergarten (50 pupils), preliminary grades (50 pupils), 6 grades of elementary school (300 pupils), and 4 classes of high school (150 pupils) with a total of 550 pupils and 35 teachers (8 Jewish). The Jewish subjects taught are Bible, Hebrew, Yiddish, and Jewish history which are given 10–12 hours weekly in the elementary school and 9 hours in the high school. Principal: Dr. David Gross. There are also students groups in the high school devoting themselves to general Jewish matters. Principals: Dr. Margot Labunska and Henoch Finkel. About 1,000 children and adults attend Chirstian schools. The yearly budget of the Colegio is $170,000.

Centro de Cultural Hebrea "Scopus," located in the Colegio. 55 members, mostly university students. Pres.: Jacobo Carciente.

Joven Israel, membership: 30 students. Pres.: Dr. J. Abrami, Apartado 3540.

Library, maintained by the Union Israelita.

MARACAIBO
(350 Jews—300 East European, 40 Sephardim, 10 German-speaking)

Sociedad Israelita de Maracaibo, Calle 24 de Julio No. 6. Bella Vista, Apartado 524. Located in its own building. Embraces all the Jews in the city. Affiliated with the World Jewish Congress. Pres.: Ch. Gelman. It is now erecting a building for the synagogue and the school.

Colegio Hispano-Hebrao "Biluh," maintained by the Sociedad Israelita. It consists of a kindergarten with 35 children and 4 teachers. The first grade of an elementary school was recently opened. Pres.: Moris Shonfeld. 35 children attend Christian schools. There are 25 Jewish university students.

Library.

WIZO, 72 members. Pres.: Mrs. Aida Eidelman.

MARACAY (150 Jews)

Centro Israelita. Pres.: Luis Shadah.

VALENCIA (120 Jews)

Comunidad Israelita. 34 members. Pres.: M. Starosta.

OTHER JEWISH SETTLEMENTS:

There are also 50 Jews in *Barquisimeto,* 30 in *Puerto La Cruz,* 30 in *Coro,* 60 in *San Cristobal,* 10 in *Ciudad Bolivar,* and 100 in the province of *Los Andes.*

PUBLICATIONS:

El Mundo Israelita, Sociedad a Troposos, 4 Altor-Oficina 26, Caracas. Weekly.

Nuestro Camino, Weekly. Avda. Francisco Javier Ustariz, Ap. 3540, San Bernardino. Dr. J. Abrami.

Paginas Hebreas. Monthly. Avenida Ustariz, Edif. San Vicante. Apt. 10, San Bernardino.

VIRGIN ISLANDS

JEWISH POPULATION: 85

This group of islands in the Carribean Sea consists of St. Thomas, St. John, and St. Croix. The Dutch ruled them from 1657–1917, when the United States purchased them from Denmark. The earliest Jew known to have lived in the Virgin Islands was Gabriel Milan who was governor of St. Thomas from 1684–1687.

In 1789, there were 9 Jewish families on St. Thomas. In 1796, the first synagogue named "Bracha Veshalom" was erected on St. Thomas. The building was enlarged in 1833. The census of 1837 counted 400 Jews and that of 1850, 500. Since then, their number has decreased. There was no anti-semitism under Dutch rule. Most of the Jews were Sephardic and Orthodox, and, therefore, were reluctant to obey the order of the Dutch kings that boys and girls of all religions be confirmed. The first rabbi of the Virgin Islands, Benjamin Cohen Carillon, an advocate of Reform, confirmed the girls also. His successor, N. M. Nathan, returned to Orthodoxy. He was succeeded by David Cardozo, and in 1919, Moses D. Sasso took office as religious leader of the Community.

Jews played an important role in public life, especially the Moron, DeSala, Cardozo, and Sasso families. Major Wolff was governor of St. Thomas. When the United States took possession of the Virgin Islands, the Jewish population shrunk to about 60. These maintained their organized Jewish communal life on St. Thomas, one of the first Jewish communities in the Western Hemisphere.

The Jews are nearly all native-born, constituting an economically important group, and are composed of merchants, government officials, and employees of American companies. The present American governor of the Virgin Islands is Morris Decastro, an active member of the Jewish Community of St. Thomas. In 1950, the Legislative Assembly passed a law barring discrimination in public places. All owners of club facilities must file an affidavit with the government attesting that there is no discrimination in the use of their premises.

ST. THOMAS (85 Jews)

Jewish Community "Bracha Veshalom." Rabbi: Moses D. Sasso. The numerically small congregation maintains the historic synagogue.

NORTH AMERICA

ALASKA

JEWISH POPULATION: 120

Jewish merchants, mainly from San Francisco, visited Alaska frequently and were the pioneers in introducing the fur trade there. They established the "Alaska Company" which was instrumental in the acquisition of the territory by the U.S.A.

There were abortive attempts to organize a Jewish congregation in Alaska, but Emil Teichman, in his book "A Journey to Alaska in the year 1868," reports that one Friday evening, he saw in the warehouse of a Jewish trader in Sitka an assembly of some twenty Jews holding their Sabbath services under the leadership of the oldest man present who took the place of a rabbi. Teichman was very impressed by "this religious gathering in so strange a setting which said a great deal for the persistence with which the Jews everywhere, even in the most remote countries practice their emotional exercises."

In 1869, S. Kaplan, a resident of Sitka visiting San Francisco, reported to the periodical "The Hebrew" in San Francisco that there were only 14 Jewish residents in Sitka and they intended to organize a congregation which, however, did not materialize. (See: Rudolf Glanz, "The Jews in American Alaska 1867–1880," New York 1953).

Of the 500 Jews now living in Alaska, only 120 are permanent residents, while the remaining 380 are U.S. Army personnel. The largest settlement of civilian Jews —approximately 70—is in the city of *Anchorage*. About 20 Jewish families are scattered throughout the other cities in Alaska. Some of them have intermarried and have lost their Jewish identity.

There have been a number of Jewish communal organizations in Anchorage for the last few years. The Jewish Community Council is now defunct. The most active group is the newly formed J.W.B. (Jewish Welfare Board) Armed Services Committee, organized by the representative of the J.W.B. in Alaska, Mr. Jack Frankel. Mr. Frankel also conducts a course in Adult Jewish studies at the U.S.O. Club in Fairbanks. The newly designated Jewish chaplain for Alaska, Rabbi Jacob Rubenstein, along with Mr. Jack Frankel, are active in the military communities and have included Jewish civilians in their activities.

Among the prominent Jews of Alaska are Zachary Loussac, construction man and former mayor of Anchorage and Robert Bloom, who came to the country from Ireland 60 years ago. Mr. Bloom was a pioneer who came with the Klondike

Gold Rush in 1905 and helped found the city of Fairbanks. He also made several unsuccessful attempts to form a Jewish Community in Fairbanks. A small Jewish cemetery still remains there.

ANCHORAGE (20 Jewish families)

Jewish Welfare Board Armed Services Committee, Box 26, Spenard. Pres.: Burton Goldberg. Sec.: Miss Diane Bloomfield.

Chaplain: Rabbi Jacob Rubenstein. Conducts services for military and civilians.

Hadassah Women's Organization, 1439 Hollywood Drive. Pres.: Mrs. Dorothy Drickey.

Jewish Education Association c/o Rabbi Jacob Rubenstein, Elmendorf AFB.

FAIRBANKS (6 Jewish families)

Representative of the Jewish settlement: Robert Bloom, 531½ Third Avenue.

Adult Jewish Studies Course, c/o USO CLUB Fairbanks. Director: Jack Frankel. 20 pupils. 1 teacher.

Jewish Education Association, c/o Chaplain Jacob Rubenstein, Elmendorf AFB. Organized 1954.

Other small Jewish groups exist in the city of Juneau where their representative is Mr. Charles Goldstein and in the city of Kodiak, represented by Mr. Herbert Spiegel. Box 344, Kodiak.

PUBLICATION:

Alaskan Star. Military publication. Editor: Arnold Forman. Circulation: 200.

CANADA

JEWISH POPULATION: 241,000

Jews were prohibited by law from living in Canada while it was a French possession. Nevertheless Jews came from the South of France—David Gradis, a wealthy merchant and shipowner of Bordeaux, founded the "Society of Canada" in 1748, and his son, Abraham Gradis, had a large share in the commercial development of the Colony.

Jews played a part in the British occupation of Canada. A Jewish captain, later Sir Alexander Schomberg, commanded a ship at the capture of Quebec under General Wolfe. Half a dozen Jewish officers, including Aaron Hart whose descendants played important roles in Jewish and Canadian life for several generations, were members of the expeditionary force which occupied Montreal. A num-

ber of Jews settled at an early date in that city, where the Spanish and Portuguese Synagogue, Shearith Israel (still existing) was established in 1768. Not until 1845 was a second congregation formed in Toronto. In the 19th century, Jewish immigrants from England arrived in some numbers, and communities were established in the more important centres. A new era in the history of Canadian Jewry began at the close of the century when emigration on a large scale from Eastern Europe began. Montreal, Toronto, and to a lesser degree, Winnipeg became the seats of large Jewish communities. There were attempts to limit Jewish civil rights. In 1807, Ezekiel Hart was elected to the Quebec Assembly. He was expelled from the Assembly because he was not permitted to be sworn in in accordance with the Jewish religion. He was, however, reelected the following year and again expelled. When the Assembly sought to frame a law prohibiting Jews from holding office, the Governor, James Craig, dissolved the legislature. Not until 1832 did the Canadian Jews receive full civil rights with the passage of a bill called "Jews' Magna Charta."

There are Jews occupying important governmental and civic positions. Two Jews are members of the Federal parliament. Toronto elected a Jew, Mr. Nathan Phillips, as its mayor. The following towns have Jews as their mayors: Medicine Hat (Alberta), Flin Flon (Manitoba), and Humboldt (Saskatchewan).

In 1900, the Jewish population reached 16,000; in 1911 their number was 75,000. The census of 1931 listed 157,000 Jews.

The United Jewish Teachers' Seminary is located in Montreal. In 1954, fifteen teachers were graduated from its three year course. The Hebrew Teachers Seminary "Midrasha Lemorim" was established in Toronto in 1953 with 23 students. In 1954, the Council of Jewish Educational Institutes was organized in Montreal representing all types of schools; yeshivot, Talmud Torahs and secular Yiddish schools as well as the congregational Sunday schools.

There are 93 Jewish schools in Canada of which 16 are in Montreal, 15 in Toronto, 5 in Winnipeg, and 57 in 48 other Jewish communities, mostly Talmud Torahs and congregation schools. Besides the above mentioned two teachers' seminaries, there are 6 yeshivot: 4 in Montreal

and 2 in Toronto. The total number of pupils attending Jewish schools in 1954 was 15,000, constituting about 50% of the Jewish children of school age.

The number of children attending Jewish schools in Montreal in 1954 was 6,700 or 47% of all Jewish children. Of these, 50% attended Jewish day schools, 45% attended five-day afternoon schools, and only 5%, Sunday schools.

In Toronto, 60% of all Jewish children were enrolled in Jewish schools. In the smaller communities of Ontario, 80% of the Jewish children attended Jewish schools in 1954, of whom 58% attended Talmud Torahs, 10% Yiddishist schools, and 32% Sunday schools.

Of the 186 Jewish congregations, Montreal has 54 and Toronto 49 and there are 83 congregations in 62 other places. Of these, 165 are Orthodox with 83 Rabbis, 18 Conservative with 18 Rabbis, 3 Reform with 3 Rabbis. In Montreal, a Synagogue Council was formed in 1953 comprising 12 Orthodox, 5 Conservative and 1 Reform Congregation.

Jewish immigration to Canada from 1945 until 1954 was 40,672 consisting of only 4% of the total immigration to Canada. The number of Jews admitted in 1951–1957 was—20,414; 1951 — 3,561; 1952—7,478; 1953—5,092; 1954—3,712. In 1954, the percentage of Jewish immigrants decreased to 2%.

The Jews played an important role in the economic development of Canada especially in trade, the merchant marine, the fishing industry, and telegraph and telephone communications.

The Jews introduced the clothing, fur and tobacco industries into Canada.

Since 1874, several attempts were made to establish Jewish farm colonies. In 1892, the Ica and the Baron Hirsch Institute of Montreal settled 47 families at the Hirsch Colony. Other Jewish Agricultural settlements were founded in Saskatchewan Province: Lipton in 1901, Edenbridge 1906, and others. The total Jewish farm population of the 17 settlements amounts to about 2,200.

In 1953, the House of Commons passed a Fair Employment Practice Bill introduced by the Federal government to prevent racial and religious discrimination.

NATIONAL ORGANIZATIONS AND INSTITUTIONS:

Canadian Jewish Congress, 493 Sherbrooke Street, Montreal.

Established 1919, reorganized 1934, recognized by the federal, provincial, and municipal governments as the central Jewish representative body in Canada. It is the representative central body of Canadian Jewry and is associated with the world Jewish Congress.

The Congress holds Biennial Plenary Sessions to which delegates nominated by the congregations, Zionist organizations, *landsmannschaften,* Jewish fraternal orders, Jewish labor organizations, and members of the community at large are elected by all communities. The delegates at the Biennial Plenary Session elect a Dominion Council which in turn elects a National Executive Committee from its membership. Pres.: Samuel Bronfman; Chmn, Exec. Com.: Michael Gerber; Executive Director: Saul Hayes.

Actions Committee of the Labour Zionist Movement in Canada. Est. 1939. Pres.: M. Dickstein; Exec. Direc.: L. Cheifetz (5101 Esplanade Ave. Montreal).

Association of Hebrew Schools (Igud), 493 Sherbrooke St. West, Montreal. Est. 1942. Pres.: E. Shuchat. Exec. Direc.: S. Lerner.

B'nai B'rith. Est. 1875. 15 lodges.

Canadian Hebrew Culture Organization (Keren Hatarbuth), 5815 Jeanne Mance St., Montreal. Pres.: S. S. Gordon. Exec. Direc.: L. Kronitz.

Canadian Jewish Historical Society c/o Canadian Jewish Congress, Montreal. Pres.: B. G. Sack.

Canadian Ort Committee, 373 St. Catherine St., W. Montreal, Est. 1937. Pres.: H. S. Greenwood.

Hadassah Organization of Canada. Est. 1917. Pres.: Mrs. A. Slavouski. Sec.: Mrs. Esther Waterman, 2025 University St. Montreal. There are 220 Chapters in most of the principal Jewish centers.

Hashomer Hadati of Canada, 5402 Park Ave. Montreal, 396 Markham St., Toronto. Reorganized 1943. Youth organization, affiliated with Torah Va-Avodah Movement of Canada.

Jewish Colonization Association of Canada. Est. 1907. Pres.: Samuel Bronfman. Manager: S. Belkin, 493 Sherbrooke St. W. Montreal.

Jewish Immigrant Aid Society of Canada. Est. 1919. Pres.: J. Segall. Exec. Dir.: M.A. Solkin, 4221 Esplanade Ave. Montreal, 3 branches.

Jewish Labour Committee in Canada. Est. 1936 Pres.: Michael Rubinstein. Exec. Dir.: Kalman Kaplansky, 4848 St. Lawrence Blvd. Montreal.

United Jewish Teachers Seminary, Montreal. Maintained by the Canadian Jewish Congress. Chairman: S. Harvey.

Mizrachi Organization of Canada. Pres.: H. Tannenbaum. Sec.: N. A. Levitsky, 5402 Park Ave., Montreal.

Mizrachi Women of Canada. Pres.: Mrs. R. Bessin. Exec. Sec.: Miss Q. Hershovich.

National Council of Jewish Women, Canadian Division, 44 St. George St. Toronto, Ont. Est. 1933. Pres.: Mrs. Harold Louis. Sec.: Mrs. S. Lerner, Mrs. G. M. Pearcy.

Poale Zion Zeire Zion Organization. Sec.:

Leon Cheifetz, 5101 Esplanade, Ave., Montreal.

United Jewish Relief Agencies. Est. 1939. Pres.: Samuel Bronfman. Exec. Dir.: Saul Hayes, 493 Sherbrooke St. W. Montreal.

Zionist Organization, 2025 University St. Montreal. Est. 1892. Ex. Dir.: Rabbi Jesse Schwartz.

MONTREAL (Quebec)
(Jewish population: 100,000)
CENTRAL ORGANIZATIONS:

Community Council, 3575 St. Lawrence Blvd. Founded 1922. Pres.: I. Cohen.

Federation of Jewish Community Service, Pres.: Abe Bronfman.

Montreal Council of Orthodox Rabbis, 3575 Lawrence Blvd. Pres.: Rabbi S. Hershorn.

Board of Ministers, 3460 Stanley St. Pres.: Rabbi S. Cass.

Congregations: 46 Synagogues with 12 Rabbis.

Shearith Israel, 5471 Lemieux Ave. Founded 1768. This is the oldest synagogue in Canada Pres.: S. Rosenberg. Rabbi: Dr. S. Frank, Sephardic.

Temple Emanuel, 4128 Sherbrooke St. West. Founded 1882. Pres.: H. Grover. Rabbi: Dr. H. J. Stern, Reform.

CULTURAL AND EDUCATIONAL INSTITUTIONS:

Hebrew Academy and United Talmud Torah, Main Building 269 St. Joseph Blvd. W. Six branches: Montreal Hebrew Academy; Hebrew High School; Anshe Sephard, 4094 Clark St.; Beth Sholem, 6675 Marquette St. Pres.: Ben Beutel.

Jewish Writers' Association, 4099 Esplanade Av. Sec.: M. M. Husid.

Jewish Public Library, 4099 Esplanade Av. Pres.: S. Winkler.

Jewish People's Schools, 5210 Waverley St. Pres.: J. Berman.

Tomchei Tmimim Lubavitcher Yeshiva, Rabbinical College of Canada, 5265 Park Ave. Dir.: Rabbi L. Kramer.

Jewish Peretz School, 120 Duluth St. East. Pres.: L. Zuker.

Mercaz Hatorah Yeshiva. Pres.: S. Drazin.

Morris Wintchefsky School. Princ.: S. Stern, 30 Villeneuve St. W.

Hillel Foundation. Dir.: Rabbi S. Cass.

Y.M.-Y.W.H.A., Mount Royal Building, 265 Mt. Royal Ave. Snowdon Building, 5500 Westbury Ave. Pres.: J. Rubin.

HOSPITALS:

Mt. Sinai Sanatorium, Office: 493 Sherbrooke St. West. Sanatorium: Sainte Agathe Des Monts, Quebec. Pres.: C. B. Fainer.

Jewish General Hospital, 3755 St. Catherine Rd. Pres.: Allan Bronfman.

BELLEVILLE (ONT.) (130 Jews)

Sons of Jacob Foundation Congregation, 122 Pinnacle St. Pres.: Ben Safe. Rabbi: Babb.

BRANDON (MAN.) (122 Jews)

Congregation B'nai Israel, Fourth and Princess Sts. Founded 1900. Pres.: M. Crystal.

BRANTFORD (ONT.) (228 Jews)

Jewish Federation. Pres.: M. Sherman. Sec.: Mrs. G. Harris, 29 Albion St.

Congregation Beth David, Palace & Albion Sts. Pres.: Louis Hankle. Rabbi: Martin Fisher.

BROCKVILLE (ONT.) (53 Jews)

Hebrew Centre. Pres.: N. Hyman. Sec.: S. A. Jacobson.

CALGARY (ALTA.) (2,600 Jews)

Congregation House of Jacob, 323 5th Av. E. Founded 1894. Pres.: E. Shapiro. Rabbi: D. Barenholtz.

Congregation House of Israel, Corner 18th Av. and Centre St. Pres.: E. Cohen. Rabbi: E. Ebner.

CORNER BROOK (NEWFOUNDLAND) (14 Jewish families)

Hebrew Congregation. Pres.: Arthur Cohen. Sec.: B. Lavin. Rabbi: Kutziner.

CORNWALL (ONT.) (183 Jews)

Community Council. Pres.: A. Dover. Sec.: Mrs. A. Miller.

EDMONTON (ALTA.) (1,748 Jews)

Jewish Community Council. Pres.: George Levine.

Jewish Federation, 10261 108th St. Est. 1938. Pres.: W. Margolis. Sec.: Fred Swartz.

ESTEVAN (SASK.)

Congregation Beth Jacob. Sec.: M. Mandel.

FORT WILLIAM (ONT.) (214 Jews)

Lakehead Jewish Council, 707 South Mark St. Pres.: S. Stitt.

Hebrew Congregation Shaare Shomayim, 137 Finlayson St. Pres.: Dr. M. L. Stitt. Rabbi: H. Goldwater.

FREDERICTON (NEW BRUNSWICK) (185 Jews)

Congregation Sgoolai Israel, Westmoreland St. Pres.: J. Budovitch. Sec.: I. Ellman.

GLACE BAY (NOVA SCOTIA) (328 Jews)

Congregations Sons of Israel, Prince St. Pres.: S. Shore. Minister, Rev. J. Mayer

GUELPH (ONT.) (198 Jews)

Community Council. Pres.: S. Acker. Sec.: J. Adler.

HALIFAX (NOVA SCOTIA) (1,159 Jews)

Community Council. Pres.: Dr. M. Jacobson. Sec.: Mrs. Chas. Arron, 25 Connaught Ave.

Robie St. Synagogue. Pres.: F. Zabberman. Rabbi: A. Greenspan.

HAMILTON (ONT.) (3,158 Jews)

Council of Jewish Organizations, 57 Delaware Ave. Est. 1934.

HOFFER (SASK.)

Congregation Beth Jacob. Pres.: Israel Hoffer.

KINGSTON (ONT.) (302 Jews)

Jewish Community Council, Est. 1947. Pres.: S. J. Cohen. Sec.: H. Millman, 117 Earl St.

KIRKLAND LAKE (ONT.) (150 Jews)

Congregation "Adath Israel," Station Rd. Pres.: M. J. Ross. Rabbi: A. Kauffman.

KITCHENER (ONT.) (434 Jews)

Beth Jacob Synagogue. Pres.: Mr. Brown, 36 Albert St.

Federated Jewish Charities, 587 King St. E. Est. 1943. Pres.: Allan Rosenberg.

LETHBRIDGE (ALTA.) (225 Jews)

Hebrew Congregation. Minister: S. W. Susman.

LONDON (ONT.) (1,000 Jews)

Jewish Community Council. Pres.: Bernard Wolf. Sec.: A. B. Gillick.

Synagogue B'nai Israel, Wellington St. and Grey St.

Synagogue B'nai Moshe Ben Yehuda, Horton St. and Colborne St. Pres.: S. Leich. Rabbi: David Kirshenbaum.

MEDICINE HAT (ALTA) (130 Jews)

Congregation Sons Of Abraham.

MELVILLE (SASK) (105 Jews)

Beth Jacob Synagogue. Pres.: S. Nagler.

MONCTON (N.B.) (268 Jews)

Tiferet Israel Congregation, 48 Steadman St. Pres.: A. M. Levine.

MOOSE JAW (SASK.) (146 Jews)

Beth Israel Hebrew Congregation, Caribou & 3rd Ave. Pres.: J. Dorfman. Minister: Rev. Joel Stall.

NEW GLASGOW (Nova Scotia) (52 Jews)

Agudas Achim Synagogue. Pres.: H. Goodman.

NEW WATERFORD (Nova Scotia) (99 Jews)

Congregation Sons Of Israel. Pres.: Louis Gorelick.

NIAGARA FALLS (ONT.) (116 Jews)

Jewish Federation. Pres.: Joseph Greenspan. Sec.: I. I. Ackerman.

Congregation B'nai Jacob, 1328 Perry St. Pres.: J. Greenspan.

NORTH BAY (ONT.) (105 Jews)

Sons Of Jacob Hebrew Congregation, Incorporated 1924. Pres.: Henry Wiseman, 694 McIntyre St. W.

OSHAWA (ONT.) (374 Jews)

Hebrew Congregation, 318 King St. E. Pres.: M. Palter. Sec.: M. Fopp. Rabbi: M. Norden.

OTTAWA (ONT.) (4,520 Jews)

Jewish Community Council. Pres.: Samuel Berger.

Va'ad Ha'ir of Ottawa, 171 George St. Pres.: T. Sachs'. Sec.: H. Hochberg. Rabbi: E. L. Lipschutz. There are 6 congregations in Ottawa.

OWEN SOUND (ONT.)

PERTH (ONT.) (11 Jewish families)

Agudath Achim Hebrew Congregation. Pres.: L. Karakowsky. Sec.: B. Karakowsky.

PETERBOROUGH (ONT.) (232 Jews)

Beth Israel Hebrew Congregation, Reid St. Pres.: H. Schwarz. Minister: Rev. J. Mayer.

PORT COLBORNE (ONT.)

Congregation Agudath Achim. Pres.: Richard Dwor.

PORTAGE LA PRAIRIE (MAN.) (61 Jews)

Congregation Beth Jacob, Main St. S. Founded 1914. Pres.: W. Glesby.

PRINCE ALBERT (SASK.) (90 Jews)

Congregation Beth Jacob, 10th St. Founded 1914. Pres.: Alexander Fayerman. Rabbi: Rev. J. Pepper.

QUEBEC (QUE.) (416 Jews)

Congregation Beth Israel, Ohev Sholem, 78½ Cremazie St. Branch at 52 Marguerite St.

Pres.: Maurice Pollak. Rabbi: Joshua Epstein. Reverend: I. Kleinman.

REGINA (SASK.) (740 Jews)

Regina Hebrew Federated Community, 2060 Halifax St. Founded 1913.

ROUYN NORANDA (QUE.) (30 Jewish families)

Hebrew Congregation. Pres.: Michael Korman. Rev.: M. W. Katz.

ST. CATHERINE'S (ONT.) (550 Jews)

Council of Jewish Organizations. Pres.: S. A. Hoffman. Sec.: Miss M. Zalavinsky.

ST. JOHN'S (NEWFOUNDLAND) (130 Jews)

Hebrew Congregation of Newfoundland, 17 Henry St., (P.O.Box 59). Pres.: S. B. Wilansky. Sec.: M. I. Wilansky. Minister: Rabbi R. Mellor.

SAINT THOMAS (ONT.) (60 Jews)

Hebrew Congregation and Jewish Centre. Pres.: H. Jackson. Sec.: Henry Caplan.

SARNIA (ONT.) (185 Jews)

Jewish Community Council. Pres.: Roy Smith. Sec.: L. Glait, 116 College Ave.

SASKATOON (SASK.) (687 Jews)

Agudath Israel Congregation, 202 Avenue E. Founded 1910. Pres.: M. Aarons. Rabbi: Adler.

SAULT STE. MARIE (ONT.) (116 Jews)

Congregation Beth Jacob, Bruce St. Pres.: Alan Torgov. Sec.: Jack Fishman.

SHERBROOKE (QUE.) (197 Jews)

Agudath Achim Synagogue, 85 Montreal St. Pres.: M. Smith. Sec.: B. Hyman.

SUDBURY (ONT.) (184 Jews)

Jewish Community Centre, 140 Cedar St.

SYDNEY (Nova Scotia) (407 Jews)

Jewish Community Council. Pres.: Harvey Webber.

THREE RIVERS (QUE.) (61 Jews)

Hebrew Association. Pres.: S. Vineberg. Sec.: M. Budd.

TIMMINS (ONT.) (202 Jews)

B'nai Israel Synagogue, 23 Cedar St. N. Pres.: M. Bucovetsky. Rabbi: A. Matts.

TORONTO (ONT.)
(Jewish population: 77,000)

United Jewish Welfare Fund, 150 Beverly St. Founded 1937. Chairman: Arthur E. Gelber. Exec. Dir.: Florence Hutner.

EDUCATIONAL INSTITUTIONS:

Central Bureau of Jewish Education, 455 Spadina Ave. Pres.: S. Posluns. About 60% of the Jewish children are getting Jewish instruction.

Hillel Foundation (at the Univ. of Toronto), 186 St. George St. Dir.: Rabbi Aaron Kamerling.

Young Men's Hebrew Association, 15 Brunswick Ave. Pres.: Borsok.

Borochov School and Kindergarten, 330 Lippincott St. Pres.: Dr. L. Jessel.

Jewish National Workers' Alliance Folk Schools, 110 St. George St. and 476 Euclid Ave. Pres.: I. Freeman.

D'Arcy Street Talmud Torah, 68 D'Arcy St. Princ.: J. I. Wohlegelernter. Sec.: G. Goldwasser.

Associated Hebrew Free Schools, 9 Brunswick Ave. Princ.: Dr. L. Jacober.

ZIONIST INSTITUTIONS:

Toronto Zionist Council, 651 Spadina Ave. Pres.: J. Devor. Sec.: Mrs. L. Kert.

Hadassah Administrative Board, 651 Spadina Ave. Pres.: Mrs. M. A. Levy. There are 14 Chapters.

Mizrachi Organization of Toronto, 461 Spadina Ave. Pres.: Rabbi J. Washer.

Poale Zion Council. Pres.: A. Wallerstein, 110 St. George St.

Tora V'Avoda Movement of Canada, 396 Markham St. Toronto.

VANCOUVER (B.C.) (7,000 Jews)

Je···· Community Council, 2675 Oak St. Founded 1932. Pres.: Dr. J. V. White. Dir.: Louis Zimmerman.

Talmud Torah Association, 27th Ave. and Oak St. Pres.: I Lipsky.

Peretz School. Pres.: Saul Wyne.

VICTORIA (B.C.)

Congregational Emanu El. Est. 1863. Pres.: S. Bricher. Sec.: Raymond Rose.

WELLAND (ONT.) (107 Jews)

Jewish Federation of Welland. Pres.: Harry Carrel. Sec.: Sidney Goldsmith.

WINDSOR (ONT.) (2,600 Jews)

Jewish Community Council, Palace Theatre Bldg. Quellette Ave. Est. 1938. Pres.: Eli C. Cohen. Sec.: Mrs. F. Geller.

Talmud Torah. Pres.: M. Mossman, 166 MacDougall St.

I. L. Peretz School. Pres.: R. Madoff, 1870 Ypres Avenue.

WINNIPEG (MAN.)
(Jewish population: 20,000)

The Jewish Community of Winnipeg is about 65 years old. There were only two Jews there in 1879.

Talmud Torah and Hebrew Free School, Corner Mateson and Powers Sts. Pres.: H. B. Mitchell.

Peretz Folk Schools and Institute, 418 Aberdeen Ave. Pres.: B. Mayman.

Keren Ha-Tarbuth. Pres.: J. Wolinsky, 126 Machray Avenue.

Sholem Aleichim School, 410 Pritchard Ave. Pres.: J. Yanovsky.

United Jewish Welfare Fund, 123 Matheson Ave. Est. 1938. Pres.: M. Nathanson. Dir.: A. B. Feld.

Mount Carmel Clinic, Selkirk Ave. E. Pres.:
J. King. Dir.: L. Schubert.

Vaad Ha'Ir, 1206 Main St. Pres.: D. Salter.
Sec.: H. Frank.

YARMOUTH (N.S.) (110 Jews)

Agudath Achim Congregation. Rabbi: P. D.
Cohen, Sec.: Hubert Lynch.

YORKTON (SASK.)

Shaaray Shomaim Congregation, Betts Ave.

Bulletin du Cercle Juif (French), 493 Sherbrooke St., West, Montreal. Monthly.

PUBLICATIONS:

Bulletin du Cercle Juif (French), 493 Sherbrooke, W. Montreal. Monthly.

The Canadian Jewish Magazine, 1500 St.
Catherine St., W. Montreal. Monthly.

Canadian Jewish Review, 265 Craig St., W.
Montreal. Weekly.

Canadian Zionist, 2025 University Ave., Montreal. Monthly.

Congress Bulletin, 493 Sherbrooke St., West,
Montreal. Monthly.

The Daily Hebrew Journal, 409 College St.,
Toronto.

Dos Wort, 5101 Esplanade Ave., Montreal.
Monthly. Yiddish.

Israelite Press, 221 Flora Ave., Winnipeg.
English-Yiddish.

Jewish Daily Eagle, 4075 St. Lawrence Blvd.,
Montreal.

Canadian Jewish Chronicle, 4075 St. Lawrence
Blvd., Montreal. Weekly.

Canadian News, 525 Dundas St. W., Toronto.
Yiddish. Weekly.

Jewish Post, 213 Selkirk Ave., Winnipeg.
Weekly.

Jewish Standard, 43 Yonge St., Toronto.
Fortnightly.

Jewish Western Bulletin, 2675 Oak St., Vancouver, B.C. Weekly.

Kanader Stimme (Yiddish), 130 Laurier W.,
Montreal. Monthly.

Vochenblatt (Yiddish-English). Weekly.   304
Brunswick Ave., Toronto.

Western Jewish News, 303 Times Bldg., Winnipeg. Weekly.

Windsor Jewish Community Bulletin, 405
Pelissier St., Windsor. Monthly.

HAWAII

JEWISH POPULATION: 1,000

Jews have lived in Hawaii for more than 150 years, but the descendants of the early settlers have either moved away or are no longer identified as Jews. The present Jewish residents have come to Hawaii within the past 32 years. Their number is estimated at 1,000. Almost all of them live in Honolulu. The rate of intermarriage is very high.

Temple Emanu-El, the only Jewish Congregation in the Territory of Hawaii, was chartered by the Territory in 1938 under the name "Honolulu Jewish Community." The name was changed in 1948 to "Congregation of the Honolulu Jewish Community" and in 1954, to its present name, Temple Emanu-El. Until 1950, the Congregation of the Honolulu Jewish Community was little more than an appendage to the National Jewish Welfare Board. It had a membership of not more than 40 families. From 1947 to 1950, it had a part-time Rabbi, a graduate of the Yeshiva College, who was the Director of the National Jewish Welfare Board Activities in Hawaii. In 1950, the National Jewish Welfare Board closed its offices in Hawaii. In 1951, the Congregation purchased a building which it remodeled into the first house of worship ever owned by the Jews of Hawaii. The same year, the Congregation engaged Rabbi Francis Hevesi, former Chief Rabbi of Budapest, as its first full time rabbi. Upon the death of Rabbi Hevesi in 1952, the Congregation voted to adopt the Reform ritual and elected Rabbi Alexander Segel, a graduate of the Hebrew Union College, as its rabbi, and purchased a home for him. The Congregation is affiliated with the Union of American Hebrew Congregations. Its sisterhood is affiliated with the National Federation of Temple Sisterhoods and its Men's Club is affiliated with the National Federation of Temple Brotherhoods. The Congregation has a membership of approximately 115 families. Bernard H. Levi son, an attorney, has been President of the Congregation since May, 1950.

HONOLULU (1,000 Jews)

Temple Emanu-El, 2207 Oahu. Pres.: Bernard H. Levinson, 328 Merchandise Mart Bldg. Sec.: Samuel Landau. Membership: 115 families. Reform congregation. Rabbi: Alexander Segel, 2207 Oahu Avenue.

Religious School, 2207 Oahu Avenue. 6 teachers. 40 pupils. Dir.: Rabbi Alexander Segel.

Temple Emanu-El Institute of Jewish Studies, 2207 Oahu Avenue. 1 teacher. 15 pupils. Dir.: Rabbi Alexander Segel.

EUROPE

ALBANIA

JEWISH POPULATION: 200

The 52 Jewish families living in Albania are mostly Sephardim who escaped from Greece during World War II and now reside in the capital, Tirana. There are also small Jewish settlements in the towns of Scutari and Valona, according to a report in the Australian *Jewish Herald* of Melbourne on April 10, 1953.

TIRANA (200 Jews)

Jewish Community. Pres.: Itzhak Cohen.

AUSTRIA

JEWISH POPULATION: 12,000

It is probable that Jews came to the Danube with the Roman colonists. The first definite evidence of the presence of Jews in Austria is in the vicinity of 900. Under the Holy Roman Empire, in the 13th century, the situation of the Jews was rather favorable. The first synagogue in Vienna was built in 1204. Under Duke Frederick II, Jews were granted many privileges. Until 1421, there existed a central organization of Jewish communities. From the 14th century on, the situation of the Jews, which had been relatively fortunate in the previous five centuries, worsened. Jews were systematically exploited; their property confiscated; they were often murdered. In 1420, they were expelled from the country. Emperor Frederick III allowed them to return in 1451. In the following centuries, the Jews were tolerated, but their burden of taxation was excessive. When the Vienna Jews again began to grow in numbers, Ferdinand II granted them, in 1624, a suburb of Vienna as a place of residence, later known as Leopoldstadt and the most densely populated Jewish area of Vienna. Outside of Vienna, in the 17th century, there were between 3,000 and 4,000 living on the estates of the aristocracy. For this privilege, they paid a special tax. However, there was another period of excessive persecution which culminated in the second expulsion of Jews from Austria in 1670.

Individual Jews were soon again tolerated in Vienna after their expulsion in 1670, although they were subject to restrictions. A period of oppression set in with the reign of Maria Theresa (1740–80), but restrictions were lifted by Joseph II in 1782. The constitution of April 25, 1848, granted Jews equality of rights and abolished old Jewish taxes. But it was not until 1867 that all limitations were removed, and Jewish communities were formed in the larger and smaller cities. Jews took part in the founding of many industries in the Austrian provinces and attained respectable positions in government service, legislative bodies, the army, and in the universities.

The first World War imposed heavy demands upon the Jews of Austria and brought a great influx of fugitives, mostly from Galicia and Bucovina. After the War, most of them returned to their homes, many under the pressure of anti-Semitic measures of the municipalities of Vienna, Prague, and other cities. The collapse of Austria-Hungary resulted in excesses against the Jews. The Austrian Republic, which was established following the Revolution of 1918, extended complete emancipation to the Jews of the country.

The crisis of 1934–35 and the collapse of the Viennese banking house of Rothschild and its affiliates caused havoc in the economic and political status of the Austrian Jews. The new constitution of 1934 curtailed the rights of Jews in schools. From 1934 to 1938, the government apparently made efforts to check the rising tide of anti-Semitism but failed. In December 1937 and February 1938, there were anti-Jewish riots and demonstrations. In March 1938, the republic was overrun by the armies of Hitler. This was followed by barbaric persecutions against he Jews. Many escaped by emigration and others were sent to concentration camps. In 1943, the destruction of this glorious Jewish community was completed.

After the liberation in 1945, only 29 Jewish children were left in Vienna. Owing to the small number of Jewish pupils in the public schools of Vienna, only one Jewish afternoon school and 6 centers for Jewish religious instruction were operating during 1953–54 for a total of 246 pupils—124 boys and 122 girls —with 5 teachers. There are 228 Jewish students, of whom 198 are in Vienna, in Austrian institutions of higher learning. Only 680 Jews live in the Austrian provinces outside Vienna, and Jewish cultural life is thus practically non-existent there.

Almost the same parties that were active in 1930, when Austrian Jewry numbered over 200,000 and the Jewish population of Vienna alone amounted to about 180,000, exist today. They are: the Bund Werktaetiger Juden (the Jewish Socialists); the Jewish Confederation (various Zionist parties and the Torah-true Jews); the Jewish Unity (the Left Wing). The orthodox Jews of Mizrachi and Aguda recently organized their own congregation outside of the Kultusgemeinde alleging that the Kultusgemeinde does not provide for their religious needs.

Bundesverband der Israelitischer Kultusgemeinden (Federal Union of Jewish Communities in Austria), Schottenring 25, Vienna 1.
Coordinates the activities of the Communities of Vienna, Gras, Linz, Salzburg and Innsbruck and is practically directed by the Jewish Community in Vienna. The Union is an affiliate of the World Jewish Congress.
Pres.: Dr. Emil Maurer.
Sec.: Wilhelm Krell.

VIENNA ,9,100 Jews)

Israelitische Kultusgemeinde Wien (Jewish Community), Schottenring 25, Vienna 1. It is recognized by law and represents the interests of Jewry before the authorities. It organizes Jewish religious instruction at the public elementary and high schools.
Pres., Dr. Emil Maurer.
Sec.: Wilhelm Krell.
Chief Rabbi: Dr. Akiba Eisenberg.
Temple of the Jewish Community, Seitenstettengasse 4, Vienna I.
Hospital of the Jewish Community, Seegasse 9, Vienna IX. Dir.: Dr. Mathias Reich.
Agudas Israel, Falkenstr. 6, Vienna I.
Pres.: B. Schreiber.
Bne Akiba, Judenplatz, 8, Vienna I. Youth organization of Mizrachi.
Gordonia, Seitenstettengasse 2. Youth organization of Mapai in Austria.
Hakoah, Seitenstettengasse 4, Vienna I. Jewish sport Union.
Pres.: Rudolf Bohmer.
Hanoar Hazioni, Universitatsstrasse 4/4. Youth organization of the General Zionists.
Hashomer Hatzair, Alserstrasse 18, Vienna IX. Youth organization of Mapam of Austria.
Herzl Club, Eschenbachgasse 11, Vienna I. Zionist non-political club.
Chairman: Dr. Bernard Klamer.
Sec.: Prof. Berthold Hirschl.
Vereinigung Judischer Hochschuler in Osterreich, Seitenstettengasse 2, Vienna I. Union of Jewish students.

Chairman: Leon Zelman.
Sec.: Otto Kahn.
Zionistische Federation von Osterreich, Seitenstettengasse 4. The Zionist Federation of Austria coordinates Zionist activities throughout the country.
Chairman: Gustav Leitner.
Sec.: Dr. David Schlang.
Zionistischer Landesverband in Osterreich, Universitatsstrasse 4, Vienna IX. Organization of the General Zionists for Austria.
Chairman: Dr. Wolf Herzberg.
Sec.: Fritz Mueller.
Zionistisch-Revisionistische Union, Rechte Wienseile 37, Vienna IX. Zionist Revisionist Union of Austria.
Chairman: Alfred Reischer.
Sec.: Siegfried Lazar.
Mapai, Poale Zion Hitachduth Osterreich, Seitenstettengasse 2. Organization of Mapai, Poale Zion Hitachduth.
Pres.: Hugo Lowey.
Sec.: Benjamin Bohrer.
Mapam, Alserstrasse 18, Vienna IX. Central board of Mapam in Austria.
Misrachi, Judenplatz 8, Vienna I. Union of religious Zionists.
Pres.: Chief Rabbi Dr. Akiba Eisenberg.
WIZO, Seitenstettengasse 4, Vienna I.
Pres.: Mrs. Ada Neuspiel.

GRAZ (232 Jews)

Israelitische Kultusgemeinde Graz (Jewish community), Grieskai 58.
Dir: Knoepelmacher.
Union of Jewish Students, Postfach 51.
Chairman: Boris Dov Drujan.

INNSBRUCK (160 Jews)

Israelitische Kultusgemeinde Innsbruck (Jewish community) Anichgasse 7.
Pres.: Rudolf Brull.
Union of Jewish Students, Sillgasse 15b.

LINZ (171 Jews)

Judische Kultusgemeinde Linz (Jewish community), Bettelheimstrasse 26.
Pres.: Schwager.

SALZBURG (729 Jews)

Israelitische Kultusgemeinde Salzburg, Mertens-
strasse 7.

Pres.: Herman Einziger.

PUBLICATIONS:

MONTHLIES: *Die Stimme,* Universitatsstrasse
4/4. German. (General Zionists).

Juedisches Echo, Seitenstettengasse 2, Vienna
I. German. (Jewish students).

Neue Welt, Hutweidengasse 34, Vienna XIX.

Renaissance, Seitenstettengasse 2, Vienna,
(Mapai).

Tribune, Judenplatz 8, Vienna I. German.
(Mizrachi).

BELGIUM

JEWISH POPULATION: 35,000

The first reliable accounts place Jews in Belgium as early as the 4th century. The situation of the Jews in this country was, in general, favorable, although they were at times subject to persecution. In the 8th and 9th centuries they were accorded full rights and privileges by the reigning monarchs.

From the end of the 9th to the 13th century, however, they were severely persecuted. In the 13th century, the situation slightly improved, although they were forced to pay heavy taxes. The Black Death (1348–49) had disastrous effects on the Jews, culminating in the Brussels Massacre of 1370 which completely destroyed the Belgian Jewish communities.

In the 16th century, Spanish and Portuguese Marranos settled in Antwerp, but they were oppressed by the Austrian and Spanish rulers of the time. Increased Jewish immigration into the country began at the outset of the 18th century. When Belgium came under Dutch rule, the Jews attained full civil rights. With the establishment of Belgian independence in 1830, Jews were granted religious freedom under the country's constitution.

The first organization of Jewish communities probably came at the time when the country was under French control; under Dutch rule, in 1814, these communities became subject to the Jewish Consistorial Council of Holland. When Belgium became independent, Jews were permitted to have their own communal organization with a central consistory and chief rabbinate in Brussels.

With the advent of the Hitler regime, Belgium received many refugees kindly. By 1940, there were nearly 100,000 Jews in the country, mainly in Antwerp, Brussels, Liege, Ghent, and Charleroi.

During the Nazi occupation, thousands of Jews fled the country. Some of them returned and, together with refugees from other countries, renewed Jewish communal life in Belgium. 90% of the Jews in Belgium are non-citizens.

Jewish education in Brussels is rather neglected. Due to the fact that the Jewish residents are scattered, no schools were developed besides the Yesod Hatorah day school with 120 pupils, and smaller institutions where more than 500 children receive Jewish instruction. In Antwerp the situation in this respect is much better. There are well organized Jewish schools, such as Tachkemoni, with 450 pupils; Jewish primary Yesode Hatorah, with 600 pupils; Shomre Hadas; the ORT school, with 240 students. In government elementary and high schools Jewish religious instruction is assured through the Jewish congregations of the respective cities.

BRUSSELS (20,000 Jews)

Consistoire Central Israelite de Belgique, 2, rue Joseph Dupont. The central Jewish body in Belgium, its board is composed of representatives of all Jewish communities and synagogues; recognized by Government.
Pres.: E. E. Wiener.
Grand Rabbi: Solomon Ullman.

Communaute Israelite de Bruxelles, 2, rue Joseph-Dupont, Jewish community of Brussels. Affiliated with the Consistoire Central.

Synagogues: Synagogue of Brussels, 32, rue de la Regance; Synagogue of Anderlecht, 67a, rue de la Clinique; Synagogue of Schaerbeek, 192, rue Josaphat; 42, rue Quatrecht, 20, rue Rogier, 27, rue Gendebien; "Beth Israel" Synagogue, 18, rue de Lenglentier; Synagogue du Misrahi, 1 rue d'Ardenne; Sephardi Synagogue, 2, rue Joseph Dupont; Consistorial Synagogue, 2, rue Joseph Dupont.

Federation Sioniste de Belgique, 6, rue de Grayer. Central Zionist body.
Pres.: Nesanel Lewkowicz.
Gen. Sec.: Marc Anisfeld.

Comite Central Israelite, 54, rue de Venise. Its work is mostly of a religious nature. Maintains a children's home in Antwerp.
Pres.: M. Diamant.

Comite du Congres Juif Mondial, 38, Ave. de Pantheon, Brussels. Representatives: J. Rosenberg; Marcel Marihower.

Conseil des Associations Juives de Belgique, 190, Blvd. M. Lemonnier. Co-ordinate activities of all Jewish associations in Belgium.
Pres.: Abraham Ryba.
Sec.: Jacques Rosenberg.

Organisation des Sionistes Religieux Misrachi en Belgique, 41, rue de Chartreux.
Pres.: Ch. Mauer.
Sec.: Zilberberg.

Office Palestinien, 17 rue de Pascale.

O.R.T. Belge, 67, rue Van Soust, Bruxelles—Anderlecht.
Pres.: Roger Van Praag.
Sec.: Maurice Heiber.

Aide Aux Israelites Victimes de la Guerre, 10, rue de la Vallee. Aids Jewish victims of the war; supports 3 children's homes.
Pres.: Alfred Goldschmidt.
Gen. Dir.: Guy Mansbach.

Agence Juive pour la Palestine (Jewish Agency for Palestine), 6, rue de Grayer.
Dir.: Israel Weis.
Gen. Sec.: S. Altman.

Alliance Israelite Universelle, 48, rue de l'Eremitage.

American Joint Distribution Committee, 76, rue Mercelis.

B'nai B'rith (*Fraternelle*), 28, rue General-Gratry.
Pres.: S. Silberberg.

Association Sportive Maccabi, 11, rue de la Concorde.

Cercle Amical "Arbeiter-Ring", les Amis des Enfants, 96, Blvd. de la Revision. The two societies, The Workmen's Circle and the Children's Aid Society work together.

Comite de l'Union des Sionistes Generaux de Bruxelles, 78, rue de Ruysbroeck.
Pres.: Nes Lewkowicz.
Sec.: Tewia Wybrancyk.

Communaute Israelite Orthodoxe, 76a, rue de la Clinique.
Pres.: Perle.
Sec.: J. Zalcman.

Synagogue and *Beth-Midrash*, rue Chapeau, Bruxelles-Anderlecht.

Jessode Hatorah, 67a, rue de la Clinique. Religious school.

Hanoar Hazioni, Haoved Hazioni, 78, rue de Ruysbroeck.

Mizrachi, 1, rue d'Ardenne. Under this group are: *Hapoel Hamizrachi, Bachad, Bne Akiba, Social Section, Agricultural and Artisan's School of the Bachad.*

Poale Agoudath Israel—Agoudath Israel, 27, rue Gendebien.

Poale Sion, Hashomer Hatzair, Leachdouth-Mapam, 43, rue Bara.

Secours Mutual Juif, 43, rue Bara. Provides social aid, especially for aged Jews.
Gen. Sec.: Chaim Monk.

Societe de Beinfaisance Israelite Sepharadite de Belgique, 36, rue Jourdan. Sephardic welfare society.
Pres.: Conrad Franco.
Sec.: Zacharie Levy.

Beith Israel Synagogue, 34, rue de la Colonne, Bruxelle-Molenbeck.
Pres.: Berkowick.
Sec.: Muchinsky.

Union des Etudiants Juifs de Belgique, 34, chaussee de Charleroi.
Pres.: Dr. Unger.

Union Europeenne des Juifs Turcs, 66, rue de Livourne.

WIZO, 109, rue de la Source.

ANTWERP (11,000 Jews)

Communautes Israelites Reunies d'Anvers (Jewish community), Terliststraat 35.
Rabbis: Dr. S. Sapira, M. J. Zweig, Chaim Kreiswirt.

Synagogues: Israelietische Gemeente (Schilderstraat 10), Machsikei Hadas (Oostenstraat 43), Moryah (Terliststraat 35), Synagogue of Portuguese Ritual (Hovenierstraat 20), Machsikei Hadas Beth Hamidrash (Oostenstraat 43), Eisenmann Synagogue (Oostenstraat 27), Menachem Aweilim (Lange Kievitstraat 134), Agudath Israel (Oostenstraat 42), Beth Hamidrash (Stoomstraat 9), Beth Hamidrash (Sterreborgstraat 13), Beth Hamidrash Misrachi (Van Spangenstraat 14).

General Zionist Organization, 1200 members.

Poale Zion—Mapai, 650 members.

Communaute Israelite "Shomre Hadaas", (Schildersstraat 10). Hebrew School.
Rabbi: Dr. S. Sapira.
Pres.: H. Schamisso.

Communaute Isralite "Machsike Hadaas". Community for Russian ritual.

Commnaute du Rite Portugais, Hovenierstraat 20. Pres.: J. Chalhon.

Jesode-Hatora—Beth-Jacob, 18–22, Longue rue Van Ruusbroeck. Jewish orthodox school consisting of a kindergarten, primary school and seminary, French and Flemish sections.
Dir.: S. Ostersetzer.
Sec.: S. Klagsbald.

Mizrachi, 14, rue Van Spagan, 700 members. Under it are *Bachad* and *Bne Akiba*.

Tachkemoni, Institut Israelite, 313 Longue rue d'Argile. Mizrachi Jewish school, giving preparatory, primary, and secondary instruction. Has French, Flemish, and Hebrew sections.
Dir.: J. Goldberg.
Pres.: B. Hakan.
Sec.: D. Seifter.

O.R.T., 27, Belgielei. Pres.: Marcel Ginsburg.

Agoudath Israel en Belgique, 42, de l'Orient.
Pres.: S. Klagsbald.
Sec.: L. Pinkusevitz.

CHARLEROI (2,000 Jews)

Communaute Israelite (Jewish community), 56, rue Pige-au-Croly.
Pres.: N. Linker.
Sec.: M. Gorzaleranz.

Ecole Hebraique Israelite, 56, rue Pige-au-Croly. Hebrew school.
Pres.: Mr. Kirschweg.
Sec.: I. Lipzyk.

Federation Sioniste, 56, rue Pige-au-Croly.
Pres.: Chaim Kirschenzweig.
Sec.: Ephraim Posner.

ARLON

Communaute Israelite (Jewish community),
22, rue des Martyrs.
Pres.: Georges Garey.

GHENT

Communaute Israelite (Jewish community),
4 Roskamerstraat.

LIEGE

Communaute Israelite (Jewish community).
Organisation Sioniste, 6, rue Dcuffet.
Pres.: Raphael Janowski.
Sec.: J. Rabine.

OSTENDE

Societe Culturelle de la Communaute Israelite
(Jewish community), 1 Blvd. Alphonse
Pieters.
Pres.: Kleiner.
Sec.: Jacques Kalter.

PERIODICALS:

FORTNIGHTLY: Tribune Sioniste, French. 6,
rue de la Crayer, Bruxelles.
MONTHLIES: Kehilatenu. 2, rue Joseph Du-
pont, Bruxelles.
Lebn un Shalom (Yiddish), 375, rue Haute,
Bruxelies.
Menorah, 11, rue de la Concorde, Bruxelles.

BULGARIA

JEWISH POPULATION: 6,000

There is evidence that Jewish communities existed in Bulgaria as early as
the 2nd century C.E. In the 10th century, the Byzantine conquest of Bulgaria
brought a fresh stream of Jews into the
land. In the 13th and 14th centuries,
when Bulgaria was again independent,
an important Jewish community grew up
at Trnovo, then the capital. In the second half of the 14th century, the Jewish
population of Bulgaria was increased
through the immigration of Jews banish-
ed from Hungary.

In 1396, Bulgaria was conquered by
the Turks, and under the Ottoman regime the Jewish communities increased
and prospered. At the end of the 15th
century, large numbers of Sephardic
Jews came from the Iberian peninsula
and German-speaking Jews from Bavaria.
After the liberation of Bulgaria from

Turkish rule, Jews were granted all civil
and political rights and full equality with
the Christian population in the terms of
the peace treaty drawn up at the Congress of Berlin in 1878. However, anti-
semitism began to make great strides
shortly thereafter and reached peaks of
violence during the First World War, in
1925, and especially with the advent of
Fascism in 1933.

Before the Second World War, Bulgaria's
48,000 (as of 1940) Jews were predominantly Sephardic. Almost three-fifths
lived in Sofia. The affairs of the various
Jewish communities were administered
by a consistory patterned after the
French model and by a chief rabbi. Zionism was fairly popular.

Bulgarian Jewry survived the Second
World War, despite the Nazi domination
of this country. Their number at the end

of the war was about 49,000, of whom 38,000 emigrated to Israel in the period 1948-1953. The great majority—35,000 —left in the second half of 1948, immediately after the establishment of the Jewish State.

According to the report of the Fifth Conference of the Jewish People's Committees, held in Sofia in April, 1952, Bulgarian Jews numbered 7,676 at the end of 1951. Since 1952, about 600 more Jews have emigrated to Israel. The total number of Jews left in Bulgaria can therefore be estimated at 7,000.

In addition to Sofia, the following 13 Jewish communities sent their represen· tatives to the above-mentioned Jewish Conference of 1952: Plovdiv, Ruse, Stanke Dimitrov, Stalin, Yambol, Vidin, Kyustendil, Burgas, Stara Zagora, Lom, Kolarovgrad, Kazanlik, and Pleven.

The law of 1951 made all Jewish communities and their Central Consistory non-religious lay institutions. A separate Central Israelite *Religious* Council was established in Sofia, and similar local councils were supposed to be organized in the provinces. Jewish library and reading room associations, which had existed in many communities, were all taken over by municipal authorities and transformed into local libraries for general use. The Jewish vocational "ORT" school in Sofia was closed in 1952, taken over by the government and converted into a general model technical school named after the Communist leader Kirov. The Jewish Scientific Institute in Sofia was also closed by the government on the basis of a decision of the Consistory and

its properties taken over by the Bulgarian Academy of Science. In 1954, however, the Consistory again mentioned the existence of the Scientific Institute, enumerating the following Jewish scholars among its members: Nathan Zak, Azarieh Polikarov, Eli Ashkenazi.

The only Jew who occupies an important position in the government is the Minister of Culture, Reuben Levi, a publicist. A second Jew, Israel Meir, heads the Department of Cultural Relations with Foreign Countries.

In 1953, a number of Jews were ousted from the Ministry of the Interior and Ministry of Foreign Trade and from municipal institutions and the militia.

SOFIA (4,260 Jews)

Central Consistory of Jews in Bulgaria, The Consistory was established in 1949 as a lay organization. It is the central representative body of Bulgarian Jewry. It supports 300 needy persons with small allowances from funds left by the Joint. The Executive is composed of 6 members and the Board of the Consistory of 24 mmbers.
Pres.: David Yerokham.
Sec.: Isak Frances.

Jewish Community of Sofia, Pres.: Mrs. Nastia Isakova. The president and the board of the Sofia community as well as the presidents of the communities in the provinces are appointed by the Central Consistory.

Central Israelite Religious Council, Established 1951, as the central body for Jewish religious matters. It is headed by the Chief Rabbi.

Committee for Jewish Culture. It arranges performances for Jews. There are no other forms of Jewish social life. All Jewish schools were closed in 1948.

Synagogue, The Synagogue is partly used by the University. The services are held in a small room on the second floor of the building. During the week, 15 persons attend the services and on Friday evenings, 70. During the holidays, about 400 persons participate in the worship, but the youth is absent even then.

Chief Rabbi: Dr. Asher Hananel, Ekzarh Josef Street 16, Sofia.

A. Ventura Orphanage. It is the only institution directed by the Jewish community.

Evreiski Vesti, Sofia. Monthly publication consisting of 2 pages. Organ of the Consistory.

CYPRUS

JEWISH POPULATION: 160

The most important historical event of the Jews in Cyprus took place in 115–117 when the Jewish community there was involved together with the Jews from Cyrene, Egypt, and Mesopotamia in the great revolt against Rome.

By the 7th century a new Jewish settlement was formed which is said to have taken part in the rebellion of Cyprus against the Emperor Heraclius in 610. The traveller Benjamin of Tudela found a Jewish community there which observed the Sabbath from daybreak to daybreak.

Don Joseph Nassi, the Duke of Naxos, urged Turkish Sultan Selim to conquer Cyprus, which was then under Venetian rule, and was promised the crown of the island should the expedition succeed, but he did not receive the reward.

With the British occupation of Cyprus in 1878, experiments began to form Jewish agricultural settlements there. In 1883, 1885, and 1891 unsuccessful attempts were made by Russian and Rumanian Jews to establish farm colonies. Later, ICA began to take an interest in ths colonization. In 1897, a Jewish colony was founded in conjunction with the "Ahavath Zion" society of London followed by another abortive experiment by Rumanian Jews. All attempts failed; most of the settlers left for Palestine and now only two farmers remain. A few German Jewish refugees have settled there since 1933. After the second world war, the population was vastly increased by the so-called illegal immigrants to Palestine who were intercepted at sea and interned there. These finally proceeded to Palestine after the proclamation of the Jewish State.

In view of the proximity of Cyprus to Israel, the Jews in Cyprus have a very strong interest in it and perform an important function in maintaining friendly relations between Cyprus and Israel, thus aiding the Israel Vice-Consul in Nicosia.

The Jewish population in June 1941, when it was removed by the British authorities to places of greater security, was 252. Many of these have returned; and they, together with those of the original Jewish population who remained in the island, now number 160: 54 in Larnaca, 13 in Famagusta, 60 in the capital

Nicosia, and the remainder in small centers.

There are three Jewish-owned factories in Cyprus, all in Larnaca, and a number of citrus growers. There is no rabbi in Cyprus. The leader of the community, Mr. Pershitz, an orange-grower, stems from Palestine. The community is now making efforts to erect a Jewish Center with a permanent synagogue.

The Committee of the Jewish Community of Cyprus, P.O.B. 95, Larnaca.

Pres.: Jacques Weiner.

Sec.: G. M. Berdy.

Treas.: Ida Pershitz.

The Jewish Community, P.O. Box 616, Nicosia.

CZECHOSLOVAKIA

JEWISH POPULATION: 23,000

The history of Jews in Bohemia can be traced to the 10th century. One of the oldest Jewish settlements in this country is in Prague, to which Jews came probably from Germany, Hungary, and the Byzantine Empire. During the Crusades, the Jews were severely persecuted, and many were forcibly baptized. In the 13th century, under King Ottocar II their situation became more favorable. During the 14th century, they were again persecuted, and King Charles IV (1347-78) was the first ruler to claim the Jews as his "imperial serfs" (Kammer knechte), an idea soon widely adopted. Wenzel IV (1378-1419) seized the property of Jews who had been killed in a massacre in Prague, and the murderers were not prosecuted. Under the rulers Podebrad (1458-71) and the Jagellons (1471-1526), anti-Jewish royal decrees were issued undermining the economic position of the Jews. In the course of the 16th century, the Jews were expelled several times, particularly from Prague. In 1625, when Bohemia fell to the Hapsburg rulers of Austria, the lot of the Jews continued to be unfavorable, and heavy taxes were imposed on them.

In 1670, the Jewish population of Bohemia increased greatly as a result of the expulsion of Jews from Vienna and of the Chmielnicki pogroms in Poland (1648-49). Their number in Prague grew from 4,000 to 12,000 by 1708. They were, however, still subject to the provisions of the ghetto, and the number of their marriages was explicitly restricted. In 1744, the Empress Maria Theresa issued orders expelling all Jews by 1745, and this was partly carried out.

With the Edict of Toleration of Joseph II in 1781, the history of Bohemian Jews merged with that of the Jews in other parts of Austria. Their full emancipation came only in 1867.

Bohemia had many famous Jewish leaders such as Isaac ben Mordecai and Isaac ben Jacob Halaban in the 12th century, Loew ben Bezalel (Maharal mi-Prague), Lippman Geller, Isaiah Horowitz (Sheloh), Jonathan Eybeshuetz, and others in the 18th century, and Rapaport, Zunz, and Michael Sachs in the 19th. Prague was especially noted as one of the great Jewish intellectual centers.

There were approximately 385,000 Jews in Czechoslovakia in 1938. The largest proportion lived in Ruthenia, where they formed over 15% of the total population, in eastern Slovakia, and in the cities of Prague, Bratislava, Brno and Moravska-Ostrava. *Ruthenia,* which until World War I was a part of Hungary, had 105,000 Jews in 1938, a large percentage of whom were employed in the rural sections as farmers and agricultural and forest workers. The largest Jewish community of Ruthenia was Mukacevo with 10,000 Jews.

Slovakia in 1938 had approximately 150,000 Jews. Bratislava contained the most important Jewish community in Slovakia, and its Yeshiva was one of the most prominent in Europe. The Jews of *Bohemia* and *Moravia* numbered about 80,000 in 1938 and constituted the most progressive segment of Czechoslovakian Jewry.

The political status of the Jews in Czechoslovakia was favorable. The Jews were represented both among government officials and in the army. Czechoslovakia was the first country to recognize Jewish nationality. The country became a haven to many refugees from Nazi Germany. However, when German troops occupied the country in 1939, the situation of the Jews deteriorated completely and they were put at the mercy of violent anti-Semitism.

At the end of World War II, only 35,000 of Czechoslovakia's 385,000 Jews remained. Of these, 24,000 emigrated to Israel from 1945 to 1953. At the end of 1953, there were 17,500 Jews in the country 9,000 of whom were in Slovakia. At the beginning of the Communist regime, many Jews held positions as officials and directors of nationalized enterprises. Their number was also relatively large in the liberal professions. However, the Slansky trial and feeling against "intellectualism" and "cosmopolitanism" hit the Jews severely. Many lost their jobs and only during the summer of 1953 did many of them manage to find re-employment.

There are four rabbis in the whole country as compared to 300 before World War II. The chief rabbi is Dr. Gustav Sicher of Prague. The number of synagogues is considerably reduced. The property of the Jewish communities has not been returned and they subsist on the small allowances of the Ministry of Religions. Since the end of the war, no special schools have been opened for Jews.

At the end of November 1953, a congress of the Jewish religious communities in the thirteen Regions of Bohemia, Moravia, and Silesia was held at which a *Council of Jewish Communities* in these regions was established on clearly formulated principles approved by the Communist Government. A new constitution was accepted which limits the activities of the communities to the status of a religious congregation. The constitution provides that all Jewish communal activities must be carried out in agreement with the principles of the People's Democratic

Order and the Laws of the Republic. A Kehillah can be established in any place where there is a minimum of 10 persons of the Jewish faith living in accordance with Jewish religious tradition. The supreme authority is vested in the *Council of Jewish Communities* in Czechia which will appoint rabbis and teachers of religion. The constitution also provides for the position of a chief rabbi and the formation of a council of rabbis.

In 1950, the Joint Distribution Committee and other relief organizations were banned, local Jewish welfare organizations nationalized, and Jewish emigration, halted. In 1951, the Zionist organizations in Czechia and Slovakia were closed and many Zionists and Jews "under suspicion" were arrested.

In 1952, the anti-semitic trial of Rudolph Slansky and his "associates" started. Of the 14 accused, 11 were Jews. Eight of the 11 sentenced to hanging were Jews; the rest were condemned to life imprisonment. At the end of 1951, two Israeli citizens, Simon Orenstein and Mordechai Oren, were arrested during their visit to Prague and later appeared as witnesses of the prosecution at the Slansky Trial. In September 1953, Ornstein was sentenced to life imprisonment and Oren to 15 years. Orenstein was released in October, 1954, and Oren, in May 1956.

BOHEMIA AND MORAVIA
(8,000 Jews)

Rada Jidovskych Nabozenskych Obci (Council of Jewish Religious Communities), Prague. The supreme religious Jewish body in Bohemia and Moravia, it represents the whole Jewish community in the Czech districts. It is a legal entity under public law and is governed by the above-mentioned recently adopted constitution.
Pres.: Emil Neumann.
Sec.: Dr. Rudolf Iltis.
Chief Rabbi: Dr. Gustav Sicher.

PRAGUE (5,000 Jews)
Jewish Religious Community (or District Community).
Pres.: Artur Busch.
Sec.: Ernest Frank.
Chevra Kadisha.
Chief Rabbi: Dr. Gustav Sicher.

Of the 300 Jewish children, 50 attend one hour a week of religious instruction with the special permission of the authorities.

PUBLICATION:
Vestnik Zidovskych Nabozenskysh Obci v Ceskoslovensku (Bulletin of the Jewish religious communities in the Czechoslovak Republic). The only publication for the Jews in Czechoslovakia. Appears monthly in Czech and Slovak. Editor: Dr. Rudolf Iltis.
Altneuschul, The historic synagogue.
Other Jewish Communities in Bohemia and Moravia.

In Bohemia and Moravia, there are 8 other Jewish religious communities: In Brno, Karlovy Vary (Pres.: Tiberius Ney); Kyjov; Liberec (Pres.: Leopold Smilovic); Olomouc (Pres.: Dr. Hirsch); Ostrava; Plzen (Pres.: Max Popper, Rabbi Ravidovitz); and Usti n. L. (Pres.: Max Goldberger). In addition, there are a number of so-called "Sinagogalni Sbory" or kehilloth which were established in any place where there was a minyan. These are headed by the rabbi of the respective district. Such kehilloth exist in the following places: Ceske Budejovice, Ceská Lípa, Chomutov, Hodonín, Holesov, Hradec Kralove, Jablonec n. N., Klatovy, Kromeriz, Marianske Lazne, Nachod, Opava, Orlova, Pardubice, Písek, Lazne Podebrady, Prostejov, Pribram, Tábor (Synagogue restored 1954), Teplice, Trutnov,

Turnov, Uh. Brod, Varnsdorf, Vsetin, and Zatec.

Homes for the Aged: One in Lazne Podebrady; another in Marianske Lazne.

RABBIS:

Dr. Richard Feder, district rabbi for the districts Brno, Gottwaldov, Jihlava, Olomouc, Ostrava.

Emil Davidovic, district rabbi for the districts Ceske Budejovice, Pardubice, Plzen, Prahavenkov.

Dr. Bernard Farkas, district rabbi for the districts Liberec, Karlovy Vary, Hradec Kralove, Usti n. L.

SLOVAKIA (15,000 Jews)

Ustredny Svaez Zidovskych Nabozenskych Obci Na Slovensku (Central Federation of Jewish Religious Communities in Slovakia),
Pres.: Josef Lipa.
Chief Rabbi: Elias Katz (of Bratislava).
The structure of the communities seems to be similar to the ones in the Czech districts.

BRATISLAVA (4,000 Jews)

Jewish Community, The largest in Slovakia.
Chief Rabbi: Elias Katz.

Other Jewish communities in Slovakia are known to exist in Hlohover, Kosice (Rabbi Steiner), Nitra, Nové Zámky, and Zvolen.

DENMARK

JEWISH POPULATION: 6,500

The history of the Jews in Denmark begins in 1622 with a letter of King Christian IV inviting the Sephardic Jews of Holland to come to his newly founded city of Glückstadt in Schleswig-Holstein in order to develop commerce. The letter was written on the advice of the King's Jewish physician, Dr. Jonah Charizi. In 1657, King Frederick III allowed Sephardim to settle in Denmark without restrictions, while German Jews needed a special passport. In 1684, the first synagogue for German Jews was opened in Copenhagen owing to the efforts of Israel David and Meyer Goldschmidt of Altona. The German cities Altona, Hamburg and Mansbeck, which were then Danish provinces, had larger Jewish communities and jointly elected a chief rabbi under Danish supervision. At the close of the 17th century, Copenhagen had its first

rabbi, Solomon of Rausnitz. His successor, Rabbi Israel ben Issachar, is known by his book "Ohel Israel" on Shehita. In 1745, at the request of the Jews in Copenhagen, the Danish King addressed an appeal to the Empress Maria Theresa not to banish the Jews from Prague.

In 1817, a governmental decree bestowed on the Jews all civil, but not political rights. Only the constitution of 1879 granted to the Jews full equality with all citizens.

Notwithstanding their scanty number, many Danish Jews won distinction. Naphtali Herz Wessely (1725–1805) and Isaiah Euchel (1758–1809) were famous Hebrew writers and Moses Mendelssohn's coworkers in the Haskala period. Isaac Noah Mannheimer of Copenhagen (1793–1865) served there as preacher and later became famous as rabbi in Vienna. D. Simonsen, chief rabbi of Copenhagen, was a noted Jewish scholar and bequeathed his famous Hebrew library to the Royal Library. Denmark had a number of distinguished Jewish writers, scholars, and artists, among them Henry Nathanson and Georg Brandeis.

In 1870, there were 4,290 Jews in Denmark. Because of mixed marriages and a low birth rate, this number dwindled to 3,476 in the ensuing thirty years. However, there was some Jewish immigration from Eastern Europe in the beginning of the 20th century which somewhat checked the decline. Of the present Jewish population, about 1,500 Jews are the descendants of the Sephardic immigrants of the 18th century, the remainder came from Eastern Europe and the Baltic countries after the Russian revolution of 1905. Many Jews are businessmen and artisans and a number are professionals. Their economic situation is rather fair. The relationship with non-Jews is friendly, and antisemitic manifestations are very rare. During World War II, many Danes risked their lives and exposed themselves to persecution in order to save their Jewish neighbors from Nazi massacre in 1943 and to help them escape to Sweden.

There is an important Jewish Section of the Royal Library in Copenhagen which is a valuable repository of Jewish books including the collection of the late Chief Rabbi Simonsen which he bequeathed to the Royal Library. The librarian of the Jewish Section is Dr. Rafael Edelman.

Besides the Jewish community in Denmark proper, the first Jewish congregation in the Arctic was recently established at Thule, U.S. Air Base in Greenland.

There are two religious schools and one Talmud Torah. Religious instruction is also given in the public schools.

During the second World War, almost all Jews fled to Sweden to avoid persecution by the Nazi invaders. After the war, all of them returned to Denmark. The Swedes, as well as the Danes, extended all possible help to the Danish Jews during their escape to Sweden and their subsequent repatriation.

COPENHAGEN (6,000 Jews)

Det Mosaiske Troessamfund l Kobenhavn (Jewish community). Ny Kongensgade 6. Founded in 1684. The first cemetery, which still exists, was founded in 1692.
Pres.: Karl Lachmann.
Sec.: Fritz Rothenberg.
Chief Rabbi: Dr. Phil Marcus Melchior, Forchlammersvy 20.
Synagogue. Krystalgade 12.
Pres.: Jul. Margolinski.

Dansk Zionistenforbund, Ny Kongensgade 6, Danish Zionist Union.
Pres.: Benjamin Slor.
Sec.: Miss Bella Katzenstein.
The Union is made up of five organizations:

Awodah. The Mapai group of Denmark, founded in 1938.
Pres.: S. Bentow.

Dansk Sionistenforening, General Zionist's group, founded in 1902.
Pres.: Richard Gelvan.
Misrachi, Founded 1912. Pres.: Joseph Schild.
Zeire-Misrachi. Founded 1933.
Pres.: Joseph Kahn.
WIZO, Founded 1946.
Pres.: Kamma Melchior.

Agudas Jisroel, Vesterbrogade 44, Kobenhavn V.
Pres.: Josef Kahn.
Sec.: E. Winkler.

B'nai B'rith, Forchhammersvy 20. Founded 1912.
Pres.: Marcus Melchior.

Brith Ivrith Olamith, Norre Sogade 13. Association for Hebrew culture.
Pres.: S. Friedman.

De Jodiske Religionsskole, Jewish religious school, in cooperation with the community.
Pres.: Walter Bachman.

Carolineskolen—Jodisk Faelleskole, Jewish primary school. Dir.: Harry Pihler.

Cheder Lejaldey Jeshurun, Ole Suhrsgade 12. Jewish religious school. Founded 1913.
Pres.: Dr. M. Schalimtzek.

Hasomir, Jewish Choral Society. Chrus for men founded in 1912.
Pres.: Jizchak Feder.
Chorus for women founded in 1948.
Pres.: Mrs. Dober Karakowsky.

HIAS—Kobenhavn, Frederiksborggade 54 Kobenhavn—K. Delegate, Jul. Margolinsky.

Idraetsforeningen "Hakoah," Blankavej 12. Jewish sport club, affiliated with Maccabi World Union. Founded 1924.
Pres.: Bernhard Bodnia.

Jiddische Bibliothek, Hovedgade 102, Koben-havn-Soborg. Yiddish library. Founded 1906.
Pres.: S. Beilin.

Jivo-Kobenhavn, Hallsallee 4. Founded 1925.
Pres.: Abraham Krotoschinsky.

Jodisk Ungdomsrorening Kobenhavn, Krystalgade 11. Jewish youth association.
Pres.: Moritz Schwarz.

Machsike Hadas, Ohle Suhrsgade 12. Orthodox Synagogue.
Pres.: Josef Kahn.

O.R.T., Kobenhavn, Ehlersvej 11.

O.S.E., Kobenhavn, Westerbrogade 82.

Skandinavisk Jodisk Ungdomsforbund, Dron, Tvargade 29. Union of the Jewish youth of Scandinavia.
Pres.: Harry D. Levitan.

PUBLICATIONS:

Israel monthly published by Dansk Zionistenforbund, Ny.
Kongensgade 6, Copenhagen.
Editors: Herbert Sundik, Bent Melchior.

Judish Samfund. Monthly.
Editor: Torben Meyer.

ENGLAND

JEWISH POPULATION: 450,000

The evidence for the settlement of Jews in England begins with the Norman Conquest of 1066. Jewish immigrants arrived during the reign of William the Conqueror and settled in London, Lincoln, and other places.

Under King Stephen the Jews had to pay heavy taxes to the king. During his reign, the first recorded blood accusation against the Jews was brought in Norwich (1144). In 1189–1190, massacres of Jews occurred in London, York, Lynn, and Bury St. Edmunds.

In 1274, Edward I issued the "Statute of Judaism" according to which Jews were actually deprived of the possibility of earning a living. In 1278, the whole English Jewry was imprisoned and 293 Jews were executed in London.

As a consequence of the discrimination imposed on the Jews by the Church prohibiting any intercourse between Christians and Jews, Edward I issued writs to all English counties in 1290, expelling the Jews from England. 16,000 Jews were deported. They were allowed to carry their portable property, but many were robbed and others were drowned on their way to France.

Between the expulsion of the Jews in 1290 and their return in 1655, no manifestation of Jewish life can be traced, with the exception of a few Jewish visitors who got special permits or Marranos from Spain who formed a secret congregation in London toward the middle of the 17th century.

Oliver Cromwell invited Rabbi Manasseh ben Israel from Amsterdam to plead for the readmission of Jews into England. Despite the Council's opposition, Cromwell gave informal permission to the Jews in 1655 to reside and trade in England.

In 1753, the *Jew-Bill was* adopted by the Parliament according to which the Jews were allowed to become citizens by application to Parliament. The bill, however, was repealed a year later due to intense protests and strong opposition of the population.

In 1847, Baron Lionel de Rothschild was the first Jew elected to Parliament but was unable to obtain his seat because of the oath of office containing the words "upon the faith of a Christian." He was again elected in 1850. This time Parliament rejected an amendment to the oath wording. Not until 1858 was the oath form modified to enable Baron de Rothschild to take his seat as the first Jewish member of Parliament.

The struggle for Jewish emancipation in England lasted until 1890 when complete equality was granted to Jews and Roman Catholics.

The Board of Deputies of British Jews came into existence in 1760 as a joint committee of the Sephardic and Ashkenazic communities to represent English Jewry at Court. In 1836, it obtained statutory recognition. It had taken part in all activities for the defense of the political and civil rights of English Jewry and, in many cases, of the Jews abroad. All properly constituted synagogues and some charitable and secular institutions in England were entitled to representation in the Board of Deputies.

In 1800 the number of Jews in England was about 8,000, of whom 6,000 lived in London. In 1881, the outbreak of pogroms in Russia forced many Jews to emigrate, and a number of them settled in England, increasing the Jewish population to 60,000. In 1901, there were 160,000 Jews in England. Due to Nazi persecution, a new immigration of German Jews took place from 1933.

British Jewry now numbers 450,000 of whom some 290,000 reside in London and the remainder in some 110 scattered communities. The following Jewish population figures in the larger English cities are according to the book "A Minority in Britain," by M. Friedman, London, 1955.

Under the leadership of the late Chaim Weizmann, afterwards the first President of Israel, the Zionist movement obtained in 1917 the historic Balfour Declaration from the British government, and Britain became the mandatory power over Palestine until the establishment of the State of Israel in 1948. Britain appointed Sir Herbert Samuel as first High-Commissioner for Palestine.

Education. About 40% of the Jewish children receive some kind of Jewish education. Hebrew and religious classes are attached to nearly all synagogues. Central organizations of Jewish education are the Central Council for Jewish Religious Education; London Board of Jewish Religious Education, Woburn House, Upper Woburn Place, London W.C.1; Jewish Day School Trust, 27 Creechurch Lane, E.C.3; Jewish Secondary School Movement, 86 Amburst Lk. N.16. There are 11 day schools, over 50 privately owned day schools and 4 boarding schools, and 11 Talmud Torahs in London alone and many more in other larger and smaller communities. The two rabbinical seminaries are Jew's College in London, for training rabbis for Jewish communities in England, and the other recently established in Ramsgate, for Sephardic students, mainly from North Africa. 3,500 Jews are attending English universities, more than 2,200 of them in London, 310 in Oxford, and 170 in Cambridge.

Board of Deputies of British Jews.
Woburn House, Upper Woburn Place, London W.C.1.
Tel.: Euston 3952, Teleg.: Deputies, Kincross, London.
Pres.: B. Janner, M.P.
Vice-Pres.: Ald. A. Moss.
Sec.: A. G. Brotman.
The Board appoints the following committees: Executive; Law, Parliamentary and General Purposes; Foreign Affairs; Jewish Defense to combat anti-Semitism; Finance; Eretz Israel; Aliens; Charities registration to supervise charitable institutions; Education.
The Chief Rabbinate, 4 Creechurch Place, Aldgate, London.

EC 3—Tel.: Mansion House 0292/3.
The Chief Rabbinate of the British Commonwealth has developed out of the office of the Rabbi of the Ashkenazic Great Synagogue in London. The first rabbi of the Great Synagogue who extended his authority beyond London was Aaron Hart (1704–1756). At present, the Chief Rabbi has authority over the United Hebrew Congregations of the British Empire which includes all the congregations contributing to the Chief Rabbinate Fund. The jurisdiction of the Chief Rabbi, however, is recognized by a large number of other congregations.

Chief Rabbi: Israel Brodie.
Sec.: Michael Wallach.
Beth Din of the Chief Rabbi: Adler House, Adler Street, London E.1.
Dayanim of the Beth Din: Rabbis Dr. I. Grunfeld, L. Grossmann, A. Rapoport, and Dr. M. Lew.
Haham of the Spanish and Portuguese Jews of Great Britain: Rabbi Dr. Solomon Gaon, 2 Ashworth Rd., London W.9.
World Jewish Congress
British Section, Congress House, 55 New Cavendish St., London W.I. Tel.: Welbeck 0335–9
Pres.: The Marchioness of Reading.
Chairman: Jacob Halevy.
Gen. Sec.: Dr. S. Roth.
Branches of the British Section of the World Jewish Congress exist in Birmingham, Bradford, Glasgow, Hull, Leeds, Liverpool, Manchester, St. Annes, and Southport as well as in various districts of London. Over 190 organizations in Great Britain are affiliated with the British Section.

World Jewish Congress
European Executive, Congress House, 55 New Cavendish St. London W.I.
Tel.: Welbeck 0335–9.
Chairman: Israel M. Sieff.
Exec. Sec.: Dr. C. Roth.
Anglo-Jewish Association, Woburn House, Upper Woburn Place, London W.C.1.
Tel.: Euston 5937/8.
Teleg.: Anjewglo, London.

Pres.: R. N. Carvalho.

Sec.: Ch. S. Spencer.

Founded 1871. The Association has branches in Australia and New Zealand as well as in various cities in England.

World Zionist Organization, and Jewish Agency for Israel,

77 Great Russell St. London, W.C.1.

Tel.: Museum 3815.

Teleg.: Zioniburo.

Head of London Office: Dr. S. Levenberg.

Zionist Federation of Great Britain and Ireland,

77 Great Russell St. London W.C.1.

Pres.: B. Janner, M.P.

Chairman: Dr. I. S. Fox.

Sec.: L. Bakstansky.

WIZO, 107 Gloucester Place, London W.1.

Pres.: Mrs. Rebecca D. Sieff.

Chairman: Mrs. I. Bloch.

Sec.: Mrs. R. Gassman.

Jewish National Fund, 65 Southampton Row, London W.C.1.

Pres.: L. Gestetner.

Sec.: H. J. Osterley.

Mizrachi Organization, 35 Great Russell St. London W.C.1.

Chairman: H. Landy.

Sec.: Barry Mindol.

Mizrachi Women's Organization, 35 Great Russell Street, London W.C.1.

Pres.: Mrs. Isaac Wolfson.

Sec.: Miss M. Liebster.

Poale Zion, 2 Bloomsbury Place, London W.C.1

Chairman: S. Goldberg.

Sec.: Harry Myer.

Hapoel Hamizrachi, 275 Willesden Lane, London N.W.2.

Chairman: A. Bornstein.

Sec.: Joseph Halpern.

Bachad, Religious Chalutzim, 24 Tottenheim Court Rd., London W.1.

Habonim, Zionist Youth and Chalutzic movement. 36 Wellington St., London W.C.2.

Zionist Revisionist Organization, 73 Great Titchfield St., London W.1.

Chairman: A. Abrahams.

Sec.: E. Barnett.

Agudath Israel, 257 Seven Sisters Rd., London N.7.

Chairman European Exec.: H.A. Goodman.

Sec.: M. R. Springer.

Teleg.: Centraguda.

Jews' College, Woburn House, Tavistock Sq. London, W.C.1.

Established 1855. Rabbinical Seminary, training also teachers.

Pres.: Chief Rabbi I. Brodie.

Chairman: Alan A. Mocatta.

Principal: Rabbi Dr. Isidore Epstein.

Jewish College, Lady Montefiore in Ramsgate.

Established 1869 by Moses Montefiore in memory of his wife. In 1952 reorganized by the Jewish Agency Department for Torah Education and Culture as a Sephardic Rabbinical and Teachers' Seminary.

Hon. Principal: Haham Dr. S. Gaon.

Hon. Sec.: H. M. Cansino, 13 Burgess Hill, London, N.W.2.

Association of Jewish Friendly Societies,

265-7 Whitechapel Rd. London E.1.

Established 1915 to coordinate the activities of its 25 Orders and Societies in London and other cities.

B'nai B'rith of Great Britain and Ireland,

Woburn House, Upper Woburn Place, London W.C.1.

Pres.: J. Morrison.

Sec.: Miss E. Mitzman.

League of Jewish Women, Woburn House, Upper Woburn Place, London W.C.1.

Pres.: Miss H. M. Schlesinger.

Sec.: Miss S. Prins.

HIAS, 9 Dryden Chambers, 119 Oxford St. London W.1.

JCA, Jewish Colonization Association,

46 Queen Anne's Gate, London S.W.1.

Pres.: Henry d'Avigdor Goldsmid.

Dir.: Victor Girmounsky.

B'rith Ivrith Olamith, British Branch for Hebrew Language and Culture.

Pres.: Rev. J. K. Goldbloom.

Sec.: Mrs. Hedva Cedric, 51 Hurstwood Rd. London, N.W.11.

World Sephardi Federation, New House, 67-68 Hatton Gdn., London E.C.1.

Pres.: A. Benroy.

Sec.: O. Camby.

World Union for Progressive Judaism,
Founded 1926.
51 Palace Court, London W.2.
Hon.Pres.: Rabbi Dr. L. Beck.
Chairmen: Rabbis Leslie I. Edgar and Dr. W. van der Zyl.
Sec.: B. Woyda.

Association of Synagogues in Great Britain (Reform).
Pres.: Rabbi Dr. Leo Beck.
Sec.: H. Arbeid, 33 Seymour Place, London.

Central British Fund for Jewish Relief and Rehabilitation,
Woburn House, Upper Woburn Place, London W.C.1.
Hon. Pres.: Viscount Samuel.
Pres.: Chief Rabbi I. Brodie.
Chairman: Anthony G. de Rothschild.

Jewish Trust Corporation for Germany Ltd.,
Woburn House, Upper Woburn Place, London W.C.1.
To claim heirless property of former Jewish communities in the British and French Zones of Germany.
Chairman: Henry d'Avigdor Goldsmid.
Sec.: Dr. C. I. Kapralik.

United Restitution Office, Ltd.,
8 Fairfax Mansions, London, N.W.3.
To assist claimants in the recovery of property in Germany.
Chairman: Prof. Norman Bentwich.

LONDON (280,000 Jews)

United Synagogues,
Woburn House, Upper Woburn Place, London W.C.1.
Founded 1870. Comprises: 25 constituent Synagogues, 20 District Synagogues, 31 Affiliated Synagogues. Maintains religious, welfare and cultural institutions, as well as the Beth-Din of the Chief Rabbi.
Pres.: Ewen S. Montagu.

Federation of Synagogues,
64 Lemon St. London E.1.
Founded 1887 by Lord Swaythling. Com-

prises 4 federated and 57 affiliated orthodox Synagogues.
Pres.: M. Lederman.
Exec. Dir.: Julius Jung.

Union of Orthodox Hebrew Congregations,
126 Green Lanes, London N.16.
Founded 1926 (Comprises 43 Synagogues and smaller prayerhouses).
Rabbi Dr. Solomon Schonfeld.

Community of Spanish and Portuguese Jews,
Heneage Lane, London E.C.3.
Founded by Marranos 1657. Comprises now the Louderdale Rd. Synagogue; the Holland Park Synagogue, mainly of Jews from Salonica; Revis Marks Synagogue and Stamford Hill Synagogue of Persian and Bukharan Jews.
President of the Sephardic Congregations: Ch. E. Sebag-Montefiore.
Haham: Rabbi Dr. Solomon Gaon.

Reform Synagogues,
The 6 Reform Synagogues in London are constitutents of the above-mentioned Association of Synagogues in Great Britain.

Liberal Synagogues,
The 8 Liberal Synagogues in London are constituents of the aforementioned Union of Liberal and Progressive Synagogues.

AMERSHAM (80 Jewish families)

Amersham, Chesham and District Hebrew Congregation, Woodside Hall, Woodside Rd. Amersham.

BIRMINGHAM (6,300 Jews)

One of the oldest Jewish communities in England. The first synagogue was established 1780, and a Jewish cemetery already existed there in 1718.

Representative Council of Birmingham Jewry,
43 Cannon St., Birmingham.
Pres.: Ivan Shortt.
Sec.: Harry Faber.
The Council coordinates the following 4 congregations: Hebrew Congregation, Central Synagogue, New Synagogue, Pershore Rd. Synagogue.
There is also a small Liberal Synagogue.

Hebrew and Religious Instruction Committee.
Hebrew School, St. Luke's Rd., Birmingham.

BLACKPOOL (2,000 Jews)

United Hebrew Congregation, 19 Clayton Street
Pres.: M. Gordon.
Sec.: L. Saldman.
Progressive Jewish Congregation,
Pres.: S. Gorwitz.
Sec.: Mrs. R. Comor, 26 Longton Rd.

BOURNEMOUTH (1,500 Jews)

Jewish Community Centre
Chairman: L. Corren, 36 Southbourne Grove
Synagogue, Wotton Gardens; Reform New
Synagogue, Old Chrischurch Rd.

BRADFORD (700 Jews)

Jewish Representative Council.
Chairman: O. M. Stroud.
Sec.: H. S. Bergman, 29 Oak Lane.
Bradford Hebrew Congregation. The Brad-
ford Synagogue.

BRIGHTON and HOVE (4,500 Jews)

Jewish Council
Chairman: H. Middleburgh.
Sec.: J. Sawyer, 3 Stillwood Rd.
2 Orthodox and one Liberal Synagogue.

BRISTOL (410 Jews)

The Jewish Community was founded be-
fore 1754, and was one of the principal
Jewish centres in medieval England.
Synagogue, Park Row.
Pres.: S. Jacobs.
Sec.: A. Steinberg, Stoke Paddock Rd.
Bristol 9.
Rabbi: Harold Lerner.

CAMBRIDGE (200 Jews)

The Cambridge University Jewish Society.
Aim: To assist Jewish students in all Jewish
activities.
Pres.: A. P. Samuel.
Sec.: Mr. B. Priestley.
Synagogue, Ellis Court, Thompson's Lane.

CHELTENHAM (120 Jews)

Hebrew Congregation, St. James Square.
Sec.: H. Bazar, King Hall, North St.

COVENTRY (220 Jews)

Synagogue, Barras Lane.
Pres.: C. Angel.
Sec.: M.L. Hyam, 84 Harefield Rd.

DARLINGTON (195 Jews)

Hebrew Congregation, 9 Victoria Rd.
Pres.: A. Richardson.
Sec.: E. M. Goldstein, 44 Daneside Rd.

DERBY (205 Jews)

Representative Council.
Sect.: L. V. Fraser, 6 Arlington Rd.
Hebrew Congregation, 270 Burton Rd.

GATESHEAD-ON-TYNE (350 Jews)

Synagogue, Bewick Rd. and 22 Claremont Place.
There are a Yeshiva, 179 Bewick Rd.; Beth
Midrash Lemorim Ulemoroth, 6 Gladstone
Terrace; and the Institute for Higher Rab-
binical Studies, 22 Claremont Place.

GRIMSBY (400 Jews)

Sir Moses Montefiore Synagogue, Holme Hill,
Henerge Rd.
Pres.: H. Rachkind.
Sec.: H. Goodman, 118 Hainton Ave.

HARROGATE (300 Jews)

Hebrew Congregation, St. Mary's Walk.
Pres.: E. G. Bernard.
Sec.: H. Cope.

HIGH WYCOMBE (120 Jews)

Hebrew Congregation, 7/8 Queen Square.
Pres.: J. Silverstone.
Sec.: Mrs. R. Weiss, 33 Hampdon Rd.

HULL (2,000 Jews)

Jewish Representative Council.
Pres.: H. Rosen.
Sec.: J. Rose, 165 Pickering Rd.

There are 3 synagogues: The Old Hebrew Congregation, Osborne St.; The Central Synagogue, Park Street; The Western Synagogue, Linnaeus St.

LEEDS (25,000 Jews)

Jewish Representative Council. Brandsby Lodge, 98 Chapeltown Rd.
Pres.: Mark Laboritch.
Sec.: K. C. Cohen.
Zionist Council, 307 Chapeltown Rd.
There are branches of Mizrachi, Poale Zion, Poale Mizrachi, Mapam, Wizo, and Pioneer Women.
United Hebrew Congregation, 98 Chapeltown Rd. Comprising 4 synagogues.
Rabbis: S. Brown and I. Lerner.
There are 11 more synagogues not affiliated to the United Hebrew Congregation.
Beth Din, 98 Chapeltown Rd.
Members: Rabbis Dr. H. Medalle, Chairman; Dr. M. Kranz; J. Apfel.
Educational and Cultural Institutions: Talmud Torah; Talmudical College; Jewish Institute; Tarbut Association; Leeds University, Union Jewish Students' Association.

LEICESTER (1,100 Jews)

Hebrew Congregation, Highfield St.
Pres.: D. Cooklin.
Liberal Jewish Group. Sec.: S. David, 31 Somerville Rd.

LETCHWORTH (250 Jews)

Hebrew Congregation, 40 Hall Mead.
Rabbi: O. Feuchtwanger.
Sec.: O. Pressburger.

LIVERPOOL (7,500 Jews)

Merseyside Jewish Representative Council.
Pres.: Dr. I. J. Lipkin.
Sec.: E. Felton, 5 Oxford St.
Liverpool and District Rabbinate.
Rabbi: Z. Slitchnik.
Synagogues, There are 12 synagogues. The oldest of them is Old Hebrew Congregation founded 1790.
Rabbi: Stanley Woolf.

Merseyside Council for Jewish Education.
Chairman: H. Beacon.
Sec.: A. Barron.
Educational Institution and Endowed Schools.
Talmud-Torah School, Talmudical College, Yeshiva.
Zionist Central Council.
Pres.: Dr. H. Woolwich.
Sec.: E. L. Fagin, 8 Princess Rd.
There are branches of Mizrachi, Torah Va'Avoda, Habonim, Poale Bion.

LUTON (800 Jews)

Synagogue Bury Park
Rabbi H. D. Rivto, 45 Westbourne Rd.

MANCHESTER (31,000 Jews)

Council of Manchester and Salford Jews, 11 Albert Sq.
Pres.: S. Glicker.
Sec.: N. Jacobs.
Beth Din, 149 Cheetham Hill Rd.
Chairman: Rabbi Dr. A. Altman.
Manchester and Salford Synagogue Council, 149 Cheetham Hill Rd.
Pres.: Rabbi Dr. A. Altman.
There are 40 synagogues. The oldest is the Great Synagogue founded 1780.
Central Board for Hebrew Education, Bent St. Cheetham.
Pres.: Rabbi A. Altman.
Sec.: H. Stone.
There are 5 Jewish schools, a Yeshiva, and the Institute of Jewish Studies.
Zionist Central Council, Mamlook House, 142 Bury Old Rd. Mizrachi, Poale Zion, Mapam, Torah Va-Avoda, Habonim, Tarbuth Society, and Bachad.

MARGATE (300 Jews)

Synagogue, Godwin Rd. Cliftonville.
Rabbi: B. Landau.
Pres.: P. H. Black.
Sec.: H. Taylor.

MIDDLESBROUGH (450 Jews)

Synagogue, Park Rd., South. Rabbi: B. Kersh.
Sec.: D. Morrison.

NEWCASTLE (2,300 Jews)

Representative Council. Chairman: L. Myers.
Sec.: A. A. Ross, 66 Cragthorne Gardens.
Synagogues, There are 4 synagogues, the oldest
is Old Hebrew Congregation, Leazes Park Rd.
Zionist Association, Mizrachi, Daughters of
Zion, Young Zionist Association.

NEWPORT (180 Jews)

Synagogue, Queen's Hill.

NORTHAMPTON (425 Jews)

Hebrew Congregation, Overstone Rd.
Pres.: I. Necus.
Sec.: J. Maizels.
Zionist Society. Wizo.

NORWICH (135 Jews)

Synagogue, 3 Earlham Rd.

NOTTINGHAM (2,500 Jews)

Jewish Communal Council.
Pres.: J. Levin.
Sec.: A. Litman, 16 Cavendish Ave.
Synagogue, Shakespeare Street.
Rabbi: Dr. J. Posen.
Pres.: W. M. Snapper.
Sec.: M. Greenberg.

OXFORD (500 Jews)

Jewish Congregation, Richmond Rd.
Pres.: Prof. S. H. Frankel.

PLYMOUTH (350 Jews)

Hebrew Congregation, Catherine St.
Rabbi: D. Jasowic.
Pres.: S. Marks.
Sec.: M. Overs.

PORTSMOUTH (600 Jews)

Synagogue. The Thicket, Southsea.
Rabbi: I. Cohen.

PRESTON (160 Jews)

Jewish Council.
Pres.: A. J. Royce, 9 Carlisle Ave.
Synagogue, Avenham Place.

RAMSGATE (106 Jews)

Synagogue, Spanish-Portuguese, Hereson.
Pres.: C. E. Sebag-Montefiore.
Rabbi: B. Rodrigues-Pereira.
Montefiore College and Museum.
Recently established, as already mentioned,
as a rabbinical seminary for North-African
students.

READING (500 Jews)

Synagogue, Goldsmid Rd., Russell St.
Rabbi: Philip Isaacs.
Pres.: I. Auerbach.

ST. ANNES-ON-SEA (375 Jews)

Hebrew Congregation, Oswald Rd.
Rabbi: I. Weinberger.

ST. ANNES-ON-SEA (375 Jews)

Hebrew Congregation, Orchard Rd.
Rabbi: E. Feldinger.

SHEFFIELD (1,850 Jews)

Representative Council.
Pres.: A. Roseby.
Sec.: D. Brown, 123 Dobroft Rd.
United Hebrew Congregation, Wilson Rd.
Rabbi: I. Chait.
Pres.: M. Waldenberg.
Sec.: B. Miller, 53 Snig Hill.
Hebrew Education Board, Psalter Lane.
Dir.: Dr. M. Friedlander.
Zionist Association; Wizo.

SOUTHAMPTON (150 Jews)

Synagogue, Albion Place, High St.
Rabbi: R. Restab.
Pres.: A. Bernfield.
Sec.: S. Burke.

SOUTHEND & WESTCLIFF (3,500 Jews)

Synagogue, 99 Alexandra Rd.; Westcliff-On-Sea
Rabbi: P. Shebson.
Pres.: L. Feitelson.
Zionist Society, Hebrew Education Board.

SOUTHPORT (3,000 Jews)

Synagogue, Arnside Rd.
Rabbi, Dr. A. E. Silverstone.

New Synagogue, West Street Club.
  Rabbi: E. Cahn.
Hebrew Education Board; Hatikvah Society;
Mizrachi.

SOUTH SHIELDS (115 Jews)

Hebrew Congregation, 25 Beach Rd.

STAINES (450 Jews)

Staines & District Synagogue, Tothill St.
  Rabbi: J. Rosenberg.

STOCKPORT (220 Jews)

Hebrew Congregation, 211 Chestergate.
  Rabbi: E. Groundland.

STOKE-ON-TRENT (200 Jews)

Hebrew Congregation, Birch Terrace, Hanley.
  Rabbi: B. M. Starr.

SUNDERLAND (1,100 Jews)

Hebrew Congregation, Ryhope Rd.
  Rabbi: M. Turetsky.
  Pres.: M. Cohen.
Education: Hebrew School; Talmudical College & Yeshiva; Talmud Torah.
Joint Zionist Council.
  Pres.: Ch. Gillis.
  Sec.: M. H. Minchom, 20 Beresford Park.

WALLASEY (280 Jews)

Hebrew Congregation, 27a Falkland Rd.
  Rabbi: A. Cohn.

WELWYN GARDEN CITY (195 Jews)

Jewish Community, Handside Lane.
  Pres.: L. Simmonds.

WHITLEY BAY (175 Jews)

Hebrew Congregation, 2 Oxford St.
  Rabbi: S. Balanow.
  Pres.: E. G. Markus.

WOLVERHAPMTON (230 Jews)

Synagogue, Fryer St.
  Rabbi: A. Bernstein.
  Pres.: Dr. L. Seaton.

CARDIFF, WALES (3,000 Jews)

United Synagogue. Address: A. Hauser, Queens St., Arcade Chambres.
  Rabbi: B. Ragosnitzky.
  Pres.: G. Cohen.
Cardiff New Synagogue, Moira Terrace.
  Rabbi: Dr. L. G. Graff.
  Sec.: Dr. P. Simon, 53 Butleigh Av.
Zionist Representative Council.
  Pres.: D. N. Curitz, 15 Dumfries Place.

MERTHYR TYDFIL (150 Jews)

Synagogue, Church St.
  Rabbi: A. Cohen.
  Pres.: I. Hamilton.

SWANSEA (510 Jews)

Hebrew Congregation, Christina St.
  Rev.: A. Pryzs.
  Pres.: N. Seal.
  Sec.: Dr. J. Shibko, 45 Sketty Rd.

ABERDEEN, SCOTLAND (70 Jews)

Hebrew Congregation, 74 Dee Street.
  Pres.: Dr. J. Fackenheim.

EDINBURGH (1,400 Jews)

Hebrew Congregation, 4 Salisbury Rd.
  Rabbi: I. Cohen.
  Pres.: R. Cohen.
  Sec.: J. Levison, 34 Hatton Place.
Hebrew and Religious School. Jewish Literary Society, Univ. Jewish Society.

GLASGOW (13,400 Jews)

Jewish Representative Council, 16 Turiff St.
  Pres.: Dr. I. E. Burton.
  Sec.: A. M. Samuel.
Beth Din, 16 Turriff St.
  Pres.: J. D. Lurie.
United Synagogue Council, 52 Thistle St.
  There are 14 synagogues.
Board of Jewish Religious Education, 16 Turiff St.
  Pres.: Joseph Woolfson.
  Sec.: L. Pickles.
Hebrew College. Yeshiva. Jewish Institute. Tarbuth Org. Council for Advanced Hebrew Education.

Zionist Organization.

WIZO. Mizrachi. Poale Zion. Torah V'Avoda.
Smaller Congregations of under 100 are in the following places:
Aldershot (34 Jews), Barnet, Barrow-In-Furness (54), Birkenhead (50), Blackburn (70), Bolton (80), Chester (30), Colchester (45), Doncaster (98), Dunstable (60), Durham (15), Eastbourne (60), Epsom, Exester (20), Huddersfield (70), Ligh-On-Sea, Maidenhead North Shields (16), Peterborough (80), Potters Bar (28 families), Slough, Stockton-on-Tees (55), Sutton, Swindom (24), Watford, West Hartlepool (80), Worcester (60), Worthing, York (20), *In Wales*: Abernon (25), Aberdare (42), Bangor (34), Brynmawr (30), Colwyn Bay (24), Liandundo, Slanelly (95), Contypridd (80), Porthcawl (90), Rhyl in Scotland: Ayr (68), Dundee (89), Inverness (12).

JEWISH PERIODICALS

1. NEWS AGENCIES

Jewish Chronicle News Service,
37 Furnival Street, London E.C.4.
The Jewish Telegraphic Agency,
58 Fleet Street, London E.C.4.
Jewish World News Agency (Yiddish),
66 Woodlands, London N.W.11.
Weekly News Digest,
77 Great Russell Street, London W.C.1.
World Jewish Affairs, News and Feature Service,
55 New Cavendish Street, London W.1.

2. WEEKLIES

Jewish Chronicle,
32 Furnival Street, London E.C.4.
Jewish Echo,
252 Crown Street,Glasgow, C.5.
Jewish Gazette,
151, Cheetham Hill Road, Manchester 8.
Jewish Observer and Middle East Review,
129 Salisbury Square House, London E.C..4
Jewish Telegraph,
Levi House, Bury Old Road, Manchester 8.
Jewish Voice (Yiddish)
11-13 New Road, London E.1.

3. FORTNIGHTLIES

Jewish Post (English-Yiddish),
257 Seven Sisters Road, London N.4.
Jewish Review,
45 Great Russell St. London, W.C.1.
Jewish Vanguard,
2 Bloomsbury Place, London, W.C.1.

4. MONTHLIES

A.J.R. Information,
8 Fairfax Mansion, Finchley Road, London N.W.3.
Iton Bnei Akivah,
345 Grays Inn Road, London, W.C.1.
Jewish Gazette,
3 Centreville Road, Liverpool, 18.
Jewish Recorder,
51 Westfield Road, Birmingham 16.
Labour Israel,
37 Broadhurst Garden, London N.W.6.
Liberal Jewish Monthly,
28 St. John's Wood Rood, London N.W.6.
Loshen un Lebn (Yiddish),
129-131 Cavell Street, London, E.1.
Maccabi Times,
73 Compayne Gardens, London, N.W.6.
Synagogue Review,
3 Seymour Place, London, W.1.

5. BI-MONTHLIES

Boneh,
36 Wellington St. London, W.C.2.
Pioneer Woman's News,
57 Eton Avenue, London, N.W.3.
Tarbuth (Hebrew),
77 Great Russell Street, London W.C.1.
Wiener Library Bulletin,
19 Manchester Sq. London W.1.

6. QUARTERLIES

A.J.A. Quarterly,
Woburn House, Upper Woburn Place, London, W.C.1.
Cajex,
71 Canada Road, Heath, Cardiff.
Gates of Zion, (Hebrew-English)
77 Great Russel Street, London W.C.1.
"Habimah,"
Savile Mount, Leeds 7.

Hamoreh,
   28 East Bank, London N.16.

Illustrated Technion News,
   83 Wimpole St., London, W.1.

Jewish Quarterly
   68, Worcester Cresent, London, N.W.7.

Jewish Youth,
   33 Berner St., London, E.1.

Journal of Jewish Studies,
   Stenecourt, Singleton Road, Salford 7.

Le Judaisme Sephardi (English-French),
   67/68 Hatton Garden, London, E.C.1.

Menorah,
   Woburn House, Upper Woburn Place,
   London W.C.1.

Sheffield Jewish Journal,
   23 Bowling Green St., Sheffield, 3.

Youth Aliyah Review,
   233 Baker Street, London, N.W.1.

7. PERIODICALS

Bulletin of the Technion,
   83 Wimpole St., London W.1.

Chayenu,
   345 Cray's Inn Road, London, W.C.1.

Jewish Academy,
   1 Endsleigh St., London, W.C.1.

Jewish Clarion,
   27 Bedford St., London, W.C.2.

Sifrut,
   77 Great Russell St., London, W.1.

Yidische Shriften (Yiddish)
   31 Balfour Road, London, N.S.1.

8. ANNUALS

Jewish Annual,
   Clifton House, Worship St., London E.C.2.

Hashanah,
   6 Dixon St., Glasgow.

Jewish Yearbook,
   37 Furnival Street, London, E.C.4.

Joint Palestine Appeal Year Book,
   75 Great Russell Street, London W.C.1.

Moledet,
   65 Southampton Row, London W.C.1.

Shalom,
   Zion House, 8 Princes Road, Liverpool, 8.

Zionist Year Book,
   77 Great Russell Street, London W.C.1.

FINLAND

JEWISH POPULATION: 1,800

When Finland was transferred from Sweden to Russia in 1809, after having been part of Sweden from about the 12th century, most of the medieval Swedish laws with regard to the Jews were maintained. In 1685, Jews were forbidden to enter or settle in Sweden, and this prohibition applied to Finland. Swedish laws passed in 1734 confirmed the earlier prohibition. In 1806, a royal edict forbade anew the entry of Jews into Finland. The first Jews in Finland after 1825 were Jewish soldiers who came to Viipuri and Helsinki with the Russian army. They were able to remain in Finland because of the imperial decree which permitted Russian soldiers to remain in the land after finishing their army service. After 1875, other Jewish settlers from Russia and Poland came to Viipuri and Helsinki.

In 1889, the Finnish Senate permitted the Jews who were already in the country to remain as temporary residents, but they had to obtain a certificate of residence from the governor every six months. In 1899, further restrictions were imposed on the rights of Finnish Jews. They were allowed to reside only in Abo, Helsinki, and Viipuri; they were denied freedom of movement; and they were barred from the liberal professions and from working as artisans. In addition, they had to pay heavy taxes.

A little Jewish immigration into Finland, mostly from Lithuania, Poland, and other parts of Russia, began under Russian domination but was hampered by antiquated statutes. After the March revolution in Russia and Finland's declaration of independence in 1917, a constitution was adopted which granted equality to all residents of the country including the Jews. They enjoyed all rights of citizenship, although they were still subjected to unfavorable treatment. In the early 1920's, a Hebrew school and a Jewish social center were built in Helsinki. In 1932, Dr. Simon Federbusch became the chief rabbi of a federation of the Jewish communities of Viipuri, Helsinki, and Abo which he had previously organized. In 1938, the government tried to dissolve the Fascist party which had carried on anti-Jewish and anti-government agitation. In the same year, the Finnish cabinet permitted 55 Austrian Jewish refugees to enter the country; later, another 150 were allowed to enter. By 1939, there were about 250 Jewish refugees, mostly from Germany and Austria, in Finland. At the close of the Russo-Finnish war in 1940, the entire Jewish community of

Viipuri was ceded with that part of Finland to Russia. However, these Jews left the area and went to Abo and Helsinki. In 1940, the Finnish government agreed to admit a number of Jewish doctors, dentists, and skilled workers from among the German Jewish refugees most of whom had fled Denmark and Norway.

Centralradet for De Judiska Forsamlingarna I Finland, Malmagatan 26, Helsinki.
The Central Council represents the three Communities of Helsinki, Abo, and Tampere. Each of the three communities is governed by a separate Board of Administration which sends its representatives to the Central Council. Each Community comprises the religious, social, and charitable associations existing in its respective area.
Pres.: I. Davidkin.
Sec.: Josef Lefko.

Finlands Zionistforbund Hazohar, Malmbrinken 2, Helsinki. Zionist-Revisionist group.
Pres.: Jonas Jakobson.
Sec.: Jacob Kamras.

HELSINKI (1,350 Jews)

Judiska Forsamlingen I Helsingfors (Jewish community), Malmgatan 26.
Forwaltningradet (Administrative Council).
Pres.: I. Davidkin.
Synagogue. Pres.: David Motzkin.
Forwaltningradet (Administrative Council).
Pres.: Abraham Schwartzmann.
Sec.: Leo Miramo.
Bicur Cholim, Centralgaten 6. Religious welfare organization.
Pres.: Samuel Rosenblom.
Hachnosas Orchim, Batsmansgatan 5.
Pres.: M. Waprinsky.
Sec.: D. Motzkin.
Hamerkas Hazioni B'Finland, c/o Kangasythyna L. Robertsgatan 13.
Embraces all Zionist groups.
Pres.: Davidkin.
Sec.: Dr. H. Strascheffsky.

Helsingin Juutalinen Yhteiskoulu, Grasviksgatan 3. Secondary Jewish school for boys and girls.
Pres.: Abraham Schwartzman.
Sec.: Scholem Bolotovsky.

Idrottsforeningen Makhabi, Lonnrotsgatan 45. Maccabi sport club.
Pres.: A. Livson.
Sec.: S. Geronik.

Judiska Akademiska Klubben I Finland, Bermansgatan 7. Students' association.
Pres.: M. Steinbock.
Sec.: D. Morduch.

Judiska Scoutkaren Kefir, Lotsgatan 10, C. 14. Jewish scouts.

Judiska Brid Gelubben, Museigatan 21. B'nai B'rith.
Pres.: Israel Polarsky.

Judiska Fruntimmers Valgorentsforening, Idrottsgatan 18. Jewish women's welfare association.
Pres.: Mary Rung.

Judiska Handelsforeningen, Tolotorgatan 7. Jewish tradesmen's association.
Pres.: R. K. Salutski.

Judiska Sangforeningen, Lonnrotsgatan 28. Jewish choral club.
Pres.: S. Rasko.
Sec.: P. Wardi.

Keren Kayemeth Leisrael, c/o Kangashyhtna A/B L. Robertsgatan 13.
Pres.: I. Davidkin.
Sec.: S. Bolotovsky.

WIZO Helsingfors, Auroragatan 17.
Sec.: Mrs. E. Millner.

Zionistika Ungdomsforeningen Hatchijo, Nylandsgatan 15. Zionist youth group.

Pres.: A. Hasan.
Sec.: Mrs. B. S. Hasan.

ABO (400 Jews)

Judiska Forsamlingen i Abo (Jewish community).
Pres.: Hirsch Hasan.
Sec.: Abel Kasan.
Comprises a synagogual section, cultural section, and social section.

Judiska Idrottsforeningen Makkabe, Jewish sport club.
Pres.: Leo Kaplan.

Judiska Fruntimmersforeningen, Association of Jewish women for social work.
Pres.: Mrs. Sonja Zewi.

Judiska Klubben Achwa, Pres.: David Zewi.
Sec.: Bernhard Krawts.

Zionistica Ungdomsforeningen Kadimah.
Pres.: Jacob Salutskij.
Sec.: Miss Hannele Scheiman.

Oy Ahawat Hesed Ab, Jewish loan association.
Sec.: Mrs. Sara Millner.

Chevro Bikur Cholim, Jewish sick fund.
Pres.: Abraham Schapira.

WIZO, Pres.: Mrs. Bertha Eckert.

Zionistika Kommiten, Zionist committee.
Pres.: Beni Katro.

TAMPERE (50 Jews)

Tampereen Juutalainen Seurakunta (Jewish community), Nasilinnankatu 27.
Founded in 1946.
Pres.: Sholem Beregoffsky.
Sec.: S. Steinbock.

In 1955, the community purchased a building of its own to house the synagogue and other communal institutions.

FRANCE

JEWISH POPULATION: 250,000

There is no documentary evidence of the presence of Jews in Gaul (France) earlier than the 4th century, but they were certainly there before that period. When Christianity became the state religion of the Roman Empire (325), the Jews in Gaul were forbidden to marry Christians, and in 439, they were deprived of all public positions. Jews were active in agriculture, crafts, and commerce. In the Frankish Empire, there were many discriminations against them, and finally, Dagobert I forced them to be baptized or to emigrate (629).

Under Charlemagne (768-814), Jews constituted an important economic factor, dominating the entire export and import fields. The Crusades, however, brought persecution to the Jews. In the second Crusade, many Jews were killed. Philip IV arrested all the Jews (1306) and exiled some 10,000 of them, confiscating their property. By 1315, they were recalled by the people, who were being victimized by Christian money lenders. In 1322, they were again expelled and once more readmitted to be expelled again in 1394.

During the Middle Ages, significant Jewish cultural centers existed in Champagne and Provence. The most famous scholars of the time were Rashi (1040–1105), Jacob Tam (1100–70), the founder of the Tosafists School, the philologists of the Kimhi and Ibn Tibbon families and many others.

As a result of the French Revolution of 1789, some, though not all, of the Jews were granted equal rights. In 1807, Napoleon convened the Jewish Sanhedrin in Paris which declared the willingness of the Jews to orientate themselves to European civilization, Napoleon's prerequisite for their emancipation. Napoleon's decrees of 1808 did not, however, grant equal rights to the Jews of France. It was not until 1818, when these decrees expired, that Jewish emancipation came into force. The equality of the Jewish religion was recognized by the law of 1831 whereby the rabbis were to be supported by the national treasury as were the Christian priests. During the term of Isaac Rudolph Cremieux, Jewish minister of justice, a decree was issued in 1870 which made the Jews of Algeria full-fledged French citizens.

The prominent positions Jews were able to achieve in France aroused an anti-semitic movement whose champion was Edward Drumont; the National Anti-Semitic League was founded in 1886. This became conspicuous especially during the Dreyfus Case in 1894. Dreyfus was re-tried and finally exonerated due to such staunch defenders of the Jews as Emile Zola.

France became a haven of refuge for persecuted Jews, mainly from Russia. The Jewish population at the beginning of the 20th century and especially during the Nazi regime in Germany increased.

60,000 Jews fought in the French army during the Second World War.

The collapse of France in 1940 resulted in the flight of about half of the country's 350,000 Jews; the rest were trapped in the occupied territory. Under the Vichy regime, the Jews were discriminated against in accordance with the racial laws issued by the government, and the French citizenship of the Algerian Jews was revoked. From the German-occupied part of France, approximately 120,000 Jews were sent to annihilation camps in Poland.

After the Second World War, many Jews returned to France, reinforced by a new influx of Jews from the Iron Curtain countries of Eastern Europe. Great efforts have been made to reestablish Jewish communal life.

According to a recent survey, there are about 30,000 Jewish children of school age in France. Of these, only 10% receive Jewish instruction. There are 4 religious day schools 3 of which are in Paris — the Lucien-Hirsch elementary school, the Javne high school, the Rambam high school. One day school, the elementary and high school "Akiba," operates in Strasbourg. Almost every synagogue affiliated with the Consistory has courses for prayers and Hebrew for beginners. At the Paris synagogues outside the Consistory there are 6 Talmud-Tora schools. There are also 4 Yeshivoth in the country: in Aix-les-Bains, for French Jewish pupils; and for North African pupils in Brinoi, Montmorency and Feblin sponsored by the Libawitz group. The Orthodox opened evening courses "Pet-ronage" where the Jewish pupils of the public schools are given religious instruction. In Orsai, near Paris, daily Jewish courses for university students are given. Outside Paris, there are courses in Jewish instruction in Lyons, Rouen, Toulouse, Nancy, Marseilles and in a few other places. Paris is also the seat of the Rabbinical Seminary of the Consistory. Also, there are 13 Jewish children's homes in France, 7 of them in Paris. The overwhelming majority of French Jewry is Ashkenazic. The Sephardic group amounts to approximately 70,000 of whom about 45,000 live in Paris.

PARIS (150,000 Jews)

Union des Associations Cultuelles Israelites de France et D'Algerie, 44, rue de la Victoire. (Consistoire Central Israelite de France et d'Algerie).

The Union was founded in 1906 after the proclamation of the separation of church and state. It replaced the former Israelitic Consistory of France. It unites the associations of various rituals which acknowledge its status. Its aim is to support, preserve, and defend Jewish religious interests in France and Algeria. It is considered the qualified representative of the French Jews by the Jews of the country as well as by the government.
Pres.: Baron Guy de Rothschild.
Sec.: H. Levi.

Conseil Representatif des Juifs de France (C.R.I.F.), 45, rue de la Bruyère-9e. It represents French Judaism before public authority and opinion and before Jewish organizations of other countries.
Pres.: Dr. Vidal Modiano.
Hon. Pres.: Leon Meiss.
Federation des Associations Cultuelles Israelites de France et d'Algerie — Association des Rabbins Francais, 17 rue Saint-Georges.
Federation of the religious communities in

France and Algeria and association of the French Rabbis.

Hon.Pres.: Leon Meiss, Raoul Bloch-Laroque.
Pres.: Baron Guy de Rothschild.
Rabbis: Grand Rabbi J. Kaplan, Rabbi Salzer.

Rabbis in Paris:

Grand Rabbi of Paris, Jakob Kaplan, 1, rue Andrieux. Rabbis: Paul Bauer, 43, rue Blanche Paris; Feuerwerker, 14, place des Vosgess; Gourevitch, 24, rue Rennequin; Jais, 16, rue José-Maria-de-Heredia; Liber, 64, rue de Montreuil, Versailles; M. Salm, 17, rue St. Georges; Schilli, 14, rue Chasseloup-Laubat; Jean Schwartz, 70, rue Secrétan; Elie Munk, 10 rue Cadet; Rubinstein, 40, rue de Belleville; Stern, 8, rue Ambroise-Thomas.

Synagogues in Paris and Precincts:

15, rue Notre-Dame-de-Nazareth; 25, rue de Rosiers; 10, rue Pavée; 21, rue de Turenne; 10, rue Cadet; 4, rue Saulnier; 10, rue Dieu; 32, rue Basfroi; 24, rue Copernic (Liberal); 31, rue de Montevideo (Traditional); 5, rue Duc; 9, passage Kusner; 20, rue Villiers-de-l'Isle-Adam; 17, rue des Rosiers; 24, rue du Bourg-Tibourg; 6, rue Ambroise Thomas; 3, rue Clermont-Tonnerre, Aulnay-sous-Bois. *Consistorial synagogues:* 9, rue Vauquelin; 44, rue de la Victoire; 14, rue Chasseloup-Laubat; 13, rue Saint-Isaure; 75, rue Julien-Lacroix; 21, bis, rue Tournelles; 28, rue Buffault (also Sephardic); 43, rue des Abondances, Boulogne-sur-Seine; 19, rue de Villiers, Champigny; 47, rue de Malleville, Enghien les-Bains; 19, allee Chatrian, Le Raincy-Villemomble; 21, rue Ancelle, Neuilly-sur-Seine; 30, rue Celine-Robert, Vincennes. *Sephardic synagogues:* 18, rue Saint Lazare; 7, rue Poincourt.

Seminaire Israelite de France (Anciennement Ecole Rabbinique de France) 9, rue Vauquelin. Founded first in Metz in 1829; in Paris, since 1859. Educates and furnishes rabbis for Jewish communities of France and French-speaking countries.

American Jewish Committee,
European Headquarters: 30 Rue La Broedie, Paris VIII.
Dir.: Zacharia Shuster.

American Jewish Joint Distribution Committee,
European Bureau: 119 Rue Saint-Dominique, Paris VII.
Dir.: Moses W. Beckelman.
Sec.: H. Katz.

Association Consistoriale Israelite de Paris,
17, rue Saint-Georges.
Jewish consistorial association. Maintains and operates 17 synagogues and houses of prayer in Paris.
Chief Rabbi: Jacob Kaplan.
Pres.: Baron Alain de Rothschild.
Hon. Sec.: E. Levy.

Agence Juive pour la Palestine, 135 Avenue de Wagram.

Agoudath Israel de France, 38 rue des Blancs-Mainteaux.

Alliance Israelite Universelle, 45, rue La Bruyère. Founded in 1860, it has 135 schools with more than 51,000 pupils in the Mediterranean area.
Pres.: Rene Gassin.
Sec.: Eugene Weill.

Association des Amis Israelites de France, 10, rue Lancry.

Association des Artistes Peintres et Sculpteurs a Paris "Amanouth," 47 rue Chabrol. Assoc. of painters and sculptors.
Pres.: Mane Katz.

Association Cultuelle Israelite-Agoudas Hakehilos, 10, rue Pavée. Founded 1913. Supports orthodox Jewish life in Paris and the Department of Seine.
Grand Rabbi: S. Rubinstein.
Pres.: A. Rozemberg.

Association B'nai B'rith, 46ter, rue Saint-Didier.
Pres.: Gaston Kahn.
Sec.: G. Jacob.

Association Cultuelle Sepharadite de Paris, 13, rue Saint-Lazare.
Pres.: Edgar Abravanel.
Sec.: Albert Cohen.

Association Sioniste Sepharadite de Paris, 55, rue Richard Lenoir.
Pres.: M. Angel.

Brit Hatzoar (Sionistes Revisionnistes de France), 13, rue de Lancry.

B'rith-Ivrith, 29, rue St. Lazare. Founded in 1939 as Union for Hebrew language and culture. Publication: Mahbaroth.
Pres.: J. Fink.

Bund (Union des socialistes Juifs), 110, rue Vielle-du-Temple. Publication: Yiddish daily "Unser Stimme."

Centre de Documentation Juive Contemporaine 10, rue Marbeuf. (Contemporary Jewish documentation center). Since its foundation in 1943, it has collected all documents relative to the persecution of the Jews in various European countries. Publication: 'Le monde Juif" (monthly).
Pres.: Isaac Schneerson.

Chambre de Commerce France-Israel, 2, rue Meyerbeer.

Congres Juif Mondial, 78, Avenue des Champs-Elysees.
Sec. Gen.: Armand Kaplan.
Conseil Consltatif Francais.
Pres.: Edmond Fleg.

Conseil de la Jeunesse Juive, 27, Avenue de Segur. (Council of Jewish Youth). Associated organizations: Bahad, Borochov, Dror., Eclaireurs Israelites de France, Hanoar Httzioni, Hehaloutz, Jeunesse Sepharadite, Jeunesse Socialiste, Bund, Maccabi, M.J.S.U. Gorodnia, Yeschouroun, Cadets de l'U.J.R.E. Hachomer Hatzair, Jeunesse Liberale, Jeune WIZO, Union des Etudiants Juifs.
Pres.: Dr. Simon.
Sec.: Sternschein.

Confederation Mondiale des Sionistes Generaux Executif pour l'Europe et l'Afrique du Nord, 31 bis, Avenue Foch.
Sec.: Dr. Frey.

Conseil pour l'education et la Culture Juives en France, 45, rue La Bruyère. Council for Jewish Education and Culture in France.
Pres.: Kanapa.
Hon. Pres.: Jules Braunschvig.

SCHOOLS:

Ecole Normale Israelite Orientale, 59, Rue d'Auteuil. Teachers Seminary of the Alliance Israelite.
Dir.: E. Levinas.

Ecole Maimonide, 11, rue des Abondances. French lyceum with Hebrew courses.
Dir.: Marc Cohn.

Ecole Primaire Israelite, 70 Avenue Secrétan.
Dir.: Theo Dreyfus.

Ecole de Travail, 4 rue des Rosiers.
Dir.: A. Cremieux.

Federation des Societies Juives de France, 29, rue St. Lazare.
Founded 1923 to coordinate activities of different societies.
Publications: Editions Kyoum (books); Almanac "Kyoum," literary review (monthly; Yiddish).
Pres.: Marc Jarblum.
Hon. Pres.: Jefroykin.

Federation Sioniste de France, 135. Avenue de Wagram. Founded 1919.

Fondation de Rothschild, 76, rue de Picpus. Consists of a hospital, orphanage, and home for the aged.
Pres.: Baron Guy de Rothschild.

Hechalutz-France, 83 Avenue de la Grande-Armee. Founded 1936 to prepare Jewish youth for agricultural colonization in Israel.

Mizrahi, 5, rue d'Alsace. Founded 1900. Traditional religious and Zionist activities.

Poale Zion—Hitachdouth, 45 rue de Chabrol.
Pres.: Marc Jarblum.

Hapoel Hamizrahi de France et d'Afrique du Nord, 27, Boul. des Italiens.

WIZO, 24 rue de Mont-Thabor. Has chapters in Strasbourg, Mulhouse, Colmar, Saverne, Thann, Sarrebourg, Nancy, Metz, Epinal, Thionville, Lille, Rouen, Lyon, Clermont-Ferrand, Grenoble, Limoges, Toulouse, Pau, Bordeaux, Marseille, Cannes, Grasse, Nice, Monte Carlo.
Hon. Pres.: Mrs. Leon Filderman, Mrs. Jacob Kaplan.

Yechouroun (Mouvement de le Jeunesse Traditionalliste), 194, rue de Rivoli. Founded

1926. Board: Th. Klein, Lucien Lazare, L. Muller.

AGEN (*Lot-et-Garonne*).

Association Cultuelle Israelite d'Agen et du Lot-et-Garonne, 4, Place du Maréchal Foch. Jewish community.
Pres.: Dr. Henri Muller.

AMIENS (Somme)

Association Culturelle Israélite du Département de la Somme (Jewish community), 13, rue du Cloître-de-la-Barge. Founded 1933; maintains own synagogue.
Pres.: S. Lehr.

AVIGNON (Vaucluse)

Association Cultuelle Israelite (Jewish community), 7 rue Laboureur.
Rabbi: M. Sal.

BAR-LE-DUC (Meuse)

Communaute Israelite de Bar-Le-Duc (Jewish community).
Pres.: B. Finkel.

BAYONNE (Basses Pyrennées)

Consistoire Israelite des Basses—Pyrennes et des Landes, 35, rue Maulec. Founded 1492 by Jews from Spain.
Pres.: S. Salzedo.

BELFORT

Association Cultuelle de Belfort (Jewish community), 6, rue de l'As-de-Carreau. Founded before 1814.
Rabbi: Marc Kahlenberg.
Pres.: Jacob Guggenheim.

BESANCON (Doubs)

Association Cultuelle Israelite (Jewish community), 2, rue Mayence. Founded about 1825.
Rabbi: Grand Rabbi Avram.

BEZIERS (Hérault)

Association Cultuelle Israelite (Jewish community), 9, rue Alphonse—Mas.
Pres.: Schimenowitz.

BISCHWILLER (Bas Rhin)

Communaute Israelite de Bischwiller (Jewish community).
Pres.: Joseph Levy.

BORDEAUX (Gironde) (4,000 Jews)

Association Cultuelle Israelite de la Gironde, (Jewish community), 213, rue Ste. Catherine
Grand Rabbi: Joseph Cohen.
Pres.: Roger Gomez—Vaez.

CAEN (Calvados)

Union des Etudiants Juifs de France, 168, rue Caponière. Section of Union of Jewish Students in France.

CANNES (Alpes-Maritimes)

Association Cultuelle Israelite de Cannes (Jewish community), 2, rue des Mimosas. Has temple and house of worship.
Pres.: Dr. M. Machtou

CHALONS SUR MARNE (Marne)

Association Cultuelle Israelite (Jewish community), 30, rue Pasteur.
Pres.: Ulmann.

CHÂTEAUROUX (Indre et Loire)

Communaute Israelite (Jewish community).

CLERMONT-FERRAND (Puy-de-Dôme)

Association Cultuelle Israelite (Jewish community), 14, rue des Quatre-Passeports. Founded 1861. Has synagogue; gives course of religious instruction.
Pres.: Joseph Enkaoua.

COLMAR (Haut-Rhin)

Consistoire Israelite du Haut-Rhin (Jewish community), 4, rue des Têtes. Founded 1808.
Pres.: Gaston Picard.

DAUENDORF (Bas-Rhin)

Communaute Israelite (Jewish community).
Pres.: Kauffmann.

DIJON (Côte-d'Or)

Association Cultuelle Israelite de Dijon (Jewish community), 5, rue de la Synagogue. Rabbi: I. M. Choucroun.

DIEPPE (Seine-Inférieure)

Association Cultuelle de Dieppe (Jewish community).

ELBEUF (Seine-Inférieure)

Association Cultuelle Israelite (Jewish community), 36, rue du General-de-Gaulle. Founded in 1872 by Jewish emigrees from Alsace-Lorraine.
Pres.: Maurice Blin.

EPERNAY (Marne)

Association Cultuelle Israelite (Jewish community), 2, rue Placet.
Pres.: Dr. Rene Netter.

EPINAL (Vosges)

Communaute Israelite (Jewish community), 6, rue Parmentier.
Pres.: Albert Netter.

GRENOBLE (Isère)

Association Cultuelle Israelite (Jewish community), 20 rue de Paris. Synagogue, 7, rue Jean Jacques Rousseau.
Rabbinate, 4, rue Fourrier.
Rabbi: Ignace Kahan.
Pres.: Rodolphe Fischl, Prof. Mosse.

GUNDERSHOFFEN (Bas-Rhin)

Communaute Israelite (Jewish community). Pres.: Math. Corbeau.

HAGUENAU (Bas-Rhin)

Communaute Israelite (Jewish community), 1, Fosse des Tanneurs, rue des Juifs. Existed by 12th century.
Synagogue built in 1821.
Rabbi: Joseph Bloch.
Pres.: Joseph Strauss. Talmud Thora; dir.: Rabbi Joseph Bloch.

HERRLISHEIM-OFFENDORFF (Bas-Rhin)

Communaute Israelite (Jewish community). Pres.: Paul Kahn.

LAFERTE-SOUS-JOUARRE (Seine-et-Marne)

Association Cultuelle Israelite (Jewish community), 18, rue du Port-aux-Meules. Pres.: M. Meyer.

LAUTERBOURG (Bas-Rhin)

Communaute Israelite (Jewish community). Pres.: Meyer.

LE HAVRE (Seine-Inférieure)

Association Cultuelle Israelite (Jewish community), 5, Impasse des Ormeaux. Reconstruction of synagogue, destroyed during last war, under way.

LE MANS (Sarthe)

Association Cultuelle Israelite (Jewish community), 32, rue du Bourg-Belé.
Pres.: Sulim.

LENS (Pas-de-Calais)

Communaute Israelite (Jewish community), 19 Avenue Raoul-Briquet. Founded 1930. Pres.: I. Schwartz.

LILLE (Nord) (2,000 Jews)

Association Cultuelle Israelite de Lille (Jewish community), 5, rue Auguste-Angellier.
Pres.: Georges Gerschel.

LIMOGES (Haute-Vienne)

Communaute Israelite de Limoges (Jewish community), 11, rue Banc-Leger.
Pres.: Julien Alexandre.

LUNEVILLE (Meurthe-et-Moselle)

Association Cultuelle Israelite (Jewish community), 5, rue Costara.
Pres.: Sam Job.

LYON (Rhône) (11,300 Jews)

Association Cultuelle Israelite (Consistoire de Lyon) (Jewish community), 13, Quai Tilsitt. Founded 1852.

Grand Rabbi: S. Poliakoff.
Pres.: Marcel Levy.

Communaute Israelite Sepharadite, 47, rue Montesquieu. Sephardic Congregation; founded 1919.
Rabbi: Benjamin Assouline. Talmud Tora.

MARSEILLES (Bouches-du-Rhône)

Consistoire Israelite (Jewish community), 117, rue de Breteuil.
Grand Rabbi: Israel Salzer.
Pres.: Fédia Cassin.

Ecole de Marine O.R.T. — Ligue Maritime Juive, 7, Avenue de Monaco. Maritime school and section of O.R.T.
Dir.: Mauduit-Larive.

MERTVILLER (Bas-Rhin)

Communaute Israelite (Jewish community).
Pres.: Henri Herzog.

METZ (Moselle) (2,800 Jews)

Communaute Israelite de Metz (Jewish community), 39, rue de l'Arsenal. Founded about 1850.
Grand Rabbi: Nathan Netter.
Pres.: Eugene Weill.
Maintains a kindergarten called Pouponniere

MOISSAC (Tarn-et-Garonne)

Association Cultuelle Israelite (Jewish community), 18, Quai du Port.
Pres.: Simon.

MONTAUBAN (Tarne)

Association Cultuelle Israelite (Jewish community), 8, rue d'Elie.
Pres.: Elie Fisch.

MONTBÉLIARD (Doubs)

Communaute Israelite (Jewish community), Maison Ducas.
Pres.: Bernheim.

MONTPELLIER (Hérault)

Association Cultuelle Israelite (Jewish community), 5, rue des Augustins.
Pres.: César Uziel.

Union des Etudiants Juifs de France, 5, Faubourg St. James. Union of Jewish Students in France.
Pres.: Elie Levy.

MULHOUSE (Haut-Rhin) (2,000 Jews)

Communaute Israelite de Mulhcuse (Jewish community), 2, rue des Rabbins.
Rabbi: Edgard Weill.
Pres.: Joachim Bloch.

MUTZIG (Bas-Rhin)

Communaute Israelite (Jewish community).

NANCY (Meurthe-et-Moselle) (2,000 Jews)

Association Cultuelle Israelite de Nancy (Jewish community), 16, rue du Grand-Rabbin-Haguenauer. Founded 1785.
Grand Rabbi: Simon Morali.
Publication: "La Revue Juive de la Lorraine" (Jewish Revue of Lorraine), monthly.
Ed.: Grand Rabbi Morali.

Association Cultuelle Israelite, 55, rue des Ponts. Polish community.
Pres.: Pierre Kobrinek.

NANTES (Loire-Inférieure)

Association Cultuelle Israelite de Nantes— Bretagne—Vendee (Jewish community), 5, Impasse Copernic. Founded 1854.

Congres Juif Mondial, 16, ave. Les Primevères.
Pres.: Leon Schenker.
Regional section of the World Jewish Congress for Western France.

NICE (Alpes-Maritimes) (7,000 Jews)

Association Cultuelle Israelite (Jewish community), 7, rue Gustave-Deloye.
Rabbi: G. Scialtiel.
Pres.: Emile Cassin.

Association Talmud Torah, 7, rue Gustave Deloye. Founded 1952.

Temple Aschkenazi du Boulevard Dubouchage, 26, Bld. Dubouchage. Independent Ashkenazic congregation.
Rabbi: Syngalowsky.

NIEDERBRONN-LES-BAINS (Bas-Rhin)

Communaute Israelite (Jewish community).
Pres.: Alphonse Levy.

NIMES (Gard)

Association Cultuelle Israelite (Jewish community), 40, rue Roussy.

OBERNAI (Bas-Rhin)

Communaute Israelite (Jewish community).

ORLEANS (Loire)

Association Cultuelle Israelite (Jewish community), Place de la Salle des Fêtes. Founded 1806.
Pres.: Lang.

PAU (Basses-Pyrennées)

Association Cultuelle Israelite (Jewish community), 8 rue des Trois-Frères-Bernadac. Founded 1880.
Pres.: George Theodore.

PERIGUEUX (Dordogne)

Communaute Israelite (Jewish community), 3, rue Thiers.

PERPIGNAN (Pyrennées-Orientales)

Association Cultuelle Israelite (Jewish community), 3, rue de la Pinte.

POITIERS (Indre et Loire)

Communaute Israelite (Jewish community).

PONT-A-MOUSSON (Meuse)

Association Cultuelle Israelite (Jewish community), 28, rue de Barclay.

REICHSHOFFEN (Bas-Rhin)

Communaut: Israelite de Reichshoffen (Jewish community).
Pres.: Baer.

REIMS (Marne)

Association Cultuelle Israelite (Jewish community), 49, rue Clovis.
Pres.: Paul Grass.

RENNES (Ille-Et-Vilaine)

Association Cultuelle Israelite (Jewish community), 1, Rue d'Antrain.
Pres.: Douegnas.

ROANNE (Loire)

Association Cultuelle Israelite (Jewish community), 25, rue Chassain-de-la-Plasse. Maintains a Hebrew school.
Pres.: Baruch Grynberg.

ROUEN (Seine-Inférieure)

Association Cultuelle Israelite (Jewish community), 55, rue des Bons-Enfants. Existed by Middle Ages; founded 1871. Pub.: Monthly "Bulletin de l'Association Cultuelle Israelite de Rouen." Synagogue reconstructed 1950.

SAINT-ETIENNE (Loire)

Association Cultuelle Israelite (Jewish community), 34, rue d'Arcole. Founded 1863.
Pres.: Dr. Nordmann.

SAINT-FONS (Rhône)

Association Cultuelle Israelite (Jewish community), Monte Croz B.C.
Pres.: H. Bentitou.

SAINT-QUENTIN (Aisne)

Association Cultuelle Israelite (Jewish community), 11, Bld. Henri-Martin.
Pres.: Dugowson.

SAVERNE (Bas-Rhin)

Communaute Israelite de Saverne (Jewish community).
Rabbi: Armand Bloch.

SEDAN (Ardennes)

Association Cultuelle Israelite (Jewish community), 15, Bld. Faber.
Pres.: P. Troller.

SOULTZ-SOUS-FORETS (Bas-Rhin)

Communaute Israelite (Jewish community).
Pres.: Julien Weil.

STRASBOURG (Bas-Rhin) (8,000 Jews)

Communaute Israelite de Strasbourg (Jewish community), 29, rue Oberlin. Founded 1784. Synagogues: 18, Place Broglie; 28a, rue Kageneck, rue de la Nuée Bleue.
Grand Rabbi: Abraham Deutsch.

Consistoire Israelite du Bas-Rhin, 23, rue Sellenick. Founded 1844. Central body for all communities in Bas-Rhin. Pub.: "Bulletin de nos Communautes."
Grand Rabbi: Abraham Deutsch.
Pres.: Lucien Gromback.

Association "Aquiba," 9, Rue du Fossé-des-Tanneurs. Supports the "Aquiba" School, a primary and secondary school for Hebrew language and Jewish tradition.
Dir.: Benjamin Gross.
Pres.: Grand Rabbi Deutsch.

Kadima, 42, Avenue de la Forêt-Noire. Local organization of General Zionists.
Pres. Dr. Levy-Dreyfus.

Union Regionale des Sionists de l'Est de la France, Regional union of Zionists in Eastern France.
Pres.: Lilienbaum.

TARBES (Hautes Pyrennées)

Association Cultuelle Israelite (Jewish community), 10, rue Brauhauban.
Pres.: Rene Bloch.

TOULON (Var)

Association Cultuelle Israelite (Jewish community), 32, Bld. du Maréchal-Joffre. Founded 1949.
Pres.: Maurice Rebouah.
Rabbi: Isaac Sameh.

TOULOUSE (Haute-Garonne)

Association Cultuelle Israelite (Jewish community), 2, rue Palaprat.
Rabbi: Andre Chekroun.
Maintains Talmud Tora. Pub.: "Bulletin intérieur de la Communaute."

TOURS (Indre et Loire)

Association Cultuelle Israelite (Jewish community), 37, rue Parmentier.

Rabbi: Pierre Blum.
Pres.: David Levy.

TROYES (Aube)

Association Cultuelle Israelite (Jewish community), 10, rue Charles-Dutreix.
Pres.: Albert Blum.

VALENCIENNES (Nord)

Association Cultuelle (Jewish community), 36, rue de l'Intendance.
Pres.: Léon Enten.

VERDUN (Meuse)

Association Cultuelle Israelite (Jewish community), Impasse des Jacobins. Founded 1875.
Pres.: G. Daltroff.

VERSAILLES (Seine et Oise)

Association Cultuelle Israelite (Jewish community), 10, rue Albert-Joly. Founded before 1788.
Pres.: R. Weill.

Ecole de Service Social Paul-Baerwald, 47, rue du Parc-de-Clagny. "School of Social Service" founded in 1949 by AJDC to train specialized social workers for Jewish communities in Europe, Israel, and North Africa.
Dir.: Dr. Henry Selver.

VICHY (Allier)

Association Cultuelle Israelite (Jewish community), 2 bis, rue du Maréchal-Foch.
Pres.: Marcel Bloch.

VILLEURBANNE (Rhône)

Communaute Israelite (Jewish community), 33, Avenue Henri-Barbusse.
Pres.: Jules Levy.

WESTHOFFEN (Bas-Rhin)

Communaute Israelite (Jewish community).
Pres.: Auerbacher.

WOERTH (Bas-Rhin)

Communaute Israelite (Jewish community).
Pres.: Kahn.

PUBLICATIONS:

YIDDISH DAILIES: *Naje Presse,* 127, Fg. Pois-sonnière, Paris, 9e. *Unzer Stimme,* 20, 1ue Ferdinand Duval, Paris, 4e. *Unzer Wort,* 45, rue de Chabrol, Paris 4e.

WEEKLIES: *Tsionistiche Schtime* (Yiddish), 2, square Trudaine, Paris, 9e. *Unzer Weg* (Yiddish), 4, rue Martel, Paris, 10e.

FORTNIGHTLIES: *Arbeter Wort* (Yiddish), 15, rue Béranger, Paris, 3e. *Journal de la Com-munautes,* 17, rue St. Georges, Paris, 9e. *Bulletin de nos Communautés,* 18, rue de l'Observatoire, Strasbourg. *Terre Retouvee,* 12, rue de la Victoire, Paris, 9e.

MONTHLIES: *A Jovö* (Hungarian), 56, rue St. Georges, Paris, 9e. *Al Hamischmar,* 17, rue de la Victoire, Paris, 9e. *Ami,* 14, rue Geor-ges Berger, Paris, 8e. *Amif-Association des Médicins Israélites de France,* 7, rue de Bucarest, Paris, 8e. *Amities: France-Israel,* 135, Avenue de Wagram, Paris, 17e. *Bulletin d'Information de l'Association Culturel Is-raelite de Grenoble,* 20 rue de Paris, Gren-oble. *Bulletin Mensuel de la Circonscription Consistonale Israélite de Lyon,* 13, quai de Tilsitt, Lyon. *Cale Bianca,* 44, rue Blanche, Paris, 9e. *Conversation avec les Jeunes,* 80, rue St. Antoine, Paris, 4e. *Evidences,* 30, rue la Boëtic, Paris, 8e. *La Femme-Pionniere* (French-Yiddish), 106, rue Vieille du Tem-ple, Paris, 4e. *La Voix Sioniste,* 2, Square Trudaine, Paris, 9e. *Le Rayon,* 24, rue Copernic, Paris, 16e. *Le Revue Juive de Lorraine,* 16, rue du Grand Rabbin Haguen-auer, Nancy. *Les Cahiers de l'Alliance Israé-lite Universelle,* 45, rue la Bruyère, Paris, 9e. *Notre Drapeau,* 13, rue de Lancry, Paris, 10e. *Notre Volonté* (French-Yiddish), 18, rue des Messageries, Paris, 10e. *Renaissance,* 117, rue de Breteuil, Marseilles. *Revue de la WIZO,* 24, rue du Mont-Thabor, Paris, 1er. *Theater Spigel* (Yiddish), 25, rue de Lancry, Paris, 11e. *Trait d'Union,* 31, rue de Montevideo, Paris, 16e.

QUARTERLIES: *Fonds Social Juif Unifié,* 19, rue de Teheran, Paris, 9e. *Frailand* (Yiddish) 6, rue Quatrefages, Paris, 5e. *Le Mond Juif,* 27, rue Génégaud, Paris, 6e. *Les Lettres Juives Francaises,* 17, rue Saint-Georges, Paris, 9e.

PERIODICALS: *Agir,* 46, rue St. Didier, Paris, 16e. *Far Ounzere Kinder* (Yiddish), 36, rue Amelot, Paris, 11e. *Freie Horizonten* (Yid-dish), 306, rue des Pyrénées, Paris, 20e. *Images de la Vie,* 232, rue de Charenton, Paris, 12e. *Kadimah,* 6, rue Lalande, Paris, 14e. *La Revue de la Pensée Juive,* 24, rue Copernic, Paris, 16e. *La Revue d'Histoire de Médecine Hébraique* (French-Hebrew), 55, rue de Clichy, Paris, 9e. *La Revue Juive de Champagne,* 16, rue Charbonnet, Troyes. *La Vie Juive,* 78, Avenue des Champs-Elysées, Paris, 8e. *Les Cahiers Séfardis,* 18, Boulevard Bineau, Neuilly-sur-Seine. *Notre Communauté,* 6, rue de l'As de Carreau, Belfort. *Targoum,* 89, rue de Seine, Paris, 6e. *Volksguezunt* (Yiddish), 2 bis, avenue de Villars, Paris, 7e.

IRREGULARS: *La Semaine Juive,* 23 bis, rue Dufrénoy, Paris, 16e. *Les Eclaireurs Israélites* 27, avenue de Ségur, Paris, 7e.

GERMANY

A. WEST GERMANY FEDERAL REPUBLIC

JEWISH POPULATION: 25,000

According to the official census of 1925, the Jewish population of Germany was 564,379. By 1933, the number had decreased to 525,000, according to an estimate of the Jewish communities.

From 1925 to 1951, the number of Jews emigrating to Israel and other countries because of the persecutions was 295,000, while 250,000 were exterminated by the Nazis. The Jewish survivors in Germany consist mostly of the aged.

It is estimated that only about 2,000 Jews live in communist East Germany.

After vehement controversy in Jewish quarters about the advisability of negotiations with Germans and following 1½ years of negotiations, an agreement was reached on September 1952 between Germany on the one hand and Israel and the Conference on Jewish Material Claims against Germany on the other, according to which West Germany has to pay the State of Israel $715,000,000 as reparations for confiscated and destroyed Jewish property and an additional $107,000,000 to the Conference. Payment is to be made in 12 to 14 annual instalments. Western Germany has also committed herself to substantial improvements of existing laws which would allow greater indemnification to individual victims of the Nazi regime. The Central Council of German Jews estimates that in addition to the 28,000 registered with Jewish communi-

ties there are 15,000 unaffiliated Jews in Germany. There are 2,500 Jewish youngsters of whom 1,200 are of school age. The number of teachers is 35.

Zentralrat der Juden in Deutschland (Central Council of Jews in Germany), Fischerstrasse 49, Düsseldorf. Founded 1950. It is the general representative body of all Jews in Germany. Aims: to represent the common interests of German Jewish communities before the governmental authorities and foreign Jewish organizations and support Jewish cultural and social activities. Chairman, Heinz Galinski; Gen. Sec., Dr. Henry G. van Dam; Adm. Sec. Dr. Schafer.

Arbeitsgemeinschaft der Jüdischen Gewerbetreibenden und Industriellen ("The Committee for Cooperation of Jewish Tradesmen and Industrialists"), Fischerstrasse 49, Düsseldorf. Pres., Hans Schiller. Local branches exist in Berlin-Charlottenburg, Niebuhrstrasse 61 (Manager: Ludwig Deutsch-Rosenberg); Frankfurt am Main, Hebelstrasse 17 (Manager: Otto Schafer); München, Trogerstrasse 10 (Manager: Alfred Neuhardt).

Arbeitsgemeinschaft Jüdischer Juristen ("The Committee for Cooperation of Jewish Lawyers"), Fischerstrasse 49, Düsseldorf. Founded to protect the special professional interests of Jewish lawyers and notaries.

Zentralwohlfartsstelle der Juden in

Deutschland E.V. ("The Central Welfare Board of the Jews in Germany"), Rothenbaumchaussee 38, Hamburg. Founded in 1952 to ensure the cooperation of all local Jewish welfare organizations in Germany. Pres., Dr. Ewald Allschoff (Frankfurt), Siegfried Heimberg (Hamburg).

WEST BERLIN (5,000 Jews)

Jüdische Gemeinde zu Berlin (Jewish Community of Berlin), Joachimsthalerstrasse 13. Chairman, Heinz Galinski.
  Synagogues: (1) Berlin-Charlottenburg, Pestalozzistrasse 14/15; (2) Berlin N.O. 55, Rykestrasse 53; (3) Berlin S.O. 36, Fränkelufer 10-16; (4) Berlin W. 15, Joachimsthalerstrasse 13; (5) Berlin N. 65, Iranischestrasse 3; (6) Berlin-Niederschönhausen, Moltkestrasse 8-11.
Jüdischer Weltkongress (World Jewish Congress), Joachimsthalerstrasse 13, Berlin W15.
Jewish School in the Frenkl Synagogue. 25 pupils. Twice weekly.
Jüdische Studentenvereinigung in Berlin (Association of Jewish Students in Berlin), Joachimsthalerstrasse 13, Berlin W 15.
Koordinationsausschuss der Jüdischen Studentenvereinigungen in der Bundesrepublik und Berlin (The Coordinating Committee of the Students' Union of Berlin and the German Federation), Joachimsthalerstrasse 13, Berlin W 15. Founded 1951. Local branches in Berlin, Heidelberg, Munich, Marburg-Giessen and committees in Göttingen and Hannover. Pres., Georg Majewski; Sec., Babette Moser.
American Joint Distribution Committee, Pestalozzistrasse 14, Berlin-Charlottenburg. Dir., Gerhard Schaefer.
Ort Union, Joachimsthalerstrasse 13, Berlin W15.

LANDESVERBAND DER JÜDISCHEN GEMEINDEN VON NORDRHEIN-WEST-FALEN (Federation of Jewish Communities of North Rhine-Westphalia), Arnoldstrasse 6, Düsseldorf. Chief Rabbi for Northwest Germany, Dr. P. Holzer (Dortmund, Schwanenwall 29), Pres., Julius Dreifuss.
Jüdisches Altersheim Rosenau (Jewish Home for the Aged), Rosenau. Maintained by the Federation of Jewish Communities of Nordrhein-Westfalen. Manager, Mrs. Girod.

AACHEN

Jüdische Gemeinde Aachen (Jewish Community), Wilhelmstrasse 10. Reorganized in 1945. Pres., Walter Voss.

BONN

Synagogengemeinde Bonn (Jewish synagogal community), Quantiusstrasse 4. Pres., Siegfried Leopold.

DUISBURG

Jüdische Gemeinde Duisburg (Jewish community), Könenstrasse 13. Pres. Paul Goldfischer.

DUSSELDORF

Synagogengemeinde Düsseldorf (Jewish synagogual community), Arnoldstrasse 6. Pres. Alfred Sieradz.

ESSEN

Jüdische Gemeinde Essen (Jewish community), Steelerstrasse 29. Pres. Siegfried Levy.

KOELN

Synagogengemeinde Köln (Jewish synagogual community), Ottostrasse 85; Röntgenstrasse, Köln-Ehrenfeld. Reorganized 1945. One of the largest communities. Pres. Moritz Goldschmidt.
Jüdisches Altersheim (Home for the Indigent and the Aged), Blankenheimerstrasse 55, Köln-Sülz.

KREFELD

Synagogengemeinde Krefeld (Jewish synagogual community), Bismarckstrasse 118. Pres. Fritz Leven.

MUELHEIM-RUHR

Jüdische Gemeinde Mülheim (Ruhr), (Jewish community), Kampstrasse 7. Pres., Salomon Lifsches.

MUENCHEN-GLADBACH

Jüdische Gemeinde München-Gladbach (Jewish community), Albertusstrasse 54. Reorganized 1945. Maintains a house of prayer. Pres. Kurt Hecht.

OBERHAUSEN-WESEL

Jüdische Gemeinde Oberhausen-Wesel (Jewish community), Reeser Landstrasse. Pres. Alex Russel.

RHEYDT

Jüdische Gemeinde Rheydt (Jewish community), Königstrasse 62. Pres. Emil Heymann.

SIEGKREIS RUPPICHTEROTH

Jüdische Gemeinde Siegkreis Ruppichteroth (Jewish community), Wilhelmstrasse 17. Pres. Erich Bendix.

WUPPERTAL

Jüdische Gemeinde Wuppertal (Jewish community), Friedrich-Ebertstrasse 73. Reorganized 1945. Pres. Josef Heinmann. The community acts as the central Jewish body for the towns and rural settlements in the districts of Wuppertal, of which the main ones are Solingen-Ohligs, Remscheid-Lennep, Velbert, Mettmann, Langenberg, Neviges, and Heiligenhaus.

LANDESVERBAND DER JÜDISCHEN GEMEINDEN VON NORDRHEIN-WESTFALEN, WESTFALEN SECTION (Federation of Jewish communities of North Rhine-Westphalia), Schwanenwall 29, Dortmund. Pres. Siegfried Heimberg; Sec., Max Rosenbaum.

BIELEFELD

Jüdische Kultusgemeinde Bielefeld (Jewish community), Stapenhorststrasse 35. Pres. Max Hirschfeld.

BOCHUM

Jüdische Religionsgemeinde Bochum (Jewish community), Rombergstrasse 10. Pres., Siegbert Vollmann.

DORTMUND

Jüdische Gemeinde Gross-Dortmund (Jewish community), Schwanenwall 29. Pres. Siegfried Heimberg.

GELSENKIRCHEN

Jüdische Gemeinde Gelsenkirchen (Jewish community), Schwindtstrasse 28. Pres., Robert Jessel.

HAGEN-WESTFALEN

Jüdische Kultusgemeinde Hagen und Umgebung (Jewish community), Potthofstrasse 14. Pres. Richard Hirschfeld.

HAMM

Jüdische Gemeinde Hamm (Jewish community), Marker Allee 1. Pres. Max Consirowski.

HERFORD

Jüdische Gemeinde Stadt- und Landkreis Herford (Jewish community), Ortsieckerweg 11. Reorganized 1945. Pres. Hans Grabowski.

HERNE

Jüdische Religionsgemeinde Herne (Jewish community), Schäferstrasse 14. Pres., Edgar Wahl.

LIPPSTADT-SOEST

Jüdische Gemeinde der Kreise Lippstadt-Soest (Jewish community), Erwitterstrasse 12. Pres. Albert Heumann.

MINDEN

Jüdische Gemeinde für Stadt- und Landkreis Minden, Lübbecke, und Schaumburg-Lippe (Jewish community), Königswall 5-9, Minden. Pres. Emil Samuel.

MUENSTER IN WESTFALEN

Jüdische Gemeinde Münster und Umgebung (Jewish community), Am Kanonengraben 4. Pres. Siegfried Goldenberg.

PADERBORN

Jüdische Gemeinde Paderborn (Jewish community), Fürstenbergstrasse 33. Pres., Hermann Steinheim.

RECKLINGHAUSEN

Jüdische Gemeinde Recklinghausen (Jewish community), Paulusstrasse 6. Pres. Mrs. M. Aron.

SIEGEN

Jüdische Gemeinde Siegen (Jewish community), Untere Kaiserstrasse 54, Siegen-Geiswald. Pres. Julius Löwenstein.

WARBURG

Jüdische Gemeinde Warburg und Höxter (Jewish community), Am Markt 7, Warburg-Altstadt. Pres. Otto Baruch.

WITTEN RHUR

Jüdische Gemeinde Witten (Ruhr), (Jewish community), Bahnhofstrasse 34, Witten (Ruhr). Pres. Fritz Grünebaum.

LANDESVERBAND DER JÜDISCHEN GEMEINDEN IN HESSEN (Federation of Jewish Communities in Hessen), Hebelstrasse 17, Frankfurt am Main. Chief Rabbi: Dr. Zwi Harry Levy; Pres., Dr. Ewald Allschoff.

BAD HOMBURG VOR DER HOEHE

Jüdische Gemeinde Bad Homburg (Jewish community), Kisseleffstrasse 11. Pres. Robert Schlesinger.

BAD NAUHEIM

Jüdische Gemeinde Bad Nauheim (Jewish community), Karlstrasse 34. Pres., A. Kornblüth. A Jewish boarding school was established in 1954.

DARMSTADT

Jüdische Gemeinde Darmstadt (Jewish community), Osannstrasse 11. Pres., Joseph Fränkel.

FRANKFURT AM MAIN (2,000 Jews)

Jüdische Gemeinde Frankfurt am Main (Jewish community), Baumweg 5–7. Originated in the 13th century. Reorganized in 1945. Pres., Max Meyer. *Synagogues:* Westend Synagogue, Freiherr-vom-Stein-Strasse, Baumweg 5–7. *Beth Hamidrasch,* Röderbergweg 29.

Jüdisches Altersheim, Gagernstrasse 36. Jewish Home for aged and indigent.

American Joint Distribution Committee, Emigration Service, Eschenheimer Landstrasse 92. Manager, Mrs. G. Kermisch.

Ilias, Friedrichstrasse 29.

Jüdischer Weltkongress (World Jewish Congress), Hebelstrasse 17.

40 children in the Talmud Torah.

FULDA

Jüdische Kultusgemeinde Fulda (Jewish community), von Schildeckstrasse 13. Pres., Max Gerson.

GELNHAUSEN

Jüdische Gemeinde Gelnhausen (Jewish community), Rückingen über Gelnhausen. Director, J. Lilienfeld.

KASSEL

Israelitische Kultusgemeinde Kassel (Jewish community), Heubnerstrasse 19. Ancient community, reorganized 1946. Pres., Max Levy.

MARBURG

Jüdisches Hilfskomittee Marburg (Jewish aid committee), Schulstrasse 7.

OFFENBACH

Israelitische Gemeinde Offenbach (Jewish community), Goethestrasse 1-5. Pres.: Max Willner.

WIESBADEN

Israelitische Gemeinde Wiesbaden (Jewish community), Geisbergstrasse 24. Ancient community, reorganized 1945. Pres., N. Rottenberg.

LANDESVERBAND DER JÜDISCHEN GE-MEINDEN IN NIEDERSACHSEN, Ellernstrasse 7, Hannover. Federation of the Jewish communities of Lower Saxony. Organized in 1945. Pres., Norbert Prager.

BRUNSWICK

Jüdische Gemeinde Braunschweig (Jewish community), Steinstrasse 4. Pres. Carl Mosberg.

CELLE

Jüdisches Komitee Celle (Jewish committee), Im Kreise 24. Pres., M. Goldberg.

EMDEN

Jüdische Synagogengemeinde Emden (Jewish synagogual community), Petkumerstrasse 48. Pres., A. Pels.

GOETTINGEN

Jüdische Gemeinde Göttingen (Jewish community), Planckstrasse 12. Old community, originated about 1700; refounded 1945. Pres., E. Engwicht.

GOSLAR

Jüdische Gemeinde für den Stadt- und Landkreis Goslar (Jewish community), An der Doktorwiese 1, Goslar (Harz). Old community of the 17th century. Refounded 1945. Pres., Kurt Steinberg.

HANNOVER

Jüdische Gemeinde Hannover (Jewish community), Ellernstrasse 7. Ancient community reorganized 1945.
Pres.: Norbert Prager.
ORT, Schleiermacherstrasse 10.

HILDESHEIM

Jüdische Gemeinde Hildesheim (Jewish community), Goethestrasse 17. Pres., Siegfried Gros; Sec., Rudolf Schönfeld.

LUENEBURG

Jüdische Gemeinde Lüneburg (Jewish community), Gartenstrasse 96. Pres. Rudolf Lilienfeld.

NORTHEIM

Jüdische Gemeinde Northeim (Jewish community), Göttingerstrasse 35.

OLDENBURG

Jüdische Kultusvereinigung — Synagogengemeinde Oldenburg (Jewish community), Hochheider Weg 15. Ancient community, reorganized 1945. Pres., Adolf de Beer. Room for public worship: Cäcilienweg 9.

OSNABRUECK

Jüdische Gemeinde des Regierungsbezirkes Osnabrück (Jewish community for district of Osnabrück), Hasenauerstrasse 6a. Pres., Rudolf Stern.

SEESEN (Harz)

Jüdische Gemeinde Seesen (Jewish community), Jacobsonstrasse 9.

WINSEN-LUHE

Jüdisches Komitee Winsen-Luhe (Jewish community), Ludhorferstrasse 96, Winsen-Luhe, Kreis Harburg-Land. Reorganized 1946. Pres., Friedel Käppler.
Jüdische Gemeinschaft Schleswig-Holstein (Jewish community for Schleswig-Holstein), Kronshagener Weg 38, Kiel.
Synagogue: Lübeck.

KIEL

Jüdische Gemeinde Kiel (Jewish community), Kronshagener Weg 88. Pres., Heinz Salomon.

LUEBECK

Jüdische Gemeinde zu Lübeck (Jewish community), St. Annenstrasse 11.
Pres.: Josef Seliger. Synagogue.

EUTIN

Jüdische Gemeinde Eutin (Jewish community), Albert Mahlstedtstrasse 31.
Pres.: Hyneck Lewitt.

FLENSBURG

Jüdisches Komitee Flensburg (Jewish community), Burgstrasse 28.

VERBAND DER JUDISCHEN GEMEINDEN NORDWEST-DEUTSCHLANDS, Rothenbaumchaussee 38, Hamburg. Federation of the Jewish Communities of Northwestern Germany.
Pres.: Julius Dreifuss.

BREMEN

Israelitische Gemeinde Bremen (Jewish community), Osterdeich 17.
Pres.: Carl Katz.

HAMBURG

Jüdische Gemeinde in Hamburg (Jewish community), Rothenbaumchaussee 38.
Pres.: Harry Goldstein, Dr. Henry G. van Dam, Dr. Herbert Pardo, Dr. Berthold Simonsohn.
WIZO, Pres.: Mrs. Bella Alexander.
American Joint Distribution Committee, Rothenbaumchaussee 38.
Pres.: Miss I. Boehm.
HIAS, Rothenbaumchaussee 38.

LANDESVERBAND DER JUEDISCHEN GEMEINDEN VON RHEINLAND-PFALZ An der Liebfrauenkirche 11, Koblenz. Federation of tthe Jewish Communities of Rhineland-Palatinate.

BAD KREUZNACH

Jüdische Kultusgemeinde fuer die Kreise Kreuznach und Birkenfeld (Jewish community for the districts of Kreuznach and Birkenfeld), Herlesweiden 14, Bad Kreuznach. Founded 1945.

KOBLENZ

Jüdische Gemeinde Koblenz (Jewish community), An der Liebfrauenkirche 11.

LANDAU

Israelitische Kultusgemeinde Landau (Jewish community), Reiterstrasse 10.

MAINZ

Jüdische Gemeinde Mainz (Jewish community), Untere Zahlbacherstrasse 11.
Rabbi: Samuel Neumann, Rochusstrasse 23.

NEUWIED

Jüdische Gemeinde Neuwied (Jewish community), Engerserstrasse 4.

NEUSTADT AN DER WEINSTRASSE

Jüdische Kultusgemeinde der Rheinpfalz (Jewish community), Ludwigstrasse 20.

TRIER

Jüdische Gemeinde Trier (Jewish community), Saarstrasse 47.
Oberrat der Israeliten Badens, Kriegsstrasse 154. Karlsruhe in Baden. The Supreme Council of the Jews of Baden. Council reorganized 1945.
Pres.: Otto Nachmann.
Sec.: H. Freund.
Grand Rabbi: Dr. Robert Raphael Geis.

FREIBURG

Israelitische Landesgemeinde fuer Suedbaden (Jewish community), Hans Jacobsstrasse 8, Freiburg i. Breisgau.

HEIDELBERG

Jüdische Kultusgemeinde Heidelberg (Jewish community), Häusserstrasse 10/12.

KARLSRUHE

Jüdische Gemeinde Karlsruhe (Jewish community), Kriegsstrasse 154.
Pres.: Leopold Ransenberg.

MANNHEIM

Jüdische Gemeinde Mannheim (Jewish community), Quadrat R. 7, Nr. 24.

ISRAELITISCHE KULTUSVEREINIGUNG WUERTTEMBERG UND HOHENZOLLERN (Jewish central community), Hospitalstrasse 36, Stuttgart.
Chief Rabbi: Dr. Neufeld.

LANDESVERBAND DER ISRAELITISCHEN KULTUSGEMEINDEN IN BAYERN (Federation of the Jewish Communities of Bavaria), Herzog-Maxstrasse 7, München.

Israelitische Kultusgemeinde Augsburg (Jewish community), Halderstrasse 6a, Augsburg. Membership 68.
Pres.: Hugo Schwarz.

Israelitische Kultusgemeinde Bamberg (Jewish community), Promenade 4. Bamberg. Membership 72.
Pres.: N. Sandyk.

Jüdische Gemeinde Fuerth (Jewish community) Blumenstrasse 31. Fürth. Membership 197.
Pres.: Lev Rosenthal.

Israelitische Kultusgemeinde Muenchen (Jewish community), Herzog-Maxstrasse 7, München. Membership 1,900.
Pres.: Siegfried Neuland.
Rabbis: Snieg, Friedmann, Ros.

ORT, Möhlstrasse 10, München.

American Joint Distribution Committee, Siebertstrasse 3, München 27. Head Office for Germany. Dir.: Samuel L. Haber. Deputy Dir. for Germany: Dr. A. Kohane.

Israelitische Kultusgemeinde Nürnberg (Jewish community), Wielandstrasse 6, Nürnberg. Membership 182.
Pres.: P. Baruch.

Jüdische Gemeinde Regensburg (Jewish community), Schäffnerstrasse 2. Membership 166.
Pres.: Chaim Schwert.

Chief Rabbi: Prof. Yaqov Simha Avidor. Regensburg is the residence of the chief rabbinate for the districts ot Bayern, Oberpfalz, and Oberfranken.

Israelitische Gemeinde Würzburg (Jewish community), Valentin-Beckerstrasse 11, Würzburg. Membership 67.
Pres.: D. Rosenbaum.

PERIODICALS:

Allgemeine Wochenzeitung der Juden in Deutschland, Hildenerstrasse 35a, Duesseldorf-Benrath. Weekly. German.

Neue Jüdische Zeitung, Haeberlstrasse 7, Munich. Weekly. Yiddish. Editor: Garfinkel.

Muenchener Jüedische Nachrichten, Liebher Strasse 19, Munich. German. Fortnightly. Editor: Moses Lustig.

Frankfurter Jüdisches Gemeindeblatt, Hebel Strasse 17, Frankfurt a. Main. Monthly.

Jüdische Illustrierte, Hildener Strasse 35a, Duesseldorf-Benrath. Monthly.

Jüdische Sozialalarbeit, Hebel Strasse 17, Frankfort a. Main. Monthly.

Mitteilungsblatt der Israeliten Badens, Kriegsstrasse 154. Karlsruhe, Monthly.

Baderech, Joachimstaler Strasse 13. Berlin, W. 15. Quarterly.

B. EAST GERMANY

(JEWISH POPULATION: 2,280)

BERLIN (1,500 Jews)

Jüdische Gemeinde, Oranienburgerstrasse 28.
Synagogue Bruckertrasse. Reform. Used only during High Holidays. Weekly Sabbath services held in adjacent Beth Hamidrash for a congregation of 30.
Rabbi: Martin Reisinger.
Only 8 children are given instruction in Hebrew and Jewish history by Rabbi Reisinger.

DRESDEN (150 Jews)

LEIPZIG (150 Jews)

The congregation has a cantor but no rabbi, 9 children receive Jewish religious instruction.

ERFURT (100 Jews)

The congregation has only a cantor.

Smaller Jewish communities also exist in Halle, Magdeburg, Schwerin, Chemnitz, and Plauen.

Sec.: E. Barnett.

GIBRALTAR

JEWISH POPULATION: 650

In 1473, a suggestion was made that the promontory should be reserved for Marranos. The present Jewish Community was founded by immigrants from North Africa shortly after the British annexation in 1704. In the middle of the 19th century, the Jewish population reached about two thousand. In 1941, during the Second World War, nearly all the Jews were removed to England, the West Indies, and the Portuguese islands as a measure of protection. The Jewish population before this evacuation was less than 1,000. In 1954, a Jew was elected chairman of the Gibraltar City Council.

Managing Board of the Hebrew Community, Bomb House Lane.
Pres.: D. Benaim.
Rabbi: Joseph Pacifici.
Communal Centre, Hebrew School Building, Bomb House Lane.

Synagogue, Shaar Hashamayin, Engineer Lane.
Founded before 1749; rebuilt 1768.
Pres.: M. Mattana, Minister, Rev. M.H.S. Benzimra.
Synagogue, Nefusot Yehudah, Line Wall Rd.
Founded 1799.
Pres.: Haim Hassan. Minister, Rev. S. Edery.
Synagogue, Es Hayim, Irish Town.
Founded 1759.
Pres.: S. Tedesqui.
Principal, The Hon. D. Benaim.
Synagogue, Abudarham, Parliament Lane.
Founded 1820.
Pres.: Isaac Garson.
Hebrew School, Bomb House Lane.
Pres.: D. Benaim.
Yeshibat Or Torah, Bomb House Lane.
Pres.: D. Benaim.
Beiro's Home for Aged and Needy Jews.
Hebrat Shaar Hashamayim.
Pres.: Rev. M. H. S. Benzimra.
Hebrew Poor Fund.
Ozer Dalim (Sick Poor Relief Society).
Founded 1866.
Pres.: D. Benaim.

GREECE

JEWISH POPULATION: 6,000

Already in the third century B.C.E. an alliance between Sparta and the Jews existed and was renewed by the high priest Jonathan (161-143 B.C.E.), according to the Book of Maccabees. Philo tells of important Jewish settlements in Greece in the first century B.C.E. After Christianity became the state religion, the condition of the Jews in the Eastern Roman Empire deteriorated. Marriages between Jews and Christians were forbidden after 399. Leo III (717–41) and Leo VI (866–912) endeavored to convert the Jews through forcible baptism. In the 14th and 15th centuries, the position of the Jews improved and Jewish scholarship flourished.

Under Turkish rule and after the expulsion of the Jews from Spain (1492), many Jews came to Salonika and other towns. During the revolt of Greece against Turkish dominion, Jews were exposed to frequent hostile outbreaks of the Greeks. In 1891, a charge of ritual murder led to a pogrom in Corfu, and 1,500 Jews fled from there to Italy, Turkey, and Egypt. Anti-semitic riots occurred in 1898 in Larissa, Volos, and Trikala, and Jews were accused of siding with the Turks. In 1912, the Greeks occupied Salonika, and the old hostility toward Jews flared up anew. Outbreaks of anti-semitism occured in the years 1931-32. Despite anti-Jewish sentiment, the government subsidized Jewish religious, educational, and philanthropic institutions.

A large proportion of the Jews were employed as sailors and harbor workers, but their economic situation worsened considerably after the return of 1½ million Greek refugees from Turkey who endeavored to take over the economic positions of the Jews.

During World War II, 7,000 Jews were enlisted in the Greek army fighting on the Albanian front. They distinguished themselves heroically and a captured Albanian town was named "Frizis" in honor of Colonel Mordecai Frizis, a Jewish officer who was killed in action.

The barbarous liquidation of the ancient Greek Jewish community of 75,000 began with the Nazi invasion of Greece in April, 1941. 60,000 of them were deported and died in the Nazi gas chambers and by 1944 only about 11,000 survivors were left. Since then, 2,122 have emigrated to Israel and about 1,000 to the United States. These statistical figures of Jews in Greece and the various communities are based on the 1954 census of the Athens Jewish Community.

Attempts to bring a rabbi from Israel to act as chief rabbi have so far failed.

By a legislative act, the OPAIE (Organization of Assistance and Rehabilitation for Greek Jews) was formed for the purpose of recovering heirless property of the Nazi victims, estimated at a value of 10 million dollars, which is to be used for the rehabilitation of needy Jews in Greece and Israel.

The Greek government is sympathetic toward Israel, but as yet has not extended *de jure* recognition to her because of the pressure exerted by Egypt, where 200,000 Greeks live.

Central Board of the Jewish Communities,
    Odos Ipitu, Athens I.
    Pres.: Israel Noah. Sec.: Isaac Emanuel.

The Central Board is recognized by the Government. An annual General Assembly, representing the 24 Greek Jewish communities, elects the Administrative Council and the Executive. The communities maintain, with the help of the Government, two Jewish day schools, one in Athens and the other in Larissa.

ATHENS (2,828 Jews)

Jewish Community, 5 Rue Melidoni.
    Pres.: Zaharia Vital.

The largest community in Greece, it is headed by an Administrative Council consisting of 9 members. The Council is the executive committee of a General Assembly of 50 members elected every third year.

Relief Committee, subsidized by the Central Board and operating for Jews out of Athens. Has a dispensary for the public

and gives medical and financial assistance.
Pres.: Maurici Beraka.

Jewish School, supported by the Jewish Community. The nursery school, conducted by an Israeli teacher, is attended by a considerable number of children.

Synagogue Beth Shalom,
Rabbi: Elias Barzilai.
There is also a second synagogue.

ORT School. 100 students. 3 modern courses. Founded in 1950.
Director: Isidore Noah.

WIZO, Pres.: Miss Joseph Nehemia.

SALONIKA (1,341 Jews)

Jewish Community, 24 Rue Vassileos Heracliou.
Pres.: Jeshua Parakia.

The second largest community in Greece, headed by an Administrative Council consisting of 9 members and elected by the General Assembly of 50 members. The Community gives medical and financial assistance to a large number of sick and poor people. According to a recent report of Mr. Abr. Recanati of Israel a former Jewish leader of Salonika, after a visit to the city, the Jewish community is in peril of complete disintegration. The once famous community cannot today (1954) provide any Jewish education for the children and even the synagogue services on Sabbaths and holidays have been discontinued.

Synagogue of the Monastiriotes. Of the remaining synagogues, only this one is in operation.

Alliance Israelita, Banque Union, Gr. Hermes.
Chairman: Joseph Nechama.

LARISSA (THESSALY) (460 Jews)

Jewish Community, The Community of Larissa is headed by an Administrative Council composed of 6 members and elected by a General Assembly of 25 members.
Jewish School for religious instruction.
Synagogue and rabbi.

VOLOS (THESSALY) (320 Jews)

Jewish Community.
Synagogue. Rabbi: Moise Simeon Pessah.

IOANNINA (EPIRUS) (103 Jews)

Jewish Community.
Synagogue and rabbi.

There are small Jewish Communities also in the following places:

Trikala (Thessaly province)	130	Jews
Khalkis (Central Greece)	132	"
Corfu (Is.)	115	"
Demotika (Thrace)	40	"
Kavalla (Macedonia)	54	"
Varria "	40	"
Kastoria "	32	"
Phlorina "	29	"
Drama "	20	"
Arta (Epirus)	46	"
Patras-Agrinion (Peloponnesus)	28	"
Zante (Is.)	11	"

HUNGARY

JEWISH POPULATION: 100,000

Jews were present in Hungary in large numbers at the close of the 11th century. During the 12th century, there was no special legislation affecting the Jews and they rose to high positions in the economic life of the country. During the reign of the Arpads, from the 10th century to the 14th, the Jews of Hungary enjoyed the friendly disposition of the rulers and the people. In Hungary, as elsewhere in Europe, the Jews were indispensable assets in the growing commercial economy of the country.

The beginning of the 15th century brought a series of calamities for the Jews of Hungary. The first charge of ritual murder was made against them at this time, and several Jews were burned at the stake. Further anti-Jewish outbreaks followed in the first years of the 16th century. The Jews were well treated by the Turks who occupied part of the country in the 16th century. However, the Jews were severely persecuted after the Turks were driven from Hungary.

In the first half of the 18th century, the number of Jews in Hungary was increased by Moravian Jews, and then by Jews from Poland, who transplanted the study of the Talmud into Hungary. According to statistics, there were 11,621 Jews in Hungary in 1735. By 1840, there were about 200,000 Jews in the country.

The reign of Joseph II (1780-90) brought a turn for the better in the condition of Hungarian Jewry. They were permitted to establish their own schools as well as to attend public schools, and were allowed to settle in the royal cities which had previously been closed to them. During the 19th century, despite their unfavorable political situation, the Jews played an important part in the life of the country. In 1867, the complete political emancipation of the Jews was effected, and in 1896, a law was passed recognizing the Jewish faith as legally on a par with Christian denominations.

After the advent of Nazism in Germany, in 1933, Hungary adopted Nazi anti-Jewish measures until, finally, Hungarian Jews were deported for forced labor and to concentration camps.

On March 19, 1944, the Nazis overran Hungary and set up governments in their own image. These governments of Sztojay and Szalasi destroyed 564,000 of the 725,007 Hungarian Jews. At the time of the liberation, there were Jews only in Budapest (119,000). The rest had been deported to various concentration camps. Some of the surviving inmates of the camps returned to the country. The number of Jews at the end of 1946 was about 130,000. They were decimated, pauperized, their families broken. Yet the Hungarian Jews set to work to rebuild their shattered life. The number of births rose rapidly, and in 1946 they exceeded, for the first time in many years, the number of deaths.

All pre-war national Jewish organizations were re-established (the Zionist Organization; the national bureaus of the Orthdox and Liberal Jews). Of the former 473 Jewish communities, 266 resumed their activities. The places of the martyred rabbis were filled. The Budapest Rabbinical Seminary trained young rabbis.

New Jewish writers appeared; a number of memoirs were published; the Budapest Congregation established a Jewish free university and reopened the Jewish museum, 23 parochial elementary schools, and 8 Jewish high schools. A portion of the lost properties was recovered. However, there were about 50,000–60,000 needy orphans, aged invalids, and widows for whom the American Joint Distribution Committee, the World Jewish Congress, and HIAS cared.

In 1945, a pogrom broke out in Kunmadaras. In 1946, not less than 108,500 Jews expressed a wish to emigrate, according to a joint memorandum of the national Jewish organizations (March, 1946).

A heavy blow struck Hungary's Jews when, in 1948, the Communist Party seized power. In this year and the next, industries and trade and retail stores, most of which were owned by Jews, were nationalized. The new Hungarian Constitution of August 20, 1949, proclaimed the separation of Church and State, thus depriving the congregations of their right to levy taxes on their members. The Government agreed, however, to accord the congregations subsidies for 20 years at a declining rate (December 10, 1948). In order to tighten control over them, the religious organizations were centralized. The Gov-

ernment pushed through the unification of all groups (orthodox, reform, liberals) of Hungarian Jewry (February 20, 1950). In each city or town there could be only one congregation, and the congregations were subordinated to one of the eight districts over which the National Bureau exercises supreme authority.

The Law of June 1948 provided for the nationalization of all parochial schools with the exception of rabbinical schools and Hebrew religious schools. The IMIT (Hungarian Jewish Literary Society) and OMIKE (National Hungarian Jewish Cultural Association) were liquidated in 1950, and their work was taken over by the Budapest Jewish Congregation's Cultural Department. The Jewish hospitals, some of them ranking among the largest in the country, and orphanages were nationalized.

The only source of real help was the American Joint Distribution Committee, which yearly spent millions of dollars to help in the establishment of co-operatives and which maintained a vast network of public kitchens, orphanages, and homes for the aged, and which subsidized the religious and cultural organizations. In 1953, the Joint Distribution Committee, together with the other American Jewish agencies, was closed by the government.

In May 1949, about 5,000 Jews fled through Czechoslovakia. The Hungarian Government, however, put an end to this movement. Later, it permitted the emigration of 3,000 Jews to Israel, but it was two years before all of these people reached their destination.

The leaders of the Zionist movement

were persecuted. In June 1949, ten of them were arrested. Seven of them were sentenced to heavy terms. In November 1949, 36 members of the Hashomer Hatzair were reported to have been arrested. In 1953, the leaders of the Budapest Congregation, including Lajos Stőkler, the president of the Budapest Jewish Congregation and of the National Organization of Hungarian Jews were arrested, but later released.

In 1951, the Government began to arrest Jews on a mass scale. Most of them were sent to villages or farms in the country as servants; others were shipped for forced labor to Soviet Russia. The number of Jews affected is estimated at 6,000. However, a wave of protests, among them from President Truman, Dean Acheson, the Lord Chancellor of Great Britain, the French Government, and Church dignitaries put a halt to the deportations. In 1953, a number of the deportees were reported to have been released and returned to their homes.

According to a bulletin of the Hungarian Legation in Israel dated October 21, 1954, there are at present 150 Synagogues and houses of prayer in Hungary, of which 50 Synagogues and Batey Midrashim are in Budapest.

The synagogues in the capital are full of Jews Friday evening. Some synagogues of historical significance, such as those of Szeged and O-Buda, were restored with the help of the government. There were before the 1956 rebellion 89 rabbis in Hungary of whom 8 were on the level of Catholic Bishops. One of these rabbis is designated Chief Rabbi of Budapest. The government assists the Jewish communities in obtaining Kosher meat and matzoth, as well as in establishing Mikvas, and in forming special co-operatives for Sabbath observers. The Rabbinical Seminary in Budapest is also supported by the government and is headed by Dr. Sandor Sheiber. Two Yeshivoth, one in Paks and one in Soltvadkert were liquidated at the end of 1956. In all larger Jewish communities courses are maintained for the study of the Torah and Talmud. The name of the present central religious body is the Hungarian Jewish Synagogue.

The Jewish library, connected with the Rabbinical Seminary in Budapest, has 60,000 volumes. The Jewish Museum in Budapest contains many historical objects.

A reliable private report of 1955 reveals that the Budapest Talmud Torah school has about 500 children. Instruction is in Hungarian and Yiddish but there is a shortage of prayerbooks and Bibles. About 500 persons then attended Friday evening service in the Kazinczy Synagogue. Of the 70,000 Jews in Budapest about 4,000 are Orthodox. There is a kosher restaurant in Budapest.

From Oct. 23, 1956, at least 25,000 Jews fled Hungary. A large number of rabbis, cantors, and ritual slaughterers departed leaving a serious shortage in the community.

NATIONAL ORGANIZATION:

The National Bureau of Hungarian Jews, (The Hungarian Jewish Synagogue, Central Religious Representative Body.)
Sip-utca 12, Budapest

Chairman: Dr. Endre Sós.
Vice-Chairman: Miklós Vida.
Sec.: László Jenő; Pál Graber; Marcel Steiner; Ernő Somosi.
Honorary Pres.: Prof. László Fleischmann.
An Executive Committee represents all the congregations in the country.
National Rabbinical Council, Chairman: Dr. Benjamin Schwarcz.

REGIONAL ORGANIZATIONS:

The country is divided into the following eight Districts, whose officers supervise the congregations within their region:

SZOMBATHELY
KAPOSVÁR
PÉCS
SZÉKESFEHÉRVAR
GYÖR
SZOLNOK
BÉKÉSCSABA
SZEGED

BUDAPEST (70,000 Jews)

The Jewish Congregation of Budapest, 12 Sip-utca, (liberals), 35 Dob-utca (orth.).
Rabbis: Dr. Imre Benoschofsky, Dr. Miklós Bernát, Dr. István Dér, Dr. Henrik Fisch, Dr. József Katona, Dr. Miklós Mandel, Dr. József Neumann, Dr. László Salgó, Dr. Benjamin Schwarcz, Dr. Mór Schwarz. Pres.: Dr. Benjamin Fischer.
There were 18 before the 1956 revolt.

JEWISH COMMUNITY OF GREATER BUDAPEST: 18 Districts.

Budapest Jewish Theological Seminary, József-Kőrut 27.
Director: Dr. Sándor Scheiber.
Hungarian Jewish Museum, Dohany-u 2.
Dir.: Fülöp Grünvald.
National Jewish Library, József-Kőrut 27.
2 Secondary Schools. József Kőrut 27.
Dir. boys' school: Fülöp Grünvald; girls: Dr. Jenő Zsoldos.

Hospital of the National Bureau of Hungarian Jews
Home of Aged, Alma-u.
Bikur Cholim Society for Aiding the Sick, Dessewfy-u. 23.
Chevra Kadisha, Chmn.: Marcel Steiner.
2 Orphanages.

PROVINCIAL CONGREGATIONS:

SZEGED (800 Jews)

DEBRECEN (2,800 Jews)
Rabbi: Dr. Miksa Weisz.

MISKOLC (1,000 Jews)
Provincial Congregation. 711 members.

NYIREGYHAZA (250 Jews)

PÉCS (600 Jews)
Pres.: László Poigár.
Rabbi: Dr. József Schweitzer.

KISVÁRDA (200 Jews)

GYÖR (300 Jews)

HÓDMEZÖVÁSÁRHELY (250 Jews)

MAKÓ (200 Jews)

KISKUNHALAS (150 Jews)

OROSHÁZA (150 Jews)
Provincial Congregation. Pres.: Géza Nádas.

KARCAG (100 Jews)

BAJA (200 Jews)
Home for Aged

SÁTORALJÚJHELY (150 Jews)

RÁKOSPALOTA (100 Jews)

GYÖNGYÖS (402 Jews)

PÁPA (200 Jews)

SOPRON (200 Jews)

NAGYKANISZA (250 Jews)

SZÉKESFEHERVÁR (200 Jews)

There are also congregations in the following places:

Balassagyarmat, Békéscsaba, Berettyóujfalu, Bonyhád, Csepel, Eger, Eehérgyarmat, Hajdunánás, Kecskemét, Makó, Mátészalka, Nyirbátor, Salgótarján, Szombathely, Vásárosnamény.

IRISH REPUBLIC

JEWISH POPULATION: 5,400

There is definite proof of the existence of a ~ermanent Jewish settlement in Ireland in 1232. In 1290, like the Jews of England, the Jews were expelled from Ireland, and did not return until 1655 in the time of Cromwell.

Jews have held a number of public offices there. Ralph Bernal-Osborne represented Waterford in Parliament in 1870. Countess Ellen Odette Desart served in the Irish Senate, 1922-1933.

Robert Briscoe of Dublin was several times elected deputy in the Irish House of Representatives. In the 20th century, the Jewish community increased considerably by immigration from Eastern Europe.

Dublin has two large and 5 small Orthodox congregations. The oldest Hebrew congregation was established in 1822, as a revival of the first Irish synagogue founded by Sephardic Jews in 1660. There is also a Jewish Progressive Congregation. In 1918, the office of the Chief Rabbi was established, the first incumbent being Rabbi Isaac Herzog, now Chief Rabbi of Israel.

There is one Jewish day school and several afternoon Talmud Torahs at the synagogues. The total enrollment is 300 pupils, with 8 teachers.

DUBLIN (5,200 Jews)

Jewish Representative Council.
Pres.: H. Good.
Sec.: I. Isaacson.
Zion School, Bloomfield Avenue, Dublin.
Rabbinate:
Chief Rabbi: Dr. I. Jakobovitz, 33 Bloomfield Avenue, S.C.R., Dublin.
Dayyan: Rabbi Z. Alony, 79 S.C. Road, Portobello, Dublin.
Minister (Cork), Rev. S. Barron, "Villa Antoine," Douglas Road, Cork.

SYNAGOGUES:

Dublin Hebrew Congregation, Adelaide Road. Founded 1892. Membership 294.
United Hebrew Congregation, Greenville Hall, S.C.R., Dublin. Founded 1914. Membership 209.
Terenure Hebrew Congregation, Rathfarnham Road, Dublin. Founded 1936. Membership 200.
Lombard Street Hebrew Congregation, Lombard Street, S.C.R., Dublin, Founded 1900. Membership 100.
Walworth Road Hebrew Congregation, Founded 1912. Membership 120.

Lennox Street Hebrew Congregation, Lennox Street, S.C.R., Dublin. Founded 1876. Membership 70.

St. Kevin's Parade Hebrew Congregation, St. Kevin's Parade, S.C.R., Dublin. Founded 1876. Membership 40.

Talmud Torah and Zion Jewish Day School, Bloomfield Avenue.

Stratford College, Stratford House, Embraces kindergarten and preparatory and secondary department with Hebrew instruction.

Zionist Council. Pres.: W. A. Freedman. Sec.: M. Abrahamson, 40 Fitzwilliam Pl.

Mizrachi, Pres.: B. Shillman. Sec.: Dr. E. Teller 28 Leinster Rd.

Tora Va'avodah. Pres.: D. Steinberg, 32 Longwood Ave.

Hebrew Speaking Society, Pres.: I. Fine.

Jewish Students' Union, Pres.: N. Gruson. Sec.: B. White, 18 Green Park, Rathgar.

New Jewish Literary and Social Club, 3 Harrington St. Pres.: S. Brown. Sec.: H. Wine.

CORK (200 Jews)

Hebrew Congregation, 10 South Terrace.
Rev.: S. Barron.
Pres.: S. Vard.
Sec.: I. T. Clein.

Hebrew School, 9 South Terrace.
Sec.: I. T. Clein.

Jewish Periodicals:
1. *Monthly*
   Halapid, 28-29 Upper O'Connell Street, Dublin.
2. *Irregular*
   Nachlath Dublin, Zion School, Bloomfield Avenue, Dublin.
3. *Annual*
   Irish Jewish Year Book, Zion School, Bloomfield Avenue, Dublin .

ITALY

JEWISH POPULATION: 33,000

Jews have lived in Italy since the 2nd century BCE. About 144 BCE, envoys of Jonathan the Maccabean already found a Jewish community there. In 19 CE, the first expulsion of the Roman Jews took place, but a few years later a new community was founded.

Jewish communities also existed in antiquity in Naples, Venice, Aquileia, Concordia, Bologna, Ferrara, Ravenna, Milano, Genoa, Pompei, Salerno, Syracusa, Palermo, Messina, as well as in Sicily, Sardinia, and many other places. Their position under the Roman emperors was generally favorable. When Christianity became the state religion in the 4th century, the situation of the Jews deteriorated con-

siderably. Under the Ostrogoths, their position improved again. In the Lombard period, the Popes left them undisturbed, and religious literature then began to flourish in Italy; 1230-1550 was the golden era for Jewish literature. The later anti--Jewish decrees, however, of Popes Benedict XIII and Eugenius IV temporarily imperiled the Jewish position (1413-1447).

In 1492, an influx into Italy of Jewish fugitives from Spain, chiefly Marranos, increased the Jewish population. Don Isaac Abravanel was received in the court of Ferdinand I in Naples.

In the middle of the 16th century the position of the Jews in Italy was undermined by the establishment of the Inquisition. and concentrated in the ghettos of Rome and Ancona.

In the 19th century, the Jews were emancipated by Napoleon. After his downfall, however, Pius VII reinstituted the Inquisition and divested the Jews of all their rights. 1870 brought the final Jewish emancipation in the Papel States by the champions of a United Italy. Among the Jews who played a prominent part in the development of Italy were: General Giuseppe Ottolenghi, Minister of War; Sansone d'Ancona, Minister of Finance; Luigi Luzzatti, the Grand Old Man of Italy, who was Prime Minister and many times Minister of the Treasury, as well as many others prominent in scientific and public affairs.

In World War I, the Jews distinguished themselves, and more than 1,000 citations for gallantry were bestowed upon Jewish soldiers. The Italian Army had 11 Jewish generals.

The advent of Fascism (1919) aroused apprehension as to the future of Italian Jewry. In the beginning, the Fascist regime left the Jews undisturbed, but after the formation of the "Rome-Berlin Axis," Mussolini began introducing Nazi racial legislation in Italy, too. Foreign and naturalized Jews were expelled and the Italian Jews were subjected to severe persecution. 530 lawyers, 500 physicians, 350 engineers, 200 chemists, and 115 journalists were deprived of their livelihood. About 5,600 Jews emigrated from Italy mostly to Palestine and America.

The Italian people, however, did not follow the anti-Semitic policy of the Government. Many Italians protected and sheltered even Jewish refugees who had escaped from Nazi-occupied countries. As soon as the Fascist regime collapsed, friendly relations between Italy and its Jewish population were fully resumed. The sufferings during the Fascist and war period had weakened and reduced the numerical strength of the Jews. Numerous efforts are being made by the Jewish communities in Italy to rehabilitate and consolidate their position.

The main Jewish communities are at present those of Rome (12,000), Milan (4,928) and Turin (3,007). Jewish youth is organized in the Italian Jewish Youth Federation, the Boy Scout Movement, Hechalutz, and the Union of Jewish Students.

EDUCATION:

In 16 communities throughout the country 25 Jewish schools of the Sunday School, Talmud Torah, Elementary School, or High School type are sponsored by the communal administrations, with the State contributing a share of the teachers' salaries.

ROME (12,000 Jews)

Union delle Comunità Israelitiche Italiane, Lungotevere Sanzio 9, Roma.

The Union of Jewish Communties in Italy was founded in 1930 for the coordination of religious, cultural, and social work of the Jewish communities and associations of Italy. The Executive Committee of the Union is elected at quinquennal congresses held every 5 years to which all the existing 23 Jewish communities delegate representatives. The Union is affiliated with the World Jewish Congress.

Pres.: S. Piperno.
Vice-Pres.: Renzo Levi.
Sec.: Dr. Giulio Anau.
Chief Rabbi: Dr. Elio Toaff.

Zionist Federation, comprising all Zionist parties, with branches in almost all Jewish communities in the country.

Federazione Giovanile Ebraica d'Italia (F.G.E.I.), Corso Vittorio Emmanuele 173, Roma. The federation of Jewish youth in Italy was founded in 1948 in Florence. Functions: Courses in Hebrew and Jewish history, sports, camps, excursions to Israel. Publication: "Ha-Tikvah." Monthly. Youth centers exist in Ancona, Bologna, Casale, Ferrara, Florence, Genoa, Milan, Naples, Perugia, Pisa, Rome, Trieste, Turin, Venice.

World Jewish Congress, Lungotevere Sanzio 9, Roma. Italian Section of the World Jewish Congress.

Comunità Israelitica di Roma, Lungotevere Cenci (Tempio).
Pres.: Dr. O. Cagli.
Jewish activities date back 2,000 years. In 1624, the Jewish community was founded as a "Jewish university" with a status approved by Pope Clemens VI, and then again approved in 1883.
The university status remained valid until the enforcement of the law of 1930 when the name was changed to "Comunità Israelitica di Roma".

Temple, Lungotevere Cenci.
Publication: "La voce della Comunità Israelitica di Roma".

ALESSANDRIA

Comunità Israelitica, Via Milano 3, Alessandria.

The community was probably founded early in the 16th century, just after the expulsion of the Jews from Spain. Its community works in close coordination with the Jewish communities of *Acqui* and *Asti,* and their welfare associations.

The administrative council consists of 1 president, 2 counsellors, 1 secretary.

ANCONA

Comunità Israelitica, Via Lazzaro Bernabei 12, Ancona. Formerly established as a university. The activity of the community dates back to ancient times. The administered documents date back to 1440.
Pres.: Bruno Ascoli.
Centro Giovanile Ebraico—(Hebrew Youth Center).

BOLOGNA

Comunità Israelitica, Via Gombruti 9, Bologna. Officially recognized by the law of 1930.
W.I.Z.O.
Centro Giovanile Ebraico (Jewish Youth Center).
Zionist Organization.
Grand Rabbi: Dr. Sergio Sierra.
Pres.: Eugenio Heimann.

CASALE MONFERRATO

Comunità Israelitica, Vicolo Salomone Olper 24, Casale Monferrato.
Pres.: Giuseppe Ottolenghi.
Temple: Vicolo Salomone Olper 24.

FERRARA

Comunità Israelitica, Via Mazzini 95, Ferrara. Officially founded in 1481.
Pres.: Prof. Ferruccio Ravenna.
Confraternite Riunite (United Federations).
Zionist Organization
Ospizio "Cavalieri Sanguinetti" (Hospital "A. Cavalieri Sanguinetti," home for the poor and aged).

FIRENZE (1,500 Jews)

Comunità Israelitica, Via Carlo Farini 4, Firenze.
Pres.: Dr. Alfredo Orvieto.

GENOVA (800 Jews)

Comunità Israelitica, Via Giovanni Bertora 6, Genova. Founded about 1750.

GORIZIA

Comunità Israelitica, Via Ascoli 13, Gorizia. Founded about 1700.
Pres.: Steno Donati.

MANTOVA (200 Jews)

Comunità Israelitica, Via Gilberto Govi 11, Mantova. Originated about 1389. Membership amounted to about 1,500–2,000 until about 1800.

Casa "di Ricovero". Home for the aged. Founded in 1925.

Asilo Infantile, Home for poor children. Founded in 1827.

Pio Istituto Trabotti. For charity and aid to the sick. Founded by Samuel Trabotti in 1834.

MERANO

Comunità Israelitica, Via Manzoni 25, Merano. Pres.: Gualtiero Windspach.

Institution for aiding the poor, Office: Via Manzoni 25, Merano. Founded Oct. 23, 1872. Now combined with the asylum for T.B. patients; controlled by the community.

MILANO (6,000 Jews)

Comunità Israelitica di Milano, Via Guastella 19, Milano. Established officially on October 30, 1930.

Grand Rabbi: E. Friedenthal, Via Guastella 19, Milano.

Pres.: Aw. G. Ottolenghi.

Scuola Ebraica (Hebrew School), Via Eupili 6.

Publications: Bollettino della Comunità Israelitica di Milano (monthly).

O.S.E. and *O.R.T.* (both: Via Unione 5).

Gruppo Sionistico, Via Unione 5.

Casa Riposo (Rest Home), Via Jomelli 18.

Alliance Israélite Universelle, Albergo Marino, 5, Piazza della Scala.

MODENA (200 Jews)

Comunità Israelitica, Piazza Mazzini 26, Modena. Dates back to the 11th century. The community was already established in 1930, and the "Israelitic University" was founded in 1500. Later this university was transformed into the actual community.

Functions originating in ancient times are: Rachamim-Misericordia Uomini ("Rachamim," Men's Association for Charity).

So'ed Holim—Misericordia Donne (So'ed Holim, Women's Association).

Talmud-Torah—Pia Istituto Israelitico per Istruzione (Talmud-Torah, religious institution for Hebrew instruction).

NAPOLI (500 Jews)

Comunità Israelitica, Piazza della Borsa 33, Napoli.

Pres.: Lamberto Foà.

Chief Rabbi: Isidoro Kahn.

Temple, Via S. M. Cappella Vecchia 81 (Adm. Piazza della Borsa 33).

Asilo Rothschild (Jewish institution, joint elementary courses). Via Cappella Vecchia 31.

PADOVA

Comunità Israelitica, Via S. Martino e Solferino 7, Padova. In existence since the 14th century. First Jewish cemetery 1384. First Synagogue built in 1467.

Pres.: Cav. Michelangelo Romanin Jacur.

Home for Children.

Opere Pie Israelitiche Unite (United Jewish religious functions).

Confraternita Israelitica "Sovvegno" (Jewish federation for mutual assistance)

Circolo di Cultura Ebraica "Shemuel David Luzatto."

PARMA

Comunità Israelitica di Parma, Vicolo Cervi 4, Parma.

Pres.: Dr. Giulio Richetti.

PISA (520 Jews inc. Lucca and Vioreggio)

Comunità Israelitica, Via Palestro 8, Pisa.

TORINO (3,000 Jews)

Comunità Israelita, Via Pio V, 12. Already existed in 1600 (former membership 5,000).

Grand Rabbi: Prof. Dr. Dario Disegni.

Pres.: Enrico Malvano.

Scuola Elementare e Media Inferiore (elementary and high school).

Orfanotrofio Educatorio (educational orphanage).

Ospizio Dei Vecchi (home for the aged).

Scuola Materna (maternity school).

Confraternita di Beneficenza (welfare and charity federation).

Centro Giovanile Ebraico (Hebrew Youth Center); Zionist groups.

Circolo di Cultura Ebraica.

Pres.: Dario Disegni.

VENEZIA (1,100 Jews)

Comunità Israelitica, Castello 4765, Venezia. The first Jewish community of Venice was established shortly after 1200 in the "Ghetto of Venice."

Grand Rabbi: Leone Leoni.

Pres.: Cavaliere Vittorio Fano.

Synagogue: Schola Grande Tedesca; Temple Italiano; Schola Canton, Tempio Levantino; Tempio Spagnolo.

Educational and social institutions:

Scuola Elementare Ebraica (Hebrew elementary school).

Asilo Infantile (Home for Children).

Casa di Riposo per Vecchi a S. Nicolo di Lido (Home for the aged "S. Nicolo di Lido")

A.D.E.I. (W.I.Z.O.)

Centro Giovanile Ebraica (Hebrew Youth Center)

Circolo Ebraico "Cuore e Concordia"

Gruppo Sionistico.

VERCELLI

Comunità Israelita, Via Foà, Founded in the 18th century.

Pres.: Ing. Albo Cingoli.

Asilo Infantile "Levi" (Home for Children)

Collegio Foà ("Foa" Institute for Studies)

Compagnia Misericordia (charitable association)

VERONA

Comunità Israelitica, Via Portici 3. Founded about 1600. Active in Jewish affairs since 1200.

Rabbi: Dr. Emanuele Weiss-Levi.

Pia Opera di Misericordia (Religious charitable activity).

W.I.Z.O.

Centro Giovanile Ebraico (Hebrew Youth Center).

(See the separate entry *Trieste,* which has in the meantime been divided between Italy and Yugoslavia.)

PUBLICATIONS:

Weeklies: Israel, Corso Vittorio Emanuele 173.

Monthlies: Bollettino della Comunità Israelitica, Via Guastella 19, Milano.

Hechalutz, Tel Broshim, S. Marco, Cevoli (Pisa).

Rassegna Mensile di Israel. Lungotevere Sanzio, 9, Roma.

Voce della Comunita di Roma, Lungotevere Cenci (Tempio), Roma.

LICHTENSTEIN

JEWISH POPULATION: 30

Hilfsverein der Juden in Lichtenstein, Schaan (Lichtenstein).

Founder and Representative: Kurt Schönlank (Vaduz).

Presidents: Beno Sommer, Max Alexander.

Secretary: Fritz Baum.

The Jewish Aid Society was founded in Lichtenstein in 1941 for the support of the needy. The society's activities started when a considerable number of emigrants were residing in Lichtenstein. Orthodox Jews joined the neighboring Jewish communities for their religious needs, particularly the community of St.-Gall in Switzerland. The Lichtenstein community was reduced after the war by emigration to Israel or to other foreign countries. On the High Holidays, religious services are conducted by the President of the Jewish Aid Society. Once a year the Jewish group is visited by the Rabbi of St. Gall, Dr. Rothschild.

LUXEMBOURG

JEWISH POPULATION: 1,200

The earliest document mentioning Jews in Luxembourg is dated 1276. The cities of Luxembourg and Echternach were among the places where Jews were martyred in 1349. In 1370, all Jews were expelled from the country. In 1443, they were re-admitted. The country's surrender to Spain in 1555 once more deprived the few Jews of the right of residence.

Under French rule (1795), the Jews were granted equal rights. In 1899, the Jewish community was fully recognized by the Government of Luxembourg, and in a short time Jewish communities were also organized in 4 other cities.

In 1935, there were 3,144 Jews in the dutchy due to increased immigration from Nazi-Germany. They participated in industry and trade. In 1940, the German invasion occurred, and the German racial laws were imposed on the country. All Jews were expelled. Hundreds of them were shipped in freight cars to the Portuguese border; many were deported to Poland. 250 Jews, allowed to stay in the country, were later killed.

After World War II, some former Jewish residents returned to Luxembourg and, with a number of new refugee immigrants, reestablished the Jewish community there.

Consistoire Israelite de Luxembourg (Jewish community)
11, rue de la Porte-Neuve, Luxembourg.
The Jewish community of Luxembourg in the capital, which is recognized as a legal body, is administered by the Consistory elected by the entire membership. There are smaller Jewish communities also in Esch, Ettelbruck, Mondorf-les-Bains, and other places which have their own local administrations. No central body exists so far; only the Grand Rabbi has country-wide competence. The communal administrations provide for religious instruction. The Grand Rabbinate publishes a monthly bulletin.

Grand Rabbi: Dr. C. Lehrmann (10, rue Marie Adelaide).
Pres.: Edmond Marx (14, rue de Goethe).
Affiliated with the community: *Esra-Entraide Israelite*—Jewish welfare and mutual aid association. Pres.: Dr. Henri Cerf.
Association Luxembourgeoise pour la Reconstruction Religieuse du Judaisme, 44, Av. Guillaume, Luxembourg. In close cooperation with the Consistoire de Luxembourg. Its aim is the advancement of Orthodox Judaism.
Hon.Pres.: Grand Rabbi Dr. Ch. Lehrmann.
Pres.: Dory Oppenheim.
Thora-Avoda, Poalei Mizrachi group
Gemiluth Chassadim, Charitable association.
Les Amis d'Israel (Friends of Israel), 13, d'Armes, Luxembourg
Pres.: Emile Lemmer.
Union des Dames, 55, Av. de la Liberté, Luxembourg. Welfare organization.
Pres.: Mrs. Rose Salomon.
Union des Jeunes Gens Israélites, 17, rue Val-Saint-Croix, Luxembourg. Union of the Jewish youth.
Pres.: Julien Meyer.
W.I.Z.O., 66 Bld. de Stalingrad, Luxembourg.
Pres.: Mrs. Rose Salomon.
B'nai Brith, Luxembourg.
Pres.: Dory Oppenheim.

ESCH-SAR-ALZETTE
Communauté Israélite, pres.: René Hermann.

ETTELBRUCK
Communaute Israelite, Pres.: Jacques Kann.

MALTA

JEWISH POPULATION: 42

There have been Jews in Malta since the period of the Romans, although their number has never been considerable. A community originating in North Africa arose at the end of the eighteenth century.

Jewish Community of Malta.
Pres.: Fortunato Habib.
Sec.: George D. Tayar, 91a Bishop St., Valletta. The Community is recognized by the goverment.
Synagogue, 9 Spur St., Valletta.
Minister: Rabbi N. Ohayon.

NETHERLANDS

JEWISH POPULATION: 25,000

There were Jewish settlements in the Netherlands by the 13th century. Conditions were tolerable until the Black Death in 1349, when Jews were severely persecuted and martyred.

Following the establishment of the Inquisition in Spain and Portugal, a steady stream of Marrano immigrants began coming to the Netherlands. However, Charles V, in 1550, issued an edict which expelled all Marranos from the Netherlands. When the Spaniards were driven from the country at the end of the 16th century, Portuguese Marranos were permitted to emigrate to the Netherlands and carry on trade. All medieval regulations degrading to the Jews were lifted by the states-general in 1619, and in 1657, Jews were declared subjects of the state.

The second group of Dutch Jews was made up of migrants from Germany who began coming to the Netherlands throughout the 17th century. A third group was composed of Polish refugees who also came in the 17th century. In some places, however, the Jews were not allowed to practice their religion or carry on trade.

In 1795, when the Netherlands was under the rule of the French Republic, the Jews were granted complete civil equality. In 1815, the kingdom of the Netherlands again became an independent state under the rule of the House of Orange, and the position of the Jews remained very favorable up to the year 1940. Jews distinguished themselves in politics, science, art, literature, and the economic life.

In the course of the 19th century, the number of Ashkenazic Jews increased considerably while that of the Sephardic Jews declined. The Jews usually settled in the large cities. The kings of Holland more than once participated directly in the organization of Jewish communal affairs and gave their attention to building up the

Jewish school system. In 1870, a Central Commission was established which, until 1940, administered all the Jewish communities in the country, with the exception of the two Sephardic communities in Amsterdam and The Hague. The Orthodox group was officially in the majority and preponderant.

After Hitler came to power in 1933, Holland was very active in aiding German Jewish refugees. The Christian population gave many signs of its sympathy for the persecuted Jews, and there was very little anti-Semitism. But, when the Nazis occupied the country in 1940, persecution of the Jews began. Dutch Jewry, which had numbered about 150,000 in 1939, has been reduced to 25,000, of whom about 6,000 are returnees. Jewish education suffers from a serious shortage of teachers. Only Amsterdam has regular daily Jewish instruction. In other places, Jewish instruction is provided by visiting teachers. The Jewish High School in Amsterdam, which is subsidized and supervised by the state, gave, in 1952, final examinations to 171 students. The Hebrew Seminary, sponsored by the Jewish Agency, was opened in the same year and provides advanced courses in Hebrew subjects. The ORT opened vocational courses in Amsterdam, Rotterdam, Amersfoort, and Apeldoorn for about 900 pupils.

Permanente Commissie tot de Algemeene Zaken van het Nederlandsch-Israelietische Kerkgenootschap, Plantage Parklaan 9, Amsterdam C. Central Board of the Jewish Communities of the Netherlands, comprising Ashkenazic, Sephardic, and Liberal organizations.

Pres.: Dr. I. Dasberg.
Sec.: B. W. de Jongh.

Nederlandsche Zionistenbond, Joh. Vermeerstraat 22, Amsterdam Z. Central Zionist organization, composed of all Zionist parties. Branches in almost all communities.
Pres.: Prof. Dr. S. Kleerekoper.

Nederlandse Advies-Commissie voor het Joodse Wereldcongres, Joh. Vermeerstraat 22, Amsterdam Z. Committee of the World Jewish Congress. Members: Mrs. M.B. Nordheim van Amerongen, S. Eisenmann, Gerard Polak, Prof. Dr. S. Kleerekoper, Dr. A. Rodrigues Pereira.

Contact Commissie der Joodse Coordinatie Commissies in Nederland, Joh. Vermeerstraat 18, Amsterdam Z. Contact Commission for the Jewish Coordinating Commissions in the Netherlands. Protects Jewish interests; welfare activities.

HIAS, Rokin 69, Amsterdam.

Nederlandse Mizrachie, Kromme Mijdrechstraat 31, Amsterdam.
Sec.: Mrs. P.L. v. Rijk-Keller.

Stichting Joods Maatschappelijk Werk "J.M.W." Joh. Vermeerstraat 18, Amsterdam. Central Jewish organization for social work in the country.
Pres.: M. Acohen.
Sec.: N. Keizer.

Verbond van Joodse Instellingen voor Kinderbeschirming in Nederland, Joh. Vermeerstraat 24, Amsterdam Z. Union of Jewish institutions for the protection of children. Maintains orphanages and homes for Youth Aliyah in Amsterdam, Apeldoorn, Bilthoven, Bussum, Deventer, Dieren, Gouda, The Hague, Hilversum, Laren, Zantpoort.

AMSTERDAM (13,000 Jews)

Nederlands Israelietische Hoofdsynagoge Amsterdam, Plantage Parklaan 9. Jewish community, founded about 1635. Consists of a Central Consistory—Rabbinic Council, Rabbinate, Section for Instruction, Social Section for Instruction, Social Section, Section for Cultural Activity, Youth Section.
Pres. of Central Consistory: E. Spier.

Sec.: B.W. de Jongh.

Grand Rabbi: Dr. Aaron Schuster.

Synagogues: Jacob Obrechtpleinhoek Heinzestraat; Lekstraat 61—Gerard Doustraat 238—Polderweg 2; Swammerdamstraat 71, Nw. Kerkstraat 149.

Liberal Joodse Gemeente, Jekerstraat 41. Jewish liberal community.

Rabbi: I. Hammelburg.

Portugeesch-Israelietische Gemeente te Amsterdam, Rapenburgerstraat 197. Amsterdam C. Jewish Sephardic (Portuguese) community.

Grand Rabbi: Rodrigues Pereira.

Pres.: P.D.M. Lopes-Cardozo.

American Joint Distribution Committee, Joh. Vermeerstraat 24, Amsterdam Z.

Agoedas Jisroeil, v. Miereveldstraat 13.

Sec.: I. Zadoks.

Beth Am, Joh. Vermeerstraat 26. Jewish cultural center.

Bergstichting, Le-Ezrath Hajeled, S.A. Rudelsheimstichting, Joh. Vermeerstraat 24. For child welfare.

Centraale Financierings Actie voor Sociaal Werk in Nederland, Joh. Vermeerstraat 18, Amsterdam Z. Central organization financing social, cultural, and social work in the Netherlands.

Centraale Vereniging voor de Joodse Geestelijke Volksgezonheid, Joh. Vermeerstraat 24, Amsterdam A. Central association for Jewish mental health.

Commissie "Het Joodse Boek," Weesperplein 1, Amsterdam C. Dissemination of Jewish literature and culture.

Histadroeth Hachaloetsiem Beholand, Hachsjarah en Alijah, Joh. Vermeerstraat 22, Amsterdam Z. Youth Aliyah.

Igud Cheruth-Hazohar, Pieter van der Doesstraat 88.

Joodse Jeugdfederatie, Joh. Vermeerstraat 28. Federation of Jewish youth.

Maccabi Sportvereniging, Gaapetraat 7, Amsterdam Z.

Nederlandse Instelling van Sociale Arbeid, Diamantbeurs, Kamer 105. Weesperplein 4. Dutch institution for social work.

O.R.T. Amstel 240.

Pekidim en Amarcalim voor de Israelietisch Gemeensen in het Heilige Land, Diezestraat 31, Amsterdam Z. Collecting funds for the Orthodoxy in Eretz Israel.

Pres.: S. Eisenmann.

Socialistisch-Zionistisch Verbond "Poale Zion," Tolstraat 76, Amsterdam Z.

Sec.: H. Voz.

Stichting "Het Joodsch Bijzonder Onderwijs," Tintorsttostraat 21/II. Jewish School. Consists of Kindergarten at 103 Van Ostadestraat, primary school, Van Ostadestraat 103, and secondary school at Stadstimmertuin 2. Chairman: N. Keizer.

Verbond van Midden Enoost Europese Jooden in Nederland, Weesperplein 1. Union of Mid and East European Jews.

Vrouwengroep van de Nederlandsch Zionistenbond (WIZO) Parnassusweg 10-11 Amsterdam Z.

THE HAGUE (1,700 Jews)

Israelietishe Gemeente, W. Molstraat 13.

Synagogue: Wagenstraat 103.

Nederlandse Zionistenbond, Broekslootkade 50.

Agoedas Jisroel, P. Bothstraat 57.

Mizrachie, Wagenstraat 105.

Sec.: A. Manuskowsky.

Verbond van Liberad Religieuze Jooden in Nederland. Jozef Israelslaan 55. Union of Liberal Jews in the Netherlands. Dutch Section of the World Union for Progressive Judaism.

ROTTERDAM (780 Jews)

Nederlands Israelietische Gemeente Rotterdam (Jewish community), Mathenesserian 223.

Synagogue: Joost van Geelstraat 66.

Nederlandse Zionistenbond, Grooswijkse Singel 32. Local Zionist Organization.

Joodse Jeugdefederatie Hechaloetz Hatsair, Heemraadssingel 28a. Federation of Hechalutz Hatzair.

HIAS, Schieweg 56 d.

ORT, Schieweg 56 d. Sec.: A.J.U. Cohen.

Bnei Akiba, Westersingel 20.

Sec.: M. Rynderman, Poel Mizrachi Youth.

Young Israel, Bergweg 338.

ARNHEM (400 Jews)

Israelietische Gemeente, Kippenmarkt 1.

GRONNINGEN (400 Jews)

Israelietische Gemeente, Niewivestad 28.

UTRECHT (1,400 Jews)

Israelietische Gemeente, Springweg 164.
Smaller Jewish communities or groups exist in
the following places:

Aalten, Almelo, Amersfoort, Apeldoorn, Beek,
Beilen, Beverwijk, Bilthoven, Borculo, Borne,
Breda, Bussum, Coevorden, Delft, Deventer,
Dieren, Dordrecht, Eibergen, Eindhoven,
Emmen, Enkhuizen, Enschede, Gouda, Haar-
lem, Hattem, Heerlen, Den Helder, Hengelo,
S'Hertogenbosch, Hilversum, Hoogeveen,
Laren, Leeuwarden, Leiden, Maastricht,
Meppel, Middelburg, Monnikendam, Nijkerk,
Nijmegen, Oldenzaal, Oss, Sneek, Stadska-
naal, Steenwijk, Tilburg, Veenendaal, Vught,
Winschoten, Winterswijk, Zanspoort, Zaan-
dam, Zutphen, Zwolle.

PERIODICALS:

De Joodse Wachter. Fortnightly Johannes Ver-
meerstr. 22, Amsterdam, Z.
Nieuw Israelietisch Weekblad. Weekly. Utrecht-
sestraat 44, Amsterdam, C.
Niw Hanoar. Monthly. Utrechtsestraat 44
Amsterdam C.

NORTHERN IRELAND

JEWISH POPULATION: 1,800

There was a Jewish community in Belfast about the year 1771, but the present
community was founded in 1870 by Jews
from Germany. In 1889, the immigration
of Jews from Eastern Europe began. In
1904, the leadng member of the Belfast
community, Sir Otto Jaffe, who had previously been High Sheriff, was elected
Lord Mayor of the city. The present Recorder (Chief Judicial Magistrate) is
Judge B. J. Fox. The great majority of
Jews live in Belfast, only a small number
living in towns and villages scattered
throughout the country.

BELFAST (1,600 Jews)

Jewish Congregation and Synagogue, Annesley
St., Carlisle Circus. Office: "Northleigh,"
Somerton Rd. Orthodox. Founded 1872;
constructed 1904.
Pres.: B. H. Hurwitz.

Sec.: M. W. Frank.
Rabbi: A. Carlebach.
World Jewish Congress, Chairman: M. Berwitz,
Sec.: Dr. J. Lewis, 202 West Circular Rd.
Belfast Jewish Charitable Trust Fund,
Pres.: ᴾ. H. Hurwitz.
Ladies' Benevolent Society, Founded 1896.
Pres.: Mrs. A. Diamond.
Chevra Gemara, Est. 1888.
Pres.: Rabbi, A. Carlebach.
University Jewish Students' Union,
Pres.: D. Saltoun.
Sec.: E. Freeman, Students' Union, Queen's
University.
Beth Hasepher, Jewish School.
Pres.: C. Rose.
Sec.: L. A. Kaitcer.
Jewish Institute, Ashfield Gardens.
Chairman: J. Hurwitz.
Sec.: M. Williams.
Friends of the Hebrew University,
Chairman: Judge B. J. Fox.
Sec.: Leslie Morris, 13 Lombard St.
Mizrachi Society, Chairman: N. Nemtzow.
Sec.: David Cohen, 16 Marmont Gardens.

NORWAY

(JEWISH POPULATION: 1,000)

In 1814, all Jews were expelled from the country, and only after long and bitter struggles was this law rescinded (1851). In 1875, there were about 30 Jews in Norway. In 1939, two congregations, the first organized in 1892, the second in 1917, were merged.

From 1914 on, Oslo had a number of charitable institutions. The younger generation belonged to the Jewish Youth Society, which was formed in 1909. From 1910 on, Oslo also had a Zionist organization. In Trondheim, besides its congregation formed in 1905 with a synagogue built in 1925, there were a youth society, a branch of the Zionist Organization, and a women's organization.

Anti-Semitic feeling in Norway was practically non-existent. However, in the late 1920's, the slaughtering of cattle according to Jewish ritual became the object of parliamentary attack on the part of some farm groups, and to a lesser extent also of the labor group, although the attitude of the majority of government officials has always been friendly to the Jews.

Up to the Nazi occupation of the country in 1940, most Jews in Norway were merchants. In industry, chiefly in the shoe and tobacco branches, there are a number of prominent Jewish firms. Large Jewish concerns are engaged in manufacturing.

The Norwegian population never failed to show its sympathy for the Jews. 750 Jews were deported from Norway to Germany and exterminated by the Nazis. 600 foreign Jews were admitted after World War II. Besides the two Jewish communities in Oslo and Trondheim, there are smaller groups of 6 to 8 Jews scattered throughout the country who sometimes travel 12 to 14 hours to Oslo or Trondheim in order to attend religious services on the High Holidays.

OSLO (700 Jews)

Det Mosaiska Trossamfund Oslo (Jewish Community), Calmeyergatan 15.
Founded 1892.
Synagogue inaugurated May 21, 1920. 620 members.
Pres.: Harry Koritzinski.
Vice-Pres.: Aksel Scheer.
Sec.: Willy Rodner.
Rabbi: Zalman Aronzon.

American Joint Distribution Committee, Wm. Thranegt. 6 B.
Dir.: Marcus Levin.

B'nai B'rith, Calmeyergt. 15.
Pres.: Rabbi Zalman Aronzon.
Vice-Pres.: Mendel Bernstein.

Jodisk Barne Og Gamelehjem, Holbergegt. 21 (Jewish home for children and the aged).
Pres.: Harry M. Koritzinski.

Jodisk Ungdomsforening, Sorkedalsveien 5, (Jewish youth organization).
Founded 1909.
Pres.: Ch. Philipsohn.
Sec.: Ruth Rodner.

Mosaisk Kvinneforening Og Wizo, Lovenskioldsgate 3. Jewish women's association combined with the local section of Wizo.
Pres.: Mrs. Regi Milner.
Vice-Pres.: Mrs. Rosa Levin.
Sec.: Bl. Steinmann.

Norsk Zionistenforening, Calmeyergt. 15. Zionist Organization.
Sec.: I. Brande.
Religious School, Stasjonsvei 47. B.
Pres.: Oscar Mendelsohn.
Enrollment 23 pupils up to 13 years of age.
World Jewish Congress, Tollbugt. 4 v. 518.
Pres.: Rabbi Zalman Aronzon.
Vice-Pres.: Alex Koritz.
Skandinavisk Jodisk Ungdomsforbund (Scandinavian Jewish Youth Association), c/o Kai Feinberg, P.O.Box 740, Oslo.
Pres.: Leon Bodd.
Sec.: Kai Feinberg.
2,000 members in Norway, Sweden, Denmark, and Finland.

PUBLICATIONS:

S.J.U.F. Bladet, Monthly. Publisher: Skandinevisk Jodisk Ungdomsforb. Norwegian-Swedish Non-political. Hovedledelsen, P.O. B. 740, Oslo.

TRONDHEIM (150 Jews)

Dee Mosaiske Trossamfund (Jewish Community), Trondheim, 130 members.
The world's most northern Jewish congregation.
Pres.: Moses Cohn.
The newly erected structure for the Jewish Community Center contains the synagogue, Jewish school, and the office of the congregation.
Jewish school, Enrollment, 35 pupils.
Jodisk Ungdomsforening, Pres.: Abrahamsen.
Sec.: J. Kommissar.
Mosaisk Kvinneforening and Wizo, Munkegat. 31. Pres.: Evy Kahn. Sec.: Rita Paltiel.

POLAND

JEWISH POPULATION: 35,000

As early as the 9th century, Jewish merchants from Germany journeyed to the still pagan region of today's Poland, and some settled there. At the close of the 11th century, Jews immigrated to Poland from Bohemia and the Rhine provinces to escape the persecutions of the Crusaders. In the 13th and 14th centuries there already existed organized Jewish communities in Plock (1237), Kalisz (1287), Krakow (1304), Poznan (1330), Lwow (1356 and others.

The Polish rulers welcomed the Jewish immigrants because of what they might contribute to the economy of the country and granted them charters with the rights to reside in Poland and earn a living as merchants and artisans. Such charters, which also protected Jewish life and property as well as religious freedom, were issued by Miczyslaw III (1173), Boleslaw the Pious (1264), Casimir the Great (1364), and some later rulers. The church, however, pursued a policy of segregation and discrimination against the Jews. The Jews were frequently victims of mob violence incited by religious fanaticism and by German immigrant traders and artisans who regarded the Jews as their competitors.

In the 17th century, the Jewish population reached the number of 350,000, constituting 10% of Poland's total inhabitants at this time. The Jewish communities enjoyed a great measure of internal autonomy in religious and social matters. The central representative, legislative, and administrative body of Polish Jewry was the "Council of the Four Lands" called Vaad Arba Aratzoth because the annual conferences of the Council were attended by delegates from four Polish provinces.

In the 16th and 17th centuries, Poland became the most important center of Jewish learning in the Diaspora. Famous rabbis and scholars such as Moses Iserles (known by his initials, Rema; 1520-1572), Solomon Luria (Marshal, 1510-73), Joel Sirkis (d. 1640), David Halevi (1586-1667), Sabbatai Cohen-Shach (1621-62), and many others were recognized by all of world Jewry as its spiritual leaders and authorities.

During the Cossack Wars (1648), Cossack hordes lead by Bogdan Chmielnicki invaded Poland and extermined all Jews they met on the way. In Galicia, Ukraine, Volhynia, and Podolia only a tenth of the Jewish population survived. More than 700 communities were ruthlessly destroyed. Soon, however, the great movement of Hassidism founded by Rabbi Israel Baal-Shem-Tov, which contributed considerably toward the moral and spiritual rehabilitation of the shaken Jewish community, emerged. A revival in Jewish learning initiated by the great Rabbi Eliahu, called the Gaon of Vilna, and his disciples also occurred.

During World War I, the 2,000,000 Jews in Poland suffered severely from the Russian authorities. In the period of restored Polish sovereignty (1918-39), cruel persecutions of Jews did not cease. The Minority Treaty concluded between Poland and the victorious Allied Powers in 1919 guaranteeing equal rights and a religious cultural autonomy for Jews was not honored by the Poles. The Jews formed their own political parties and succeeded in electing Jewish Deputies to the Polish Parliament. The Jewish Parliamentary representation vigorously defended the threatened civil and collective rights of the Jewish population but were unable to stem the increasing wave of racial hatred and persecutions.

Despite anti-Jewish policies and oppression, Polish Jewry constituted the most creative Jewish community of the Diaspora. Political and cultural activities were carried on with admirable intensity. Zionist, religious, and socialist parties were very active. The Chalutz movement training pioneers for Palestine had its backbone in Polish Jewry. They maintained their own large Jewish school network in Hebrew and Yiddish. There were several literary and artistic associations. Hundreds of books were published in Hebrew and Yiddish annually. Many Jewish dailies and periodicals appeared in Hebrew, Yiddish, and Polish. There was an intense religious life comprising Yeshivoth, Hassidic movements, and renowned Talmudical scholars. Moreover, Jews made important contributions to Polish culture in literature, arts, and science.

Almost all of Polish Jewry, numbering over 3,000,000 was exterminated by the Nazi hordes during the Second World War. In the ghettos, concentration camps, and crematoriums in Poland 3,000,000 Jews of other countries who were deported to Poland were annihilated. The heroic revolts of the Jewish youth in the ghettos of Warsaw, Bialistok, and other cities and in the underground partisan resistance forces was the last chapter of this great martyred Jewry.

Approximately 35,000 Jews live in post-war Poland. They are partly those who succeeded in surviving in Poland and partly repatriated refugees from Russia. Of the 200,000 Jewish refugees who returned from Russia to Poland after the Second World War, over 115,000 went to Israel between 1946–1957. The Polish government halted emigration to Israel from 1952 to 1957. Considerable numbers began reaching Israel in the latter year.

Most Polish Jews are now manual workers mainly in the metallurgy and leather industries and in coal mines.

In the field of *Culture and Education* we quote the following data from the information bulletin issued by the Polish Embassy in Washington on April 1954. There are 30 cultural clubs in various places. Each of these clubs have a Yiddish library. In Wroclaw a permanent Yiddish theatre exists. The Jewish publishing house in Warsaw puts out 30 Yiddish books annually. All these activities are subsidized by the government.

The following Jewish State Schools conducted in Yiddish are located in Lower Silesia: Wroclaw, Dzierzoniow, Walbrzych Legnica, Klodzko, Ziembice, Zomkowice, Lodz and Szczecin. The schools in Wroclaw, Legnica, Lodz and Szezecin also have high-school classes.

The statistical figures of Poland's Jewish population have changed considerably during 1957, following the renewed emigration of the Jews to Israel. The total number of the Jews in Poland is, therefore, currently estimated not to exceed 35,000. Accordingly, the Jewish population of the local communities has also been reduced.

WARSAW (5,000 Jews)

Social and Cultural Association of Polish Jews, Ulica Nowagrodzka 5, Warsaw. The central secular organization of Polish Jewry. According to an official the Association has 10,000 members in 35 branches in various cities.
Chairman: Hersch Smolar.
Vice-Chairmen: Samuel Hurwitz and Jacob Wasserzturm.
Sec.: Dr. David Spard.
Union of Congregations of the Jewish Faith in Poland, Warsaw, Ulica Krajowej Rady Narodowej.
Chairman: Dr. Alexander Libo.
Vice-Chairman: Isaac Frankel.

According to a government report, there are 21 Jewish communities affiliated with the Union throughout the country. The aged Rabbi of Warsaw, Ber Perkowicz, 80, is also active as Chief Rabbi of Poland. The Jewish religious congregations receive subsidies from the government and provides facilities for religious observances such as synagogues, religious education, and kosher food.
Local Jewish Religious Congregations,
Pres.: Mordechai Lichtenstein.
Synagogue: Ulica Krajowej Rady Narodowej 6.
There exists only one synagogue in Warsaw. Services are held on Saturdays, 20–30 congregants attending, according to a report of the New York Times, September 1955. On Rosh-Hashana about 100 were assembled in the Synagogue. Only on Yom Kippur was the synagogue filled to overflowing.
Jewish Historical Institute,
Director: Berl Mark. Publishes the Yiddish Quarterly "Bleter Far Geshichte" and the Polish "Biuletyn."
Jewish Writers' Club, Section of the Union of Polish Writers.

Chairman: Ber Mark.
Vice-Chairman: Binem Heller.
Yiddish Buch, Publishing House of Yiddish Books. Editor: Dr. David Sfard.

LODZ (5,000 Jews)
Jewish Religious Congregation,
Rabbi: Moshe Weinberg.
Jewish Library, 10,000 Volumes.
Jewish School, 400 Pupils.

WROCLAW (15,000 Jews)
Jewish Religious Congregation,
Rabbi, Aaron Muszel.
Yiddish Theatre.
Directress: Mrs. Ida Kaminska.

KRAKOW (5,000 Jews)
Jewish Religious Congregation,
Synagogue. The oldest synagogue in Poland, recently restored.
Rabbi: Moshe Lessman.
Jewish School.

SZCZECIN (5,000 Jews)
Jewish Religious Congregation,
Synagogue. *Jewish School*.

WALBRZYCH (3,000 Jews)
Jewish Religious Congregation.
Synagogue. *Jewish School*.

PUBLICATIONS:
Folksztyme. 4 times a week. Yiddish.
Editor: Hersz Smolar. Nowogrodzka 5, Warsaw.
Idisze Szriften. Monthly. Yiddish.
Editor: Binem Heller. Nowogrodzka 5, Warsaw.
Bleter Far Geszichte, Quarterly. Yiddish.
Published by the Jewish Historical Institute, Ul. Gen. Swierczewskiego 79, Warsaw.
Biuletyn Zydowskiego Instytutu Historycznego.
Quarterly. Polish. Published by the Jewish Historical Institute, Ul. Gen. Swierczewskiego 79, Warsaw.

PORTUGAL
JEWISH POPULATION: 2,000

Portugal was colonized by Jews before it became an independent state under that name early in the 12th century. While its Jews could not match the number and importance of the Jews of Spain, their economic and social positions were almost equal. They were organized under a stricter state supervision in Portugal than was customary in the Middle Ages. At the head of the communities, from the end of the 13th century on, stood the Chief Rabbi as supreme judge to the government; he bore the coat of arms of Portugal and made laws in the name of the king.

However, the succeeding centuries are filled with opposition on the part of the church and the populace toward the support given the Jews by the crown.

The new king, João I (1385-1433) took the Jews energetically under his protection. He prevented the anti-Jewish movement then raging in Spain from overflowing to Portugal and encouraged Jews who had fled from Spain. Jews who were baptized during the persecutions were allowed to return to their original faith in Portugal.

King João II (1481-95) opened his country to the Marranos who fled from the Spanish Inquisition. His successor, Manuel (1495-1521), followed a wavering policy toward the Jews and, under the influence of Queen Isabella of Castille, issued a decree (December 4, 1496) which ordered all Jews to be expelled from the country by the end of October, 1497. He had the Jewish children taken away and forcibly converted over the opposition of his counselors. Approximately 20,000 adults who wished to emigrate were summoned by him to Lisbon and declared slaves. He sent priests to convert them. Many preferred martyrdom, but there was nothing left for the great mass than surrender in the hope of future escape. Thus a group of New Christians was formed. In 1506, the religious hatred of the nation agitated by the Dominicans reached its climax in a massacre of New Christians in which about 2,000 were killed. The king, Manuel, then took severe measures and renewed the New Christians' privileges. However, in the last years of his reign, he was concerned with the thought of enforcing the Inquisition. This plan materialized in 1531 under João III, his successor. From the beginning of the 19th century on, there again existed a small Jewish community in Lisbon. Besides this, there remained in various places communities of Marranos who observed many Jewish rites and whose prayers denoted their unfailing Jewish faith.

Although the Marranos attained religious freedom through the revolution of 1910, they did not avail themselves of this opportunity openly to avow their affiliation with Judaism. Through the endeavors of Arthur Carlos de Barros Basto, himself a descendant of a Portuguese Marrano family, Marranos were encouraged to return to Judaism. Jewish communities composed of Marranos were established in Lisbon, Oporto, Coimbra, Bragança and Belmonte. A monthly, *Ha-Lapid* (The Torch), founded by Barros Basto in 1927, offers material for Jewish education.

After the advent of the Nazi regime (1933), thousands of Jews from Germany and Austria, and later from other Nazi-occupied countries, moved to Portugal. Almost all of them later left Portugal and the number of Jews has thus been considerably reduced.

LISBON (Jewish population: 800)

The expulsion of Jews from Portugal took place in 1497, but by 1852, 2,500 Jews were living there again. Their number, however, decreased considerably in the following years. Jewish religious and welfare activities can be traced from 1864. In 1940, the Jewish population was estimated at over 2,000, but, it has decreased since then because of emigration.

Communidade Israelita de Lisboa, Rua Alexandre Herculano 59. Founded in 1912, this, the central body of the Jews in Portugal, is recognized by the government. It concerns itself with Jewish education and religious and charitable activities. The Board is elected every three years.

Pres.: Prof. Dr. Moses B. Amzalak.

Sec.: Dr. Semtob D. Sequerra.

Synagogue: 59 rua Alexandre Herculano.

Jewish Center of Portugal (for Zionist activities), Rua Rosa Aranjo 10.

Pres: David Halpern.

Keren Kayemeth Leisrael (section of Jewish National Fund), Av. Aliante Reis Lei.

Representative: M. Ruten.

OPORTO

Communidade Israelita de Oporto, Rua Guerra Junqueiro 340.

Synagogue, same address as above.

Besides the above-mentioned 850 Jews in Portugal, a group of about 250 Marranos now openly professing Judaism live in Oporto.

RUMANIA

JEWISH POPULATION: 190,000

From the second half of the 17th century on, lawfully constituted Jewish communities recognized by the princes came into being in Rumania. There were important Jewish communities in 1740 at Galati, Bacau, Berlad and Roman. Due to oppression, the Rumanian peasants fled the country in large numbers so that towards the middle of the 18th century, the two Rumanian principalities of Moldavia and Wallachia were thinly populated. Consequently, the boyars invited Jews to settle in the country and secured for them certain privileges in the form of decrees from the princes. They came in large numbers and founded 63 towns and villages in Moldavia. This immigration movement slackened off about 1850 and stopped in 1860.

The Jews of Rumania played an active role in transforming the old feudal system into a modern economy. They also participated in developing the cultural and intellectual standards of Rumania. Among the eminent Rumanian Jewish poets were A. Steuerman-Rodion, B. Nemtzeanu, A. Toma and Adrian Verea; among the novelists, I. Ludo, I. Peltz and M. Sebastian; among the scholars, Iuliu Barasch, Moses Gaster, Lazar Saineanu, Henry Tiktin, and Candrea.

The Jews suffered from anti-semitism in varying degrees of violence and were always the scapegoats in the struggle between the ruling classes and the unhappy peasants. Jews began to be considered foreigners at the time of the Russian occupation of the principalities (1828–1834). Numerous anti-Jewish laws and regulations were issued between 1880 and 1916. This situation resulted in extensive emigration; more than 70,000 Jews left the country between 1900 and 1906.

The years 1918 to 1937 were known as the period of emancipation during which time the Jews were granted equal rights. During this period, according to official statistics, there were between 760,000 and 850,000 Jews in the the country. The anti-Semitic movement, however, began anew after the first World War and increased in 1922 and 1923. Jews were deprived of their citizenship in 1938. Finally, under the Iron Guard regime of General Ion Antonescu, an era of horrors began for the Jews which far surpassed all that had gone before.

By the time Rumania was liberated from the Nazis, 385,000 Jews had been exterminated. The Nazi regime in Hungary was responsible for the annihilation of 115,000 Jews in North Transylvania, the territory which Hitler awarded to her in 1940. Nazi Rumania accounted for 270,000 Jews deported to Transnistria or murdered during the massacres of 1941. The surviving 376,000 Jews of the country were pauperized through the extortion and expropriation measures of the Antonescu regime which inflicted on them losses amounting to one billion dollars.

After the return of the remnants of the

deportees from Auschwitz and Transnitria and the immigration of 50,000 Jews from the country's Soviet-annexed territories into Rumania, the number of Jews grew to nearly 400,000.

After the liberation, the Jews revived their communal life. The Uniunea Evreilor Romani, their central body, was again headed by its leader, Dr. William Filderman. The Jewish Party as well as the Zionist organizations resumed their work. A network of Jewish and Hebrew schools was established. Sixteen Jewish weeklies and periodicals appeared in the country.

The situation changed radically after the Communists took over the government in 1946. The Jewish Party was liquidated. The Zionist organizations, with 108,000 members, were also forced into "self-liquidation." The Jewish Democratic Committee was transformed into a purely Communistic organization, becoming the sole representative of Rumanian Jewry. The nationalization of trade and industry caused the complete pauperization of the Jews. It is estimated that 37,000 of them left the country in 1946–7. The Jewish Democratic Committee launched a campaign of unparalleled vehemence against the Zionists.

In the period of 1950–1954, many Jewish and Zionist leaders, including Dr. A. Beneviste, A. L. Zissu, Dr. Lowenstein, Dr. Rohlich and Dr. L. Haber were arrested and sentenced, some to life imprisonment. Most of them were released in 1955 and reached Israel a year later. In the earlier period, until 1952, emigration to Israel had been permitted by the Rumanian Government. All in all, 247,000 Rumanian Jews migrated legally or otherwise to Israel from 1948.

In 1948, Church and State were separated, and in the following year, Jewish congregations of all leanings (Orthodox and Reform) were merged into one unified organization. The congregations of the country formed a National Federation headed by the Supreme Council of Rabbis. The shortage of spiritual leaders is not alleviated by a rabbinical college, established by M. Rosen the "Chief Rabbi," since it fails to recruit students in the anti-religious atmosphere prevalent in the country.

In Bucharest, there still exist the Great Synagogue (The Carol Schul) and three other synagogues, all full during the holidays. The chief rabbi of the Bucharest community is Moshe Rosen. There are now 32 rabbis in the entire country, whereas there were 92 at the end of the war. Most of the synagogues in Transylvania have been closed for the lack of congregations. In 1948, 69 Yiddish elementary schools and 23 high schools were closed. All Jewish hospitals and homes for the aged were nationalized. In 1953, only 3 Jewish elementary schools, a lyceum, and 5 kindergartens remained.

In 1952, many thousands of Jews were deported from the cities to remote rural districts or labor camps. The majority of Rumanian Jews are anxious to emigrate to Israel, but since 1952, the Government has stopped the issuance of emigration permits. At the end of 1953, only 250,000 Jews remained in Rumania.

There is a tendency to purge the Jews from government offices. In 1952 and

1953, a number of Jewish officers were ousted from the army, and in oil companies, Jewish engineers were replaced by non-Jews.

On January 27th, there was a pogrom at the University of Jassy which resulted in injuries to over 60 Jewish students. Anti-Zionist actions were conducted by the Jewish Democratic Committees and the cultural Ikuf organization. The Democratic Jewish Committee was dissolved in 1953.

According to a report released in 1954 by the Rumanian Legation in Paris, 126 Jewish communities exist in Rumania. There are 50 synagogues in Bucharest, 75 in Jassy and 45 in Botosani, ritual slaughter-houses in all Jewish communities, and 32 Talmud Torahs. A number of synagogues have been rebuilt with grants from the State.

Federation of Rumanian Jewish Communities, Bucharest.
Central Religious Body.
Pres.: Dr. M. Popper.
Sec.: H. Leibovici.
Supreme Rabbinical Council, Bucharest.
Consists of 12 members appointed by the Ministry of Religion upon the recommendation of the Federation.
Pres.: Chief Rabbi, Moses Rosen.

BUCHAREST (43,492 Jews)
Dr. Singer Library.
Dr. Nimirover Archive for History.
YKUF (Yidisher Kulturfarband). Also in other cities.
Yiddish Theatre. Also in Jassy.
Rabbis: Chief Rabbi Moses Rosen, Dr. Abraham Beck, Leib Halper, Marcus Franke¹, David Landman, Jacob Almuli, Nathan Strulovitz, Dr. Chaim Alpern, Alexander L. Rubin.

Larger Jewish Communities Outside Bucharest:

ARAD (13,200 Jews)
Jewish Community.
Rabbis: Dr. Miklós J. Schoenfeld, Zimon Z. Miller.

BOTOSANI (19,500 Jews)
Jewish Community.
Rabbi: Jacob Schmukler.

GALATI (7,185 Jews)
Jewish Community.
Rabbi: Jacob Margulies.

DOROHOI (7,600 Jews)
Jewish Community.
Rabbi: David Schechter.

IASI (16,677 Jews)
Jewish Community.
There is a permanent Yiddish State Theatre.
Rabbis: Israel Gutman, Menachem Gutman.

PIATRA-NEAMT (8,000 Jews)
Jewish Community.

ROMAN (7,900 Jews)
Jewish Community.

SUCEAVA (18,865 Jews)
Jewish Community.
Rabbi: Mordecai Goldenberg.

TIMISOARA (12,784 Jews)
Jewish Community.
Rabbi: Dr. Meier Neuman.

ORADEA (5,144 Jews)
Jewish Community.
Rabbi: Zev Pollack.

CLUJ (3,000 Jews)
Jewish Community.
Rabbi: Abraham Schoenfeld.

SATU-MARE (7,500 Jews)

Jewish Community.
Rabbis: Dor Dachner, Schmaria Deutsch.

BAIA-MARE (7,489 Jews)

STALIN (3,934 Jews)

PUBLICATIONS:

Viata Noua, Matei Bararab St. 2a. Bucharest.
Weekly. Rumanian.

SAAR

JEWISH POPULATION: 415

The pre-war Jewish community of Saarbrücken and surroundings had about 4,500 members. In 1935, their number reached 7,000, distributed in 23 communities throughout the country. In the same year, the Saar returned to Nazi Germany following a plebiscite. All Jews were forced to sell their properties at a nominal price and emigrate. It is estimated that 30-40% of the Saar's Jews were killed. After the liberation in 1945, only a small number returned. Of these, 60% were French citizens. The financial status of the community is good. The resources of the community are derived mainly from an 8% tax which is imposed directly on all Jews in order to take care of welfare cases and support Zionist work. 10% of the total communal income is turned over for aid to Israel. In January 1951, the reconstructed synagogue was inaugurated.

Congregation Synagogengemeinde Saar, Lortzingstrasse 8, Saarbrücken.
Pres.: Alfred Levy (also president of the Saar Senate).
Rabbi and Gen. Sec.: Walter Kasel.
Sec.: Eva Lehmann.

Fursorgeverein der Synagogengemeinde.
Pres.: S. M. Wachsmann.
Vice-Pres.: M. Simon.
Treasurer: J. Borg.
Sec.: W. Kasel.

Maccabi-Saar.

B'nai-Akiba (Poel Mizrachi Youth)

Frauenverein der Synagogengemeinde Saar,
Pres.: Mrs. Thekla Lehman.
Vice-Pres.: Martha Blum.
Treasurer: Hilde Cahn.

Religious School (26 pupils), Dir.: W. Kasel. All Jewish children attend the school. All Jewish high school students also receive instruction in Hebrew and Jewish history.

WIZO (membership: 80). Pres.: Mrs. G. Levy.
Sec.: R. Salomon.

SPAIN

JEWISH POPULATION: 3,500

There is evidence of the existence of Jews in Spain from the fifth century.

The Jews actively aided the Arabs in their invasion of the country (711–828). The 10th and 11th centuries were the Golden Age of Spanish Jewry.

Conditions for the Jews deteriorated substantially when the Christian Spaniards were victorious in their campaigns against the Moslems. In 1391, anti-Jewish pogroms broke out in Seville and other cities and Jews who refused to become baptized were killed or sold into slavery. All the Jewish communities in Andalusia were annihilated. In 1481, the Inquisition, directed primarily against the Marranos loyal to Judaism, began to function. After the conquest of Granada, Ferdinand and Isabella, in 1492, decreed the expulsion of all Jews. The exiles went to Portugal, Turkey, North Africa, and Italy.

Under the reign of Alfonso XIII (1902–1931), Jews again settled in Spain, although in very small numbers. When a part of Morocco was given to Spain (1906), a considerable number of Jews—about 25,000—came under Spanish rule.

After the Government issued an edict of religious freedom (1931), a Federation of Jewish Communities was organized. In Madrid, a small community had already existed under the religious supervision of the chief rabbi of Tetuan, Spanish Morocco. In 1934, a Zionist society was formed. In Barcelona, however, the Jewish community was much larger. It had originated

in the first years of the 20th century and had increased in numbers after the First World War. In 1935, Spain grandiosely celebrated the 800th anniversary of the birth of Maimonides.

During the civil war (1936), the situation of the Jews in Spain and in Spanish Morocco deteriorated. Heavy contributions were exacted from them and numerous Jews fled. By 1936, less than 500 Jews were left in Barcelona. In the first years of Franco's rule, antisemitism became rampant. German Jewish refugees in 1940 were rounded up and sent to special camps. In 1942, all synagogues and Jewish centers were closed. At the end of 1942, after the Nazi occupation of Vichy France, many Jews fled from France to Spain, where they were interned in camps.

Since the end of the Second War, the condition of the Jews has improved. However, their communities are merely tolerated, having no legal status. According to a decree of Primo de Rivera in 1924, Sephardic Jews may regain their Spanish nationality. General Franco promulgated a law on December 29, 1948, which recognized as Spanish subjects certain categories of Sephardim. The leaders of the Jewish community in Madrid maintain that the decrees of Primo de Rivera and Franco amount to a cancellation of the expulsion law. This interpretation, however, is not shared generally by Jewish quarters outside Spain. There have been no legislative gestures on the part of the Spanish government to abrogate expressly the old expulsion law and restore legal recognition to the organized Jewish communities in the country.

All Jews living in Spain today immigrated to the country during the Republican regime. The Sephardim have been able to obtain their citizenship but the Ashkenazim cannot unless they convert to Catholicism.

There is a Hebrew chair at the Madrid University now headed by a Catholic professor and a magazine named "Sepharad" for Jewish history and literature in medieval Spain is published bi-annually by Catholic scholars. Maimonides' birthplace in Cordoba is maintained by the government as an historical shrine.

MADRID (1,000 Jews)

Comunidad Sefardita de Madrid, 76 members.

The Executive Committee is composed of a president, vice-president, treasurer, and 4 members. Recently, the membership of the community increased from 36 to 76. Sabbath services are held with the approval of the authorities in a small hall and are conducted by Jewish university students from Spanish Morocco. The Community appointed a Cultural Committee for lectures and meetings. There is a group of 50 Jewish students from Spanish Morocco at the Madrid University who are studying medicine, engineering architecture, pharmacology, etc. With their Jewish background, these students are a constructive factor

in strengthening the Jewish religious and cultural life of the entire community. They organize lectures and instruct the children of Jewish parents.

Pres. of the Community: Daniel Francois Baroukh, Calle de Ayala 3, Madrid.
Ezra, Charitable society for local needy and transit immigrants from Europe and North Africa.
WIZO, Engaged in sending gift parcels.
Benoth Yerushalaim, Society for charity.
Honorary Pres.: Baroness de Ginzburg.
Synagogue, The Community obtained permission for an attendance of 20 persons at services to be held at 62 Cardinal Cisneros Street. For services during the high holidays, the Chief of Police allowed the Jews to hire rooms in the Castelland Hilton Hotel, but in 1955 this permission was denied. There were 312 persons present including representatives of the Spanish authorities.

BARCELONA (2,500 Jews)

Comunidad Israelita de Barcelona, Calle Porvenir 44.
Pres.: Louis H.A. Blitz.
Sec.: Benjamin Anavi.
The Synagogue is at the same address. Over 90% are Sephardim. The Community erected a building for the Synagogue in the center of the city containing two halls for a Sephardic and an Ashkenazic congregation and rooms for a Jewish religious school.
Organizacion Sionista, Apartado 1053. Central office for Spain.

OTHER JEWISH SETTLEMENTS:

Seville, About 30 Jews.
Valencia, 15 Jews.

SOVIET UNION

JEWISH POPULATION: 2,500,000

At a very early date Jewish merchants from Byzantium and Khazaria emigrated to the Russian territory. According to the oldest Russian chronicle, Jews from Khazaria participated in the religious disputation in 986 held in the presence of Prince Vladimir of Kiev. Kiev was the first city where Jews settled. Theodosius (1057–74), the abbot of the monastery of Kiev, instructed the faithful to live in peace with all except the Jews. When Prince Gedimin of Lithuania occupied southern Russia in 1340, he already found a considerable Jewish population there.

In Muscovy the Jews were denied permanent residence. Ivan the Terrible (1533–84) was the first to order the complete exclusion of Jews from his country. Under the Czar Fyodor (1676-82) Jewish traders were excluded from Muscovy. Those who stayed in Moscow were forced to be baptized, but some of them continued to practice Judaism in secret. In 1727, Catherine I issued an ukase banishing the Jews from all Russian cities. This law was repeated by Elizabeth (1741–62), according to which 35,000 Jews were expelled from Russia by 1753.

As a result of the first partition of Poland in 1772, more than 100,000 Jews of White Russia became Russian subjects. The Russian law recognized the Kahal organizations, which enjoyed some measure of an internal autonomy.

According to a ukase of 1791, the so-called Pale of Settlement was established which allowed Jews to reside only in some provinces. The Pale included White Russia, the provinces of Kiev, Czernigow, Poltava, Minsk, Volhynia, Podolia, Lithuania, Courland, and Bessarabia. In 1794, the government ruled that the Jews had to pay double the taxes imposed upon Christian merchants.

During the reign of Alexander I (1801–25), attempts were made to improve the desperate situation of the Jews. A committee formed in 1802 recommended a compulsory reform of the Jews to make them abandon leaseholding and inkeeping in favor of agriculture and productive labor. Jewish children were admitted to the government schools. Traditional Jewish garb and earlocks were proscribed. The general course of the government, however, remained anti-Jewish. Alexander's objective with his reforms was the conversion of the Jews to Christianity, but without practical results. The Jews however considered Alexander as a benefactor of the Jews by comparison with his successors.

During the reign of Nicholas I (1825–55), the Jewish situation deteriorated considerably. In this period, 600 laws were issued restricting the rights of the Jews. In 1827, a ukase was issued imposing military duty upon the Jews. 70,000 Jewish children from the ages of twelve to eighteen were taken from their homes and placed in the Cantonist schools in the remote provinces for military training during which they were tortured relentlessly in order to convert them to Christianity. The military service lasted 25 years. The Jewish Cantonists who endured all the unspeakable sufferings and came out of the Russian army as Jews were considered as heroic martyrs of Judaism. The Pale of Settlement was reaffirmed. The aim of the educational reforms was to promote baptism of the Jews. Some Jewish leaders unaware of these government tendencies cooperated with the government and made efforts to transplant the enlightenment of western Europe into Russia. Among these were Isaac Ber Levinson in his book "Teudah Beyisrael" (1828) and Max Lilienthal who agitated for the establishment of modern Jewish schools on behalf of the government. Moses Montefiore visited Russia in 1846 to intervene with the government to alleviate the plight of the Jews but with little success.

Under the liberal regime of Alexander II (1855–81) the position of the Jews was somehow improved. The oppressive stipulations regarding the military service of Jews were withdrawn and their economic situation became more tolerable. During the reactionary rule of Alexander III (1881-96), the Jewish position again turned desperate.

A long terrible series of pogroms against Jews began in 1881. The expulsion of Jews from Moscow in 1891 was followed by new anti-Jewish laws. Hostility toward the Jews continued unabated after Nicholas II became Czar in 1896. The Russian defeat in the war against Japan brought on the high point of the persecution of the Jews. In 1903, anti-Jewish agitation by the "Black Hundreds" led to fearful pogroms in Kishinev and Homel.

In the four elections to the Duma (1906–1913) some Jewish representatives were elected but were unable to stem the wave of oppression.

Before the first World War, the Jewish population of Russia amounted to approximately *six million* or 4.07% of the total. About 2.5% were active in agriculture, 33% in industry and handicrafts, and 37% in commerce. They were also strongly represented in the professions.

Russian Jewry was the largest Jewish community the world over. It played a central role in the cultural and social life of the Jewish people. The development of modern Hebrew and Yiddish literature and the expanding national Zionist and socialist movements reflected the devotion and vitality of this Jewry despite all disabilities.

The first World War brought to the Russian Jews new dreadful sufferings. Half a million Jews were evacuated from hundreds of towns of the border provinces for alleged reasons of military necessity. By the time of the Armistice, one and a half million Jews were living on charity supplied mainly by Jewish organizations in America.

The revolution of March 1917 abolished all anti-Jewish restrictions, but a crusade against Jewish cultural and religious life was initiated by the Bolsheviks who assumed control in October. All Jewish communities, cultural, social and religious organizations were dissolved, the Hebrew language prohibited, and Zionism outlayed. At first, cultural and educational activities in Yiddish were allowed and even encouraged, but in 1948–49 all manifestations of Yiddish culture were destroyed.

In the beginning of the Soviet regime the white armies of Denikin, Petliura, Makhno, and Balakhowitz, in their civil war against the Communists, destroyed all Jewish communities in their reach. Between 1917 and 1921, there were over 1,500 pogroms in the Ukraine and White Russia. The number of murdered Jews is estimated at 100,000 and of the orphaned children at 150,000.

In 1941, Germany invaded Russia and occupied the area where most of the Jewish centers were located. A part of the Jewish population was evacuated and settled in the interior. The Jews who were left behind, however, were indiscriminately exterminated by the Nazi invaders. Over a million Russian Jews were murdered by the Germans with the aid of the native populations, mainly in the Ukrain- and White Russia.

The Russian Jews, however, did not escape anti-Semitic outbreaks even under Communist rule.

Since the beginning of the Second World War, three anti-Semitic campaigns were launched in Soviet Russia. In 1941, the first anti-Jewish drive took place with the slogan that Jews were deserting Moscow. Many government departments and universities discharged their Jewish staffs and professors. In 1948–49, a more serious anti-Semitic outbreak occurred under the mask of "Cosmopolitanism" implying lack of Soviet patriotism. It

virtually brought to an end the entire organized Jewish life. All Jewish organizations, publishing houses, newpapers, and theatres were closed. All Yiddish writers disappeared, obviously exterminated or jailed. Jewish autonomy in the Birobidzhan region was revoked and many Jews deported from this area. The reason for this anti-Jewish action was a demonstration of Moscow Jews in honor of the first Israeli Ambassador, Golda Meyerson, on her arrival in Moscow. Jews by the thousands blocked the streets to greet her. The Kremlin saw in this mass expression of enthusiasm for the restoration of the Jewish State a "security risk" to the Soviets.

In 1947, the Soviet Union surprisingly supported the establishment of a Jewish State in Palestine, apparently with the aim of ousting Britain from the Middle East. In the following years, the attitude towards Israel became unfriendly and pro-Arab.

The third anti-Jewish campaign started with a staged "Jewish doctor-plot" in 1953 accusing prominent Jewish physicians of conspiring against the life of Communist leaders. After Stalin's death, the doctors were rehabilitated.

Since 1955, the U.S.S.R. has been supporting the Arabs openly in word and deed against Israel. Israel's war in Sinai unleashed a flood of vicious vituperation on the part of top Soviet leaders. All news from the Middle East is heavily slanted against Israel.

The role of the Jews in the political life of the Soviet Union is being reduced to a minimum. The number of Jews in the highest political bodies is almost nil. In the 1937 elections, 47 Jews were elected to both chambers of the Supreme Soviet; in 1946, only ten Jews, in 1950, five. In 1954, only two Jews were elected among the nearly 2000 members, namely Lazar Kaganovich of the Union and Rachel Fradkin of Birobidzhan. She was the only Jewish member from the "Jewish" Autonomous Region, while the other four members from Birobidzhan were Russians. In July, 1957, Kaganovich was ousted from the government.

According to recent reports, the younger generation knows virtually nothing about Judaism. Jews complain of anti-Semitism and express a desire to emigrate. A few Jews inquired about the situation in Israel, but always in whispers. Zionism, prohibited in Russia, has not died out. (H. Schwartz, N.Y. Times 11/19/55.)

The Jewish religious societies in the Soviet Union have no central governing body. Nor was there any before the Revolution. Each society conducts its activities independently, under the leadership of an elected executive board, auditing committee, and rabbi. In practice, however, the rabbis of neighboring synagogues get together to discuss religious questions of general signifance.

The appearance of Israeli delegations at the Youth Festival in July, 1957, gave Russian Jewry another chance of demonstrating their enthusiasm for Israel and marked the beginning of tighter control over Russia's Jews by the authorities.

As to the number of the Russian Jews, the late Rabbi Schlifer of Moscow estimated them at 3,000,000. Other calculations place them at two and a half million. Since official sources are not available, we must follow reliable estimates. The same applies to the size of the Jewish population in various cities mentioned beneath which are based merely on reports of visitors and newspapers. We availed ourselves of the relatively most reliable sources.

In accordance with the new Soviet policy after Stalins death of relaxing the restrictions on communication with the West, Rabbi S. Schlifer of the Moscow Synagogue, instructed by the Soviet authorities, invited in 1956 for the first time three Jewish delegations to visit Soviet Russia in order to contact the Jewish population there and investigate their spiritual and religious needs. The invited delegations were of the World Jewish Congress, the Rabbinical Council of America, and the Rabbinical Board of New York.

MOSCOW (400,000 Jews)

3 *Synagogues*—The Central Synagogue, Spasaglinshevski Street; The Synagogue at Lermontov Street; A third smaller Synagogue whose location is not mentioned.
Chief Rabbi: Judah Leib Levin.

The synagogues are the only places where Jews meet as Jews during services. All other Jewish institutions are closed. The staff of the Israeli Embassy in Moscow and Jewish visitors from abroad can see Jews in groups only in the synagogue, but even there, they are afraid to speak to foreign Jews. H. Schwartz reports (N.Y.Times, 9/27/55) that 5,000 Jews crowded into the Central Synagogue in Moscow and the neighboring streets on Yom Kippur, while the capacity of the Synagogue is only 2,000. Many spoke Yiddish. On Sabbath the attendance is about 70-80. They are mostly old people, because the younger ones are not released from work, not even on Yom Kippur.

In the Central Synagogue there are also services on workdays for aged people, and after the Mincha service they study Mishna.

KIEV (100,000 Jews)

3 *Synagogues*—Rabbi Panich. Several private rooms for prayer. Estimates on the number of Jews in Kiev vary from 100,000 to 300,000.

A Jewish immigrant from Kiev reported in Jerusalem that elderly Jews there maintain Jewish traditions, there are synagogues, a Chevra Kadisha and a kosher butcher, but the younger Jews are completely assimilated.

LVOV-LEMBERG (30,000 Jews)

An immigrant from Lvov to Israel in June, 1955 reported that in Lvov and its outskirts there are 30,000 Jews with a few synagogues remaining. The Jews in the small towns of Eastern Galicia are concentrated around the synagogues.

KISHINEV (30,000 Jews)

Synagogue.

It is estimated that there are about 25-35,000 Jews in Kishinev.

H. Shurer, Editor of Davar, visited the synagogue on a Friday evening in 1954 and found scores attending the Sabbath service, but they were afraid to speak to him as a foreigner.

BAKU (100,000 Jews)

One Synagogue.

According to a report from O. Ostin (Forverts, 1/27/54) a friend of the reporter compiling figures on the number of Jews in Russian cities writes that Baku has a larger Jewish population than Kiev and Kishinev, indicating that Baku has a Jewish population exceeding 100,000.

LENINGRAD (100,000 Jews)

One synagogue.

According to the report of a visiting Jewish student from England in 1955, the synagogue in Leningrad is much larger and more beautiful than the one in Moscow. He found it empty, only in an adjoining room were there a few Jews reciting the Psalms. There are services only on the Sabbath in the adjoining little Beth Hamidrash attended by a score or two of Jews.

MINSK (40,000 Jews)

Synagogue—Rabbi Jacob Gerber.

It is estimated that 30-50,000 Jews live in Minsk. The Germans murdered 100,000 Jews there during World War II. There are no Yiddish books or Jewish cultural institutions. In the only Minsk synagogue, a small wooden building, there were 150 elderly Jews to celebrate Succoth, and a small wooden succah decorated with palm leaves stood near the synagogue. The rabbi said that on Yom Kippur the synagogue was full and hundreds stood in the street outside. There is no Jewish school, and most Jewish children receive no religious training whatsoever.

ODESSA (170,000 Jews)

Synagogue—Rabbi Diment.

According to a report by Israeli seamen there is a Yiddish theatre in Odessa.

KHARKOV (90,000 Jews)

There is no synagogue. It was closed when the rabbi was imprisoned for alleged subversion several years ago. It is to be assumed, however, that there are private minyanim performing services. (H. Schwartz, N.Y. Times, 11/19/1955).

TASHKENT (100,000 Jews)

According to a report, Tashkent has one of the largest Jewish communities in Russia.

CZERNOWITZ (60,000 Jews)

3 *Synagogues.* A Rabbi.

Report from an immigrant arrived from Czernowitz 1954: Many Jews are in government service. Several families recently obtained permission to emigrate to Israel. The number of Jews in Czernowitz is estimated at 30,000 to 50,000.

VILNA (25,000 Jews)

3 *Synagogues.* Rabbi I. Rabinovitch.

According to a report ("Davar" of 5/29/55)

There are about 20,000 Jews in Vilna, mainly stemming from other places. There are 3 synagogues. The Jewish communal institutions are located in the Choral Synagogue, and about 20 persons attend the daily services. The other 2 synagogues are open only on Sabbath.

RIGA (30,000 Jews)

Synagogue. — Rabbi M. Masliansky.

There are about 10,000 Jews in Riga, many speaking Yiddish. The synagogue was crowded on the high holidays and a cantor from Leningrad officiated. A second synagogue was closed after the war for "reparation reasons" and was not reopened.

KOVNO (5,000 Jews)

Chor-Synagogue. Rabbi Vorkul.

Approximately 5,000 Jews live in Kovno. The only remaining synagogue is the Chor-Shul. On weekdays, only a few attend but during the holidays the synagogue is well filled. There is no Jewish school or cheder. The number of Jewish births is very small, and in the case of a boy, a mohel is brought from Vilna.

CZERKASSY (2,000 Jews)

Synagogue. Rabbi Sifeld.

Of the 10,000 Jews before the World War only 2,000 remain.

Out of the 12 synagogues, only one is left now.

BIROBIDZHAN (100,000 Jews)

The Jewish autonomous province in Birobidzhan was proclaimed in 1934 by the Soviet Union as a competition to the Zionist concept of creating a Jewish State in Palestine. The project was to establish a region with a Jewish majority through immigration where the Jews could develop their culture and thus become one of the territorial nationalities of the Soviet Union. This experiment failed. In the Yalta Papers, published by the State Department in Washington, it is recorded that Stalin told President Roosevelt, the Soviets had tried to establish a national home for the Jews in Birobidzhan, but the Jews had stayed there only two or three years and then scattered to the cities. This was apparently the official excuse for the liquidation of a Jewish Birobidzhan.

The head of the Birobidzhan administration, the Jew Lev Yefremovich Vinkevich, admitted to the reporter H. E. Salisbury (N.Y.Times, 6/22/54) that the region is more a Russian than a Jewish province since the Jews constitute only one of several nationalities there, and that the Jews use the Russian, not the Yiddish language. The Jewish population is only 50% of the total 200,000. Among the new immigrants the Jews are in a minority, the vast majority consisting of Russians, Ukrainians, and Tartars. There are two newspapers, one a Russian daily with a circulation of 10,000 and the Yiddish "Birobidzhaner Shtern," published twice weekly in 1,000 copies only. A Jewish theatre existed until a few years ago and is now closed. During Salisbury's visits to schools and factories he was never asked about Israel, Jews abroad, or other matters of Jewish interest. The officials explained it by a lack of Jewish interest, the real reason being, however, fear of the Communist officials.

* * *

There are more than 100 Jewish communities scattered throughout the Soviet Union, large and small, about which no information is available. Among them are the following mentioned occasionally in reports which reached us:

Yakutsk, There is a considerable Jewish element in Yakutsk, but no organized Jewish life. (Salisbury, N.Y. Times, 6/15/54).

Tiflis, 2 Synagogues. A Rabbi. The Rabbi of a Georgian Synagogue asserted that in contrast to all other Russian cities the Jewish children in Tiflis are getting instruction about Judaism. (Henry Schwartz, N.Y. Times 11/9/55).

Rostov, One Synagogue. Large Jewish community.

Kulaisi, Synagogue. Rabbi Haham K. D. Yeliashvili.

Zhitomir, Large Jewish population.

SWEDEN

JEWISH POPULATION: 13,000

In 1775, the first Jewish community was founded in Stockholm. Parliament permitted Jewish settlement and religious services in Stockholm and in three other towns in 1779; and in 1782 the Board of Trade allowed Jews to work in certain branches of business and industry. King Karl XIV repealed some regulations against Jews in 1838, giving them full equality in most respects with other Swedish subjects. By 1870, the emancipation of Jews in Sweden was complete.

Practically all the first Jews in Sweden came from Germany. In the last decades of the 19th century, there was a steady increase of immigrants from Eastern Europe. In 1910, there were 6,112 Jews in Sweden; ten years later, the number increased to 6,469.

Gradually, through mixed marriages and low birth rate, many Jewish families disappeared, but the Jewish population increased through immigration. With the ascendancy of Hitler, Swedish Jews again re-indentified themselves with world Jewry and their problem and began an intensive program of relief and community work abroad and at home. Today, the greater part of Swedish Jewry lives in Stockholm, Gothenburg, and Malmo with smaller centers in other towns as Boras, Halsingborg, Jonkoping, Karlstad, Kristianstad, Sundsvall, and Uppsala. Of the 13,000 Jews in the country, only 6,000 are Swedish subjects.

STOCKHOLM (Jewish population: 6,500)

Mosaiska Forsamlingen (Jewish Community of Stockholm), Wahrendorffsgatan 3. Aims: Religious, cultural, and social activity in cooperation with the local Jewish associations. Pres.: Gunnar Josephson.
Social Director: Ivar Muller.
Sec.: David Kopniwsky Kamrer.
Director of Administration: Prof. Erik Wolff.

Rabbis: Chief Rabbi Dr. Kurt Wilhelm, Vartavagen 6. Dr. E. Kronheim, Vanadisvagen 22A.

Synagogue, Wahrendorffsgatan 3. The community takes care of four Jewish cemeteries, the oldest of which exists since 1776.

Community Library.

Committee for Assistance and Support, Pres.: Ivar Muller.

Section for Refugees, President and Director: Gunnar Josephson.

Religious School, Wahrendorffsgatan 3. Pres.: Bernhard Tarschys.

American Joint Distribution Committee, Malmskillnadsgatan 38.

HIAS, Kindstugatan 11.
Swedish sections of HIAS and JOINT for the purpose of supervising emigration and assistance by both organizations. Both are combined with the community's section for refugees and are directly administrated by this board: Dr. Michaeli and Mrs. Sonja Haneryd.

Congregation Adas Jisrael, St. Paulsgatan 13.
Pres.: Josef Birnik.
Vice-Pres.: Hirsch Nissalowitz.
Sec.: Paul Rothschild.

Swedish Zionist Federation, P.O.B.14016 Stockholm. Includes representatives of the various Zionist groups.
Pres.: Fritz Hollander.

B'nai B'rith, Birialsgatan 106. Swedish Section of B'nai B'rith.
Pres.: Arne Levin.

Association of Jewish Pensioners' Home, Skulptorvagan 8, Stockholm-Johannehov. Home for old and indigent Jewish people.
Pres.: Gunnar Josephson.
Sec.: David Kopniwsky.

Association for Assistance "Rodef Chesed," Odengatan 85. Founded in 1870, it administrates a fund for various kinds of social activities.
Pres.: Josef Katz.

Sport Club Makkabi, Klippgatan 19c.
Pres.: Jack Witz.

Congregation Jeschurin, Odengatan 28. Orthodox congregation.
Synagogue: Biblioteksgatan 4.
Rabbi: A. I. Jacobson, Odengatan 28.
Pres.: John Benzion.

Jewish Association for Cultural and Social Aims, Gubbangsvagen 103.
Pres.: Goran Nisell.

Jewish Women's Association, Sigtunagatan 15. For social and cultural activity.
Pres.: Mrs. Gladys Wolff.

Jewish Students' Club, Frejgatan 28. Organized for cultural and social activities.
Pres.: Lennart Levi.

Keren Kajemet Leisrael, Valhallavagan 104.
Director and Secretary: Dr. Michael Fried.

Holiday Colony, Balsa-Enkoping, of Stockholm Jewish Community.

Holiday Colony, Vaddo-Backa, of Stockholm Jewish Community.
Pres.: Ivar Muller.

Mizrachi Organization, Odengatan 28.
Pres.: Rabbi A. I. Jacobson.
Sec.: Stephan Speyer.

Nachmansonska Stiftelsen, Gotgatan 55. This endowment takes care of the social needs of Jewish children and supports a day nursery.
Pres.: M. Grunberger.

Palestine Bureau, Odengatan 28. Committee for special Jewish questions.
Pres.: A. I. Jacobson.

World Jewish Congress, Grev Magnigatan 11. Swedish section of the W.J.C. It publishes a monthly in Swedish, "Var Rost."

WIZO, Valhallavagan 104.
Pres.: Karin Bornstein.
Vice-Pres.: Mi Goldmann.
Gen. Sec.: Mrs. Brigit Leiser.

GOTHENBURG (Jewish population: 1,400)

Mosaiska Forsamlingen Goteborg, Jewish Community.
Pres.: M. R. Henriques.

Keren Kajemet Leisrael, Spannmulsgatan 16. Local section of the K.K.L.
Pres.: Berndt Fibert.

WIZO, Fribergsgatan 4.
Pres.: Mrs. Ragne Blecher.
Vice-Pres.: Mrs. Gullan Wolff.
Sec.: Mrs. Hertha Philipson.

MALMO (Jewish population: 1,000)

Mosaiska Forsamlingen, Klostergatan 8. Jewish Community.
Pres.: Manne Benjamin.

Keren Kajemet Leisrael, Roskildevagen 27e.
Pres.: Leo Fischer.

WIZO, Halsingborgsgatan 3.
Pres.: Mrs. Gudrun Marlow.
Sec.: Mrs. Berta Winitsky.

BORAS

WIZO, Tometegatan 1b.
Pres.: Mrs. Szala Szotten.
Sec.: Mrs. Elly Polak.

HALSINGBORG

WIZO, Dorttninggatan 118.
Pres.: Mrs. Rosa Bertman.

JONKOPING

WIZO, Vastra Storgatan 37.
Pres.: Mrs. Regina Naftaniel.

KARLSTAD

WIZO, Sveagatan 5. Pres.: Mrs. Sofia Dohre.
Sec.: Miss Brigit Rubinstein.

KRISTIANSTAD

WIZO, Epidemivagan 5a. Pres.: Mrs. P. Rulf.
Sec.: Mrs. Klara Lewinschal.

SUNDSVALL

WIZO, Kyrkogardsgatan 16b.
Pres.: Mrs. Sonja Lipschutz.

UPPSALA

WIZO, Kyrkogardsgatan 29.
Pres.: Mrs. Fanny Valentin.

PERIODICALS:

Fortnightly: *Judisk Krönika,* Valhallavägen 106, Stockholm, Ö.

Monthlies: *Judisk Tidsskrift,* Rättviksvägen 30, Bromma.
Judisk Hem. Mössebergsvägen 114, Bromma.

Quarterly: *Församlingsbladet.* Wahrendorffsgatan 3, Stockholm. 7.

SWITZERLAND

JEWISH POPULATION: 20,000

Jews immigrated to Switzerland from Alsace, Southern Germany, and France. At first, they lived under the protection of the emperor, but in the 14th century, they came under the protection of the cities to whom they paid high protection taxes. Excluded from commerce and handicrafts, they were forced to live chiefly by money lending. Gradually they were replaced by Christian money lenders and were expelled from the cities, namely from Lucerne 1348, Bern 1408, Zurich 1436, Schaffhausen 1475, Thurgau 1491, and Geneva 1490. They lived grouped around the synagogue and were compelled to wear the Jews' hat. In 1348-1349, during the Black Death, Jews were burned at the stake in most cities.

At the beginning of the 17th century, a new influx of Jews started from Alsace, Baden, and Poland. In 1774, it was decided that Jews should reside exclusively in two villages, Lengnau and Oberendigen, in the canton of Baden. By 1810, their number increased to 1,000.

The establishment of the Helvetian Republic in 1789 didn't change the status of the Jews. In 1809, the great Council of Aargau passed the Jewish Bill (Judengesetz) which considerably restricted their civil rights. Full emancipation was granted to the Jews in 1877. Jewish ritual slaughtering was declared illegal in 1894 and is still prohibited.

Despite their small number, Jews took an active part in the political, cultural, and economic life of Switzerland. All Jewish communities were united in the Schweizer Israelitischer Gemeindebund, founded in 1904. The Swiss authorities repudiated anti-Semitism on numerous occasions. In 1934, in the lawsuit of the Jewish representatives against a Nazi paper, the Swiss court declared "The Protocols of the Elders of Zion" to be a forgery and fined their publisher. In 1936, a young Jew, David Frankfurter, assassinated the Swiss Nazi leader Gustloff and was found guilty. His sentence was later commuted. The verdict contained a severe repudiation of Nazi persecutions.

After the Nazis' advent to power in

Germany in 1933, over 20,000 Jewish refugees escaped to Switzerland. The majority of them were placed in internment camps by the Swiss government and supported by Jewish organizations. After the war, almost all refugees left Switzerland for Israel and other overseas countries.

Union of Swiss Jewish Communities, (Schweizericher Israelitischer Gemeindebund), Lavaterstr. 37 Zurich.
Pres.: Dr. George Brunschwig, Marktgasse 51, Bern.
Sec.: Jean Brunschwig, 33 Rue du Rhone, Geneva.
The "Gemeindebund," which has a membership of 4,000, was founded in 1904 and represents Swiss Jewry and its 26 affiliated communities.

Rabbinical Union (Rabbinerverband der Schweiz), Salistr. 33, Luzern, 11 members.
Pres.: Rab. S. Brom, Lucerne.
Vice-Pres. and Sec.: Rab. Dr. Z. Taubes, Zurich.

Union of Jewish Religious Teachers and Cantors, Steinhandlenstr. 65 Zurich.
Pres.: ˜ ʃ. Ruda, Zurich. 35 members.

Bene Brith Basel: Eichenstr. 41.
Pres.: R.Haymann.
Geneva: 10 Rue St. Leger.
Zurich: Gladbachstr. 55. Pres.: Dr. H. Weil.

Union of Jewish Women's Associations (Bund der Israelitischen Frauenvereine in der Schweiz) St. Jacobstr. 34 Basel.
Pres.: Vera Dreyfus, Basel. Membership 4,506. Branches in all Swiss cities.

WIZO, Schnetzengraben 16 Basel.
Pres.: B. Halff, Basel, Membership 2,121. Branches in all communities.

Bne-Akiwah-Bahad, Rieterstr. 37 Zurich. Membership 200.
Central Committee: Jean Blum, Basel; Esther Kessler, Zurich; Ellen Klopman, Geneva; S. Strassberg, Basel.

Brith Hazofim, Sternenstr. 19. Zurich. Membership 140. Zionist Youth Organization.

Hashomer Hazair, Weinbergstr. 3, Zurich. 150 members.

Makkabi, Jewish Sport Organization. Baeckerstr. 177, Zurich.
Pres.: David Neufeld, Zurich.
Membership 1,200.

Aguda Youth, Kaufmannweg 17, Lucerne. 250 members.

Union of Jewish Students, Nueschelerstr. 36 Zurich.
Pres.: Georges Rosenstein. Branches in other cities.

Jewish National Fund. Schreuneng 37, Zurich.
Pres.: Dr. H. Schwabacher.

Yeshiva Etz Haim, Montreux, 80 rue Colondalles, Montreux. Founded 1927.

Yeshiva Lugano, Badenstr. 274, Zurich. Founded 1952.

BADEN

Jewish Community, Seminarstr. 57 Baden. Founded 1859. 45 members.
Synagogue: Parkstrasse 17.
Pres.: A. Wolf.

BASEL

Jewish Community. Leimenstr. 24 Basel. Founded 1805. 800 members.
Pres.: A. Goetschel.
Synagogue: Corner Leimenstr. & Eulenstr.
Rabbi: Dr. Arthur Weil.

Israelitische Religionsgesellschaft (Orthodox Congregation).
Ohronstr. 14. Membership 52.
Pres.: A. Jakulbowitsch.
Synagogue: Ahronstr. 14.
Rabbi: Jacob Snyders.
Talmud Tora: Blauenstr. 18. Jewish Kindergarten Palmenstr. 1.

BERN

Jewish Community, Kapelienstr. 2, Bern. Founded 1848. Membership 188.
Pres.: Emil Raas.
Synagogue, Kapellenstr. 2.
Rabbi: Dr. Eugen J. Messinger.

BIEL

Jewish Community, Oberer Quai 22, Biel.
Founded 1848. Membership 82.
Pres.: Gabriel Picard.
Synagogue: Rueschlistr. 3.
Rabbi: Dr. A. Silberstein.

LA CHAUX-DE-FONDS

Jewish Community, 29 Rue du Temple
Allemand. Founded 1833. Membership 150.
Synagogue 63. Rue du Pare.
Rabbi: Emanuel Bulz.

FRIBOURG

Jewish Community, 5 Rue Fancigng. Fribourg.
Founded 1888. Membership 35.
Pres.: Isidore Nordman.
Synagogue: Avenue de Rome.

GENEVA

Jewish Community, 10 Rue St. Seger, Geneva.
Founded 1825. Membership 304.
Pres.: Erwin Haymann.
Synagogue: Place de la Synagogue.
Grand Rabbi: Dr. Alexander Safran.
Society Agudath Achim, 69 Rue de 31 Decembre, Geneva.
Pres.: Ch. Rabinowicz.
Synagogue: 76 Rue du Rhone.
World Jewish Congress, 1, Rue de Varembe,
Geneve 20.
Exec. Dir.: Dr. G.M. Riegner.
Sec.: Miss Miriam Becker.

LAUSANNE

Jewish Community, 54 Galeries du Commerce,
Lausanne.
Founded 1866. Membership 201.
Pres.: Gustave Dreyfuss.
Synagogue: 1 Rue Juste-Olivier.
Rabbi: Dr. G. Vadnai.

LUGANO

Jewish Community, Founded 1917. Membership 30.
Pres.: Leo Rubinfeld.
Synagogue: V. a la Stazione 12.
Rabbi: Friedmann.

LUCERNE

Jewish Community, Berglistr. 46, Lucerne.
Founded 1867. Membership 130.
Pres.: I. Bollag—Guggenheim.
Synagogue: Bruchstr. 51.
Rabbi: Samuel Brom.

ST. GALL

Jewish Community, St. Leonhardstr. 43, St. Gall.
Founded 1863. Membership 145.
Pres.: Ernst Dreyfuss.
Synagogue: Frongarstenstr. 18.
Rabbi: Lothar Rothschild.

VEVEY-MONTREUX

Jewish Community, Vevey. Founded 1908.
Membership 15.
Pres.: Dr. J. J. Bloch.
Synagogue: 2 Rue du Simplon, Vevey.

WINTERTHUR

Jewish Community, Feldstr. 55, Winterthur.
Founded 1886. Membership 48.
Pres.: H. Bloch.
Synagogue: Rosenstr. 5.

YVERDON

Jewish Community, 54 Rue Valentin, Yverdon.
Founded 1888. Membership 16.
Synagogue: 26 Rue Valentin.
Rabbi: M. Donath.

ZURICH

Jewish Community, Savaterste 37, Zurich.
Founded 1862. Membership 1,287.
Pres.: Dr. Georg Guggenheim.
Synagogue: Loewenstr. 10.
Rabbi: Dr. Zvi Taubes.
Israelitishe Religionsgesellshaft, Loewenstr. 12.
Founded 1895. Membership 229.
Pres.: J. Mannes.
Synagogue: Freigutstr. 37.
Rabbis: A. Kornfein, Dr. Th. Weisz.
Community Agudath Achim, Pflugstr. 7
Membership: 140.
Pres.: A. Glass.

Synagogue: Erikastr. 8.

Rabbi: M. J. Breisch.

Small Jewish Communities exist in the following places:

Bremgarten (15 members), Davos (7), Delémont (11), Diessenhofen (19), Kreuzlingen (23), Liestal (7), Neu-Endingen (7), Lengnau (5), Solthurn (15).

PUBLICATIONS:

WEEKLIES:

Israelitisches Wochenblatt für die Schweiz, (German-French), Uraniastr. 9, Zurich.

Juedische Rundschau - Maccabi (German-French), Postfach 14, Basel 12.

Das Neue Israel, Bederstrasse 78, Zurich.

TRIESTE, FREE TERRITORY OF

JEWISH POPULATION: 1,500

The oldest Jewish tombstone dates from 1325. The first synagogue (Ashkenazic) was built in 1748. Several years later a Sephardic synagogue was erected, to which were annexed a Jewish public school and a Jewish hospital. There were 223 Jewish families comprising 670 persons living in Trieste in 1788. They were engaged in commerce and industry, but particularly in the leather trade.

Under the fascist regime there were anti-semitic outbreaks after 1938.

Comunita Israelitica di Trieste (Jewish community), Via S. Frabcesco 19.

Pres.: Dr. Mario Stock.

Sec.: Gustavo Treves.

The Jewish Community is recognized by law as the official representation of the Jews. The Council of the Jewish Community, which includes the synagogue and the cultural clubs and social institutions of its constituents, is elected by the membership at annual meetings.

The Council of the Jewish Community maintains an elementary school which is subsidized by the Government. The Trieste Zionist Club is affiliated with the Italian Zionist Federation. For a Jewish press, Trieste depends upon that of Italy.

Elementary School "J.S. Morpurgo," Via del Monie 3.

Asylum "M. Tedeschi." For children under 5 years of age.

Pia Casa Centilomo e Casa de Riposo A. Stock, Via Cologna 29. Home for the aged.

Colonia Carlo Marpurgo, Villa Opiciana. Convalescent home for children.

YUGOSLAVIA

JEWISH POPULATION: 6,500

There were Jews in the province of Illyria as early as Roman times.

Slovenia had Jews as early as the 12th century.

Jews were continuously in Dalmatia from the times of the Romans to the present day. There were Jews in Serbia in the early Middle Ages although not in large numbers. Jewish settlements in Bitolj, Ochrida, Stip, Struma, and Pristina are attested by folk traditions and rabbinical literature. Belgrade also had an old Jewish community which grew steadily due to the influx of refugees from Germany and Hungary. At the beginning of the 16th century, numerous exiles from Spain and Portugal immigrated there. In this way, large Sephardic communities arose in Belgrade and other places.

According to the first census in 1921, there were in Yugoslavia 64,746 Jews. The second census in March 31, 1931 revealed an increase to 76,654 or 18% during this decade. The Jews in Yugoslavia were mainly concentrated in the larger cities.

Geographically and culturally, the Jews fell into four groups, corresponding to the four areas out of which the united kingdom was constituted in 1918: Serbia, Croatia and Slovenia, Bosnia and Herzegovina, and Macedonia (annexed in 1920).

Owing to Zionist initiative, the 121 Jewish communities (72 Ashkenazic, 36 Sephardic, and 13 Orthodox) with their 68,107 members formed a Federation of Jewish Communities which was officially recognized by the Government and granted full autonomy in religious matters.

The literary and intellectual life of the community was also advanced by the work of a special association of rabbis of the entire kingdom (36 rabbis and 41 Hachamim) formed in 1923. Isaac Alkalay was elected president and, shortly thereafter, Chief Rabbi of Yugoslavia.

Of significance for Yugoslavia's Jewry were the Theological Seminary and Teachers' Institute in Sarajevo, established in 1928 and headed by the historian, Rabbi Moritz Levy.

Anti-Semitism in Yugoslavia is only a recent and alien growth due almost entirely to Nazi influence. Moreover, it does not represent any genuine feeling on the part of the masses, but was the creation only of political pressure. 55,000 Jews were exterminated by the Nazis.

From 1948 to September 1953, 7,691 Jews emigrated to Israel.

Yugoslavia is the only communist country which allows Jews to affiliate with the World Jewish Congress and to maintain contact with world Jewry, and it does not restrict emigration to Israel.

Savez Jevrejskih Veroispovednih Opstina Fnrj,
(Federation of Jewish Communities), Ulica 7, Jula, No. 71, Beograd.
Pres.: Dr. Albert Vajs.
Vice-Pres.: Dr. Lavoslav Kadelburg.

Sec.: Solomon Kalderon.

Treasurer: Isak Masijah.

The Federation, based on law and administrative acts, is recognized by the Government and its authorities as the central Jewish body. It includes all the Jewish communities in the country, of which there are 35, each of them electing its own board. According to its constitution and by-laws, it directs the religious, social, cultural, and national affairs of the whole community and coordinates the work of the constituent communities, which are autonomous with respect to their local matters. The central organs of the Federation are: The Executive Board, the Main Board, and the Supervisory Board. They are elected at the National Conference of Jewish Communities held every year.

Autonomous Relief Committee, (Autonommi Odbor Za Pomoc Saveza Jevrejskih Veroispovednih), Ulica 7, Jula, No.71, Beograd.

Pres.: David A. Alcalay.

Sec.: Bata Gedalja.

Jewish Community of Serbia, The total number of Jews in Serbia is 2,564. In the city of Beograd there are 1,277 Jews, in Subotica 410, Novi Sad 274, Sombor 88, Zemun 66, Zrenjanin 36, Pancevo 34, Senta 28, Nis 25, Backa Topola 23, Kikinda 18, Apatin, Vrsac and Backa Palanka each 16, Pristina 14, Bajmok 12, Vrbas 11, Becej and Pozarevac 10 each.

Jewish Community of Croatia, In Croatia, out of a total of 2,021 Jews, there are 1,305 in Zagreb; Osijek has 175, Split 90, Rijeka 74, Daruvar 24, Susak 22, Cakovec and Dubrovnik 21 each, Slavonska Pozega 19, Belisce 16, Djakovo 15, Sibenik and Bjelovar 13 each, Donji Miholjac and Opatija 12 each,

Nova Gradiska and Virovitica 11 each, Koprivnica, Ogulin and Vinkovci 10 each.

Jewish Community of Bosnia and Hercegovina, Bosnia and Hercegovina has 1,261 Jews. Sarajevo has 1,010. Other Jewish settlements are: Mostar 58, Tuzla 37, Zenica 23, Banjaluka 19, Jajce 16, Zavidovici and Travnik 15.

According to a report in the *New York Times* of May 9, 1954, of the once relatively prosperous Sephardic community in Sarajevo of 10,000, only 600 remain. The synagogue is neglected, and Yugoslavia's only rabbi performed the Passover services with 18 worshippers. Opposite the synagogue is a tiny Jewish cultural clubroom. At the seder, 30 people of the community and only two children participated, one of them the son of the Israeli Minister to Yugoslavia. There has been no barmitzvah since 1941, and circumcision is now a rarity. Many of the Jews intermarry. The great Sephardic temple was demolished by the invading Germans; another synagogue is now used as a dancing school. One of the Jews pointed out to the reporter that a Jewish museum will be erected soon in Sarajevo and he is afraid that not much more will be left if the de-Judaization of the once glorious community continues.

Jewish Community of Slovenia, There is a total of 100 Jews in Slovenia. Ljubljana having 60, Murska Sobota 19, and Maribor 14.

Jewish Community of Macedonia, There are 99 Jews here of whom 95 reside in Skoplje. In Crna Gora (Montenegro) there are 3 Jews, 2 in Cetinje, 1 in Kotor. There are more places in Yugoslavia where less than ten Jews live.

AFRICA

ALGERIA

JEWISH POPULATION: 130,000

During the first centuries of the Common Era, under the Romans, there were small Jewish settlements in at least seven cities. Under the Roman Empire, the Jews enjoyed civic equality. Under the Byzantine Empire, some of the synagogues were transformed into churches, and the Jews became subject to discriminations.

In the 7th century, Jews fleeing from Visigothic Spain augmented the Jewish community in North Africa. Some of the native Berber tribes accepted Judaism. Arab control, beginning with the 7th century, was more tolerable to Jews than Byzantine rule. But during the Almohade dynasty (1130–1269), merciless persecutions began, forcing many Jews to flee or accept Islam and to wear a special dress. More Spanish Jews came to Algeria in 1391 to escape new persecutions. The most famous scholars immigrating with the Spanish Jews were Rabbi Isaac bar Sheshet (Ribash, 1326–1408) and Simon Ben Zemah Duran (Rashbatz, 1361–1444) After the Spanish expulsion (1492), several thousand more Jews found refuge in Algeria. Under the Turks and their rulers, the Jews were subject to humiliating restrictions. They were confined to ghettos and compelled to wear black skull caps and shoes without heels and were forbidden to ride on horseback.

With the French conquest of Algeria in 1830, Jews gradually began to adopt French culture. Due to the influence of the Jewish Minister of Justice in France, Isaac Adolphe Cremieux, 38,000 Jews were accorded French citizenship in 1870. Anti-semitism flared up in 1934 in Constantine and other towns; more than a hundred Jews were slain and hundreds wounded in the rioting. The Jewish masses are poverty-stricken. The majority are peddlers, day laborers, and artisans.

The Alliance Israelite Universelle school established in Algiers in 1900 has more than 750 pupils. Algiers also has a boys' artisan school with 1,000 students, established in 1892, supported partly by the Alliance Israelite Universelle and partly by the Jewish community of Algiers. In Algeria, which is part of Metropolitan France, religious instruction in the elementary stage is left to the local congregations. There are, therefore, private religious schools, Talmud Torahs, in every community and a Rabbinical Seminary founded by the Federation of Jewish communities. The Ort maintains five different trade schools in Algiers and Constantine.

The largest communities in this country are those of Algiers, Oran, and Constantine. A large network of charitable societies and relief committees gravitates around the consistories of the local communities. A country-wide organization is the Algerian Zionist Inter-Federation which comprises the departmental federations and centralizes Israel-oriented activities. The World Jewish Congress, Alliance Israelite Universelle, WIZO, and youth groups, such as the Algerian Sections of the French Union of Jewish Students and of the Jewish Boy Scouts of France, as well as the various Zionist youth organizations, have branches in almost all communities and display much activity.

ALGIERS (Jewish population: 30,000)

Federation des Communautes Israelites d'Algerie 11, rue Bab el Oued.

Founded in April 1947, the Federation unites all the Jewish Communal Councils throughout the country, i.e. 16 religious communities in the Department of Algiers, 15 in the Department of Oran, and 9 in the Department of Constantine, as well as the Jews in smaller places. It represents Algerian Jewry in general and its constituent religious associations in particular and provides for the maintenance and development of their institutions.

The Federation convenes biennial general assemblies which elect the administrative council, and is represented on the Consistoire Israelite de France et d'Algerie by 7 delegates from the Department of Algiers, 7 from the Department of Oran, and 6 from the Department of Constantine. The Federation is affiliated with the *World Jewish Congress.* President: Benjamin Heller. General-Secretary: Albert Lellouche.

Rabbinic Council: Grand Rabbi of Algeria, Maurice Eisenbeth (36, rue Alfred Lelluch,

Algiers); Grand Rabbi of Constantine, Fredj Halimi; Grand Rabbi of Oran, David Askenazi; Grand Rabbi of Bone, Rahmin Naouri.

SYNAGOGUES:

The Grand Temple is at Place Abraham Bloch. Other temples are at: Rue Suffred, Rue Scipion, Rue Sainte, Rue de Dijon, Impasse Boutin, Rue Medee, Alee des Muriers (Alger-Belcourt), Temple d'Alger-Saint-Eugene.

Alliance Israelite Universelle, 11 rue Bab el Oued. Pres: Samuel Lebar. Sec: Albert Confino.

Association Consistoriale Israelite, 11, rue Bab el Oued. Pres: Maurice Belicha. Sec: Sylvain Farro.

Association d'Etudes, d'Aide et d'Assistance, 56 Avenue du Frais-Vallon. Founded in 1940 to help and support Jews excluded from their professions by the Laws of Vichy. From 1940 to 1942, it concerned itself with Jewish education at Algiers for the Jewish children being excluded from French state schools. Since 1947, it is concerned with the problems of Aliyah. Pres: Raymond Jonathan.

B'nai B'rith 38, Bld. du Telemly. Pres: B. Becache. Sec: J. Lamyeche.

Comite d'Aide Aux Refugees, 11 rue Dumont-d'Urville. Section of the American Joint Distribution Committee. Director: Elie Gozlan. Sec: Jean Gozlan.

Commission Culturelle Juive d'Algerie, 1, rue Mahon. Founded in 1952 for the coordination of Jewish cultural activities, its affiliate organizations consist of:

Congress Juif Mondial (Bureau Nord-Africian), 1, rue Mahon. Pres: Benjamin Heller. Director: Jacques Lazarus.

Comite Juif Algerien d'Etudes Sociales, 21, Bld. Bugeaud. It publishes the monthly "Information Juive," edited by J. Lazarus. Pres: Ernest Dadon. Sec: Jacques Lazarus.

Federation des Communautes Israelites d'Algerie. Described in detail above.

Union des Etudiants Juifs de France, 115, rue Michelet, Union of Jewish students in France. Pres: Pierre Attal. Sec: Andre Attya.

Conseil Superieur Rabbinique d'Algerie, 11, rue Bab el Oued. Pres: Grand Rabbi of Algeria, Maurice Eisenbeth. Sec: Rabbi Abraham Fingerhut.

Eclaireurs Israelites de France, 8 rue Scipion. Algerian Section of Jewish scouts of France. Provincial Commissioner: D. Bacry. Local commissioner: Sylvain Zenou.

Ecole Rabbinique d'Algerie, 11, rue Bab el Oued. Founded in April 1947 by a decision of the Federation, its aim is to train rabbis for Algerian communities. Directors: Grand Rabbi M. Eisenbeth and Rabbi A. Fingerhut.

Interfederation Sioniste Algerienne, 26, rue d'Isly. Zionist Federation of Algeria. Pres: Prof. H. Aboulker. Sec: Edmond Teboul.

Jewish Agency B.P. 54, Alger.

Keren Kayemeth Leisrael, 10, rue Bedeau. Director of Algerian office: Edmond Blum. Pres: Jacques Albou. Sec: Elie Zerbib.

La Bienfaisante, 2, Impasse Boutlin. A welfare organization. Pres: Gaston Saffar. Sec: Louis Ayache.

ORT, 8, rue Leon-Roches. Founded in 1946. Pres: Andre Chiche. Director: Georges Ensalem.

WIZO (*Section d'Alger*), 4, Bld. Laferriere. Pres: Mrs. Colette Aboulker. Sec: Mrs. P. Djian.

AIN-TEMOUCHENT
(Jewish Population: 1,500)

Association Cultuelle Israelite (Jewish Community), Bld. National. Pres.: Leon Karsenty. Sec.: David Bennsoussan.

BLIDA (Jewish Population: 2,000)

Association Cultuelle Israelite (Jewish Community) Place du Marche. Founded in 1862. Pres: Joseph Chiche. Rabbi: Serfati.

BONE (Jewish Population: 1,100)

Association Consistoriale Israelite (Jewish Community), rue Rabbin-Kahn. Pres: Raoul Naouri. Sec: Jacques Attal. Grand Rabbi: Rahmin Naouri. *Synagogue* Rue Rabbin Kahn.

BATNA (Jewish Population: 1,100)

Association Cultuelle Israelite de Batna (Jewish Community), rue Bugeaud. Founded in 1908. Pres: Isaac Guejd. Sec: Aaron Rehby.

CONSTANTINE (Jewish Population: 14,000)

Association Consistoriale Israelite de Constantine (Jewish Community). Place Negrier. Founded in 1908 to execute Jewish religious practices. Pres: Paul Barkatz. Sec. and Grand Rabbi: Fredj Halimi.

Commission du Congress Juif Mondial, 3, rue des Fr. Beraud. Pres: Marcel Amram. Sec: Simon Allouche.

Federation des Oeuvres Sociales, 3, rue Feraud. Federation of Welfare Organizations. Pres: Max Sebbah.

Tribunal Rabbinique, Place Negrier. Pres: Grand Rabbi Fredj Halimi.

Synagogues: "Rebbi Messaoud," rue Jose Ksentine; "Kadima," Impasse rue Henri-Namia; "Djerdida," rue Damremont; "Algerois," place Negrier; "Midrach," rue Thiers; "Rebbi Benjamin" rue Pottier; "Sidi Bahi", rue Pottier; "Bellevue", Banlieue superieure; and Synagogue de Bellevue, rue Pierre Loti.

Federation Sioniste Departementale, Place Negrier. Pres: Maurice Toubiana. Sec: Mrs. Gozlan.

American Joint Distribution Committee, 3, rue Feraud. Director: Samuel Levis.

Keren Kayemeth Leisrael, Place Negrier. Pres: Charles Bouchara.

ORT, 15, rue du 3-e Chasseurs d'Afrique. Pres: Joseph Attali. Sec: Armand Sarbib.

Or Thora, rue Louis Lecont. Supports needy students and publishes religious text books. Rabbi Daniel Renassia.

Union des Etudiants Juifs de France, 4, rue Georges Clemenceau.

WIZO, 11, rue Lavedan. Pres: Mrs. Aurette Narboni. Sec: Miss Irene Zerbib.

COLOMB-BECHAR
(Jewish Population: 1,900)

Association Cultuelle Israelite (Jewish Community) Rue de Colonel-Pein. Founded in 1932. Pres: Jacob Sebban.

GHARDAIA (Jewish Population: 1,300)

Communaute Israelite (Jewish Community). Pres: Sebban Balouka.

GUELMA (Jewish Population: 1,050)

Association Cultuelle Israelite (Jewish Community), rues Mogador at Duquesne. Founded in 1907. Rabbi: Daniel Halimi. Pres: Armand Attali. Sec: Michael Gozlan.

MASCARA (Jewish Population: 1,800)

Association Cultuelle Israelite (Jewish Community), rue d'Alger. Founded in 1905. Pres: Joseph Bensadoun. Sec: Adolphe Benamour.

MOSTAGANEM (Jewish Population: 1,850)

Association Cultuelle Israelite (Jewish Community), rue de la Mina. Founded in 1901. Pres: Rene Roubache. Sec: Albert Aim.

ORAN (Jewish Population: 30,000)

Association Cultuelle Israelite (Jewish Community), 27, Bld. du Marechal-Joffre. Founded in 1850. Grand Rabbi David Askenazi. Pres: Albert Smadja. Sec: Georges Garson.

Alliance Israelite Universelle

Commission du Congres Juif Mondial, 7, rue Lamartine. Pres: A. Smadja. Sec: Georges Garson.

Federation Sioniste Departemental, 16, rue Mac-Mahon. Pres: Albert Smadja. Sec: Rabbi S. Cohen.

Keren Kayemeth Leisrael, 9, rue Pierre-Tabarot. Pres: Benayoun.

WIZO, 14, rue de la Paix. Pres: Mrs. Carcassone. Sec: Mrs. G. Serfaty.

SIDI-BEL-ABBES (Jewish Population: 3,200)

Association Cultuelle Israelite (Jewish Community), 6, rue Gambetta. Founded in 1890. Pres: Georges Charbit.

TLEMCEN (Jewish Population: 5,500)

Association Cultuele Israleite (Jewish Community), 5, rue de Rabb. Founded in 1945. Pres: Nessim Bensaken.

Smaller Jewish communities called "Association Cultuelle Israelite" exist in the following places: Affreville, Aflou, Ain-Beida, Aumale, Berrouaghia, Biskra, Boghari, Bordj Bou Arreridj, Boufarik, Bougie, Bou Saada, Djelfa, Duperre, El-Oued, Frenda, Geryville, Hussein Dey, Inkerman, Khenchela, Laghouat, Lamoriciere, Marengo, Medea, Miliana, Montagnac, M'sila, Nedroma, Nemours, Orleansville, Palikao, Perregaux, Phillipeville, Reibell, Relizane, Rio-Salado, Saida, Saint-Denis-Du-Sig, Setif, Souk-Ahras, Tebessa, Zenita.

PUBLICATIONS:

Information Juive, monthly. Published by the Comite Juif Algerien d'Etudes Sociales, 21, Bld. Bugeaud, Algiers. Editor: J. Lazarus.

l'Annuaire du Judaisme Nord-Africain, 21, Bld. Bugeaud, Algiers. Annual.

BELGIAN CONGO

JEWISH POPULATION: 2,500

The Congregation Israelite du Katanga in Elisabethville is recognized by the Government of the Colony as the spokesman for the Jewish community there. The Congregation represents all the Jews in the Congo. They live in eight major communities and a few smaller groups the overwhelming majority of which are members of the Congregation. The Congregation is administered by a 14-man committee, elected annually.

Organized Jewish religious life exists mainly in the two communities Elisabethville and Jadotville. The other Jewish settlements are linked, through membership, with the Congregation in the capital, Elisabethville.

The Government schools have instituted courses in religion and Hebrew which are attended by Jewish children of school age. Jewish publications in the Congo consist of 2 bi-weekly bulletins, published in French by the Zionist Association and the Revisionist group.

The Congregation is affiliated with the World Jewish Congress. Recently, the Congregation decided to establish a Jewish library and has undertaken a census of the Jewish population in the country.

ELISABETHVILLE—535 Jews.

Congregation Israelite du Katanga, Elisabethville, P.O.B. 931. Pres: B. Amato. Vice-Pres: J. Soriano and L. Benzakeim. Sec: S. Hassan. Grand Rabbin: Moise Levy.

Zionist Association of Belgian Congo comprises *WIZO, Habonim,* and *Union of Zionist Youth,* as well as a Revisionist group.

JADOTVILLE—60 Jews

There is a Jewish congregation and a synagogue which are affiliated with the Congregation Israelite of Elisabethville.

EGYPT

JEWISH POPULATION: 25,000

Ever since Biblical times, there have been Jewish settlements in Egypt. During the Greek and Ptolemaic periods, a widespread Jewish diaspora existed in the country. Alexandria is mentioned as a huge Jewish community. Under Arab rule, Egypt became an important Jewish center.

During the 19th century, the position of the Egyptian Jews was politically tolerable.

After the second world war, Egyptian Jewry numbered about 80,000. By 1951, the Jewish population had decreased to 45,000. 22,000 living in Cairo and 20,000 in Alexandria. Out of the 35,000 Jewish emigrants from Egypt, 25,000 settled in Israel. Egyptian Jewry is composed of three groups: Sephardim, Ashkenazim, and *Karaites*. Each of these maintains a separate congregation in Cairo. In Alexandria, all three are represented by a joint community Council. Alexandria is the only place in the world where the *Karaites* are members of a Jewish community.

There are approixmately 1,500 *Karaites* in Egypt concentrated mainly in Cairo. They have played a significant role in the spiritual life of Egypt. Many prominent writers, physicians, and artists were members of the *Karaite* community. The *Karaites* have their own publication "Al-Calim," edited by Joseph Kamal. They have two synagogues with two "hakhamim" (rabbis) Joseph Haina and Baruch Salah. Since the establishment of the State of Israel, their situation has deteriorated considerably and at least 3,000 emigrated to Israel. Sixty families founded the settlement Mazliah near Ramlah and 55 families, the village Rannen in the Negev.

When Egypt became independent after the first World War, the situation of the Jews continued to be rather satisfactory. However, since the emergence of the State of Israel, anti-Jewish feelings have become more widespread despite official statements distinguishing between "justified" hostility toward Zionists and Israelis and between Egyptian Jews. There were anti-Jewish outbreaks in 1951 when a bomb was thrown at the old Synagogue of Alexandria and during the rioting in Cairo, when Jewish merchants constituted a large portion of the victims, and in 1952, when Jewish establishments were destroyed. Since the Israel War of Liberation in 1948, discrimination against Jews has been rampant.

About 150 Jews were arrested in 1954 on charges of "Zionist activities." Thirteen Jews were sentenced by a military tribunal as "Zionist spies," one of them committed suicide in jail and two others were sentenced to death, and despite protests from many countries, they were executed. The others got long-term imprisonment. The study of Hebrew and the agricultural training of Jewish youth are prohibited. The Maccabi stadium is closed since the war against Israel. Only 1,800 children remain in Cairo, while in 1948, there were still 4,500.

Arbitrary mass arrests, discriminatory taxation, a virtual economic boycott culminating in expulsion, incarceration of thousands in concentration camps, and expropriation following Israel's Sinai campaign in the fall of 1956 describe the detertorating position of Egyptian Jewry. The total number of the Jews in Egypt has been reduced considerably and is now estimated to be below 25,000.

At lease 12,000 were forced to flee after the Sinai-Suez conflict in 1956.

The communities in Cairo and Alexandria maintain 15 Jewish schools with an enrollment of about 2,000 children. There are also two schools in Tanta with 150 pupils and two schools in Port Said with 100 pupils. The Sephardim in Cairo had a Jewish hospital in the city which was confiscated in November, 1956. Smaller Sephardic communities also exist in Tanta, Mansurah, Port Said, and Damanhur.

CAIRO (13,000 Jews)

Jewish Community. The Jewish community comprises separate congregations of Ashkenazim and Sephardim which maintain their own synagogue and schools, as well as the Jewish hospital. Pres: Salvador Cicurel. Chief Rabbi: Haim Nahum. 12 Sharia Zaki, Tewfikieh, Cairo.

ALEXANDRIA (11,000 Jews)

Jewish Community. The Jewish Community Council embraces the Ashkenazim, Sephardim, and Karaites. It maintains the Synagogues and schools. Pres.: Edwin Gohar. Interim chief rabbi: M. Angel.

ETHIOPIA

JEWISH POPULATION:
25,000 FALASHAS, 300 JEWS OF OTHER ORIGIN

There undoubtedly existed an ancient settlement of Jews in the country which exerted a strong influence prior to the appearance of Christianity.

In the 10th century, the Zaguè dynasty arose, and some of its rulers were considered to be Jewish Kings. The Zaguè dynasty ended in 1270, but some independent Jewish rulers maintained themselves in the northern part of the country until the 16th century when they were defeated by King Sara Dengel. A further massacre of the Jews by King Susenyos in 1617 wiped out the last vestiges of the independence of the Falashas.

Falashas in Ge'ez, the classical Abyssinian semitic tongue, means "immigrants" or "strangers." Falashas are, today, artisans, repudiating commerce and usury which they regard as incompatible with Mosaic law. In 1935, they were estimated to number about 50,000. Since then, their number has gradually decreased through persecutions and conversions to other religions.

Due to the efforts of Joseph Halevy of France (1867) and recently of Jacob Feitelovitch (1904), Jews in other countries have taken an interest in the plight of the Falashas and in maintaining them in their Judaism. Native teachers have been trained in Jerusalem. In 1924, a Jewish school for the Falashas was opened in the capital, Addis Ababa, with 50 pupils. In 1937, the Jewish Community in Addis Ababa numbered about 200, of whom 54 were Falashas, 60, Yemenite Jews and 40, European Jews. A Jewish community was also organized in Diredawa. After Mussolini adopted an antisemitic policy, the situation of the Falashas worsened, and the Jewish communities in Addis Ababa and Diredawa were dissolved.

After World War II, their situation improved and many of them prepared to emigrate to Israel, but they encountered difficulties. 280 succeeded in entering Israel. Most of the Falashas are scattered in the small rural districts, over the country, mainly in the mountainous north. They have their religious leaders of the priestly tribe "Cohanim" who give primitive religious instruction to the children and officiate at the religious services.

No exact figure is available as to the number of the Falashas. James Bruce, a British explorer of the 18th century, speaks of half a million Falashas. Missionary reports of the 19th century estimate their number about 200,000. In recent years, however, estimates have dropped considerably, approximately to 25,000, due to persecutions and missionary activities exploiting their economic distress. Their communities are scattered particularly in the Amhara, Tigri, and Shoa regions and in Eritrea. Many live as Marannos to avoid persecution.

Rabbi Samuel Beeri delegated from Jerusalem to Abyssinia by the Department for Tora Education and Culture of the Zionist Organization re-established a Jewish educational institution named "Niddahe Israel" in Asmara in 1954. The school is attended by 24 students consisting of 7 Cohanim, 15 other boys, and 2 girls from various Falasha villages who will return to their homes as leaders and teachers on completion of their studies. One group of 12 Falasha youngsters recently arrived in Israel to study there two years with the intention to return to Abyssinia as trained instructors and teachers.

ADDIS ABABA (125 Jews)

Jewish Community, P.O.B. 463.
Pres.: Shalom Shilomay, P.O.B. 50.
Most of the Yemenite Jews have left for Israel.
Synagogue "Succat Rahamim," maintained mainly by the Adenite Jews.

ASMARA (ERITREA) 220 Jews)

Eritrea Jewish Community, Avenue Empress Manen 96. P.O.B. 22, Asmara. The majority are Sephardim and Yemenite Jews from Aden. Affiliated with the World Jewish Congress. Prayer house and Bet Din (Rabbinical Court).
Jewish School, 15 pupils.
Hebrew Club. Serves as community center.
Rabbi: Rason Tobi.
Pres. of Community: Shoa Menahem Joseph.
Sec.: Jacob Samuel Cohen.

The Falashas are not organized in congregations but they have leaders in every region where they reside who represent them before the authorities and exert their influence upon the villages of their brethren. According to a recent report (1954) of the above-mentioned Rabbi Samuel Beeri, the Christian Mission maintains schools for poor Falasha children who attend them because of the material support distributed; this results in the conversion of many children to Christianity. Rabbi Beeri, together with the leader and learned Falasha, Mr. Jona Bugalah, aided by a committee of 5 priests (Cohanim) compiled for us the following list of Falasha settlements:

Region:	No. of Villages	Central Settlement	Leader	Population
Zohra	15	Ouzava (362 persons)	Aba Ezaria	1,486
Sekelth	23	Tevivber (99) Gayna (150)	Blatha Aitgev) Betbevu Itzhak)	1,611
Belesa	5	Belbaho Curi	Aba Mehreth) Athu Kindey)	470
Voinadega	6	Dergage	Tegenya Gember	114

Region:	No. of Villages	Central Settlement	Leader	Population
Vogara	62	Benber	Mamu Zega	
		Charvita	Itzhak Adgeh	7,563
		Brera	Itzhak Vondmageni	
Telemth	16	Falashotz Gay	Sabbathai	1,050
Smayn	32	Melata	Aba Menashe	3,200
Volkaith	11	Vofargef	Hadrai	1,150
Tegedi	9	Mezrei Gevata	Vondemneh	650
Merena	16	Avena	Sholom Shemi	1,309
Aschefer	12	Dengelber	Hazvater Meconen	300
Alefa	3	——	——	150
Coza Vogara	6	Assuha	Yisha	250
The entire Gamdar Area	totals		....	20,803
Volo area		Zastha		1,500
Thegerey		Asgedi	Noga	
Area	20	Byeth Miriam	Kes Itzhak	1,250

Falasha population 23,553

Scattered in other places not included in the above list 1,500

Thus, the total Falasha population is estimated at 25,000

KENYA

JEWISH POPULATION: 1,000

Jewish settlement in British East Africa dates from 1903, when the British Government offered the Zionist Organization a territory in the present Kenya for an autonomous Jewish settlement. Shortly afterwards, a few Jews settled in the territory. More recently, a number of Central European Jewish refugees have been admitted to the colony and given the opportunity of establishing themselves there. Jewish life and Zionist activities in Kenya are centered around the synagogues.

Board for Kenya Jewry, P.O.Box 2145, Nairobi.
President: I. Somen.
Secretary: D. Somen.

The Board, which is a central body for the Jews in the colony, has as its constituents the Hebrew Congregations of Nairobi, Nakuru, Mombasa, and of the Kitale-Eldoret District, as well as the Jewish social and charitable societies of Nairobi. Their delegates elect annually the members of the Board, including four officers. Mr. I. Somen is also Deputy Mayor of Nairobi.

East African Jewish Guild, P. O. Box 1254, Nairobi.
President: J. Gross.

Kenya Zionist Council, P.O. Box 6220, Nairobi.
Chairman: G. Farkas

Council for Training and Settlement.
President: I. Somen.
Secretary: Mrs. D. Katzler.

NAIROBI

Nairobi Hebrew Congregation, P. O. Box 990. Est. 1907.
President: S. W. Ellis.
Minister: Rev. A. H. Karwan.

WIZO, Nairobi Branch, P. O. Box 5187.
President: Mrs. B. V. Levy.

Vermont Memorial Hall Management Committee, P. O. Box 990. The Hall was built in 1938. It is the center of all local Jewish religious, educational, cultural, and social activities.

Zionist Society, President: Mrs. L. Keen.

KITALE-ELDORET

Hebrew Congregation, P. O. Box 194, Kitale.
Chairman: I. Latke.
Secretary: R. A. Haller.

WIZO, Chairman: Mrs. H. Mendel.
Zionist Society. Secretary: R. A. Heller.

MOMBASA (10 Jewish families)

Hebrew Congregation, P.O.Box 577. Est. 1940.
President: M. Freed.

WIZO, President: Mrs. L. Beck.
Secretary: Mrs. H. Strauss, P.O.Box 2012.

NAKURU

Hebrew Congregation, P.O.Box 159. Est. 1941.
President: D. Ruben.
Secretary: A. Rosenston.
Minister: Rev. H. Lichtenstein.
Zionist Society, P. O. Box 166.
WIZO. Secretary: Mrs. H. Gordon.

PUBLICATION:
East African Jewish Review. Monthly. P.O.B. 5211, Nairobi.

LIBYA

JEWISH POPULATION: 3,000

Libya, a former Italian colony in North Africa, with a population predominantly Arabic, became an independent country on December 24, 1951 by a decision of the General Assembly of the United Nations.

Israel voted in the UN for the independence of Libya. Dr. Perlzweig, representative of the World Jewish Congress, visited the Jewish community there and was authorized to represent the Libyan Jews in the Social and Economic Committee of the UN, where he succeeded in including in the constitution of the new state guarantees for the equal rights of the Jewish population.

There were about 37,000 Jews in Libya after World War II, but 33,000 of these left the country for Israel, just before or immediately after it became independent. About 3,500 Jews remain.

In spite of the fact that the constitution guarantees full equality to all of the country's citizens, regardless of creed or race, the Jews are discriminated against in many respects. They cannot vote or be elected to public office. No Jews are employed by the government. Jews are not admitted to the army or police forces. The last four Jewish police officers were dismissed recently simply because they were Jews.

Jews going abroad receive a laissez-passer valid for only six months instead of the usual five-year passport. Failure to return to Libya before expiration of this period may entail the loss of citizenship and the right of residence in Libya. A Moslem Libyan is readmitted even if he has no valid passport at all.

Foreign Jews residing in Libya have to renew their identity papers and residence permits every six months. If they go abroad for a period exceeding six months, they lose their residence permits.

Libyan Jews who leave the country are not permitted to take their belongings.

Maccabi, the Jewish sports organization, has been closed since December 1953, despite the fact that a search of the premises revealed nothing illegal or even suspicious.

Correspondence with Israel is strictly forbidden, although almost all Libyan Jews have relatives there.

Moslems who used to be friendly to Jews now avoid all contact with them. The Jewish population feels that its position is most precarious, that none of its legitimate rights can now be considered secure.

Since the mass Aliyah to Israel brought about the liquidation of the Jewish communities in the interior, there are only two communities left in Libya, namely that of Tripoli, and a smaller one in Benghazi. A relief committee and the youth club, Maccabi, are active in Tripoli. Two Jewish day schools, Citta Vecchia and Roma, are maintained by the Community in Tripoli. In addition, there are an Alliance school and 5 yeshivot.

Jewish Community of Tripolitania, 2 Via Generale Caneva, Tripoli.
President: Joseph Barda.
Secretary: Dino Yona.

Jewish Community of Cyrenaica, Benghazi.
President: Saul Legziel.
Secretary: Nessim Jona.

These two Communities, which represent the Jews of their respective regions, are recognized by the Government. Their administrative committees are elected by the members of the communities, and their work consists of fostering the religious life of their respective communities, spreading Jewish culture, and conducting charitable activities.

MOROCCO

JEWISH POPULATION: 220,000

There were numerous Jewish colonies in North Africa long before it became a Roman province (42). In 429, the Vandal king, Genserich, conquered North Africa with the aid of the Jews whom he freed from all restrictions imposed upon them. In the 6th century, many Spanish Jews emigrated to Morocco to escape persecutions under the Visigoth kings, bringing with them western culture, industry, and commerce. In the 7th century, many Berber tribes professing Judaism came into power. In 696, the heroic priestess Kahinah of the Jewish Berber tribes of Jerwa, under whose leadership most of the Berber tribes united, defeated the army of

Caliph Abdalmelek. However, the Arabs subsequently vanquished Kahinah, who fell in battle.

In the 8th and 9th centuries, the Jews lived in peace. Their residential quarter was called the "Mellah" (salted place, i.e. marsh). But in the 11th century, persecutions against the Jews were renewed. In 1032, 6,000 Jews were slaughtered in Fez and the women dragged off into slavery by the Arabs. When the liberal Almoravids came into power in 1062, the harsh conditions of the Jews were alleviated. In 1147, the Almoravids were conquered by the Almohades, who forced the Jews either to embrace Islam or emigrate. It was during the Almohades dynasty that, for the first time, Jews were forced to wear a particular costume—prototype of the Jew-badge.

The expulsion of Jews from Spain (1492) and from Portugal (1497) brought many thousands to Morocco.

In the 19th century, the Jews were again subjected to severe persecution. In 1899, about 2,500 Jewish children died in Marrakesh alone of smallpox and in 1901, an epidemic of typhus claimed 3,000 victims in four months. Besides limited Talmud Torah instruction, no training was accessible to Jewish youths. With the French and Spanish occupations, the situation improved and the humiliating restrictions were eliminated in 1907.

The present Jews of Morocco might be divided into three classes: (1) Berbers or Mountain Jews, (2) Sephardic Jews, and (3) European Jews. In 1942, there were about 30,000 *Berber* Jews in the mountainous regions and in the desert. The men are tall, healthy, swarthy, and observant. They knew little about the origins of Judaism, except for the tales about Jerusalem and Palestine that came down to them from their forefathers. Some of them speak a little Hebrew. Besides the Heder, no education is accorded to their children. Great poverty prevails. Trade, handicrafts, and begging provide the means of livelihood. About 50% of them are engaged in handicrafts.

The *Sephardic* Jews live in the European quarters of the large cities. They have their own synagogues and cultural life. They are pious, Zionistically inclined, hospitable, and charitable. The *European* Jews came to Morocco during World War II, after the Germans occupied Belgium, Holland, and France.

The adoption of anti-Jewish laws by the Vichy government in 1940 affected Moroccan Jewry, resulting in anti-Jewish demonstrations in the leading cities. Jews were ousted from government positions and ordered back into the ghetto. Following the defeat of Germany, Jewish rights in Morocco were restored but their economic position continues to be grave. Over 40,000 of them have immigrated to Israel in recent years. Arab leaders, struggling for the independence of Morocco, promised the representatives of the World Jewish Congress that the Jews would have equal rights with all citizens. The fact, however, that France granted autonomy to Morocco increased the feeling of insecurity of the Jewish population, and the emigration to Israel has risen considerably since 1955.

Educational facilities for Jewish children in Morocco are very poor. (See Steven D. Wolkowicz: "Mission to Morocco, A Report on Moroccan Jewry," published by the World Jewish Congress in 1947). Compulsory education is unknown, although about 20% (50,000) of the Jewish Moroccan population consists of children of school age. About 25% of the Jewish children receive no instruction at all. The total number of Jewish youth in schools in 1947 was 18,508. There are about 75 schools of the Alliance Israélite Universelle in Morocco, with a total enrollment of over 30,000 children. These schools are subsidized by the government and the Jewish Community. A special seminary for teachers (Magen David) was established in 1947 for the purpose of providing an intensive training course in Hebrew. Approximately 6,000 boys learn Hebrew and Talmud in the Yeshivoth and Hadarim of the organization "Otzar Hatorah." Noteworthy in the educational sphere are the Jewish day schools bearing the names of Narcisse Leven, Moise Nehon, S. Reinach, and Y. Semach.

The largest Jewish communities are Casablanca, Marrakesh, Meknes, Fez, and Rabat. Besides the communities listed below, there are about 40,000 Jews scattered in minor places in Morocco. In the Zionist field, the various parties have their own groups; numerous associations in various fields are active.

In June, 1956, the authorities of Morocco, which lately had achieved a great measure of independence from France, prohibited Jewish emigration to Israel, despite previous assurances to grant full freedom to the Jews including the right of emigration.

Conseil des Communautes Israélites du Maroc, 12, rue Delcasse, Rabat.

This is the central body of Moroccan Jewry with its seat in Rabat and on which the officially recognized local communal committees are represented. Regional delegates: for Casablanca: Joseph Abehsera, Albert Malka, Fortune Moreno, David Bergel; for Marrakesh: David Mimran, Maurice Corcos, Elie Abenhaim (Mogador); for Fez: Jacques Bensimhon; for Meknes: Mimoun Mrejen; for Rabat: Jack Ohana; for Oujda: Moise Azoulay; for Agadir: Moise Coriat. Jewish delegates at the Section for Morocco of the Governmental Council: Casablanca—Jacques Perez; Rabat—Jacques Dahan; Fez—Samuel Hamou; Meknes—Joseph Berdugo; Marrakesh—David Mimram; Oujda—Jacob Cohen. General Treasurer: Georges Benabou. Joint General Treasurers: Nessim Levy, Jacques R. Ohana. General Secretary: Jacques Dahan. Joint General Secretaries: Jacques Perez, Joseph Berdugo, Samuel Hamou. Publication: "La voix des Communautes" (monthly).

Comite Central Marocain du Congres Juif Mondial, 111, avenue General-Drude, Casablanca. The central committee for Morocco was founded in 1950. Represented are the Local Congress Committees in the larger communities of Casablanca, Rabat, Meknes, Fez, Marrakesh, Oujda, Ouezzane, Port-Lyautey, Safi, and Sefrou. The Working Committee is elected at the Annual Assembly of the delegates of the Provincial Branches. It works in close cooperation with the WJC French Section in Paris and the North African Bureau of the World Jewish Congress in Algiers.
President: Z. Schulmann.
Vice-President: Is. D. Abbou.
Secretary General: Me. Meyer Toledano.

CASABLANCA (Jewish population: 90,000)'
Communaute Israélite de Casablanca (Jewish Community), Place Djemma Es-Eouk.

Pres.: David Benazeraf.

Vice-Pres.: Jacques Perez, Joseph Abihsera.

Tres.: Max Tangy.

Sec.: Armand Assouline.

Tribunal Rabbinique, 7, Rue de la Douane. Grand Rabbi Haim Bensoussan.

Agence Juive, 55, ave. du General d'Amade.

Pres.: B. Blumenthal.

Aide Scolaire, 109, bld. Moulay Youssef. Founded in 1923 to furnish support through scholarships to poor pupils.

Pres.: Jo Levy.

Sec.: E. Sikirdji.

Alliance Israélite Universelle, Garden House, rue Azema, Casablanca-Oasis.

The section for Morocco of the A.I.U. began its activity there with the foundation of the first school at Tetuan in 1862. In 1955, it maintained 71 schools with over 30,000 pupils.

Pres.: Jules Braunschwig. Delegate of the A.I.U. for Morocco, Ruben Tajouri.

Schools of the A.I.U.: *Groupe Scolaire "William Oualid,"* 234/236 bld. Rgts., Coloniaux. Directors are Israel Sabetay (for boys) and Mrs. Elise Farache (for girls). *Ecole Rue Lesseps.* Dir.: Eliezer Sikirdji. *Ecole de Garcons,* 74, bld. Moulay-Youssef. Dir.: Nessim Levy. *Ecole N. Leven,* 85, bld. Moulay-Youssef. Dir.: Leon Arari. *Ecole M. Nahon,* 97, bld. de Bordeaux. Dir.: Miss Messodie Levy. *Ecole Professionelle Israelite,* 20, bld. Rgts. Coloniaux. Dir.: Leon Gomel. *Ecole Y. D. Demach,* 83, bld. Moulay-Youssef Dir.: Joseph Bassan. *Ecole Y. D. Semach,* 109, bld. Moulay-Youssef. Dir.: Mrs. Rachel Levy.

American Joint Distribution Committee, 80, bld. de Marseille. The section for Morocco cooperates with the O.R.T., Ozar Hatorah, the A.I.U., and, especially, with educational institutions. The principal activities: meals, service for health, and education.

Dir.: William Bein.

Association des Anciens Eleves de l'A.I.U., 46, rue Lacepede.

Pres.: Albert Bensoussan.

Sec.: Jacques Mellui.

Association de la Jeunesse Juive "Charles Netter," 33, rue Malherbe. Founded in 1930, the aim: physical and intellectual development of Jewish youth.

Pres.: Albert Levy.

Sec.: J. Lasry.

Aumonerie Militaire des Troupes du Maroc, bld. Emile Zola. Jewish religious service for the troops in Morocco.

Centre Antituberculeaux, Oeuvre de Bourses d'Etude "Abraham Ribbi," 66, rue Coli. founded in 1938 to fight tuberculosis. Supports sanitoriums.

Pres.: S. D. Levy.

Comite de la B'rith Ivrit Olamit, 33, rue Malherbe.

Pres.: Alfonso Sabah.

Sec.: Isaac Levy.

Eclaireurs Israelites de France (Jewish scouts), 33, rue Malherbe. Local groups exist in all Moroccan towns. Delegate commissioner for North Africa and director of the D.E.J.J. Edgar Gudej. Council of adm.: Pres. Emile Sebban. Vice-Pres.: Joseph Medioni.

Ecole Normale Hebraique "Maghen David" (Teachers' Seminary), rue des Sports, Casablanca-Oasis. Founded in 1945. Since 1946, a section of the A.I.U. Its aim is to educate teachers in Hebrew for the schools of the A.I.U. in Morocco.

Dir.: Rabbi I. Rouche.

Pres.: S. D. Levy.

Em Habanim, 10, rue Lusitania. Founded in 1938 to provide poor children with a Jewish education, food, clothing, and medical care.

Federation des Associations des Anciens Eleves de l'Alliance Universelle Israelite et de la Jeunesse Juive du Maroc, 33, rue Malherbe.

Home d'Enfants "Murdoch Bengio" (orphanage), 10, rue de Bally. Founded in 1944.

Pres.: Mrs. Celia Bengio.

Sec.: Mrs. Dory Marques.

Hoveve Hassafa, 15, bld. de Bordeaux. Aim: to promote the Hebrew language.

Pres.: Isaac Levy.

Sec.: Daniel Levy.

Keren Kayemeth Leisrael, 7, rue Lusitania.
Pres.: S. D. Levy.
Sec.: Elie Ohayon.

La Maternelle, rue Verlet-Hanus. Founded in 1927. Supports mothers in confinement. Dispensary and hospital. Kindergarten created in 1932.

Malbisch Aroumim (clothing for the poor), 16, rue Michael-Ange.

L'Oeuvre de Lait, 101, rue Centrale. Founded in 1941. Provides milk for babies without distinction of race.

O.S.E.—Maroc, 80, bld. de Marseille. Section for Morocco founded in 1946. Local sections at Marrakesh, Salé, Port-Lyautey, Fez, and Sefrou.
Pres.: S. D. Levy.
Sec.: Dr. I. Benzaquen.

O.R.T.—Maroc, 41, rue du General Marguerite. Founded in 1947. Maintains two professional schools. The boy's boarding school located at Ain-Sebaa. The girl's semi-boarding school is at Val d'Anaf.
Pres.: Jules Senouf.
Sec.: M. Toledano.

Otzar Hatorah, 118, rue des Anglais. Supports about 70 talmudical schools in Morocco.
Pres.: Rabbi Haim David Bennsoussan.
Sec.: Albert Malka.

Societe de Bienfaisance Israelite, 4, rue du Consulate d'Espagne. Welfare society for France, Tunisia, and Morocco. Founded in 1942.

Societe Maghen David, 6, rue Cottenest. For the promotion of the Hebrew language and literature.
Pres.: S. D. Levy.

WIZO, 62, rue Blaise Pasqual. Central body which embraces local sections of Casablanca, Fez, Rabat, and Meknes.
Pres.: Mrs. Marie Levy.

AGADIR (1,500 Jews)

Comite de la Communaute Israelite (Jewish community).
Pres.: David Moryoussef.
Sec.: Jacques Abisror.

AZEMMOUR

Comite de la Communaute Israelite (Jewish community), rue de la Casbah.
Pres.: Meyer Abichid.
Sec.: Raphael Levy.

FEDALA (500 Jews)

Communaute Israelite (Jewish community).
Pres.: Chaloum Ben David.
Sec.: Simon Malka.

FEZ (19,000 Jews)

Comite de la Communaute Israelite de Fez (Jewish Community), Boite Postale 101. The community takes care of social activities, subventioning local welfare organizations. It is especially concerned with religious education.
Pres.: Felix Serfaty.
Sec.: Moise Aflalo.

Congres Juif Mondial, 76, bld. Bouksissat.
Sec.: Moise Aflalo.

Aide Scolaire, Place du Commerce. Local section for scholarship aid.

Association des Anciens Eleves de l'A.I.U.
Pres.: Moise Aflalo.

Alliance Israelite Universelle. A.I.U. schools in Fez: *Eccle S. Levi,* place du Commerce.
Dir.: Haim Djivre.
Ecole de l'A.I.U., rue de l'Indochine.
Dir.: Elie Benozillo.

Association Juive pour la Lutte Contre la Tuberculose, Derb El Aouinet. Local section of Jewish association which fights tuberculosis.
Pres.: Isaac Aflalo.

Em Habanim. Hebrew school. Pres.: Checoury.

Hoveve Hassafa, 428, Derb El Ferd. For Hebrew language and culture.
Pres.: Samuel R. Azuelos.
Sec.: Saul Elkeslassy.

Oeuvre de Secours Aux Enfants. Hospital dispensary for children.
Pres.: Jacob Niddam.

Societe Israelite de Bienfaisance, Bld. Poeymirau. For welfare, founded in 1929.
Pres.: M. Charbit.

WIZO, 26, rue de Pologne.
Pres.: Mrs. Arrouas.

MARRAKESH (18,000 Jews)

Communaute Israelite de Marrakech (Jewish community).
Pres.: I. Larsy.

Comite de la Communaute Israelite, rue Arest-El-Maach.
Pres.: David Mimram.

Aide Maternelle. Society for help in cases of confinement.
Pres.: Mrs. David Mimram.

Aide Scolaire, rue Touareg. Aid for scholarship.
Pres.: Elias Benhamou.

Association des Anciens Eleves de l'A.I.U.
Pres.: David Mimram.

Alliance Israelite Universelle.
Dir.: A. Goldenberg. "Jacques Bigart" School
Dirs.: R. Camhy, N. Sarfaty, Miss Bemoaram. Professional school for agriculture.
Dir.: E. Harrus.

Congress Juif Mondial, 13, rue Tazi.
Pres.: David Elkaim.
Sec.: Moise Bibasse.

Oeuvre de Secours Aux Enfants, Trik Koutoubia. Aid for children.
Pres.: Joseph Israel.

MAZAGAN (3,200 Jews)

Comite de la Communaute Israelite Elkaim (Jewish community), avenue Richard d'Ivry.
Pres.: David Bergel.
Sec.: Messod Benchetrit.

Aide Scolaire, avenue Albert 1 e. Association for scholarship aid.
Pres.: Abraham Golfand.

Cercle de l'Union, avenue Commandant Lacheze.
Pres.: Santos Benatar.

MEKNES (18,500 Jews)

Comite de la Communaute Israelite (Jewish community), Portes du Vieux Mellah. Jewish activity since 15th century, officially founded in 1945. Assistance for the aged and indigent. Aid through food and clothing. Maintains holiday colonies, educational activities, home for the aged.
Pres.: Joseph Berdugo.
Sec.: Daniel Toledano.

Association des Anciens Eleves de l'A.I.U., rue Branly.
Pres.: David Mrejen.

Congres Juif Mondial, Boîte postale 51.
Pres.: Elie Berdugo.

Oeuvre de Nourriture et d'Habillement Scolaire Israelite, avenue du Mellah.
Pres.: Pinhas Mrejen.

Societe d'Assistance aux Malades Israelites, rue Branly. Association for assistance for ill and indigent persons.
Pres.: Joseph Mrejen.

Union des Dames Israelites, rue des Ecoles, Meknes-Nouveau Mellah.
Pres.: Mrs. Baruk Toledano.

WIZO, 14 avenue Polymireau.
Pres.: Miss Berdugo.

MOGADOR (8,250 Jews)

Comite de la Communaute Israelite (Jewish community), 2, rue du Lieutenant Bessede.
Pres.: Joseph D. Bohbot.
Sec.: Elie Abenhaim.

Aide Scolaire, Pres.: Joseph D. Bohbot.

Alliance Israelite Universelle, Ecole Auguste Baumier.
Dirs.: Mr. and Mrs. Bitton.

Keren Kayemeth Leisrael, B.P. 71.
Commissioner: M. Knafo.

Union des Dames Israelites pour l'Assistance Medicale.
Pres.: Rachel Benisty.

OUEZZANE (2,100 Jews)

Comite de la Communaute Israelite (Jewish community), 12, rue des Tanneurs.
Pres.: Elie M. Elhadad.
Sec.: Menachem Barcessat.

Alliance Israelite Universelle.
Dir.: Mr. and Mrs. Pinhas.

Association des Anciens Eleves de l'A.I.U.
Pres.: Leon Pinhas.

Congres Juif Mondial.
Pres.: Elie Elhadad.
Sec.: Leon Pinhas.

OUJDA (3,300 Jews)

Comite de la Communaute Israelite (Jewish community), rue Sidi-Brahim.
Pres.: Jacob Cohen.
Sec.: Elie Azoulay.

PORT-LYAUTEY (4,000 Jews)

Comite de la Communaute Israelite (Jewish community), 13, rue Benami.
Pres.: Georges Benabou.
Sec.: David Abeckjerr.

Association des Anciens Eleves de l'A.I.U., Immeuble "Tholet," bld. Clemenceau.
Pres.: David Abeckjerr.

Congres Juif Mondial, Immeuble "Peilleron," bld. Clemenceau.
Pres.: Maurice Karchen.

Oeuvre de Secours aux Enfants. Pres.: Elkain.

RABAT (15,000 Jews)

Comite de la Communaute Israelite (Jewish community), 7, rue Henri Popp.
Pres.: Joseph Berdugo.
Sec.: Benatar.

Aide Scolaire, 6 bis, rue de Kairouan. Association for scholarship. Gives food and clothing to pupils of A.I.U. schools and supports holiday colonies.
Pres.: I. Benchimol.

Congres Juif Mondial, 12, rue Rivoli.
Pres.: Felix Sicsic.

Ecoles de l'A.I.U. Boys' school "Salomon Reinach." Dir.: R. Oiknine.
Girls' school "Salomon Reinach."
Dir.: Mrs. Nahum.

Federation des Associations des Anciens Eleves de l'A.I.U., 1, rue de Bordeaux.
Pres.: Lazare Conquy.
Secs.: Bensoussan, Amar.

Haut Tribunal Rabbinique, 2, rue de Valanec. Supreme rabbinic tribunal.
Pres.: Grand Rabbi Saul Danan.
Sec.: Joseph Elmaleh.

Keren Kayemeth Leisrael, 9, Cite des Orangers.
Pres.: Charles Perez.

Union des Dames Israelites. Pres.: Mrs. Baruk.

WIZO, 12, rue Revoil. Pres.: Mrs. Sicsic.

SAFI (3,700 Jews)

Communaute Israelite de Safi (Jewish community). Pres.: N. Levy.

SALÉ (3,500 Jews)

Comite de la Communaute Israelite, (Jewish community). Pres.: Meyer Benaudis.

Association des Anciens Eleves de l'A.I.U.
Pres.: Henri Chnassia.
Sec.: Isaac Halioua.

Ecoles de l'A.I.U., Boys' school. Dir.: Lazare Conquy. Girls' school. Dir.: Miss Zalie Katalan.

Oeuvre de Secours aux Enfants. Pres.: Benaudis.

SEFROU (5,000 Jews, 700 non-Jews)

Comite de la Communaute Israelite (Jewish community), Boite postale 2. Takes care of charity, education, and instruction, 13 synagogues.
Pres.: Rahamim Tobaly.
Sec.: Isaac Botbol.

Association des Anciens Eleves de l'A.I.U. Founded in 1930.
Pres.: Abner Assouline.
Sec.: Guidaha Hamou.

Congres Juif Mondial, Correspondent: Rahamim Tobaly.

Ecole de l'Alliance Israelite Universelle.
Dir.: Torron.

Hebrat Eliahou Hanabe, Founded in 1905. Activities: funerals, circumcisions, bar-mitzvas, social service for ill persons, food and lodging for the indigent and homeless.
Pres.: Mimoun Levy.
Sec.: Meyer Mayost.

Hebrat Moshav Zekenem, Founded in 1930 for the aged.
Pres.: Youssef Mamane.
Sec.: Isaac Roben.

Ichivat "Beth David." School founded in 1939 with courses in Hebrew, Talmud, Bible, and French.
Pres.: Meyer Mayost.
Sec.: Hai Abner Azoulay.

Ichivat "Beth Rebeka." School for girls, founded in 1952. Courses in Hebrew, French, and sewing.

Pres. and Dir.: Rabbi David Obadia.

Oeuvre de Secours aux Enfants, "Assistance for Children" (O.S.E.), opened a hospital dispensary in 1949.

Pres.: Isaac Botol.

Sec.: Elie Ittah.

Societe d'Assistance aux Malades Indigents Israelites "Bikour Holim." Society for medical and social assistance for ill and indigent, founded in 1935.

Pres.: Rahamim Tobaly.

Sec.: Simon Afriat.

Societe de Bienfaisance "Em Habbanim." Talmud Torah school, founded in 1920.

Pres.: Jacob Tobaly.

Sec.: Abba Afriat.

SETTAT (1,600 Jews, 880 non-Jews)

Comite de la Communaute Israelite (Jewish community), rue de Caporal-Chef Henri Ohayon.

Pres.: David Melloul.

Sec.: Ralph Hayot.

TAZA (400 Jews)

Comite de la Communaute Israelite (Jewish community).

Pres.: Isaac Benhamou.

Sec.: Saaida Mamane.

PERIODICALS:

La Voix des Communautés, monthly, 12 rue Delcasse, Rabat.

Bulletin des Jeunes, monthly, 12 rue Prom. Casablanca.

SPANISH MOROCCO

JEWISH POPULATION: 14,300

Spanish Morocco played an important role as the cradle of the cultural life of North African Jewry.

All the Jews are Sephardim mostly deeply observant and organized in 8 communities.

The emigration of Jews from Spanish Morocco is considerable, mainly to South America, Tangier, to the French Zone, and Algeria. In the whole area, there are 8 Hebrew-Spanish schools with 20 teachers.

In Tetuan, Larache and El Kasar, there are Jewish schools maintained by the Alliance Israelite, in Tetuan with an enrollment of 430 children, Larache 150, El Kasar 200. In Tetuan, there is also a trade school, *Or Yeladim,* where 250 students are instructed in woodworking, metal

working, and electricity. This school was established by Moroccan Jews living in Venezuela and is subsidized by the Tetuan Jewish community. The Maimonides Institute was founded by the Spanish Government as a seminary for training rabbis and teachers. It has an attendance of 20 students. The Tetuan Jewish emigrants in Venezuela also support nurseries in Tetuan where 400 children are fed.

TETUAN (7,500 Jews)

Jewish Community, The Council of the community is nominated by a governmental decree.

Pres.: Isaac R. Benarroch, Tetuan, Apartado 49.

Sec.: Dr. Jacinto Gabizon.

Rabbinical Council, Pres.: Grand Rabbi Juda Leon Halfon, Tetuan, O'Donell 7.

There are 6 synagogues.

LARACHE (2,300 Jews)
Jewish Community.
Jewish School of the Alliance.

EL KSAR (2,200 Jews)
Jewish Community.
Jewish School of the Alliance.

VILLA NADOR (600 Jews)
Jewish Community.

ARZILA (570 Jews)
Jewish Community.

TERRITORY OF QUERT (325 Jews)

TERRITORY OF RIF (180 Jews)

OTHER PLACES, 535 Jews.

RHODESIA

JEWISH POPULATION: 7,200

As early as 1865 Jews lived in the territory of Lobengula, King of the Matabele.

The first Hebrew congregation was founded at Bulawayo, Southern Rhodesia, in 1894, in a tent.

The Hebrew congregation of Salisbury, the other large town of Southern Rhodesia, was founded in 1895.

A Jewish congregation was in existence in Livingstone, capital of Northern Rhodesia, until 1934. The first synagogue was opened in Livingstone in 1929, when the congregation consisted of some seventy persons and the Jewish population of Northern Rhodesia totaled about 200. At the same time, 1700 Jews lived in Southern Rhodesia.

In the mining district of Bechuanaland and Swaziland a number of Jews were active in 1943.

Rhodesian Jewish Board of Deputies (Southern and Northern Rhodesia). P. O. Box 1017, Bulawayo, and P. O. Box 442, Lusaka. An association of all organized Jewish bodies in Rhodesia, this central body is recognized by the Government and elected at biennial conferences by the delegates of its constituents, among which are all the religious congregations, the Rhodesian Zionist Council, the cultural circles, the benevolent societies, and the youth clubs. In its work the Board is assisted by regional committees in the Copperbelt, Midlands, Matabeleland, and Mashonaland. The Board is concerned with the whole field of Jewish civic and religious rights and internal communal organization.
Pres.: A. E. Abrahamson, M.P.
Sec.: M. Wagner.

Rhodesian Zionist Council, 34 Mimosa House, Ninth Avenue (Box 1162), Bulawayo. Affiliation of all Zionist bodies.
Pres.: S. Rabinovitz.
Sec.: L. Frank.

PUBLICATIONS:

Rhodesian Jewish Times, Box 1844, Salisbury. Monthly, English, Independent. Publisher and Editor: B. Goldin.

Rhodesian Jewish Journal (Supplement to South African Jewish Times, Box 2878, Johannesburg, S.A.). Monthly, English, Independent. Publisher: Sentinel Publishing Co. Editor: L. Feldberg.

SOUTHERN RHODESIA (6,000 Jews)

Bulawayo, 2,600 Jews.

Hebrew Congregation, P.O.Box 337. Founded in 1894.
Pres.: M. Abrahamson.
Membership: 510; Ashkenazim.
Community Centre. Pres.: Rev. W. Yesorsky.
Sec.: Mrs. T. Katz.
Chevra Kadisha and Free Loan Society, P.O.Box 1017.
Pres.: B. Abroms.
Sec.: E. Eliasov.
Membership: 600.
Louis Landau Hebrew School, Headmaster: Dr. C. Jacobson. 205 pupils.
Jewish Guild, Pres.: H. Eliasov.
Sec.: Mrs. S. Sher.
Bulawayo Jewish Memorial Library.
Pres.: H. Bloch.
Sec.: Mrs. H. Bloch.
2500 volumes.
Chovevi Zion Society, Founded 1897.
Pres.: A. Kramer.
Histadrut Ivrit, Pres.: A. Kramer. Sec.: M. Bina.
Yiddish Cultural Society, P.O.Box 1039.
Pres.: M. Myers. Sec.: Berkowitz.
Union of Jewish Women, 46, Pauling Road.
Pres.: D. Lazarus. Sec.: Mrs. S. Kaye.
Jewish Women's Communal League, 39a Main Street.
Pres.: Mrs. R. Jacobson.
Sec.: Mrs. D. Getz.
Chug Ivri, Bulawayo, Pres.: A. Kramer.
Women's Zionist Society, Pres.: Mrs. L. Fredman. Sec.: Mrs. D. Chai.
Habonim, Ba-Koach: S. Haimovitz.
Rabbi: W. Yesorsky, 46, Rhodes Street, Orthodox.

GATOOMA

Zionist Society and Wizo. Sec.: Mrs. B. Lewis.

GWELO

Hebrew Congregation. Pres.: M. Pearl. Sec.: M. Cohen.
Zionist Society. Pres., E. Katz.
Women's Zionist Society. Pres.: Mrs. P. Seider.
Sec.: Mrs. I. Behr.

QUE QUE

Hebrew Congregation. Pres.: S. Ashkenasia.
Sec.: R. Samson.

SALISBURY (Jewish population: 2,000)

Hebrew Congregation, Ashkenazim (Founded 1895), P.O. Box 342. Pres.: D. Shapiro.
Sec.: M. Peimer.
Salisbury Sephardic Hebrew Congregation, P.O.Box 1051.
Pres.: I. R. Rosin.
Sec.: A. Piha.
Hebrew English Nursery School, Supervisor: Mrs. M. Lewin. 35 pupils.
Salisbury Hebrew School. Headmaster: M. Bloch. 120 pupils.
Salomon Margolis Nursery School, 57 pupils.
Salisbury Jewish Benevolent Society. P.O.B.417.
Pres.: I. Lasovsky. Sec.: H. S. Court.
B'nai B'rith, P.O.Box 1719. Pres.: I. R. Rosin.
Sec.: H. E. Turkheim.
Union of Jewish Women. Pres.: Mrs. S. Kass.
Sec.: Mrs. E. Granger.
Salisbury Burial Society, P.O.Box 342. Chairman: M. E. Kaplan. Sec.: Rev. M. Konviser.
Jewish Cultural Society, P. O. Box 1579.
Pres.: E. Brod.
Phillip Bloom Communal Library, 2nd Street.
Pres.: E. Brod. Sec.: Miss E. Shwartz.
The Jewish Guild. Pres.: Dr. H. E. Gershon.
Sec.: Mrs. J. Nathan.
Zionist Society. Pres.: B. Kass. Sec.: Mrs. C. Trevis.
Women's Zionist Society. Pres.: Mrs.D. Shapiro.
Sec.: Mrs. C. Shulman, Mrs. F. Ruda.
Habonim. Pres.: L. Harris. Sec.: Miss II. Middledorf.
Rabbis: Dr. M. Papo, 111, Fife Avenue, Orthodox; Rev. M. Konviser, P. O. Box 342. Orthodox.

SELUKWE

Zionist Society, Sec.: J. S. Benatar.

SHABANI (Jewish population: 50)

Women's Zionist Society and Wizo.
Sec.: Mrs. P. Goldberg.

UMTALI

Eastern District Jewish Guild.
Pres.: B. D. Goldberg.
Vice-Pres.: L. Buddenstein.
Sec.: H. Vandenbergh.

NORTHERN RHODESIA (1,200 Jews)

Organisation of Northern Rhodesian Jewry,
c/o Miss T. Barber, Box 20, Lusaka.
Pres.: J. Mohrer.
Sec.: J. Edelstein.

BROKEN HILL

Hebrew Congregation. Pres.: H. Brin.

CHINGOLA

Hebrew Congregation. Treasurer: A. Dobkins,
H. Menashe, M. Katz.
Zionist Society, Pres.: M. Dobkins.

LIVINGSTONE (130 Jews)

Hebrew Congregation, P. O. Box 10.
Pres.: E. Kopelowitz. Sec.: A. Levy.
Rabbi: J. Szlapak, P.O.Box 278. Orthodox.
Union of Jewish Women. Pres.: Mrs. P. Rabb.
Sec.: Mrs. P. Radunsky.
Herzl Zionist Society. Pres.: A. Bean.
Sec.: Mrs. E. Bean.
Women's Zionist Society. Pres.: Mrs. P. Rabb.
Sec.: Mrs. R. Radunsky.

LUANSHYA

Hebrew Congregation. Pres.: M. Rosen.
Sec.: M. Abrahams.
Zionist Society. Pres.: J. Minchuk.
Women's Zionist Society. Pres.: Mrs. C.
Rosenfield. Sec.: Mrs. C. Rosenfield, Mrs.
G. Figov.

LUSAKA (Jewish population: 250)

Hebrew Congregation, P.O.Box 200.
Pres.: J. Mohrer. Sec.: G. Isaak.
Rabbi: S. Clayman, P.O.Box 442. Orthodox.
Union of Jewish Women. Pres.: Mrs. P. Barber. Sec.: Mrs. M. Bernson.
Zionist Society. Pres.: A. Galaun.
Sec.: H. Guttmann.
Women's Zionist Society. Pres.: Mrs. H.
Mohar. Sec.: Miss B. Clayman.

MUFULIRA

Hebrew Congregation. Pres.: V. Iljon.
Sec.: B. Epstein.
Women's Zionist Society. Pres.: Mrs. S. Schatz
Sec.: Miss B. Israel.
Zionist Society. Pres.: D. Messerer.
Sec.: B. Epstein.

N'DOLA

Hebrew Congregation, (Founded 1923), c/o
O. Schmal, Box 38.
Pres.: A. Lowenthal.
Sec.: O. Schmal.
Zionist Society. Pres.: N. Gordon.
Women's Zionist Society. Pres.: Mrs. Lowenthal. Sec.: Mrs. M. Katz.

NKANA-KITWE

Hebrew Congregation. Pres.: H. Bernstein.
Sec.: A. Kling.
Women's Zionist Society. Pres.: Mrs. A. Gersh.
Sec.: Mrs. C. Freedman.

SUDAN

JEWISH POPULATION: 346

The present Jewish residents came to Sudan at the end of the 19th century. Upon the proclamation of independence for Sudan in 1956, and since her joining the Arab League, the situation of its small Jewish community has become more precarious. All Zionist activities were prohibited, and an anti-Israel tendency is noticeable in order to demonstrate the country's solidarity with the anti-Israel policy of the

Arab League states. The Jewish Community in Khartoum is now cut off from all contact with outside Jewry. Hence there is an uneasiness about their future, despite the fact that the Sudanese people are very friendly towards them. The community has recently engaged a rabbi from Israel.

The Jews live in two small communities, in the capital, Khartoum, and in Port Sudan, both of very recent establishment.

KHARTOUM (200 Jews)

Sudan Jewish Community, P. O. Box 550.
 Pres.: David Joseph Gaon.
 Hon. Sec.: David Benzion Coshti, P.O.B.550, Khartoum, Sudan.

PORT SUDAN, *Jewish Community*.

TANGIER

(International Zone)

JEWISH POPULATION: 12,000

Comite de la Communaute Israelite de Tanger, Rue de Statut, Tangier. The Jewish Community of Tangier embraces 20 synagogues whose Governing Bodies form the Comite de la Communaute Israelite and whose membership triannually elects the 15-man Comite. The Comite, of which the president of the Rabbinical Tribunal is a member ex-officio, is a legal person recognized by the Government as the official Jewish representtion in the Zone. The Jewish Community has 3 delegates in the Legislative Assembly of the Zone.

The Community has established a special Committee to deal with World Jewish Congress affairs.

The Committee of the Community maintains a nusery school called Salvador Hassan, a Hebrew kindergarten, two primary Jewish day schools (jointly with the Alliance), and a Rabbinical Seminary attended by 70 students. Of the 1,500 Jewish children, 1,100 attended the two day schools.

 Pres.: Joe Hassan.
 Sec.: Abraham I. Laredo.
Tribunal Rabbinique.
 Pres.: Grand Rabbi Mardochee Enkaoua.
Congres Juif Mondial, Rue de Statut, Tangier.
 Members: Jack Pinco, James Nahon, Abraham I. Laredo, Stanley Abensour.
Alliance Israelite Universelle, Boy's School, 12, rue Alcazaba. Dir.: Benjamin Yanni.
 Girl's School. Dir.: Mrs. Sara Behar.
Association d'Aide a l'Enseignement Professional de la Jeunesse Juive, 75, Paseo Cenarra. Association to give aid for professional instruction of Jewish youth.
 Pres.: A. I. Laredo.
 Sec.: Albert Reinhard.
Oeuvre de Nourriture et d'Habillement des Eleves de l'A.I.U. Gives material assistance to poor pupils. Sec.: Raphael M. Laredo.
Oeuvre de Secours aux Enfants, 75, Paseo Cenarro. Branch of OSE.
 Pres.: Joe Hassan.
 Sec.: J. M. Pinto, Mrs. Coriat-Abensur.
Patronat Anti-Tuberculeux Israelite, rue Rebby Mordejay Bengio.
 Pres.: James M. Nahon.
 Sec.: Moses Labbos.

TUNISIA

JEWISH POPULATION: 75,000

According to an old tradition of Tunisian Jewry, Jews had already settled in the region before the destruction of the First Temple (586 B.C.). Many Jews came there after the destruction of Jerusalem in 70 C.E, engaging in agriculture, cattle breeding, and trade. Under the Romans and, later, under the Vandals, the Jews prospered, and their numbers increased so rapidly that Christian ecclesiastical assemblies enacted anti-Jewish measures. However, Justinian, in 534, issued an edict placing the Jews on an equal level with the pagans. Spanish refugees, fleeing persecution by the Visigothic kings, increased the Jewish population in the 7th century. When Tunisia fell under the rule of the caliphate of Baghdad, a new Jewish influx ensued. Under the Almohades (from 1146 on), the Jews experienced very difficult times. The Almohades forced them to embrace the Islamic faith or leave the country. In the first half of the 13th century, the condition of the Jews in Tunisia improved considerably. Important communities flourished in Kairouan, on Djerba Island, and in other places. However, Jews were not permitted to settle in Tunis. Later they obtained permission to live in a special section, "Hara," within the city which until 1857 remained the ghetto of Tunis. The trade and commerce of the country were controlled mainly by Jews, and they were frequently government administrators and had their own Council of Elders.

Under Spanish rule (1535-1574), Jews in Bizerte, Sousse, and Sfax suffered greatly. After Tunisia reverted to Turkish rule, Jews again acquired religious liberty and autonomy. Nevertheless, they suffered from arbitrary officials and the fanatic rabble. They were forced to wear a special costume and could ride only on saddleless donkeys and mules. Their fate changed for the better only in 1881 when Tunisia became a French protectorate and the Jews received equal rights with the Mohammedans.

In the first half of this century, the community of Tunis was composed of two large native groups, the *Touensa*, of Tunisian origin, and the *Grana Jews*, descendants of Portuguese and Italian immigrants. Each of these two groups (and of the numerous smaller immigrant groups, including Palestinian, Moroccan, Bedouin, White Russian, and other Jews– had its own charitable institutions, synagogues and cemeteries. The chief rabbi of Tunis was appointed and compensated by the state, while rabbis of the various communities were appointed by decree of the Bey and received salaries from their community. The majority of Tunisian Jewry was poverty-stricken and engaged in small handicrafts and petty shopkeeping. Most of them were religious and pro-Zionist.

There was always some anti-Jewish feeling in Tunisia. In 1917–1918, there were widespread pograms, and in 1938, the Jewish community had to turn to the

French resident and ask him to intervene, so violent was the anti-Jewish propaganda carried on by the Italians. The Vichy regime introduced anti-Semitic decrees. In late 1942 and early 1943, the Nazis reduced the Jewish population to the status of slaves; however, they were freed by the Allies in 1943.

Except for the period of Nazi occupation, when slave labor and murder were rampant, the Jews of Tunisia enjoyed physical security in the years after World War I and relations between Moslems and Jews were good, on the whole. Even during the Palestine conflict, no excesses against Jews took place. The political upheaval in Tunisia in recent years, however, brought in its wake anti-Jewish disturbances. On January 20, 1952, eight Jewish shops in Kairouan were looted by Arab mobs during clashes between Tunisian nationalists and French security forces. More anti-Jewish disturbances occured in 1952 in the ghetto of Tunis when a gang of Arabs tried to force Jewish shopkeepers to close their stores. In June, 1952, a group of young Arabs attacked the Jewish commercial center in Tunis. Five Jews and about an equal number of Moslems were injured. The nationalist Neo-Destour Party, however, condemned the attacked against the Jews, insisting that they were instigated by the enemies of the Tunisian nationalist movement. The unrest also affected Jews economically. Particularly hard hit were Jewish artisans and small shopkeepers.

An important event in the Jewish life of Tunisia was the constitution in June of an All-Tunisian representative Jewish body elected by 155 delegates from 26 Jewish communities in various parts of the country.

In 1954, Dr. M. L. Perlzweig, Political Director of the World Jewish Congress, was received by the Bey of Tunis and Mr. Tahar Ben-Amar, Premier of Tunisia. On this occasion, Mr. Ben-Amar declared that there would be no discrimination against the Jews in Tunisia with whom the friendliest relations were being maintained. The Jews would enjoy all rights granted to other citizens of the country.

From 1950–53, 11,356 Jews emigrated to Israel from Tunisia. Following the intensification of the Arab national movement, this emigration was stepped up in the second half of 1954.

Besides Tunis, the main communities today are located in Sousse, Sfax, Gabes, Nabeul, and Hara Kebira. The rest of Tunisian Jewry is scattered among more than 20 communities in the interior. The central representative body of Tunisian Jewry is the Federation des Communautes Israelites de Tunisie in Tunis. Besides the Federation, there are two central organizations the Zionist Federation and the Youth Council.

The city of Tunis contains two distinct groups of Jews: those living in the city itself and those inhabiting the ghettos (numbering about 20,000 persons). The ghetto has a scarcity of accomodations; most of the rooms are without windows; whole families consisting of 8 to 12 persons frequently live in a single room.

According to the 1946 census, 19,928 of the 70,971 Jews of Tunisian nationality were gainfully occupied. In reality, however, the number of gainfully occupied Tunisian Jews is much smaller now. A large number of Jews are permanently unemployed, unfit for work, etc. In the city of Tunis alone, there are some 15,000 Jews who require permanent or special assistance. It is estimated that over 20,000 Jewish youths between the ages of 6 and 20 require vocational training in order to become self-supporting members of the community. On the other hand, the number of Tunisian Jews in the liberal professions is increasing; in 1946, they constituted 8.9 per cent of the total gainfully employed Jewish population. The number of officials was comparatively small—320 Jews among 6,045 Europeans.

The Relief Committee is recognized and subsidized by the Government. A great number of societies and institutions are active in the fields of relief, social aid, and vocational retraining.

Religious instruction and Jewish education are given in day schools, Talmud Torahs, yeshivot, and other institutions, of which 3 are sponsored by the Alliance, with 3,000 pupils, and 3 by the ORT, and still others by private religious groups. A rabbinical seminary exists in Djerba. Altogether, about 9,000 pupils and 50 teachers are in these schools.

TUNIS (50,000 Jews)

Federation des Communautes Israelites de Tunisie, 22, rue Charles de Galle, Tunis. Pres.: Charles Saada.
Gen. Sec.: Me. Rene Cohen-Hadria.
Founded in 1948, the Federation embraces all the communities outside of Tunis, the capital.

Tunisian Commission of the World Jewish Congress, 22, rue Charles de Galle. Tunis. Composed of representatives of all organizations and groups of the community. Local World Jewish Congress Committees exist in Tunis, Beja, Djerba, Ferryville, Gabes, Sousse, and Sfax.

Grand-Rabbinat de Tunisie, 6, Impasse de Salonique, Tunis. Grand Rabbi: David Bembaron (also, chief rabbi for Tunis).

Rabbinic Council, 6, Impasse de Salonique, Tunis. The Council is presided over by the Grand Rabbi and consists of 6 members proposed by the spiritual chief and named by the ministry for one year. Members of the Council: Rabbis Ichoua El Malih, Youda Uzan, Youssef Samama, Fradji Uzan, Haim Assuied, Eliaou Raccah.

Conseil de la Communaute Israelite de Tunis (Jewish community), 10 Rue de Hoolande. Pres.: Charles Haddad.
Sec.: Roger N. Teman.
Founded in 1921.
The Jewish community maintains the following schools: Ecole Or-Thora Dir.: Jules Dana, 325 pupils, 11 teachers. Ecole Zarka, Dir.: Chalom Belhassen, 240 pupils, 5 teachers Ecole Kisraoui, Dir.: Abraham Smadja, 300 pupils, 5 teachers.

Tribunal Rabbinique, 14, rue des Tanneurs. Pres.: Grand Rabbi Meiss Cohen.
Members: Rabbis Salomon Sitruk, Masliah Mazouz, Abraham Taieb, Eliahou Guez.

Agence Juive, 12, rue Sidi-Sifiane. Dir.: Nahum Dwinger.

Alliance Israelite Universelle, 1, rue Malta-Srira. Central administration of Tunisia. Pres.: Raphael Levy.

Regional Committee of the A.I.U.
Pres.: Victor Bessis.
The Alliance maintains the following schools: Boys' School, 1, rue Malta-Srira. La Hafsia Boys' School, rue du Tribunal. Dir.: Vitalis Danon; Girls' School, 12, rue El-Mechnaka. Dir.: Mrs. Anna Levy. French-Hebrew school "Or Thora," rue Achour. The schools of the Alliance in Tunisia have a total number of 3,533 pupils, with 80 teachers.

American Joint Distribution Committee, 25,

rue de Besancon. Active in Tunisia since 1943. Dir.: Louis D. Horwitz.

Congress Juif Mondial, 8, rue des Tanneurs. Founded in 1949.
Pres.: Elie Nataf.
Correspondent: I. Shebabo.

Conseil des Mouvements de Jeunesse de Tunisie 11, rue d'Alger. Joint youth movements: Betar, Bne Akiva, Dror, E.I.F., Gordonia, Hachomer Hatsair, Hanoar Hatsioni, U.U.J.J., S.A.H., Atsmaouth, Hanoar Hamisrachi. Dir.: Ravia Yehezkel.

Federation Sioniste de Tunisie, 11, rue d'Alger. Pres. of Federal Council: Elie Eugene Guetta. Pres. of Executive Council: Meyer Bellity. Sec.: Emmanuel Fiorentino.

O.S.E., 16, rue d'Athenes. Founded in 1947, it embraces 13 recreation centers, 10 homes for babies, 11 dispensaries and 5 social services, employing 38 physicians, 18 nurses, and 10 social service workers. Main centers in Djerba, Ariana, Sousse, Sfax, and Bizerte.
Pres.: Dr. Leon Moatti.
Sec.: Dr. Lucien Tahar.

O.R.T., Km 4, Routes des Forts. Dir.: Dr. David Alberstein. Sec.: Rene Cohen-Hadria. Pres.: Me. Elie Nataf. The ORT maintains schools in which there are 406 pupils and 30 teachers.

Societe de l'Hospital Israelite de Tunis, 29, avenue de Paris. Founded in 1892 for the support of the Jewish hospital in Tunis. The hospital was founded in 1893 and the preventorium in Tunis-Ariana (Centre Doceur I.E. Hayat), in 1938. Pres.: Dr. Israel Eugene Hayat. Sec.: Mrs. Juliette Zerah-Smaja.

Union des Etudiants Juifs de France, 11, rue de Bretagne. Union of Jewish Students, founded in 1946, now has a membership of approximately 400 former students. Local sections at Sousse, Bizerte, and Sfax. Publishes "Kadimah." Pres.: Paul Halimi. Sec.: Max Sitbon.

BEJA (1,200 Jews)

Comite de la Communaute Israelite (Jewish community).
Pres.: Leon Cohen.

Sec.: Albert Olbou.
Rabbinate: Hanania Ganoun. Notaire Maatouk, Rahmine Diai.

BIZERTE (1,800 Jews)

Comite de la Communaute Israelite (Jewish community), 32, rue de Constantinople.
Pres.: Israel Archi.
Sec.: Samuel Saada.

BEN-GARDANE (500 Jews)

Comite de la Communaute Israelite (Jewish community). Pres.: Nessim Perez.

DJERBA (HARA KEBIRA) (2,00 Jews)

Comite de la Communaute Israelite (Jewish community), Boite postale No. 6.
Pres.: Samuel de K. H. Cohen.
Grand Rabbi: Mouchi Cohen Drihem.

Congres Juif Mondial. Correspondent: Samuel de K. H. Cohen.

Daber Evrith (For Hebrew language).
Pres.: David Kidouchim.
Sec.: Issakhar Haddad.

DJERBA (HARA SEGHIRA) (300 Jews)

Comite de la Communaute Israelite (Jewish community). Pres.: Victor Sarfati.

EL HAMMA (52 Jews)

Comite de la Communaute Israelite (Jewish community). Pres.: Elie Hadad.
Sec.: Meyer Cohen.

FOUM-TATAHOUINE (500 Jews)

Comite de la Communaute Israelite (Jewish community). Pres.: Mouchi Ben Dani Cohen.

GABES (3,000 Jews)

Comite de la Communaute Israelite (Jewish community). Pres.: Houati Zana.
Sec.: Simon Benattia.

HADJEB-ET-AÏOUN (40 Jews)

Comite de la Communaute Israelite (Jewish community).

GAFSA (630 Jews)

Comite de la Communaute Israelite (Jewish community).

KASSERINE (60 Jews)

Comite de la Communaute Israelite (Jewish community). Pres.: David Mimoun.

KAIROUAN (300 Jews)

Comite de la Communaute Juive (Jewish community). Pres.: Debache.

KEBILI (305 Jews)

Comite de la Communaute Israelite (Jewish community). Pres.: Zakino Allouche.

LE KEF (500 Jews)

Comite de la Communaute Israelite (Jewish community), place Logerot.
Pres.: Charles Hayoun.

MAHDIA (300 Jews)

Comite de la Communaute Israelite (Jewish community). Pres.: Mathieu Guetta.

MATEUR (400 Jews)

Comite de la Communaute Israelite (Jewish Community), Pres.: Chemla.

MEDENINE (500 Jews)

Comite de la Communaute Israelite (Jewish community). Pres.: Goussa Perez.

MEDJEZ-EL-BAB (30 Jews)

Comite de la Communaute Israelite (Jewish community). Pres.: Says Benady.

MATEUN (400 Jews)

Comite de la Communaute Israelite (Jewish community), Pres.: Chemla.

MOKNINE (400 Jews)

Comite de la Communaute Israelite (Jewish community). Pres.: Haim Hania.

MONASTIR (200 Jews)

Comite de la Communaute Israelite (Jewish community). Pres.: Victor Sebag.

NABEUL (2,200 Jews)

Comite de la Communaute Israelite (Jewish community). Pres.: Roger Mamou.
Sec.: Gabriel Haddad.
Grand Rabbi: Mouchi Haddad.

SBEITLA (200 Jews)

Comite de la Communaute Israelite (Jewish community). In conjunction with a committee for welfare. Pres.: Guide Errera.

SFAX (5,500 Jews)

Comite de la Communaute Israelite (Jewish community), 12, rue Lamoriciere.
Pres.: Charles Saada.
Sec.: Raymond Azria.
Grand Rabbi: Akiba Abitbol.

SILIANA (100 Jews)

Comite de la Communaute Israelite (Jewish community).

SOLIMAN (150 Jews)

Comite de la Communaute Israelite (Jewish community). Pres.: Youssef Levy.

SOUK-EL-ARBA (300 Jews)

Comite de la Communaute Israelite (Jewish community). Pres.: Charles Assous.

SOUK-EL-KHEMIS (200 Jews)

Comite de la Communaute Israelite (Jewish community).

SOUSSE (6,000 Jews)

Comite de la Communaute Israelite (Jewish community). Pres.: Isaac Hayat.
Sec.: Joseph Cohen.
Grand Rabbi: David Bokobza.
Congres Juif Mondial, 12, rue Villedon.
Pres.: Dr. Boujenah. Sec.: Marius Gabai.
Alliance Israelite Universelle. Dir.: Joseph Levy.

TATAHOUINE (500 Jews)

Comite de la Communaute Israelite (Jewish community). Pres.: Meyer Cohen.

TESTOUR (100 Jews)

Comite de la Communaute Israelite (Jewish community).

ZARZIS (900 Jews)

Comite de la Communaute Israelite (Jewish community). Pres.: Chalom Mazouz.

UGANDA

(EAST AFRICA)

JEWISH POPULATION: 600

The Uganda Jewish Community, Kampala, P.O.B. 3072, Uganda (Central East Africa).

Uganda is known to Zionist history as the region proposed to Dr. Theodor Herzl for the establishment of a Jewish autonomous territory. At the Zionist Congress of 1903, the proposition was vehemently opposed by the Russian Zionists. Despite receiving the support of the majority of the delegates for sending a fact-finding commission to Uganda, the project was later dropped because it would divert the efforts of the Zionist movement dedicated to the rebuilding of the Jewish National Home in Palestine.

Mr. Anthony Lipton, a lecturer in medicine at the University College of East Africa and a member of the Community's Executive Committee, reports that for several decades there had been some Jews in Uganda, but distances, poor roads between towns, and hard work made contact between the older Jewish families sporadic. During and after the second World War their number was increased by the arrival of Jews who found their way there from Europe and Palestine, in particular, professionals who were attracted by the large hospital and medical school, Makarere College, and many other institutions of learning. Besides, there are a number of Jews from India in the protectorate. In addition, the Community is now investigating the history of a group of Black Jews, apparently 40–50 farming families, living in the northern part of the country. Excluding these, the Community numbers about 60 adults who represent all shades of religious opinion. There are also quite a few children. So far they have not been able to aproach the Blacks Jews for membership owing to distance and language difficulties. But they hope to remedy this in the near future.

In December, 1955, Mr. Joseph Gillman, one of the prominent settlers, invited the Jews of Kampala (Entebbe), the capital of Uganda, to a meeting at which a caretaker committee was designated. The present Executive, embarking on constructive work, organized a communal Seder and made plans for religious services on all the major festivals. The Jews in Kampala manifest a lively interest in Zionism. A Wizo group is planned as well as the establishment of Hebrew and Jewish history lessons for children. The Executive Committee has completed negotiations for the provision of Jewish burial grounds.

Pres.: J. Gillman.
Hon. Sec.: Mrs. S. Sikoff.
Treasurer: S. Silkoff.

UNION OF SOUTH AFRICA

JEWISH POPULATION: 110,000

The Jewish Community began as an organized body at Cape Town in 1841.

The first Jewish congregation, later named Tikvath Israel, was formed in Cape Town in 1841 at the house of Benjamin Morden, who was the founder of the commercial and mining industries of South Africa. The present economic situation of the Jews is satisfactory.

The majority of the Jewish population are Ashkenazim, 80% of whom are from Lithuania. All but some 5,000 reside in urban centers. In 1891, the number of Jews was only 3,000, and by 1904 had increased to 38,000. In 1930, an immigration bill limited the immigration from Eastern and Southern Europe to 50 per annum. After 1933, a number of Jewish refugees immigrated from Austria and Germany.

There are about 200 organized Jewish communities widely scattered throughout the territory most of which have their own synagogues. Only in the larger centers, such as Johannesburg, Cape Town, Durban, Pretoria, Port Elizabeth, and Bloemfontein, do the congregations have their own rabbis. The vast majority of the Jews are Orthodox; only a few are Reform.

Dr. Joseph H. Hertz, who later became the Chief Rabbi of Britain, served as rabbi of the Johannesburg New Hebrew Congregation. He was succeeded by the prominent scholar, the late Dr. Judah L. Landau, who was appointed Chief Rabbi.

The South African Board of Education was established in 1928. It supervises two Hebrew day schools in Johannesburg, with 900 pupils, 86 congregational afternoon schools, 32 Hebrew kindergartens, and the Teachers Seminary with 32 students. There are also Yiddish folk-schools and the People's College for adult education. Forty percent of the Jewish children, about 5,000, are enrolled in the various Jewish schools. There are 1,800 Jewish university students in South Africa.

The South African Jewish Board of Deputies, founded in 1896, is the representative body of this Jewry. The Jews are active in the civic and political life of the country. Jews are members of the legislative bodies. They contributed generously to the establishment of the universities in Cape Town and Johannesburg.

The late Prime Minister of South Africa, Jan Christian Smuts, was a devoted friend of Zionism and played a leading role in the issuance of the Balfour Declaration in 1917.

During the second World War, the National Party of the Boers carried on anti-Jewish propaganda. But since the advent of this party to power under the leadership of Malan, they have displayed a fair attitude towards the Jewish population and Mr. Malan visited Israel and established a friendly policy towards the Jewish State.

South Africa has been one of the bulwarks of the Zionist movement, and its per capita contributions to Zionist funds have been the highest in the world.

UNION INSTITUTIONS

South African Jewish Board of Deputies, 124 Fox St., P. O. Box 1180, Johannesburg. Pres.: I. A. Maisels. Chairman: N. Philips. Sec.: G. Saron. The Jewish Board of Deputies for the Transvaal and Natal was founded in 1903, and a similar organization, at the Cape in 1904. The two organizations were united in 1912. The United Board consists of representatives of 365 organizations, societies, etc. The headquarters of the Board is in Johannesburg, where the executive council sits, and provincial committees exist in Cape Town, Durban, Bloemfontein, and Port Elizabeth. Chairman: J.J. Friedman. Sec.: D. Spector.

South African Board of Jewish Education, P.O. Box 2942, Johannesburg. Dir.: I. Gross. Org. Sec.: A. Misheiker.

South African Jewish Ecclesiastical Association, P. O. Box 3320, Cape Town. Pres.: Rabbi I. Abrahams.

Federation of Synagogues of the Transvaal, 24 Raleigh St., Yeoville, Johannesburg. Chief Rabbi: Dr. L. I. Rabinowitz. Sec.: H. S. Lory.

S. African Jewish Ministers' Association, 63 Sauers Bldg., Johannesburg. Pres.: Rabbi Dr. L. I. Rabinowitz.

S.A. Union for Progressive Judaism, 323 Grand National Bldg., Rissik St. (P.O.Box 8133), Johannesburg. Pres.: I. Greenberg.

Union of Jewish Women of South Africa, 47 Balfour House, St. George's St., Cape Town (P. O. Box 4500). There are 59 branches and outposts of the Union. Pres.: Mrs. R. S. Solman. Sec.: Mrs. L. Rubin.

South African Jewish Sociological and Historical Society. P.O.Box 1180, Johannesburg. Pres.: Rabbi Dr. L. I. Rabinowitz. Sec.: Mrs. Dora Sowden. Chairman: Max Geffen.

South African Hebrew Teachers' Association, Chairman: J. Rubik, 45 Shakespeare House, Johannesburg.

Histadruth Ivrith of South Africa, Chairman: M. Rutstein. Sec.: J. Batnitzky, 188 Shakespeare House, Commissioner St., Johannesburg.

South African ORT-OZE, Unity House, 100 Fox St., Johannesburg. Chairman: L. A. Lipshitz. Sec.: A. Markowitz, P. O. Box 5883, Johannesburg.

South African Zionist Federation, P.O. Box 18, 100 Fox St., Johannesburg. Chairman: S. M. Kuper. Sec.: Z. Infeld. There are Zionist societies affiliated to the Feredation in practically every Jewish center in South Africa and Women's Zionist Societies in most of them.

S. A. Women's Zionist Council, Chairman: Mrs. S. Freedman. Sec.: Mrs. I. Jacobson, P.O. Box 18, Johannesburg.

Zionist Socialist Party of South Africa, P.O. Box 2588, Johannesburg. Chairman: L. Tager. Sec.: E. Simmovitz.

Mizrahi Federation of South Africa, P.O. Box 7197, Johannesburg. Chairman: Rabbi Dr. M. Mossowsky. Sec.: E. Selbst. Constituents:

Mizrahi Organisation, Pres.: Rabbi Dr. M. Kossowsky.

Women's Mizrahi Organisation, Chairman: Mrs. M. Kossowsky.

Hashomer Hadati, Sec.: J. Shapiro.

Hapoel Hamizrahi, Sec.: E. Selbst, P.O. Box 9498.

United General Zionist Party, 208 Commissioner House, 50 Commissioner St., Johannesburg. Chairman: I. Dunsky. Sec.: R. B. Egert.

United Zionist Revisionist Party, P. O. Box 4474, Johannesburg. Chairman: J. Daleski. Sec.: H. Hurwitz.

PRETORIA (Transvaal)
(Jewish population: 3,228)

Jewish Community Council, 178 Beatrix St., P. O. Box 1222.
Chairman: G. Wegger.
Sec.: Mrs. B. Pinshaw.
Hebrew Congregation, P. O. Box 840.
Pres.: B. M. Raeburn.
Rabbi: E. Neufeld.

JOHANNESBURG (Transvaal)
(Jewish population: 53,420)

United Hebrew Congregation of Johannesburg, Est. 1915.
Synagogues: Great Synagogue, Wolmarans St.; Yeoville Synagogue, Hunter St.; Oxford Synagogue, North Avenue, Rivera. Chief Rabbi: L. I. Rabinowitz. There are 24 other Hebrew Orthodox Congregations in Johannesburg and most of them have their own rabbis and religious schools.
United Jewish Reform Congregation, Est.1946.
Temples: Temple Israel, Paul Nel St., Hillbrow, and Temple Shalom, Louis Botha Ave., Highlands North. Chief Rabbi: M. C. Weiler. Rabbi: D. H. Anew.

EDUCATIONAL AND CULTURAL ORGANIZATIONS:

United Hebrew Schools, P. O. Box 5506.
Pres.: B. I. Joffe.
Hebrew Teachers' Association,
Sec.: M. Lazarus, P.O. Box 1848.
Yiddish Cultural Federation, P.O. Box 6520.
Sec.: Mrs. F. Frierman.
Hebrew Teachers Seminary, P. O. Box 2942.
Principal: Rabbi A. Hilewitz

ZIONIST ORGANIZATIONS:

Transvaal Zionist Youth Executive, 208 Commissioner House, 50 Commissioner St.
Chairman: H. Levin.
Students' Zionist Association, c/o Students' Representative Council Office, Witwatersrand University, Milner Park.
Chairman: H. Green.
Johannesburg Zionist Association.
Sec.: Miss H. Bloch, P.O. Box 718.

Johannesburg Women's Mizrachi Organization, P.O. Box 2185. Chairman: Mrs. M. Kossowsky.
Hapoel Hamizrachi Organization, 8 Store Bros. Building, Eloff St.
Chairman: H. S. Liebgott.
Israel Society, Chairman: L. Kopillis.
Sec.: J. Katz, 292 Fox St., Jeppe.
Zionist Socialist Party, Sec.: E. Simmowitz, 46 Shakespeare House, Commissioner St.
Chairman: M. W. Friedman.

BENONI (TRANSVAAL) (1,237 Jews)

United Hebrew Institutions, P. O. Box 210.
Pres.: M. Smith.
Sec.: Miss A. Friedlander.
Rabbi: I. Freedman.

BLOEMFONTEIN (O.F.S.) (1,240 Jews)

Hebrew Congregation, P. O. Box 535.
Pres.: H. Bradlow.
Sec.: A. Arvan.
Minister: Rev. Shalom Coleman.

BRAKPAN (TRANSVAAL) (929 Jews)

United Hebrew Institutions, Chairman: N. Fine.
Sec.: M. Waisbrod, P.O. Box 145.
Minister Rev. M. Altschuler.

CAPE TOWN (CAPE PROV.) (20,446 Jews)

Great Synagogue, Government Ave. Est. 1842.
Pres.: H. Harris.
Chief Rabbi: Prof. I. Abrahams, 84 Hatfield St. Besides the Great Synagogue, there are 9 Hebrew Congregations in Cape Town.
United Council of Hebrew Congregations (Cape), Chairman: L. Gradner.
Sec.: Rev. S. Kassel, 25 Schoonder St.
South African ORT-OZE, 148 George's St.
Chairman: Dr. L. Mirvish.

EDUCATIONAL AND CULTURAL INSTITUTIONS:

Cape Jewish Historical and Museum Society, 48 Hatfield St.
Chairman: Chief Rabbi I. Abrahams.

United Hebrew Schools, 103 Hope St.
Chairman: Dr. J. Harte.
Principal: Z. Avin.
Cape Board of Jewish Education, Inchholm
Place, Hope St. Dir of Educ.: A. Moar,
supervising 4 Hebrew schools.

DURBAN (NATAL) (4,482 Jews)

United Hebrew Congregation, P.O. Box 742.
Rabbi: Harris Swift.
Jewish Reform Congregation (Temple David),
Ridge Rd., Berea, Durban.
Rabbi: Myer Miller.
Jewish Education Council, P. O. Box 746.
Chairman: Dr. B. Boshal. Dir.: S. Ernst.
United Hebrew Schools, P. O. Box 742.
Chairman: A. Stiller.
Zionist Council for Natal, P. O. Box 2833.
Chairman: J. Goldberg.

EAST LONDON (CAPE PROV.)
(1,115 Jews)

Hebrew Congregation, P. O. Box 92.
Pres.: A. M. Kawalsky.

GERMISTON (TRANSVAAL) (1,350 Jews)

United Hebrew Institutions, P. O. Box 31.
Sec.: I. Gordon. Rev.: I. Kaminer.

KRUGERSDORP (TRANSVAAL)
(1,025 Jews)

United Hebrew Institutions, P. O. Box 188.
Chairman: A. Tenenbaum. Rev.: L. Wolk.

PORT ELIZABETH (CAPE PROV.)
(2,866 Jews)

United Hebrew Institutions, P. O. Box 198.
Chairman: A. Marcow.
Hebrew Congregation. Est. 1850.
Pres.: L. Simmons.
Sec.: W. Budlender, P. O. Box 2092.
Minister: Rev. A. Levy.

SPRINGS (TRANSVAAL) (1,228 Jews)

Jewish Community Council. Sec.: Mrs. M.
Dannheisser, 6 Gilhooley Rd., Selection
Park.

OTHER HEBREW CONGREGATIONS:

Besides those mentioned above, Hebrew
Congregations exist in the following places:
Aberdeen (Cape Prov.), Aliwal North (Cape
Prov.), Beaufort West (Cape Prov.), Bellville
(Cape Prov.), Bethal (Transvaal), Bethlehem
(O.F.S.), Boksburg (Transvaal, 481 Jews),
Bothaville, Bredasdorp and Napier (Cape
Prov.), Brits (Transvaal), Bronkhorstspruit
(Transvaal), Burghersdorp (Cape Prov., 14
Jews), Caledon (Cape Prov.), Ceres-Wolseley
(Cape Prov.), Claremont (Cape Prov.), Clo-
cocan (O.F.S.), De-Aar (Cape Prov.), Del-
mas (Transvaal), Dewetsdorp (O.F.S.), Dur-
banville (Cape Prov.), Ermelo (Transvaal),
Ficksburg (O.F.S.), Frankfort (O.F.S.),
George (Cape Prov., 122 Jews), Goodwood
(Cape Prov.), Grahamstown (Cape Prov.,
100 Jews), Hennenman (O.F.S.), Harrismith
(O.F.S.), Heidelberg (Transvaal), Heilbron
(O.F.S.), Jagersfontein (O.F.S.), Keetsman-
shoop (S.W. Africa), Kimberley (Cape Prov.,
586 Jews), Kingswilliamstown (Cape Prov.),
Kinross-Leslie (Transvaal), Kirkwood (Cape
Prov.), Klerksdorp (Transvaal), Koffiefontein
(O.F.S.), Kopjes(O.F.S.), Kroonstad(O.F.S.),
Lichtenburg (Transvaal), Louis Trichardt
(Transvaal), Mafeking (Cape Prov.), Mait-
land (Cape Prov.), Malmesburg (Cape Prov.),
Marquard (O.F.S.), Messina (Transvaal),
Middleburg (Cape Prov.), Morreesburg (Cape
Prov.), Mossel Bay (Cape Prov.), Muizenberg
and Kalk Bay (Cape Prov.), Nigel (Transvaal,
293 Jews), Odendaalsrus (O.F.S., 120 Jews),
Oudtshoorn (Cape Prov., 250 Jews), Paarl
(Cape Prov., 220 Jewish families), Parow
(Cape Prov., 440 Jews), Parys (O.F.S.),
Pietermaritzburg (Natal, 120 Jews), Pieters-
burg (Transvaal), Piquetberg (Cape Prov.),
Potchefstroom (Transvaal), Queenstown (Cape
Prov., 130 Jews), Randfontein (Transvaal,
446 Jews), Reitz (O.F.S.), Riversdale and
Heidelberg (Cape Prov), Robertson (Cape
Prov.), Rondebosch (Cape Prov.), Roodepoort
(Transvaal, 371 Jews), Rustenburg (Trans-
vaal), Senekal (O.F.S.), Somerset Strand
(Cape Prov.), Somerset West (Cape Prov.),
Springbok (Namaqualand), Standerton (Trans-

vaal), Stellenbosch (Cape Prov.), Thaba
Nchu (O.F.S.), Theunissen (O.F.S.), Uiten-
hage (Cape Prov., 196 Jews), Umtata (Tran-
skei Dist.), Uniondale (Cape Prov.), Upington
(Cape Prov., 207 Jews), Ventersdorp (Trans-
vaal), Vereeniging (Transvaal), Volksrust
(Transvaal), Vrede (O.F.S.), Vredefort,
Vryburg (Cape Prov., 141 Jews), Vryheid
(Natal), Warmbaths (Transvaal), Wellington
(Cape Prov.), Wepener (O.F.S.) Willowmore
(Cape Prov.), Windhoek (S.W. Africa), Wit-
bank (Transvaal), Worcester (O.F.S.), Wyn-
berg (Cape Prov.).

PERIODICALS:

1. AGENCY: *Jewish Telegraphic Agency* (daily
bulletin), P.O. Box 7594, Johannesburg.

1. WEEKLIES: *African Jewish Newspaper*
(Yiddish), 45 Old Arcade, 100 Market St.,
Johannesburg.
Jewish Herald, 19/24 Stability Building,
Fox St., Johannesburg.
South African Jewish Chronicle, P.O. Box
2000, Cape Town.
South African Jewish Times, Eagle House,
19 Rockey St., Doornfontein, Johannesburg.
Zionist Record, Rand Daily Mail Bldgs., 176
Main St., Johannesburg.

3. FORTNIGHTLIES: *Jewish Family Magazine*
(German-English), 202 Enfield Court, Kapteijn St., Hillbrow, Johannesburg.
South African Jewish Frontier, 45 Shakespeare House, Commissioner St., Johannesburg.

4. MONTHLIES: Barkai (Hebrew), 60 Shakespeare House, Commissioner Street, Johannesburg.
Betar, Amsterdam House, Quartz St., Johannesburg.
Dapim (Hebrew), P.O. Box 5486, Johannesburg.
Dorem Afrike (Yiddish), 62 Security Building, 95 Commissioner St., Johannesburg.
Federation Chronicle, 24 Raleigh St., Yeoville, Johannesburg.
Habinyan, Vanguard House, President St.,
Johannesburg.

Hamadrich, Vanguard House, President St.,
Johannesburg.
Hamatmid, Students' Jewish Association,
University of Cape Town.
Hasholom, P.O. Box 2198, Durban.
Jewish Affairs, P.O. Box 1180, Johannesburg.
Jewish Guild Newsletter, P.O. Box 2934,
Johannesburg.
Looking Ahead, 10 Unity House, 100 Fox
St., Johannesburg.
News and Views, P.O. Box 18, Johannesburg.
Shtilim Post, Vanguard House, Cor. Troye
& Market Streets, Johannesburg.
South African Jewish Observer (Yiddish-
English), 8 Store Bros. Building, Eloff St.,
Johannesburg.
Temple David Review, 369 Ridge Road,
Durban.
World Ose News, 10 Unity House, 100 Fox
St., Johannesburg.
Zionist Mirror, 201 Commissioner House, 50
Commissioner St., Johannesburg.

5. QUARTERLIES: *Ha-Yam*, P. O. Box 4023,
Cape Town.
Judean, P.O. Box 3995, Johannesburg.
Progressive Jew, P.O. Box 8133, Johannes-
burg.

6. IRREGULARS: *Hakinor*, University of Cape
Town.
H.O.D. Journal, 138 Marshal St., Johannes-
burg.
Oif Afrike's Erd (Yiddish), P.O.Box 4241,
Johannesburg.
S.A. Maccabi News, P.O. Box 13, Johan-
nesburg.
Timorim, P.O. Box 9165, Joannesburg.

7. ANNUALS: *Jewish Guild Annual*, P.O. Box
2934, Johannesburg.
South African Jewish Year Book, Fieldhill
Publishing House, 19 Rockey St., Johannesburg.
South African Rosh-Hashanah Year Book,
|Yiddish), P.O. Box 4263, Johannesburg.
Union of Jewish Women Review, 408 Auto-
mutual House, 57 De Villiers, Johannesburg.

AUSTRALIA

AUSTRALIA

JEWISH POPULATION: 56,000

The earliest mention of Jews in Australia was in 1817 when twenty Jews in New South Wales formed a burial society. About 1828, when the Jewish population was about 300, a congregation was formed in Sydney. In April 1844, a synagogue was opened in Sydney with accomodations for 500 people. The first Jewish religious service was held in Melbourne in 1839. There were Jews in Adelaide by 1836, a permanent congregation was formed in 1848, and a synagogue consecrated in 1850. Regular services were held in Brisbane as early as the 1860's. The first Jewish congregation was formed in Western Australia, at Perth, in 1892. The discovery of gold in that decade brought a Jewish immigration, and outlying congregations were established.

The original Jewish immigrants came directly from England, though they were reinforced subsequently from other countries. The Montefiore, Levi, Solomon and Lazarus families played a very important part in the early economic development of Australia. Jews have also contributed much to Australia's public life.

Since the end of the Second World War, the Jewish population has increased from 35,535 to 56,000. Of this number, 26,000 live in Victoria, 22,443 in New South Wales, 2,874 in Western Australia, 1,492 in Queensland, 644 in South Australia, 197 in Tasmania, and 40 more in the Federal Capital Territory. Sydney and Melbourne have the largest Jewish communities with over 20,000 Jews each.

Apart from the synagogues which conduct classes or maintain Talmud Torahs, religious instruction is also provided by the Jewish congregation under Government permission in State-owned public schools, allowing religious denominations the so-called *right of entry* classes, usually one hour a week for religious instruction. About 55% of the Jewish children in Australia receive Jewish instruction in some form. One of the central Jewish educational agencies is the New South Wales Board of Jewish Education which provides religious instruction in the public schools on the basis of the above mentioned "right of entry classes." In addition to this, the Board maintains 14 educational centers in Sydney and its suburbs serving 750 children. The total number of children receiving Jewish education in some form under the control of the Board is 1,750. Besides this, there are two Jewish day schools in Sydney and a Sunday school of the liberal Temple Emanuel for 150 children.

In Melbourne, Victoria, there are six Jewish Day Schools, the largest of which is Mt. Scopus College with over 600 pupils, maintained by the Victorian Jewish Board of Deputies. The United Jewish Education Board in Melbourne is responsible for the Talmud Torahs with 400 pupils and provision for Jewish instruction in the public schools for 1,000 children. Other organizations maintain additional Jewish schools for about 1,000 children. Among these are the Hebrew schools Hascala and Bialik and two Yiddish schools, Perez and Shalom Aleichem, with 300 pupils, and the Sunday school of the liberal Temple Beth Israel, with 350 children. Also in Melbourne, the Javne Institute gives advanced courses in Jewish studies for adults.

In Perth, the Jewish school provides instruction for over 200 children, in Brisbane for 100, and in Adelaide for 40 pupils.

The continuous immigration of reactionary and anti-semitic German elements has been a source of serious concern to the Jewish population. Jewish organizations have repeatedly voiced their apprehension in this matter.

The Jews were responsible for the introduction of several important industries in Australia. Some of them have reached high positions such as Sir Isaac Isaacs, who was the first Australian Governor General, and General Monash. There are no Jews in the federal Parliament. The vast majority of Jews are Zionists, their interest in the State of Israel being considerable.

Executive Council of Australian Jewry, 243 Elizabeth St., Sydney.
Pres.: Sydney Einfeld.
Sec.: David J. Benjamin.
The Executive Council is recognized by the Commonwealth Government as the *de facto* Jewish representation and spokesman, and is affiliated with the World Jewish Congress. The constituents of the Executive Council are the six State Boards, *viz.*: New South Wales Jewish Board of Deputies, Victorian Jewish Board of Deputies, West Australian Jewish Advisory Board, Queensland Jewish Board of Deputies, South Australian Jewish Board of Deputies, and the Hobart Hebrew Congregation, each of which comprises all the Jewish organizations, congregations, institutions, and societies in its respective State. The Annual Conference of the Executive Council of Australian Jewry, at which the six State Boards are represented by their delegates, elects a Committee of Management as well as Standing Committees.

Australian Federation of Young Men's and Women's Hebrew Associations, 3 Wentworth St., Point Piper.
Pres.: S. D. Einfeld.

Australian Federation of Jewish Welfare Societies, 146 Darlinghurst Rd., Sydney.
Pres.: S. D. Einfeld.
Sec.: W. L. Brand.

Australian Jewish Historical Society.
Pres.: Rabbi Dr. I. Porush.
Sec.: S. B. Glass, 2 Castlereagh St., Sydney.

Jewish National Fund of Australia and New Zealand,
Pres.: A. Breckler.
Sec.: Dr. K. Fraenkel, 77 Bourke St., Melbourne, C. 1.

Jewish Religious Union of Australia, Temple Beth Israel, Melbourne, and Temple Emanuel, Sydney. Liberal religious organization.
Pres.: H. I. Dent.
Sec.: Dr. W. Salenger.

National Council of Jewish Women,
  Pres.: Dr. Fanny Reading, 8 Young St.,
  Sydney.
WIZO Federation of Australia, 77 Bourke St.,
  Melbourne, C.I.
  Pres.: Mrs. R. Cohen.
  Sec.: Mrs. H. Breckler.
*Zionist Federation of Australia and New Zea-
  land,* 77 Bourke St., Melbourne, C.L.
  Pres.: S. Wynn.
  Sec.: A. F. Leibler.
Mizrachi Congregation, 214 Old South Head
  Rd., Sydney, Bondi.
  Pres.: Max Mann.
  Sec.: J. E. Wolff.
  Rabbi: O. Abramson.

SYDNEY (N.S.W.) (22,000 Jews)

N.S.W. Jewish Board of Deputies, P.O.Box
  3759, 243 Elizabeth St.
  Pres.: G. de Vahl Davis.
  Sec.: Mrs. I. Robey.

SYNAGOGUES:

Great Synagogue, Elizabeth St., near Park St.,
  Erected 1875.
  Pres.: H. M. Blcom.
  Sec.: S. Schultz.
  Rabbis: Dr. I. Porush, L.A. Falk.
Western Suburbs Synagogue, 20 Georgina St.,
  Newton.
  Pres.: J. D. Pizem.
  Sec.: M. Sigalla.
  Minister: Rev. J. Rabinovitch.
Central Synagogue, Grosvenor and Grafton
  Sts., Bondi Junction.
  Pres.: F. Freeman.
  Sec.: Miss S. Finkelstein.
  Rabbi: I. L. Swift.
Bankstown Hebrew Congregation, North
  Terrace.
  Sec.: Mrs. W. Greenstein.
North Shore Synagogue, Treats Rd., Lind-
  field. Pres.: Dr. J. V. Lander.
  Sec.: Dr. E. L. Sachs.
  Minister: Rev. W. Katz.
Kingsford-Maroubra Hebrew Congregation.
  Pres.: Dr. H. H. Wachtell, 40 Nagle Ave.,
  Maroubra.

Adath Yisrael Synagogue (Orthodox), Bel-
  levue Hill.
  Pres.: A. Rabinovitch.
  Rabbi: S. D. Bernath.
South Head and District Synagogue, 214 Old
  South Head Rd., Vaucluse.
  Pres.: Emanuel Braham.
Temple Emanuel (Liberal), 5 Ocean St.,
  Wollahra.
  Pres.: David Spink.
  Sec.: Dr. W. Salinger.
  Rabbi: Dr. R. Brasch.
N.S.W. Board of Jewish Education, 146 Dar-
  linghurst Rd., Darlinghurst.
  Pres.: Dr. J. Benjamin.
  Sec.: Miss N. Goldsmith.

ZIONIST ORGANIZATIONS:

Union of Sydney Zionists.
  Pres.: M. Freilich, 4 Arthur St., Bellevue
  Hill.
WIZO State Council of N.S.W., 147 Eliza-
  beth St.
  Pres.: Mrs. F. Goldberg.
Zionist Council of N.S.W., 18 Lang Rd.,
  Centennial Park.
  Pres.: S. Steigrad.
Mizrachi Organization, 115 Glenayr Ave.,
  Bondi.
Poale Zion, Pres.: L. Markson, 194 Malabar
  Road.
Tarbuth-Zionist Cultural Organisation, Post
  Office Chambers, 333 George St.
  Pres.: S. S. Steigrad.
  Sec.: Dr. H. Kimmel.
Habonim Zionist Youth, 18 Lang Rd., Cen-
  tennial Park.
Zionist Youth League, 18 Lang Rd., Centen-
  nial Park.

OTHER INSTITUTIONS:

Beth Din, Chairman: Rabbi Dr. I. Porush,
  164 Castlereagh St.
  Sec.: Rev. E. Wolff.
Australian Jewish Welfare Society, 146 Dar-
  linghurst Rd., Darlinghurst.
  Pres.: S. D. Einfeld.
  Sec.: W. L. Brand.

Anglo-Jewish Association.
  Sec.: Orwell Phillips, 11 St. Mark's Rd.,
  Darling Point, Edgcliffe.
YIVO, Sec.: S. Stedman, c/o Australian Jew-
  ish Forum, 149 Castlereagh St.
*Sydney Council to Combat Fascism and Anti-
  Semitism,* P.O.Box 4074.
  Pres.: N. Zussman.
  Sec.: Mrs. Parker.
Young Men's Hebrew Association of Australia,
  3 Wentworth St., Point Piper.
  Pres.: E. Morris.
  Sec.: E. Berger.
Sir John Monash B'nai B'rith Lodge, 9 Darley
  St., Darlinghurst.
  Pres.: Dr. E. Huth.

ADELAIDE (S. Australia) (900 Jews)

South Australian Jewish Board of Deputies.
  Pres.: Dr. G. A. Matison.
  Sec.: M. Adelson.
Synagogue, Synagogue Place, Rundle St.
  Founded 1848.
  Pres.: L. Solomon.
  Sec.: R. J. Solomon.
  Minister: Rev. M. Benson.
Hebrew School, Headmaster: Rev. M. B.
  Benson.
S. A. Zionist Association, Pres.: G. Hines.
  Sec.: Miss B. Benjamin.
WIZO, Pres.: Mrs. N. Solomons.

BALLARAT (VICTORIA) (30 Jews)

Ballarat Hebrew Congregation, Founded 1853.
  Pres.: N. F. Spielvogel.
  Sec.: S. C. Stone.

BRISBANE (QUEENSLAND) (1,500 Jews)

Queensland Jewish Board of Deputies.
  Pres.: L. Rosenblum.
  Sec.: K. Friedlander.
Hebrew Congregation, Margaret St. Founded
  1865.
  Pres.: A. G. Myers.
  Sec.: L. Lieberman.
  Rabbi: Dr. A. Fabian.

S. Brisbane Hebrew Congregation Deshon St.
  Pres.: M. Meerkin.
  Sec.: M. Dovbov.
  Minister: Rev. S. Mendelsson.
Board of Education, Synagogue Chambers,
  Margaret St.
  Pres.: L. H. Benjamin.
Australian Jewish Welfare Society, 41 Linden
  St., Dutton Park.
  Pres.: A. Newhouse.
  Sec.: K. Friedlander.
Zionist State Council, Pres.: S. Moses.
WIZO, Pres.: Mrs. D. Nesky. Sec.: Mrs. F.
  Schoenheimer.
Zionist Youth League, Pres.: A. Newhouse.

MELBOURNE (VICTORIA) (25,000 Jews)

Victorian Jewish Board of Deputies, 325 Col-
  lins St., Melbourne, C.I.
  Pres.: Trevor Rapke.
  Sec.: A. R. Blashki.
Young Men's Hebrew Association of Australia,
  9 Elizabeth St., Melbourne, C.1.
  Pres.: J. Bercove.
Mizrachi, Pres.: D. Feiglin. Sec.: Dr. H. S.
  Ruskin, 325 Collins St.
Poale Zion, Pres.: I. Roseby. Sec.: I. Wertheim.
WIZO State Council of Victoria.
  Pres.: Mrs. J. Rapke.
  Sec.: Mrs. E. Nemenoff, 77 Bourke St., C.

SYNAGOGUES:

Melbourne Hebrew Congregation, Toorak Rd.,
  South Yaara, S.E.1.
  Rabbi: Dr. I. Rapaport.
  Pres.: S. A. Cohen.
  Sec.: H. Friedman.
East Melbourne Hebrew Congregation, Albert
  St., East Melbourne, C.2.
  Pres.: M. Rosanov.
  Sec.: B. Abrahams.
  Minister: Rev. N. Sher.
St. Kilda Hebrew Congregation, Charnwood
  Grove St., St. Kilda, S.2.
  Pres.: L. Orbuck.
  Sec.: Miss V. Lazer.
  Rabbi: J. Danglow.

Adas Israel (Orthodox), 24 Glen Eira Ave.,
St. Kilda.
Pres.: L. Newman.
Sec.: N. Rosenmann.
Minister: Rabbi Neumann.

Brunswick Hebrew Congregation, 32 Lord St.,
East Brunswick.
Pres.: J. Yoffe.
Sec.: B. Waysman.

Carlton United Hebrew Congregation, Palmer-
ston St., Carlton, N.3.
Pres.: M. Plotkin.
Sec.: I. Lachman.
Rabbi: J. L. Gurewicz.

Elwood Synagogue and Talmud Torah, 26 Avo-
ca Ave., Elwood, S.3.
Pres.: A. H. Sicres.
Sec.: S. Strelec.
Minister: Rev. Yaffe.

New Cultural Centre and Synagogue, 53 Wal-
pole St., Kew.
Pres.: T. Mahemoff.

North Carlton Beth Hamedrash, Pres.: I. Segal.

Temple Beth Israel (Liberal), 78 Alma Rd.,
St. Kilda, S.2.
Pres.: J. E. Nathan.
Sec.: Mrs. G. E. Toggert.
Rabbi: Dr. H. M. Sanger.

EDUCATIONAL AND CULTURAL INSTITUTIONS:

United Jewish Education Board, Pres.: S. Glass.
Sec.: E. A. Kingsmith, 147 Patterson Mor-
rabbiah.

Caulfield Hebrew School and Cultural Centre,
572 Inkerman Rd., Caulfield, S.E.7.
Pres.: S. Roth.
Sec.: W. Komesaroff.

Mount Scopus College (Jewish Day School),
414 St. Kilda Rd.
Pres.: A. Samuels.

Hascala Hebrew School Board (Brunswick
Talmud Torah), 961 Rathdown St., North
Carlton, N.4.
Pres.: J. Feiglin.
Sec.: I. Lachman.

St. Kilda Hebrew School, Supt., Rabbi: J.
Danglow.

Bialik Hebrew School, 973 Drummond St.,
Carlton. Pres.: J. Honig.

Talmud Torah Beth Yoseph, 12 Pitt St., Carlton. Pres.: Hirsch deVahl Stone.
Sec.: L. Stone.

YIVO, 840 Lygon St., N. Carlton, Victoria.

Jewish Youth Council, 443 Little Collins St.,
C.1. Pres.: M. Anson. Sec.: Miss N. Rechter.

OTHER INSTITUTIONS:

Beth Din, Synagogue Chambers, Toorak Rd.,
S. Yarra, S.E.1.
Chairman: Rabbi I. Rappaport.

National Council of Jewish Women,
Pres.: Mrs. S. J. Slutzkin.
Sec.: Mrs. M. Simon, 7 Byrne Ave., Elwood.

B'nai B'rith. Pres.: P. Joseph. Sec.: B. Davis.

Anglo-Jewish Society, Sec.: Mrs. J. Miller.

PERTH (W.AUSTRALIA) (ca. 3,200 Jews)

West Australian Advisory Board.
Pres.: Alec Breckler.
Sec.: N. Rosenwax.

West Australian Council of Jewish Affairs.
Pres.: H. Hyams.
Sec.: M. Lewis.

Hebrew Congregation "Sheerith Yisrael," Bris-
bane St. Founded 1896.
Pres.: A. Troy.
Sec.: H. Casper.
Minister: Rev.: L. Rubin-Zacks.

West Australian Jewish Education Association.
Pres.: Dr. A. Gild.
Sec.: M. Miller.

National Council of Jewish Women,
Pres.: Mrs. P. Luber-Smith.
Sec.: Mrs. R. Schenberg.

OTHER ORGANIZED HEBREW CONGREGATIONS:

Broken Hill (N.S.W.), *Canberra* (N.S.W., 30
Jews), *Geelong* (Victoria, 80 Jews), *Hobart*
(Tasmania, about 100 Jews), *Illawarra*
(N.S.W.), *Kalgoorlie* (W.A., 27 Jews),
Launceston (Tasmania, 40 Jews), *Newcastle*
(N.S.W.), *Parramatta* (N.S.W.).

PUBLICATIONS:

Australian Jewish Herald, Weekly. 44 Queen St., Melbourne.

Australian Jewish Forum, 149 Castlereagh St., Sydney.

Australian Jewish Historical Society Journal. Semi-annual, 2 Castlereagh St., Sydney.

Australian Jewish News. Weekly. 306 Lit. Collins St., Melbourne. English-Yiddish.

The Council Bulletin, 8 Young St., Sydney.

Great Synagogue. Monthly, 29 Alberta St., Sydney.

The Hebrew Standard. Weekly, 175 George St., Sydney.

The Jewish Post. Weekly. 44 Queen St., Melbourne. Yiddish.

Liberal Jewish Digest. Monthly. 78 Alma Rd., Melbourne.

Sydney Jewish News. Weekly. 147a King St., Sydney. English-Yiddish.

The New Citizen. Monthly. 350 George St., Sydney.

Westralian Judean. Monthly. Mc Lean's Place, Murray St., Perth, W.A.

Temple Emanuel Gazette. Bi-monthly. 7 Ocean St., Woolahra, N.S.W.

NEW ZEALAND

JEWISH POPULATION: 4,500

The settlement of Jews in New Zealand dates from the establishment of British sovereignty in 1840.

The first emigrant ship carried a number of Jews from England. But, still earlier, a few Jewish wayfarers had settled in the northern part of New Zealand. Among them were John Israel Montefiore, a cousin of Sir Moses Montefiore, who settled at Bay of Islands in 1831; Joel Samuel Polack, one of the earliest writers in the country; and David Nathan, who laid the foundation of the Jewish community in Auckland in the early 1840's. The Wellington Jewish community was founded by Abraham Hort on January 7, 1843. Communities were later established in Christchurch and Dunedin and other parts of South Island. From the earliest times, Jewish settlers have helped to lay the foundation of the commercial and industrial prosperity of the country. The first two mayors under the Municipal Corporations Act were Jews. From time to time, Jews have occupied important positions in New Zealand, including those of administrator, prime minister, and chief justice.

The majority of Jews today reside in the Auckland and Wellington provinces.

Jews share in the prosperity of the country. Relations with the non-Jewish neighbors are very friendly. In 1955, however, the Social Political League, an anti-Semitic group which obtained 123,000 votes at the 1954 elections, disseminated anti-Jewish pamphlets. In letters to the Christchurch Press, an obscure organization calling itself the League of Empire Loyalists repeated Nazi propaganda about a Jewish international conspiracy.

Assimilation poses a serious problem.

The arrival of East European Jewish immigrants and particularly the creation of the State of Israel stimulated a more active Jewish and Zionist life. The response to the Israeli funds increased. Some of the youth left for Israel. Efforts are now being made to improve Jewish education with a full-time director. In 1955, the Wellington Jewish Social Club started to publish its own monthly, besides the New Zealand Jewish Chronicle published by the Zionist Council.

United Synagogue of New Zealand, Auckland, C.I. P.O.B. 190.
The United Synagogue is the Central representative body of the Jews in New Zealand, established in 1956. The constituents of the United Synagogue are the Jewish Congregations of Wellington, Auckland, Christchurch, and Dunedin.
Chairman: Lawrence D. Nathan of Auckland.
Sec.: A. Faine of Auckland.

AUCKLAND (Jewish Population: 1,900)
"Beth Israel" Hebrew Congregation, Prince St. C. 1. Founded 1841.
Pres.: L. D. Nathan.
Sec.: H. Goodman.
Rabbi: A. Astor.
School Principal: Rabbi A. Astor.
Judean Association, Communal Hall, Bowen Av. C. 1. Founded 1932. Activities: literary and dramatic, Maccabi sports, youth and social circles.
Pres.: Rabbi A. Astor, Mrs. Astor.
Sec.: Miss I. Buetow.
Ladies' Benevolent Society, Pres.: Mrs. S. Klippel. Sec.: Mrs. H. Paykel, 17 Mt. St. John Av. S.E.3.
Union of Jewish Women, Pres.: Mrs. A. Klippel. Sec.: Mrs. S. Rubin, 23 Kelmarna Ave. W.1.
Anglo-Jewish Association, Sec.: Rev. A. Astor, Synagogue Chambers, Princess St.

United Committee for Relief Abroad,
Pres.: Rabbi A. Astor.
Sec.: G. Perl, 304 Dilworth Bldg. C.1.
Zionist Society, Pres.: L. Phillips.
Sec.: A. Faine, P.O.Box 1080.
WIZO, Pres.: Mrs. N. Solomon. Sec.: Miss S. Manoy, 25a Carlton Gore Rd. C.3.
Friends of the Hebrew University.
Pres.: Rabbi A. Astor.
Sec.: Miss O. Paykel.

CHRISTCHURCH (Jewish population: 330)
Canterbury Jewish Congregation, Gloucester St. C.1.
Pres.: Dr. Cook.
Sec.: J. P. Goldsmith.
Minister: Rev. S. N. Salas.
Philanthropic Society, Pres.: A. Rose, 48 Armagh St. C.1.
Canterbury Zionist Society, Pres.: J. Jacobs.
Sec.: E. Kaldor, P.O.Box 1546.
Welfare and Relief Society, Sec.: Mrs. G.S. Hollander, 8 Philpotts Rd.
Jewish Social Club, Pres.: J. Nunes. Sec.: Miss R. Marks, 77 Totara St. W.1.
Jewish National Fund (South Island),
Commissioner: Lutz Zelas.
Sec.: Miss L. Teplitzky, 29 Straven Rd. W.1.
WIZO, Pres.: Mrs. E. J. Jacobs. Sec.: Mrs. A. Friedlander, 77 Totara St. W.1.
Union of Jewish Women, Pres.: Mrs. D. Goldsmith. Sec.: Miss L. Burtenshaw, 178 Rossall St.

DUNEDIN (Jewish population: 100)
Synagogue, Moray Place, P.O.Box 739. Founded 1862; erected 1881.
Pres.: H. L. Boock.
Sec.: Frank S. Salinger.
Minister: E. Hirsh.
Philanthropic Society, Founded 1864.
Pres.: G. Benson.
Sec.: A. de Beer.
Ladies' Committee, Pres.: Mrs. H.L. Boock.
Sec.: Mrs. J. Horn.
Zionist Group, Pres.: Dr. S. Faine.
Sec.: E. Hirsh.

WELLINGTON (Jewish population: 2,100)

The Terrace Synagogue, P.O.Box 1069. Founded 1843; rebuilt 1929.
Pres.: J. I. Goldsmith.
Sec.: J. Benjamin.
Rabbi: H. Stransky.

The Terrace Hebrew School, Principal: Rabbi H. Stransky.

Zionist Society, Pres.: M. Gottlieb. Sec.: Mrs. H. Eidem, 101 Willis St. C.1.

WIZO, Pres.: Mrs. M. Gottlieb. Sec.: Mrs. J. Woolf.

Central Zionist Library, 86 Ghuznee St. C.2.

Hebrew Philanthropic Society, Pres.: A. Fine. Sec.: S. Greenberg.

Wellington Jewish Relief Society, Pres.: J. Lewis Sec.: G. S. Shapiro, 96 Courtenay Place,C.3.

Jewish Social Club, 86 Ghuznee St. C.2.
Pres.: A. Spolsky. Sec.: J. Ketko.

United Jewish Committee for Relief Abroad.
Pres.: J. Lewis. Sec.: G. Shapiro.

Union of Jewish Women of New Zealand.
Pres.: Mrs. M. de Woolf.
Sec.: Mrs. I. Treister.

Anglo-Jewish Association. Sec.: Rev. J. Wolman, Embassy Court, Boulcott St.

Board of Jewish Ministers of New Zealand, 128 The Terrace, C.1.
Registrar: Rev. B. Skolnick.

PUBLICATIONS:

1) *The New Zealand Jewish Chronicle,* P.O. Box 1423, Wellington, Published by The Zionist Council.

2) Monthly, published by the Jewish Social Club, Wellington.